INTERMEDIATE GCSE MATHEMATICS

Revision and Practice

David Rayner

OXFORD

Great Clarendon Street, Oxford OX2 6DP

Oxford University Press is a department of the University of Oxford. It furthers the University's objective of excellence in research, scholarship, and education by publishing worldwide in

Oxford New York

Athens Auckland Bangkok Bogotá Buenos Aires Calcutta Cape Town Chennai Dar es Salaam Delhi Florence Hong Kong Istanbul Karachi Kuala Lumpur Madrid Melbourne Mexico City Mumbai Nairobi Paris São Paulo Singapore Taipei Tokyo Toronto Warsaw

with associated companies in Berlin Ibadan

First published 2000

British Library Cataloguing in Publication Data

Data available

ISBN 0 19 914789 2 (School edition)
0 19 914790 6 (Bookshop edition)

Additonal artwork by Stephen Hill, Nick Bawden, Oxford Illustrators and Julian Page
Typeset by Tech-Set, Gateshead, Tyne and Wear
Printed and bound in Great Britain by Butler & Tanner Ltd, Frome and London

Preface

This book is for candidates working through Key Stage 4 towards a GCSE in Mathematics. It can be used both in the classroom and by students working on their own. There are explanations, worked examples and numerous exercises which, it is hoped, will help students to build up confidence. The author believes that people learn mathematics by doing mathematics. The questions are graded in difficulty throughout the exercises.

This revised edition has been written to cater for the new non-calculator papers. Future developments in the National Curriculum have also been anticipated by reference to the latest documents from the Department of Education. In response to the requests of many teachers a section of past examination questions has also been included. Teachers will note that the syllabuses and questions set by all the main GCSE boards are very similar. This book can be used with confidence when preparing for all GCSEs.

The book can be used either as a course book over the last two or three years before the GCSE examinations or as a revision text in the final year. The contents list shows where all the topics appear and an index at the back of the book provides further reference.

At the end of the book, in addition to past examination questions, there are several revision exercises which provide mixed questions across the curriculum. There are also multiple choice questions for variety.

The section on Using and Applying Mathematics contains a selection of starters for coursework projects which have been tried and tested. They can be used to provide practice in the strategies involved in attempting 'open-ended' problems.

The author is indebted to the many students and colleagues who have assisted him in this work. He is particularly grateful to Christine Godfrey for her help and many suggestions.

Thanks are also due to the following examination boards for kindly allowing the use of questions from their past mathematics papers and sample questions:

University of Cambridge Local Examinations Syndicate International	[CIE]
London Examinations, a division of Edexcel Foundation	[Edexcel]
Midland Examinations Group	[OCR]
Northern Examinations and Assessment Board	[NEAB]
Northern Ireland Council for the Curriculum Examinations and Assessment	[NISEC]
Southern Examining Group	[SEG]
Welsh Joint Education Committee	[WJEC]

The sample questions from these boards represent one stage in the development of nationally approved material and do not necessarily reflect the style currently accepted.

D. Rayner 2000

Contents

1 Number 1

1.1 Place value

- Whole numbers are made up from units, tens, hundreds, thousands and so on.

thousands	hundreds	tens	units
3	2	6	4

- In the number 3264:

  the digit 3 means 3 thousands
  the digit 2 means 2 hundreds
  the digit 6 means 6 tens
  the digit 4 means 4 units (ones)

- In words we write ‘three thousand, two hundred and sixty-four’.

Exercise 1

In Questions **1** to **8** state the value of the figure underlined.

1. $\underline{2}7$ **2.** $\underline{4}16$ **3.** $23\underline{8}2$ **4.** $51\underline{6}$
5. $\underline{6}008$ **6.** $\underline{2}6\,104$ **7.** $\underline{5}\,250\,000$ **8.** $\underline{8}26\,111$

In Questions **9** to **16** write down the number which goes in each box.

9. $293 = \square + 90 + 3$ **10.** $574 = 500 + \square + 4$

11. $816 = 800 + \square + 6$ **12.** $899 = \square + 90 + 9$

13. $6217 = \square + 200 + 10 + 7$ **14.** $5065 = 5000 + \square + 5$

15. $63\,410 = 60\,000 + 3000 + \square + 10$

16. $75\,678 = \square + 5000 + 600 + \square + 8$

17. Write these numbers in figures.
(a) Seven hundred and twenty.
(b) Five thousand, two hundred and six
(c) Sixteen thousand, four hundred and thirty.
(d) Half a million.
(e) Three hundred thousand and ninety.
(f) Eight and a half thousand.

18. Here are four number cards:

7

(a) Use all the cards to make the largest possible number.
(b) Use all the cards to make the smallest possible number.

19. Write these numbers in words.
(a) 4620 (b) 607 (c) 25 400
(d) 6 800 000 (e) 21 425

20. Here are five number cards:

(a) Use all the cards to make the largest possible *odd* number.
(b) Use all the cards to make the smallest possible *even* number.

21. Write down the number that is ten more than:
(a) 247 (b) 3211 (c) 694

22. Write down the number that is one thousand more than:
(a) 392 (b) 25 611 (c) 256 900

23. (a) Prini puts a 2 digit whole number into her calculator. She multiplies the number by 10.

Fill in *one* other digit which you know must now be on the calculator.

(b) Prini starts again with the same 2 digit number and this time she multiplies it by 1000.
Fill in all five digits on the calculator this time.

24. Write down the numbers in order, from the smallest to the largest.
(a) 2142 2290 2058 2136
(b) 5329 5029 5299 5330
(c) 25 117 25 200 25 171 25 000 25 500

25. Find a number n so that $5n + 7 = 507$.

26. Find a number x so that $6x + 8 = 68$.

27. Find a pair of numbers a and b for which $8a + b = 807$.

28. Find a pair of numbers p and q for which $7p + 5q = 7050$.

1.2 Arithmetic without a calculator

Here are examples to remind you of non-calculator methods.

(a) $\begin{array}{r} 4\,2\,7 \\ +\,5\,1\,8\,6 \\ \hline 5\,6\,1\,3 \\ \hline {\scriptstyle 1\;1} \end{array}$

(b) $\begin{array}{r} 2\,7\,{}^{7}\!\not{8}\,{}^{1}4 \\ -\;\;6\,3\,5 \\ \hline 2\,1\,4\,9 \\ \hline \end{array}$

(c) $57 \times 100 = 5700$

(d) $\begin{array}{r} 3\,7\,4 \\ \times\quad 6 \\ \hline 2\,2\,4\,4 \\ \hline {\scriptstyle 4\;2} \end{array}$

(e) $\begin{array}{r} 5\;4\;2 \\ 7\overline{)3\;7\;{}^{2}9\;{}^{1}4} \end{array}$

(f) $\begin{array}{r} 1\;3\;8 \\ 5\overline{)6\;{}^{1}9\;{}^{4}4} \end{array}$ r 4 or $138\frac{4}{5}$

Exercise 2

Work out, without a calculator.

1. $653 + 2844$ **2.** $2106 + 329$ **3.** $64 + 214 + 507$ **4.** $65\,941 + 25\,804$
5. $387 - 175$ **6.** $527 - 486$ **7.** $927 - 68$ **8.** $1024 - 816$
9. 27×10 **10.** 5×1000 **11.** 73×5 **12.** 214×4
13. 316×8 **14.** 9224×7 **15.** $340 \div 4$ **16.** $1944 \div 6$
17. $3195 \div 5$ **18.** $2600 \div 8$ **19.** $365 \div 7$ **20.** $520 \div 10$
21. $289 + 15 + 1714$ **22.** $9704 - 5135$ **23.** $6001 - 5994$ **24.** 54×20
25. $2906 - 1414$ **26.** $4716 \div 9$ **27.** 725×8 **28.** $1504 \div 8$
29. $7 + 1609 + 25$ **30.** $289 + 154 - 78$ **31.** $7 + 295 - 48$ **32.** 53×400

Speed tests

These questions can be done either:
(a) with books open
(b) read out by the teacher with books closed.

In either case *only the answer* is written down. Be as quick as possible.

Test 1

1. $30 - 8$
2. 9×5
3. $40 \div 5$
4. $24 + 34$
5. 11×7
6. $60 - 12$
7. 9×4
8. $27 \div 3$
9. $55 + 55$
10. $60 - 18$
11. 8×6
12. $49 \div 7$
13. $99 + 17$
14. $80 - 59$
15. 9×100

Test 2

1. $6 + 16$
2. $32 - 5$
3. 9×6
4. $90 \div 2$
5. $98 + 45$
6. $16 - 7$
7. $45 \div 9$
8. 13×100
9. $99 + 99$
10. $67 - 17$
11. $570 \div 10$
12. 7×3
13. $55 - 6$
14. $19 + 18$
15. $60 \div 5$

Test 3

1. 8×5
2. $17 + 23$
3. $60 \div 6$
4. $101 - 20$
5. 49×2
6. $52 + 38$
7. $66 \div 11$
8. $105 - 70$
9. 13×4
10. $220 - 30$
11. $100 \div 20$
12. $2 \times 2 \times 2$
13. $91 + 19$
14. $200 - 5$
15. 16×2

Test 4

1. 5×7
2. $36 - 18$
3. $103 - 20$
4. $56 \div 7$
5. 8×4
6. $53 + 36$
7. $51 - 22$
8. $36 \div 3$
9. 20×5
10. $99 + 55$
11. $200 - 145$
12. $88 \div 8$
13. 50×100
14. $199 + 26$
15. $80 - 17$

Inverse operations: find the missing digits

The word inverse means ‘opposite’.

- The inverse of adding is subtracting $5 + 19 = 24$, $5 = 24 - 19$
- The inverse of subtracting is adding $31 - 6 = 25$, $31 = 25 + 6$
- The inverse of multiplying is dividing $7 \times 6 = 42$, $7 = 42 \div 6$
- The inverse of dividing is multiplying $30 \div 3 = 10$, $30 = 10 \times 3$

Find the missing digits.

(a) $\square 4 \div 6 = 14$ — Work out 14×6 because multiplying is the inverse of dividing. Since $14 \times 6 = 84$, the missing digit is 8.

(b) $2\square 8 \times 5 = 1340$ — Work out $1340 \div 5$ because dividing is the inverse of multiplying. Since $1340 \div 5 = 268$, the missing digit is 6.

(c)
$$\begin{array}{r} 3\ \square\ 7 \\ +\ 2\ 5\ \square \\ \hline \square\ 3\ 9 \\ \hline \end{array}$$

Start from the right. $7+2=9$
Middle column. $8+5=13$
Check
$$\begin{array}{r} 387 \\ +252 \\ \hline 639 \\ \hline {\scriptstyle 1} \end{array}$$
Check

Exercise 3

Find the missing digits.

1. (a) $\begin{array}{r} 2\ 8\ 5 \\ +\ \square\ 1\ 4 \\ \hline 7\ \square\ \square \end{array}$ (b) $\begin{array}{r} 6\ 3\ \square \\ +\ \square\ 5\ 2 \\ \hline 8\ \square\ 9 \end{array}$ (c) $\begin{array}{r} \square\ 3\ 5 \\ +\ 3\ 4\ \square \\ \hline 9\ \square\ 9 \end{array}$

2. (a) $\begin{array}{r} 3\ 5\ 6 \\ +\ 5\ \square\ 6 \\ \hline \square\ 8\ \square \end{array}$ (b) $\begin{array}{r} 2\ \square\ 4 \\ +\ 5\ 3\ 7 \\ \hline \square\ 6\ 1 \end{array}$ (c) $\begin{array}{r} 3\ 8\ 8 \\ +\ \square\ 2\ \square \\ \hline 8\ \square\ 3 \end{array}$

3. (a) $\begin{array}{r} 4\ \square \\ \times\quad 3 \\ \hline 1\ 4\ 4 \end{array}$ (b) $\begin{array}{r} 3\ \square \\ \times\quad 7 \\ \hline 2\ 3\ 1 \end{array}$ (c) $\begin{array}{r} \square\ \square\ 1 \\ \times\quad 5 \\ \hline 1\ 6\ 0\ 5 \end{array}$

4. (a) $\square\square\square \div 3 = 50$ (b) $\square\square \times 4 = 60$
(c) $9 \times \square = 81$ (d) $\square\square\square \div 6 = 192$

5. (a) $\begin{array}{r} 4\ \square\ 5 \\ +\ 2\ 8\ \square \\ \hline \square\ 3\ 0 \end{array}$ (b) $\begin{array}{r} 4\ \square\ 7 \\ +\ \square\ 7\ \square \\ \hline 6\ 0\ 4 \end{array}$ (c) $\begin{array}{r} \square\ 3\ \square \\ +\ 2\ \square\ 4 \\ \hline 7\ 9\ 9 \end{array}$

6. (a) $\square\square \times 7 = 245$ (b) $\square\square \times 10 = 580$
(c) $32 \div \square = 8$ (d) $\square\square\square \div 5 = 190$

7. (a) $\square\square + 29 = 101$ (b) $\square\square\square - 17 = 91$

(c)
$$\begin{array}{r} \square\ 8\ 9 \\ -\ 3\ \square\ 6 \\ \hline 5\ 4\ \square \end{array}$$

(d)
$$\begin{array}{r} 3\ 3\ 5 \\ -\ 2\ 1\ \square \\ \hline \square\square\ 7 \end{array}$$

8. There is more than one correct answer for each of these questions. Ask a friend to check your solution.

(a) $\boxed{2}\boxed{3} + \square\square - \square\square = 23$

(b) $\boxed{8}\boxed{5} - \square\square + \square\square = 86$

(c) $\boxed{2}\boxed{5} \times \square \div \square = 25$

(d) $\boxed{4}\boxed{0} \times \square\square \div \square = 80$

9. Each of these calculations has the same number missing from all three boxes. Find the missing number in each calculation.

(a) $\square \times \square - \square = 12$

(b) $\square \div \square + \square = 9$

(c) $\square \times \square + \square = 72$

10. In the circle write +, −, × or ÷ to make the calculation correct.

(a) $7 \times 4 \bigcirc 3 = 25$ (b) $8 \times 5 \bigcirc 2 = 20$

(c) $7 \bigcirc 3 - 9 = 12$ (d) $12 \bigcirc 2 + 4 = 10$

(e) $75 \div 5 \bigcirc 5 = 20$

11. Write the following with the correct signs.

(a) $5 \times 4 \times 3 \bigcirc 3 = 63$

(b) $5 + 4 \bigcirc 3 \bigcirc 2 = 4$

(c) $5 \times 2 \times 3 \bigcirc 1 = 31$

1.3 Decimals

- Look at these numbers.

tens	units	•	$\frac{1}{10}$	$\frac{1}{100}$	$\frac{1}{1000}$
5	3	•	6	2	
	0	•	8	7	3

Notice that, $53{\cdot}62 = 50 + 3 + \frac{6}{10} + \frac{2}{100}$

$0{\cdot}873 = \frac{8}{10} + \frac{7}{100} + \frac{3}{1000}$

- When writing decimals in order of size it is helpful to write them with the same number of figures after the decimal point.

Here are three numbers to be written in order.

0·08, 0·107, 0·1

0·08 ⟶ 0·080
0·107 ⟶ 0·107
0·1 ⟶ 0·100

Now we can see that the correct order of these decimals from lowest to highest is 0·08, 0·1, 0·107.

Exercise 4

In Questions **1** to **8** write down each statement and decide whether it is true or false.

1. 0·3 is less than 0·31
2. 0·82 is more than 0·825
3. 0·7 is equal to 0·70
4. 0·17 is less than 0·71
5. 0·02 is more than 0·002
6. 0·6 is less than 0·06
7. 0·1 is equal to $\frac{1}{10}$
8. 5 is equal to 5·00

9. The number 43·6 can be written $40 + 3 + \frac{6}{10}$.
Write the number 57·2 in this way.

10. Write the decimal numbers for these additions.
(a) $200 + 30 + 5 + \frac{1}{10}$ (b) $60 + 7 + \frac{2}{10} + \frac{3}{100}$ (c) $90 + 8 + \frac{3}{10} + \frac{2}{100}$ (d) $3 + \frac{1}{10} + \frac{6}{100} + \frac{7}{1000}$

In Questions **11** to **18** arrange the numbers in order of size, smallest first.

11. 0·41, 0·31, 0·2
12. 0·75, 0·58, 0·702
13. 0·43, 0·432, 0·41
14. 0·609, 0·61, 0·6
15. 0·04, 0·15, 0·2, 0·35
16. 1·8, 0·18, 0·81, 1·18
17. 0·7, 0·061, 0·07, 0·1
18. 0·2, 0·025, 0·03, 0·009

19. Here are numbers with letters. Put the numbers in order and write down the letters to make a word.

A
0.2

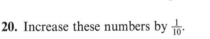

20. Increase these numbers by $\frac{1}{10}$.
(a) 32·41 (b) 0·753 (c) 1·06

21. Increase these numbers by $\frac{1}{100}$.
(a) 5·68 (b) 0·542 (c) 1·29

22. Write the following amounts in pounds.
(a) 350 pence (b) 15 pence (c) 3 pence
(d) 10 pence (e) 1260 pence (f) 8 pence

23. Write each statement and say whether it is true or false.
(a) £5·4 = £5 + 40p (b) £0·6 = 6p
(c) 5p = £0·05 (d) 50p is more than £0·42

Scale readings

Exercise 5

Work out the value indicated by the arrow.

1.

2.
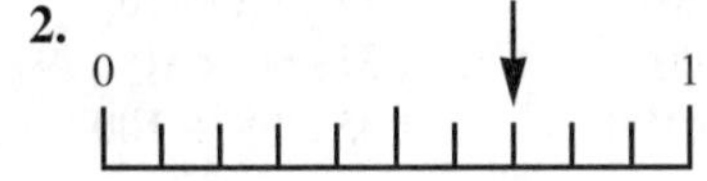

3.
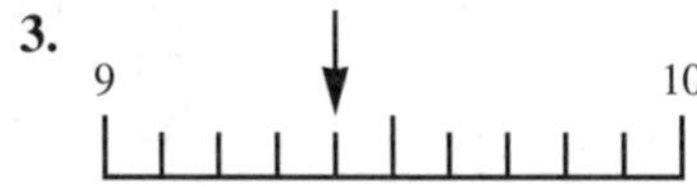

4.
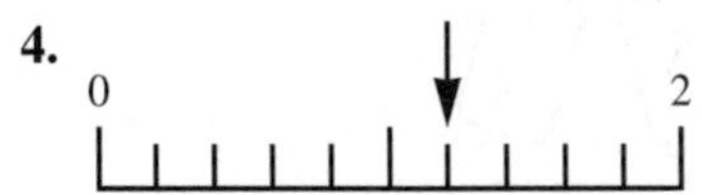

5.
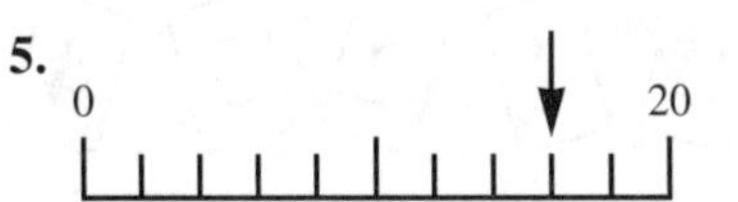

6.

7.
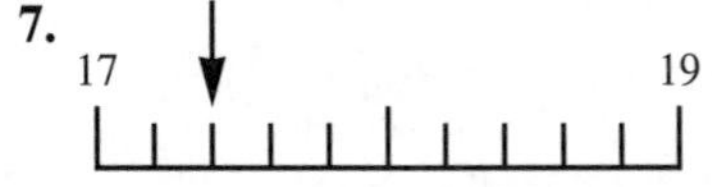

8.

9.

10.

11.
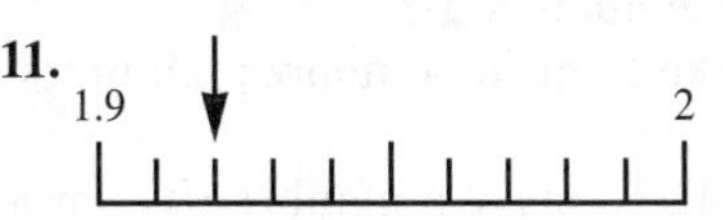

12.
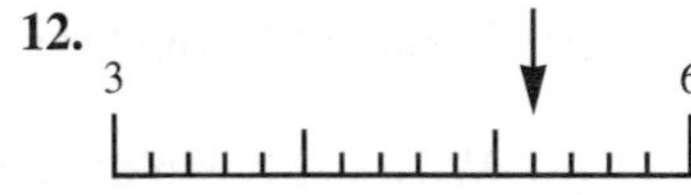

13.
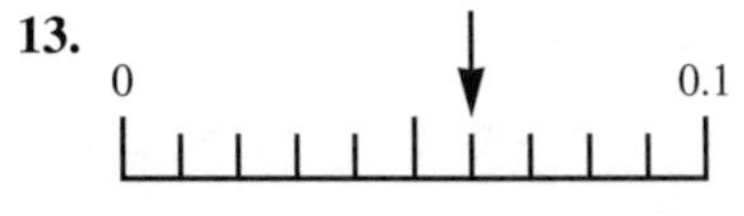

14.
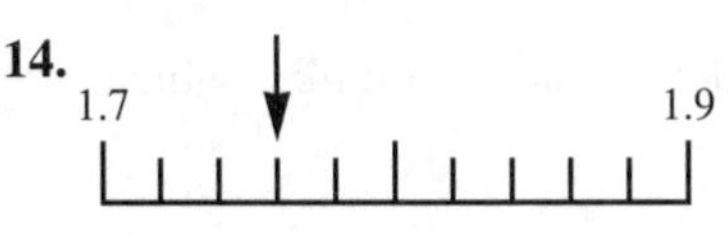

15.
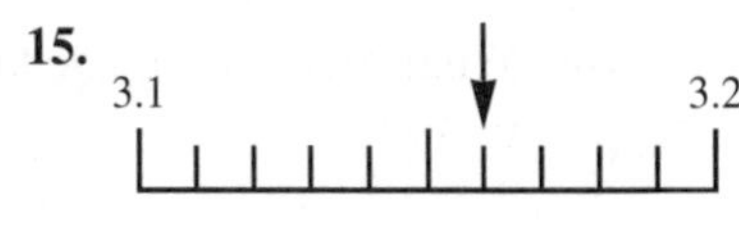

16.
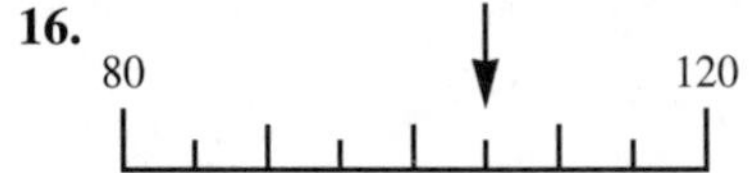

17.
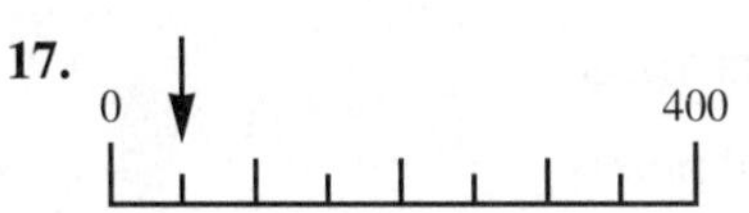

18.
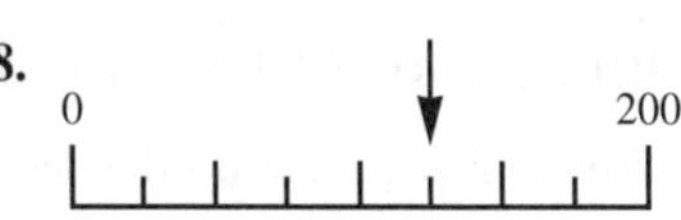

Multiplying and dividing by 10, 100, 1000

- To *multiply*, move the decimal point to the *right*.

  3·24 × 10 = 32·4

  10·61 × 10 = 106·1

  4·134 × 100 = 413·4

  8·2 × 100 = 820

- To *divide*, move the decimal point to the *left*.

  15·2 ÷ 10 = 1·52

  624·9 ÷ 100 = 6·249

  509 ÷ 1000 = 0·509

Exercise 6

Work out:

1. 0·634 × 10 **2.** 0·838 × 10 **3.** 0·815 × 100 **4.** 0·074 × 100
5. 7·245 × 1000 **6.** 0·032 × 1000 **7.** 0·63 × 10 **8.** 1·42 × 100
9. 0·041 × 100 **10.** 0·3 × 100 **11.** 0·71 × 1000 **12.** 3·95 × 10

13. 6·24 ÷ 10	**14.** 8·97 ÷ 10	**15.** 17·5 ÷ 100	**16.** 23·6 ÷ 100
17. 127 ÷ 1000	**18.** 705 ÷ 1000	**19.** 13 ÷ 10	**20.** 0·8 ÷ 10
21. 0·7 ÷ 100	**22.** 218 ÷ 10	**23.** 35 ÷ 1000	**24.** 8·6 ÷ 1000
25. 0·95 × 100	**26.** 11·11 × 10	**27.** 3·2 ÷ 10	**28.** 0·07 × 1000
29. 57·6 ÷ 10	**30.** 999 ÷ 100	**31.** 66 × 10	**32.** 100 ÷ 100
33. 42 ÷ 1000	**34.** 0·62 × 10 000	**35.** 0·9 ÷ 100	**36.** 555 ÷ 10 000

37. Here are some number cards    

(a) Jason picks the cards 1 3 and 4 to make the number 314. What extra card could he take to make a number ten times as big as 314?

(b) Mel chose 3 cards to make the number 5·2.

(i) What cards could she take to make a number ten times as big as 5·2?

(ii) What cards could she take to make a number 100 times as big as 5·2?

(iii) What cards could she take to make a number which is $\frac{1}{100}$ of 5·2?

Adding and subtracting decimals

- Remember to line up the decimal points.

(a) 4·2 + 1·76

```
  4·20 ← put a zero
+ 1·76
  5·96
```

(b) 26 − 1·7

```
  2⁵6̸·¹0
−  1·7
  24·3
```

(c) 0·24 + 5 + 12·7

```
   0·24
   5·00 ← extra zeros
+ 12·70 ←
  17·94
```

Exercise 7

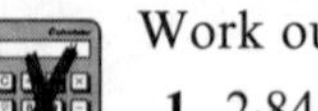

Work out.

1. 2·84 + 7·3	**2.** 18·6 + 2·34	**3.** 25·96 + 0·75	**4.** 212·7 + 4·25
5. 3·6 + 6	**6.** 7 + 16·1	**7.** 8 + 0·34 + 0·8	**8.** 12 + 5·32
9. 0·004 + 0·058	**10.** 4·81 − 3·7	**11.** 6·92 − 2·56	**12.** 8·27 − 5·86
13. 3·6 − 2·24	**14.** 8·4 − 2·17	**15.** 8·24 − 5·78	**16.** 15·4 − 7
17. 8 − 5·2	**18.** 13 − 2·7	**19.** 0·5 − 0·32	**20.** 5 − 0·99
21. 6 + 0·06 + 0·6	**22.** 12·4 + 28·71	**23.** 11 − 7·4	**24.** 8·2 + 9·54 − 11·3

25. Four rods are joined end to end. Their individual lengths are 18·3 cm, 75·2 cm, 11 cm and 0·7 cm.
What is their combined length?

26. Sue buys 3 computer games costing £11·45, £23·99 and £5·60.
How much change does she get from £50?

Multiplying decimal numbers

- The answer has the same number of figures to the right of the decimal point as the total number of figures to the right of the decimal point in the question.

(a)	(b)	(c)
$0{\cdot}2 \times 0{\cdot}8$	$0{\cdot}4 \times 0{\cdot}07$	$5 \times 0{\cdot}06$
$[2 \times 8 = 16]$	$[4 \times 7 = 28]$	$[5 \times 6 = 30]$
So $0{\cdot}2 \times 0{\cdot}8 = 0{\cdot}16$	So $0{\cdot}4 \times 0{\cdot}07 = 0{\cdot}028$	So $5 \times 0{\cdot}06 = 0{\cdot}3$

Exercise 8

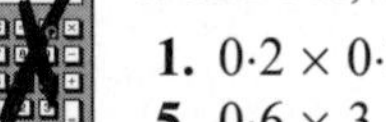

Work out, without a calculator.

1. $0{\cdot}2 \times 0{\cdot}3$ **2.** $0{\cdot}5 \times 0{\cdot}3$ **3.** $0{\cdot}4 \times 0{\cdot}3$ **4.** $0{\cdot}2 \times 0{\cdot}03$
5. $0{\cdot}6 \times 3$ **6.** $0{\cdot}7 \times 5$ **7.** $0{\cdot}9 \times 2$ **8.** $8 \times 0{\cdot}1$
9. $0{\cdot}4 \times 0{\cdot}9$ **10.** $0{\cdot}02 \times 0{\cdot}7$ **11.** $2{\cdot}1 \times 0{\cdot}6$ **12.** $4{\cdot}7 \times 0{\cdot}5$
13. $21{\cdot}3 \times 0{\cdot}4$ **14.** $5{\cdot}2 \times 0{\cdot}6$ **15.** $4{\cdot}2 \times 0{\cdot}03$ **16.** $212 \times 0{\cdot}6$
17. $0{\cdot}85 \times 0{\cdot}2$ **18.** $3{\cdot}27 \times 0{\cdot}1$ **19.** $12{\cdot}6 \times 0{\cdot}01$ **20.** $0{\cdot}02 \times 17$
21. $0{\cdot}05 \times 1{\cdot}1$ **22.** $52 \times 0{\cdot}01$ **23.** $65 \times 0{\cdot}02$ **24.** $0{\cdot}5 \times 0{\cdot}002$

Dividing by a decimal

(a) $9{\cdot}36 \div 0{\cdot}4$

Multiply both numbers by 10 so that you can divide by a *whole number*.
[Move the decimal points to the right.]
So work out $93{\cdot}6 \div 4$

$$\begin{array}{r} 2\,3\cdot 4 \\ 4\overline{)9^{1}3\cdot{}^{1}6} \end{array}$$

(b) $0{\cdot}0378 \div 0{\cdot}07$

Multiply both numbers by 100 so that you can divide by a whole number.
[Move the decimal points to the right.]
So work out $3{\cdot}78 \div 7$

$$\begin{array}{r} 0\cdot 5\,4 \\ 7\overline{)3\cdot 7^{2}8} \end{array}$$

Exercise 9

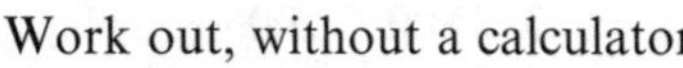

Work out, without a calculator.

1. $0{\cdot}84 \div 0{\cdot}4$ **2.** $0{\cdot}93 \div 0{\cdot}3$ **3.** $0{\cdot}872 \div 0{\cdot}2$ **4.** $0{\cdot}8 \div 0{\cdot}2$
5. $2{\cdot}8 \div 0{\cdot}7$ **6.** $1{\cdot}25 \div 0{\cdot}5$ **7.** $8 \div 0{\cdot}5$ **8.** $40 \div 0{\cdot}2$
9. $7 \div 0{\cdot}1$ **10.** $0{\cdot}368 \div 0{\cdot}4$ **11.** $0{\cdot}915 \div 0{\cdot}03$ **12.** $0{\cdot}248 \div 0{\cdot}04$
13. $0{\cdot}625 \div 0{\cdot}05$ **14.** $8{\cdot}54 \div 0{\cdot}07$ **15.** $1{\cdot}272 \div 0{\cdot}006$ **16.** $4{\cdot}48 \div 0{\cdot}08$
17. $0{\cdot}12 \div 0{\cdot}002$ **18.** $7{\cdot}5 \div 0{\cdot}005$ **19.** $0{\cdot}09 \div 0{\cdot}3$ **20.** $0{\cdot}77 \div 1{\cdot}1$
21. $0{\cdot}055 \div 0{\cdot}11$ **22.** $21{\cdot}28 \div 7$ **23.** $22{\cdot}48 \div 4$ **24.** $3{\cdot}12 \div 4$
25. $0{\cdot}7 \div 5$ **26.** $3 \div 0{\cdot}8$ **27.** $0{\cdot}3 \div 4$ **28.** $1{\cdot}2 \div 8$
29. $0{\cdot}732 \div 0{\cdot}6$ **30.** $0{\cdot}1638 \div 0{\cdot}001$ **31.** $1{\cdot}05 \div 0{\cdot}6$ **32.** $7{\cdot}52 \div 0{\cdot}4$

33. A cake weighing 4·8 kg is cut into several pieces each weighing 0·6 kg. How many pieces are there?

34. A phone call costs £0·04. How many calls can I make if I have £3·52?

35. A sheet of paper is 0·01 cm thick. How many sheets are there in a pile of paper 5·8 cm thick?

Crossnumbers

Make three copies of the crossnumber and then fill in the numbers using the clues given.

1		■	2		3	
	■	4		■		■
■	5		■	6	■	7
8		■	9		10	■
	■	■		■	11	
12		13	■	14		■
	■	15		■	16	

A.

Across
1. 13×7
2. $0{\cdot}214 \times 10\,000$
4. $265 - 248$
5. $2 \times 2 \times 2 \times 2 \times 2 \times 2$
7. $90 - (9 \times 9)$
8. 14×5
9. $2226 \div 7$
11. $216 \div (18 \div 3)$
12. $800 - 363$
14. $93 - (6 \times 2)$
15. $0{\cdot}23 \times 100$
16. $8 \times 8 - 1$

Down
1. $101 - 7$
2. $2{\cdot}7 \div 0{\cdot}1$
3. $44{\cdot}1 + 0{\cdot}9$
4. $(2 \times 9) - (8 \div 2)$
6. 9^2
8. $6523 + 917$
9. $418 \div 11$
10. $216 + (81 \times 100)$
13. $2 \times 2 \times 2 \times 3 \times 3$

B.

Across
1. $2{\cdot}4 \times 40$
2. $1600 - 27$
4. $913 - 857$
5. $2 + (9 \times 9)$
7. $0{\cdot}4 \div 0{\cdot}05$
8. $27 \times 5 - 69$
9. $4158 \div 7$
11. $2^6 + 6$
12. $5{\cdot}22 \div 0{\cdot}03$
14. $201 - 112$
15. 7 million $\div\ 100\,000$
16. $\frac{1}{4}$ of 372

Down
1. $558 \div 6$
2. $6{\cdot}4 \div 0{\cdot}4$
3. $0{\cdot}071 \times 1000$
4. $11{\cdot}61 + 4{\cdot}2 + 37{\cdot}19$
6. $(7 - 3{\cdot}1) \times 10$
8. $8 \times 8 \times 100 - 82$
9. $0{\cdot}08 \times 700$
10. $40 \times 30 \times 4 - 1$
13. $\frac{1}{5}$ of 235

C.

Across
1. $2{\cdot}6 \times 10$
2. $6{\cdot}314 \times 1000$
4. $600 - 563$
5. $0{\cdot}25 \times 100$
7. $3 \div 0{\cdot}5$
8. $0{\cdot}08 \times 1000$
9. $3{\cdot}15 \div 0{\cdot}01$
11. $1{\cdot}1 \times 70$
12. $499 + 103$
14. $1 \div 0{\cdot}1$
15. $0{\cdot}01 \times 5700$
16. $1000 - 936$

Down
1. $0{\cdot}2 \times 100$
2. $6{\cdot}7 \div 0{\cdot}1$
3. $1800 \div 100$
4. $21 \div 0{\cdot}6$
6. $420 \times 0{\cdot}05$
8. $0{\cdot}8463 \times 10\,000$
9. $0{\cdot}032 \times 1000$
10. $5{\cdot}706 \div 0{\cdot}001$
13. 5^2

Find the operation

Exercise 10

In the flow charts, the boxes A, B, C and D each contain a single mathematical operation (like +5, ×4, −15, ÷2).

Look at flow charts (i) and (ii) together and work out what is the same operation which will replace A. Complete the flow chart by replacing B, C and D.

Now copy and complete each flow chart on the right, using the same operations.

1. (i) 1 → [A] → 8 → [B] → 16 → [C] → 5 → [D] → 15

(ii) 3 → [A] → 10 → [B] → 20 → [C] → 9 → [D] → 27

(a) 4 → [A] → ? → [B] → ? → [C] → ? → [D] → ?

(b) 5 → [A] → ? → [B] → ? → [C] → ? → [D] → ?

(c) ? → [A] → ? → [B] → 28 → [C] → ? → [D] → ?

(d) ? → [A] → 16 → [B] → ? → [C] → ? → [D] → ?

(e) ? → [A] → ? → [B] → ? → [C] → 25 → [D] → ?

(f) ? → [A] → ? → [B] → ? → [C] → ? → [D] → 87

2. (i) 2 → [A] → 4 → [B] → 19 → [C] → 12 → [D] → 3

(ii) 4 → [A] → 8 → [B] → 23 → [C] → 16 → [D] → 4

(a) 6 → [A] → ? → [B] → ? → [C] → ? → [D] → ?

(b) 3 → [A] → ? → [B] → ? → [C] → ? → [D] → ?

(c) ? → [A] → 16 → [B] → ? → [C] → ? → [D] → ?

(d) ? → [A] → ? → [B] → 35 → [C] → ? → [D] → ?

(e) ? → [A] → ? → [B] → ? → [C] → ? → [D] → $2\frac{1}{2}$

(f) ? → [A] → ? → [B] → ? → [C] → ? → [D] → 8

3. (i) 2 → [A] → 17 → [B] → 34 → [C] → 12 → [D] → 3

(ii) 4 → [A] → 19 → [B] → 38 → [C] → 16 → [D] → 4

(a) 7 → [A] → ? → [B] → ? → [C] → ? → [D] → ?

(b) 10 → [A] → ? → [B] → ? → [C] → ? → [D] → ?

(c) ? → [A] → ? → [B] → 62 → [C] → ? → [D] → ?

(d) ? → [A] → $15\frac{1}{2}$ → [B] → ? → [C] → ? → [D] → ?

(e) ? → [A] → ? → [B] → ? → [C] → 208 → [D] → ?

(f) ? → [A] → ? → [B] → ? → [C] → ? → [D] → 14

4. (i) 2 → [A] → 4 → [B] → 12 → [C] → 2 → [D] → 1

(ii) 3 → [A] → 9 → [B] → 27 → [C] → 17 → [D] → $8\frac{1}{2}$

(a) 4 → [A] → 16 → [B] → ? → [C] → ? → [D] → ?

(b) 5 → [A] → ? → [B] → ? → [C] → ? → [D] → ?

(c) ? → [A] → ? → [B] → 108 → [C] → ? → [D] → ?

(d) ? → [A] → ? → [B] → ? → [C] → 182 → [D] → ?

(e) ? → [A] → ? → [B] → 3 → [C] → ? → [D] → ?

(f) ? → [A] → ? → [B] → ? → [C] → ? → [D] → 145

In Questions **5, 6, 7** find the operations A, B, C, D.

5. (i) 4 → [A] → 16 → [B] → 4 → [C] → −6 → [D] → 12

(ii) 9 → [A] → 36 → [B] → 6 → [C] → −4 → [D] → 8

6. (i) 5 → [A] → $\frac{1}{5}$ → [B] → 1·2 → [C] → 1·44 → [D] → 0·48

(ii) $\frac{1}{2}$ → [A] → 2 → [B] → 3 → [C] → 9 → [D] → 3

7. (i) −1 → [A] → 2 → [B] → 8 → [C] → −4 → [D] → 96

(ii) 7 → [A] → 10 → [B] → 1000 → [C] → −500 → [D] → −400

1.4 Properties of numbers

- **Factors** Any number which divides exactly into 8 is a *factor* of 8. The factors of 8 are 1, 2, 4, 8.
- **Multiples** Any number in the 8 times table is a *multiple* of 8. The first five multiples of 8 are 8, 16, 24, 32, 40.
- **Prime** A *prime* number has just two different factors: 1 and itself. The number 1 is *not* prime. [It does not have two different factors.] The first five prime numbers are 2, 3, 5, 7, 11.
- **Prime factor** The factors of 8 are 1, 2, 4, 8. The only *prime factor* of 8 is 2. It is the only prime number which is a factor of 8.

Exercise 11

1. Write down all the factors of the following numbers.
   (a) 6 (b) 15 (c) 18 (d) 21 (e) 40
2. Write down all the prime numbers less than 20.
3. Write down two prime numbers which add up to another prime number. Do this in *two* different ways.
4. Use a calculator to find which of the following are prime numbers.
   (a) 91 (b) 101 (c) 143 (d) 151 (e) 293

   [Hint: Divide by the prime numbers 2, 3, 5, 7, 11 etc.]
5. Prime factors can be found using a 'factor tree'.

   - Here is a factor tree for 140

   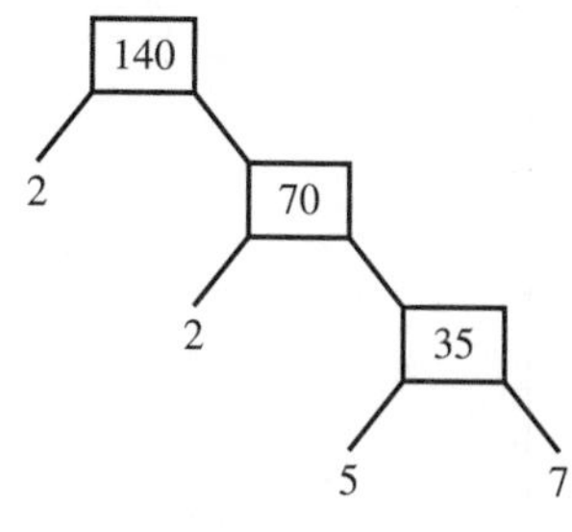

   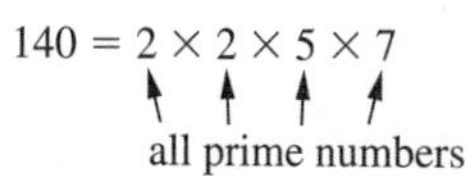

   - Here is a factor tree for 40.

   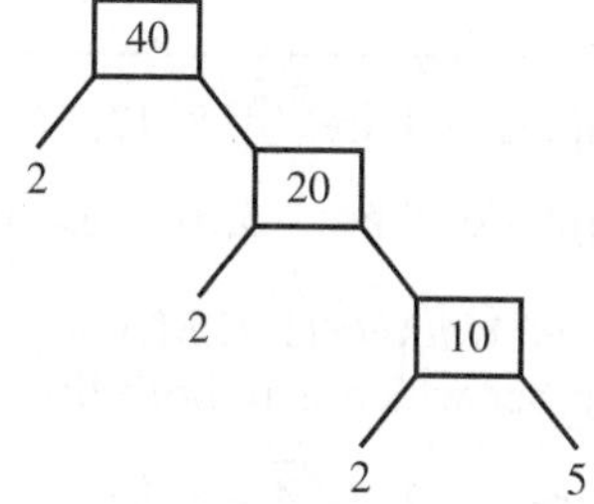

   $40 = 2 \times 2 \times 2 \times 5$

   Draw a factor tree for each of these numbers.
   (a) 36 (b) 60 (c) 216 (d) 200 (e) 1500
6. Here is the number 600 written as the product of its prime factors.

   $$600 = 2 \times 2 \times 2 \times 3 \times 5 \times 5$$

   Use this information to write 1200 as a product of its prime factors.
7. Write down the first four multiples of:
   (a) 3 (b) 4 (c) 10 (d) 11 (e) 20

8. Find the incorrect number.
(a) some multiples of 6 : 12, 18, 24, 32, 48
(b) some multiples of 9 : 18, 27, 45, 56, 72

9. Think of two numbers that are multiples of both 3 and 4.

10. Copy and complete each sentence.
(a) An [odd/even] number is exactly divisible by 2.
(b) An [ ] number leaves a remainder of 1 when divided by 2.
(c) All [ ] numbers are multiples of 2.

11. Copy the table and then write the numbers 1 to 9, one in each box, so that all the numbers satisfy the conditions for both the row and the column.

	Prime number	Multiple of 3	Factor of 16
Number greater than 5			
Odd number			
Even number			

12. Find each of the mystery numbers below.
(a) I am an odd number and a prime number. I am a factor of 14.
(b) I am a two-digit multiple of 50.
(c) I am one less than a prime number which is even.
(d) I am odd, greater than one and a factor of both 20 and 30.

L.C.M. and H.C.F.

(a) The first few multiples of 4 are 4, 8, 12, 16, (20), 24, 28 ...

The first few multiples of 5 are 5, 10, 15, (20), 25, 30, 35 ...

The *Lowest Common Multiple* (L.C.M.) of 4 and 5 is 20.
It is the lowest number which is in both lists.

(b) The factors of 12 are 1, 2, 3, (4), 6, 12

The factors of 20 are 1, 2, (4), 5, 10, 20

The *Highest Common Factor* (H.C.F.) of 12 and 20 is 4.
It is the highest number which is in both lists.

Exercise 12

1. (a) Write down the first four multiples of 6.
(b) Write down the first four multiples of 9.
(c) Write down the L.C.M. of 6 and 9.

2. (a) Write down the first five multiples of 9.
(b) Write down the first four multiples of 15.
(c) Write down the L.C.M. of 9 and 15.

3. Find the L.C.M. of:
(a) 6 and 15 (b) 20 and 30 (c) 6 and 10

4. The factors of 24 are 1, 2, 3, 4, 6, 8, 12, 24.
The factors of 32 are 1, 2, 4, 8, 16, 32.
The *common factors* of 24 and 32 are 1, 2, 4, 8.
Write down the H.C.F. of 24 and 32.

5. Find the H.C.F. of:
(a) 12 and 20 (b) 6 and 15 (c) 18 and 24
(d) 10 and 25 (e) 18 and 27

6. Write down two numbers whose H.C.F. is 8.

7. Write down two numbers whose H.C.F. is 11.

8. If we multiply together three consecutive numbers we should find that the answer is divisible by 6.
For example $2 \times 3 \times 4 = 24$, which *is* divisible by 6.
(a) See if it works for $3 \times 4 \times 5$ or $4 \times 5 \times 6$ or $7 \times 8 \times 9$ and for any other three numbers of your own choice.
(b) Can you see why the answer is always a multiple of 6?

1.5 Negative numbers

- For adding and subtracting use the number line.

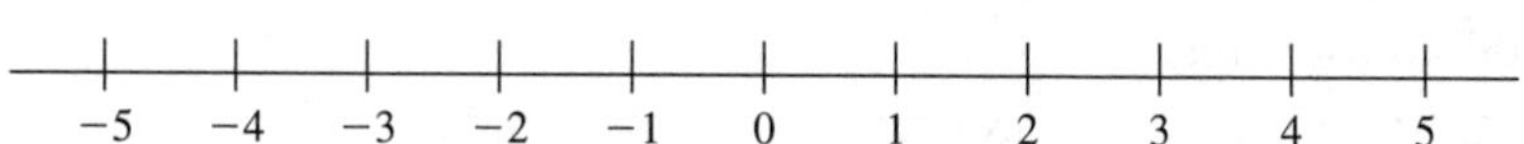

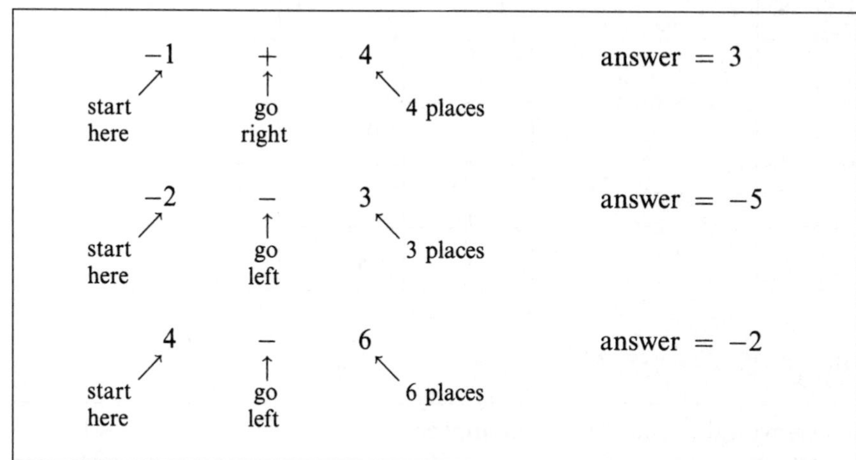

Exercise 13

Work out.

1. $-6+2$	**2.** $-7-5$	**3.** $-3-8$	**4.** $-5+2$
5. $-6+1$	**6.** $8-4$	**7.** $4-9$	**8.** $11-19$
9. $4+15$	**10.** $-7-10$	**11.** $16-20$	**12.** $-7+2$

13. $-6-5$ **14.** $10-4$ **15.** $-4+0$ **16.** $-6+12$
17. $-7+7$ **18.** $2-20$ **19.** $8-11$ **20.** $-6-5$
21. $-8-4$ **22.** $-3+7$ **23.** $-6+10$ **24.** $-5+5$
25. $-11+3$ **26.** $7-10$ **27.** $-5+8$ **28.** $-12+0$
29. $-1+19$ **30.** $20-25$ **31.** $-6-60$ **32.** $-2+100$

- When you have two (+) or (−) signs together use this rule:

  $++ = +$ $+- = -$
  $-- = +$ $-+ = -$

(a) $3-(-6) = 3+6 = 9$
(b) $-4+(-5) = -4-5 = -9$
(c) $-5-(+7) = -5-7 = -12$
(d) $8+(-8) = 8-8 = 0$
(e) $0-(-11) = 0+11 = 11$
(f) $-10-(-3) = -10+3 = -7$

Exercise 14

Work out.

1. $-3+(-5)$ **2.** $-5-(+2)$ **3.** $4-(+3)$ **4.** $-3-(-4)$
5. $6-(-3)$ **6.** $16+(-5)$ **7.** $-4+(+4)$ **8.** $20-(-22)$
9. $-6-(-10)$ **10.** $95+(-80)$ **11.** $-3-(+4)$ **12.** $-5-(+4)$
13. $6+(-7)$ **14.** $-4+(-3)$ **15.** $-7-(-7)$ **16.** $3-(-8)$
17. $-8+(-6)$ **18.** $7-(+7)$ **19.** $12-(-5)$ **20.** $9-(+6)$
21. $-3-(-2)$ **22.** $8+(-11)$ **23.** $10-(-2)$ **24.** $-7+(-2)$
25. $9-(+6)$ **26.** $7+(-7)$ **27.** $0-(-8)$ **28.** $-6-(-8)$

29. Copy and complete these addition squares.

(a)

+	−5	1	6	−2
3	−2	4		
−2				
6				
−10				

(b)

+			−4	
5			1	
		0		5
	7		6	17
		−4		

Multiplying and dividing

- When two directed numbers with the same sign are multiplied together, the answer is positive.

  (a) $+7\times(+3) = +21$
  (b) $-6\times(-4) = +24$

- When two directed numbers with different signs are multiplied together, the answer is negative.

  (a) $-8\times(+4) = -32$
  (b) $+7\times(-5) = -35$

- When dividing directed numbers, the rules are the same as in multiplication.

  (a) $-70\div(-2) = +35$
  (b) $+12\div(-3) = -4$
  (c) $-20\div(+4) = -5$

Exercise 15

1. $-3 \times (+2)$ **2.** $-4 \times (+1)$ **3.** $+5 \times (-3)$ **4.** $-3 \times (-3)$
5. $-4 \times (2)$ **6.** $-5 \times (3)$ **7.** $6 \times (-4)$ **8.** $3 \times (2)$
9. $-3 \times (-4)$ **10.** $6 \times (-3)$ **11.** $-7 \times (3)$ **12.** $-5 \times (-5)$
13. $6 \times (-10)$ **14.** $-3 \times (-7)$ **15.** $8 \times (6)$ **16.** $-8 \times (2)$
17. $-7 \times (6)$ **18.** $-5 \times (-4)$ **19.** $-6 \times (7)$ **20.** $11 \times (-6)$

21. $8 \div (-2)$ **22.** $-9 \div (3)$ **23.** $-6 \div (-2)$ **24.** $10 \div (-2)$
25. $-12 \div (-3)$ **26.** $-16 \div (4)$ **27.** $4 \div (-1)$ **28.** $8 \div (-8)$
29. $16 \div (-8)$ **30.** $-20 \div (-5)$ **31.** $-16 \div (1)$ **32.** $18 \div (-9)$
33. $36 \div (-9)$ **34.** $-45 \div (-9)$ **35.** $-70 \div (7)$ **36.** $-11 \div (-1)$
37. $-16 \div (-1)$ **38.** $1 \div (-\frac{1}{2})$ **39.** $-2 \div (\frac{1}{2})$ **40.** $50 \div (-10)$

41. $-8 \times (-8)$ **42.** $-9 \times (3)$ **43.** $10 \times (-60)$ **44.** $-8 \times (-5)$
45. $-12 \div (-6)$ **46.** $-18 \times (-2)$ **47.** $-8 \div (4)$ **48.** $-80 \div (10)$

49. Copy and complete these multiplication squares.

(a)

×	4	−3	0	−2
−5				
2				
10				
−1				

(b)

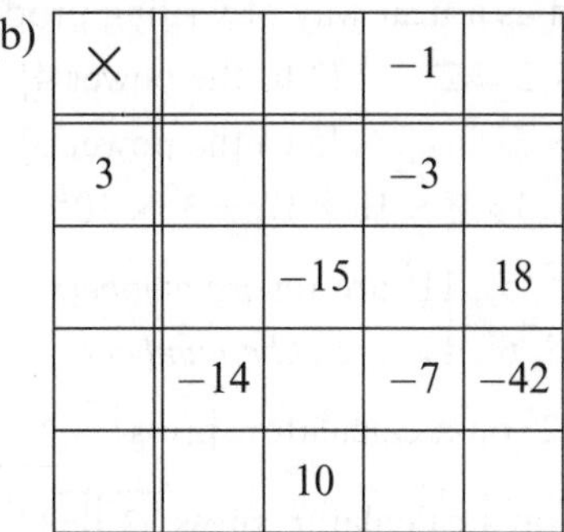

×			−1	
3			−3	
		−15		18
	−14		−7	−42
		10		

Questions on negative numbers are more difficult when the different sorts are mixed together. The remaining questions are given in the form of four short tests.

Test 1

1. $-8 - 8$ **2.** $-8 \times (-8)$ **3.** -5×3 **4.** $-5 + 3$
5. $8 - (-7)$ **6.** $20 - 2$ **7.** $-18 \div (-6)$ **8.** $4 + (-10)$
9. $-2 + 13$ **10.** $+8 \times (-6)$ **11.** $-9 + (+2)$ **12.** $-2 - (-11)$
13. $-6 \times (-1)$ **14.** $2 - 20$ **15.** $-14 - (-4)$ **16.** $-40 \div (-5)$
17. $5 - 11$ **18.** -3×10 **19.** $9 + (-5)$ **20.** $7 \div (-7)$

Test 2

1. $-2 \times (+8)$ **2.** $-2 + 8$ **3.** $-7 - 6$ **4.** $-7 \times (-6)$
5. $+36 \div (-9)$ **6.** $-8 - (-4)$ **7.** $-14 + 2$ **8.** $5 \times (-4)$
9. $11 + (-5)$ **10.** $11 - 11$ **11.** $-9 \times (-4)$ **12.** $-6 + (-4)$
13. $3 - 10$ **14.** $-20 \div (-2)$ **15.** $16 + (-10)$ **16.** $-4 - (+14)$
17. $-45 \div 5$ **18.** $18 - 3$ **19.** $-1 \times (-1)$ **20.** $-3 - (-3)$

Test 3

1. $-10 \times (-10)$ **2.** $-10 - 10$ **3.** $-8 \times (+1)$ **4.** $-8 + 1$
5. $5 + (-9)$ **6.** $15 - 5$ **7.** $-72 \div (-8)$ **8.** $-12 - (-2)$

9. $-1+8$	**10.** $-5 \times (-7)$	**11.** $-10+(-10)$	**12.** $-6 \times (+4)$
13. $6-16$	**14.** $-42 \div (+6)$	**15.** $-13+(-6)$	**16.** $-8-(-7)$
17. $5 \times (-1)$	**18.** $2-15$	**19.** $21+(-21)$	**20.** $-16 \div (-2)$

Test 4

Write down each statement and find the missing number.

1. $(-6) \times \square = 30$	**2.** $\square + (-2) = 0$	**3.** $\square \div (-2) = 10$	**4.** $\square - (-3) = 7$
5. $(-1) \times \square = -1$	**6.** $(-2) - \square = 3$	**7.** $(-2) \div \square = -2$	**8.** $\square - (8) = -6$
9. $(-12) \times (-\frac{1}{2}) = \square$	**10.** $\square + (-10) = 2$	**11.** $6 \times \square = 0$	**12.** $\square - (-8) = 0$

1.6 Powers and roots

Indices

- Indices are used as a neat way of writing products.

  $2 \times 2 \times 2 \times 2 = 2^4$ [2 to the power 4]

  $5 \times 5 \times 5 = 5^3$ [5 to the power 3]

  $3 \times 3 \times 3 \times 3 \times 3 \times 10 \times 10 = 3^5 \times 10^2$

- Numbers like 3^2, 5^2, 11^2 are *square numbers.*

  Numbers like 2^3, 6^3, 11^3 are *cube numbers.*

- To work out 3.2^2 on a calculator, press [3.2] [x^2]

  To work out 3^4 on a calculator, press [3] [x^y] [4] [=]

Exercise 16

Write in a form using indices.

1. $3 \times 3 \times 3 \times 3$	**2.** 5×5	**3.** $6 \times 6 \times 6$
4. $10 \times 10 \times 10 \times 10 \times 10$	**5.** $1 \times 1 \times 1 \times 1 \times 1 \times 1 \times 1$	**6.** $8 \times 8 \times 8 \times 8$
7. $7 \times 7 \times 7 \times 7 \times 7 \times 7$	**8.** $2 \times 2 \times 2 \times 5 \times 5$	**9.** $3 \times 3 \times 7 \times 7 \times 7 \times 7$
10. $3 \times 3 \times 10 \times 10 \times 10$	**11.** $5 \times 5 \times 5 \times 5 \times 11 \times 11$	**12.** $2 \times 3 \times 2 \times 3 \times 3$
13. $5 \times 3 \times 3 \times 5 \times 5$	**14.** $2 \times 2 \times 3 \times 3 \times 3 \times 11 \times 11$	

15. Work out without a calculator.

(a) 4^2 (b) 6^2 (c) 10^2 (d) 3^3 (e) 10^3

16. Use the [x^2] button to work out.

(a) 9^2 (b) 21^2 (c) $1{\cdot}2^2$ (d) $0{\cdot}2^2$ (e) $3{\cdot}1^2$

(f) 100^2 (g) 25^2 (h) $8{\cdot}7^2$ (i) $0{\cdot}9^2$ (j) $81{\cdot}4^2$

17. Find the areas of these squares.

(a)
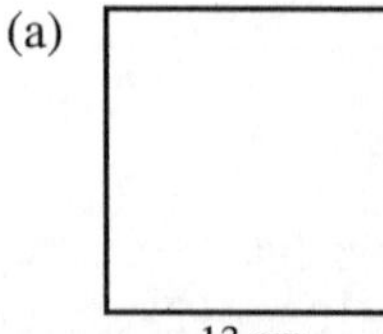
13 cm

(b)
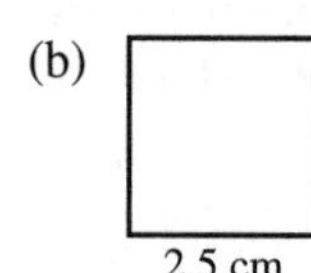
2.5 cm

(c)
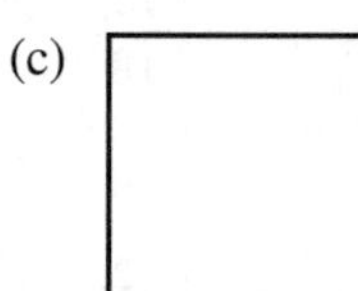
11.4 cm

18. Write in index form.

(a) $a \times a \times a$ (b) $n \times n \times n \times n$ (c) $s \times s \times s \times s \times s$

(d) $p \times p \times q \times q \times q$ (e) $b \times b \times b \times b \times b \times b \times b$

19. Use the $\boxed{x^y}$ button to work out.

(a) 6^3 (b) 2^8 (c) 3^5 (d) 10^5 (e) 4^3

(f) $0{\cdot}1^3$ (g) $1{\cdot}7^4$ (h) $3^4 \times 7$ (i) $5^3 \times 10$

20. A scientist has a dish containing 10^9 germs.
One day later there are 10 times as many germs.
How many germs are in the dish now?

21. A large garden has 2^8 daisies growing on the grass.
A weedkiller removes half of the daisies.
How many daisies are left?

22. A maths teacher won the National Lottery and, as a leaving present, he decided to set a final test to a class of 25 children. The person coming 25th won 2p, the 24th won 4p, the 23rd 8p, the 22nd 16p and so on, doubling the amount each time.

(a) Write 2, 4, 8, 16 as powers of 2.

(b) How much, in pounds, would be given to the person who came 1st in the test?

23. Sean says 'If you work out the product of any four consecutive numbers and then add one, the answer will be square number.'
For example: $1 \times 2 \times 3 \times 4 = 24$
$24 + 1 = 25$, which is a square number.
Is Sean right? Test his theory on four (or more) sets of four consecutive numbers.

Square roots, cube roots

(a) A square has an area of $529\,\text{cm}^2$.
How long is a side of the square?
In other words, what number *multiplied by itself* makes 529?

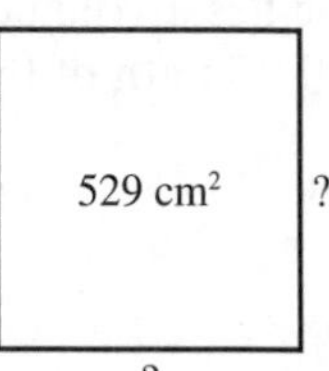

The answer is the *square root* of 529.

On a calculator press $\boxed{\sqrt{\ }}$ $\boxed{529}$ $\boxed{=}$

[On older calculators you may need to press $\boxed{529}$ $\boxed{\sqrt{\ }}$.]

The side of the square is 23 cm.

(b) A cube has a volume of $512\,\text{cm}^3$.
How long is a side of the cube?

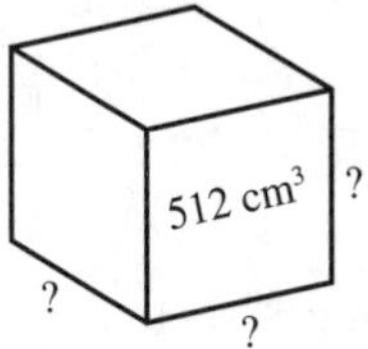

The answer is the *cube root* of 512.

On a calculator press $\boxed{\sqrt[3]{\ }}$ $\boxed{512}$ $\boxed{=}$

The side of the cube is 8 cm. [Check $8 \times 8 \times 8 = 512$.]

Exercise 17

1. Work out, without a calculator.
   (a) $\sqrt{16}$ (b) $\sqrt{36}$ (c) $\sqrt{1}$ (d) $\sqrt{100}$

2. Find the sides of the squares.

(a)

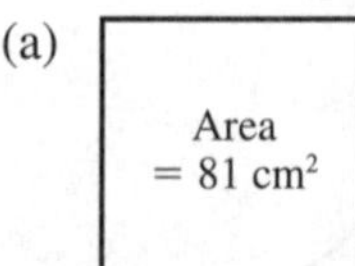

(b)

Area
$= 49\text{ cm}^2$

(c)

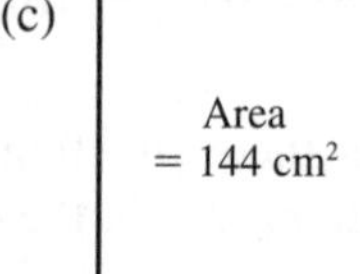

3. Use a calculator to find the following, correct to 1 d.p.
   (a) $\sqrt{10}$ (b) $\sqrt{29}$ (c) $\sqrt{107}$ (d) $\sqrt{19{\cdot}7}$ (e) $\sqrt{2406}$
   (f) $\sqrt{58{\cdot}6}$ (g) $\sqrt{0{\cdot}15}$ (h) $\sqrt{0{\cdot}727}$

4. A square photo has an area of 150 cm^2. Find the length of each side of the photo, correct to the nearest mm.

5. A square field has an area of 20 hectares. How long is each side of the field, correct to the nearest m?
   [1 hectare $= 10\,000\text{ m}^2$]

6. The area of square A is equal to the sum of the areas of squares B and C. Find the length x, correct to 1 d.p.

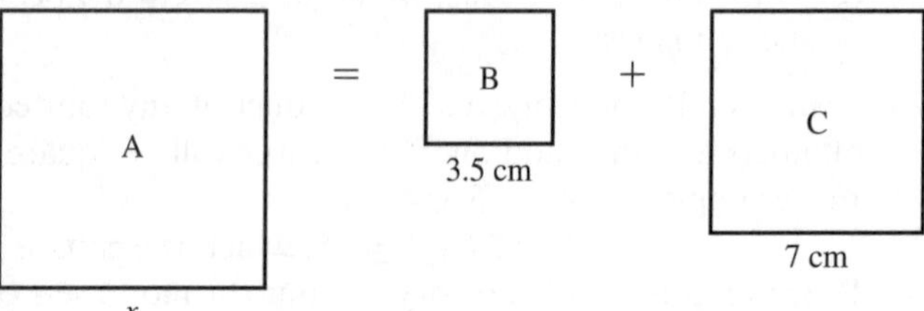

7. Find the following
   (a) $\sqrt[3]{64}$ (b) $\sqrt[3]{125}$ (c) $\sqrt[3]{1000}$

8. A cube has a volume of 200 cm^3.
   Find the length of the side of the cube, correct to 1 d.p.

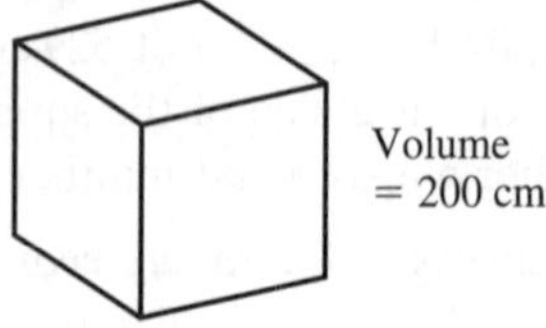

Negative indices, zero index

- Look at this sequence.

$2^4 \quad 2^3 \quad 2^2 \quad 2^1 \quad 2^0 \quad 2^{-1}$

$16 \longrightarrow 8 \longrightarrow 4 \longrightarrow 2 \longrightarrow \boxed{1} \longrightarrow \boxed{\tfrac{1}{2}}$

From left to right the index goes down by one each time as the number is divided by two each time.

we see that $2^0 = 1$
and that $2^{-1} = \frac{1}{2}$

- In general $x^0 = 1$ for any value of x which is not zero.

  In general $x^{-1} = \frac{1}{x}$

  Also $2^{-3} = \frac{1}{2^3}$ $\qquad 3^{-2} = \frac{1}{3^2}$

- The *reciprocal* of 3 is $\frac{1}{3}$. The reciprocal of 10 is $\frac{1}{10}$.

  The reciprocal of n is $\frac{1}{n}$ (which can be written n^{-1}).

Exercise 18

In Questions **1** to **12**, work out the value of the number given.

1. 3^{-1} **2.** 4^{-1} **3.** 10^{-1} **4.** 1^{-4} **5.** 3^{-2} **6.** 4^{-2}
7. 10^{-2} **8.** 8^0 **9.** 7^{-2} **10.** $(-6)^0$ **11.** 9^{-2} **12.** 1^{-7}

In Questions **13** to **32** answer 'true' or 'false'.

13. $2^3 = 8$ **14.** $3^2 = 6$ **15.** $5^3 = 125$ **16.** $2^{-1} = \frac{1}{2}$
17. $10^{-2} = \frac{1}{20}$ **18.** $3^{-3} = \frac{1}{9}$ **19.** $2^2 > 2^3$ **20.** $2^3 < 3^2$
21. $2^{-2} > 2^{-3}$ **22.** $3^{-2} < 3^3$ **23.** $1^9 = 9$ **24.** $(-3)^2 = -9$
25. $5^{-2} = \frac{1}{10}$ **26.** $10^{-3} = \frac{1}{1000}$ **27.** $10^{-2} > 10^{-3}$ **28.** $5^{-1} = 0{\cdot}2$
29. $10^{-1} = 0{\cdot}1$ **30.** $2^{-2} = 0{\cdot}25$ **31.** $5^0 = 1$ **32.** $16^0 = 0$

Multiplying and dividing

- To multiply powers of the same number *add* the indices.

$$3^2 \times 3^4 = (3 \times 3) \times (3 \times 3 \times 3 \times 3) = 3^6$$
$$2^3 \times 2^2 = (2 \times 2 \times 2) \times (2 \times 2) = 2^5$$
$$7^3 \times 7^5 = 7^8 \text{ [add the indices].}$$

- To divide powers of the same number *subtract* the indices.

$$2^4 \div 2^2 = \frac{2 \times 2 \times 2 \times 2}{2 \times 2} = 2^2$$
$$\left.\begin{aligned} 5^6 \div 5^2 &= 5^4 \\ 7^8 \div 7^3 &= 7^5 \end{aligned}\right\} \text{[subtract the indices].}$$

Exercise 19

Write in a more simple form.

1. $5^2 \times 5^4$ **2.** $6^3 \times 6^2$ **3.** $10^4 \times 10^5$ **4.** $7^5 \times 7^3$
5. $3^6 \times 3^4$ **6.** $8^3 \times 8^3$ **7.** $2^3 \times 2^{10}$ **8.** $3^6 \times 3^{-2}$
9. $5^4 \times 5^{-1}$ **10.** $7^7 \times 7^{-3}$ **11.** $5^{-3} \times 5^5$ **12.** $3^{-2} \times 3^{-2}$
13. $6^{-3} \times 6^8$ **14.** $5^{-2} \times 5^{-8}$ **15.** $7^{-3} \times 7^9$ **16.** $7^4 \div 7^2$
17. $6^7 \div 6^2$ **18.** $8^5 \div 8^4$ **19.** $5^{10} \div 5^2$ **20.** $10^7 \div 10^5$
21. $9^6 \div 9^8$ **22.** $3^8 \div 3^{10}$ **23.** $2^6 \div 2^2$ **24.** $3^3 \div 3^5$
25. $7^2 \div 7^8$ **26.** $3^{-2} \div 3^2$ **27.** $5^{-3} \div 5^2$ **28.** $8^{-1} \div 8^4$
29. $5^{-4} \div 5^1$ **30.** $6^2 \div 6^{-2}$ **31.** $3^4 \div 3^4$ **32.** $5^2 \div 5^2$

33. $\frac{3^4 \times 3^5}{3^2}$ **34.** $\frac{2^8 \times 2^4}{2^5}$ **35.** $\frac{7^3 \times 7^3}{7^4}$ **36.** $\frac{5^9 \times 5^{10}}{5^{20}}$

Further rules of indices

- To raise a power of a number to a further power, *multiply* the indices.

(a) $(x^2)^3 = x^6$	(b) $(a^4)^2 = a^8$
(c) $3x^2 \times 4x^5 = 12x^7$ — (3×4), $(2+5)$	(d) $4a^7 \times 5a^2 = 20a^9$ — (4×5), $(7+2)$
(e) $12x^5 \div 3x^2 = 4x^3$ — $(12\div3)$, $(5-2)$	(f) $(3a^2)^3 = 3^3 \times a^6 = 27a^6$

Exercise 20

Write in a more simple form.

1. $(3^3)^2$ **2.** $(5^4)^3$ **3.** $(7^2)^5$ **4.** $(8^2)^{10}$ **5.** $(x^2)^3$ **6.** $(a^5)^3$
7. $(n^7)^2$ **8.** $(y^3)^3$ **9.** $(2^{-1})^2$ **10.** $(3^{-2})^2$ **11.** $(7^{-1})^{-2}$ **12.** $(x^3)^{-1}$
13. $2a^2 \times 3a^3$ **14.** $4n^3 \times 5n^1$ **15.** $7x^4 \times 2x$ **16.** $8y^5 \times 3y^2$ **17.** $5n^3 \times n^4$ **18.** $6y^2 \times 2$
19. $3p^3 \times 3p^2$ **20.** $2p \times 5p^5$ **21.** $(2x^2)^3$ **22.** $(3a^2)^3$ **23.** $(4y^3)^2$ **24.** $(5x^4)^2$

Solve the equations for x.

25. $x^2 = 9$ **26.** $x^5 = 1$ **27.** $x^3 = 27$ **28.** $x^5 = 0$
29. $2^x = 8$ **30.** $3^x = 3$ **31.** $5^x = 25$ **32.** $10^x = 1000$
33. $2^x = \frac{1}{2}$ **34.** $4^x = \frac{1}{4}$ **35.** $7^x = 1$ **36.** $3x^3 = 24$
37. $10x^3 = 640$ **38.** $2x^3 = 0$ **39.** $10^x = 0{\cdot}1$ **40.** $5^x = 1$

1.7 Mixed problems 1

Exercise 21

1. Write down the reading on each scale.

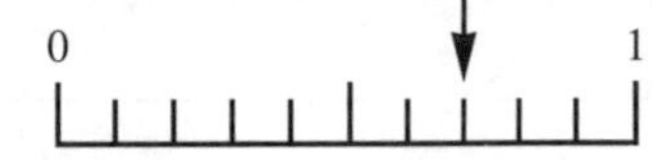

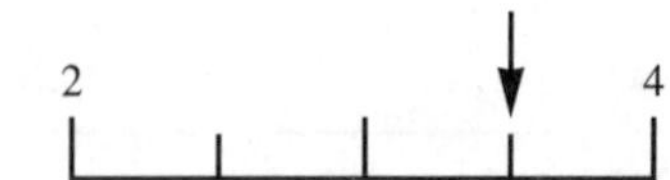

2. There are 5 people in a team.
How many teams can you make from 118 people?

3. A tree was planted when James Wilkinson was born. He died in 1920, aged 75. How old was the tree in 1975?

4. Washing-up liquid is sold in 200 ml containers. Each container costs 57p. How much will it cost to buy 10 litres of the liquid?

5. A train is supposed to leave London at 11 24 and arrive in Brighton at 12 40. The train was delayed and arrived $2\frac{1}{4}$ hours late. At what time did the train arrive?

6. Big Ben stopped for repairs at 17 15 on Tuesday and restarted at 08 20 on Wednesday.
For how long had it been stopped?

7. How much would I pay for nine litres of paint if two litres cost £2·30?

8. Here is a 'magic square'. The numbers in each row, column and main diagonal add up to to the same number.
Copy and complete these magic squares:

8	1	6
3	5	7
4	9	2

(a)

6	13	
	9	
		12

(b)

11			10
2	13	16	
		4	
7	12		6

9. A piece of wire 48 cm long is bent to form a rectangle in which the length is twice the width.
Find the area of the rectangle.

10. A rectangular floor 3 m by 4 m is to be covered with square tiles, each of side length 50 cm.
How many tiles will be needed?

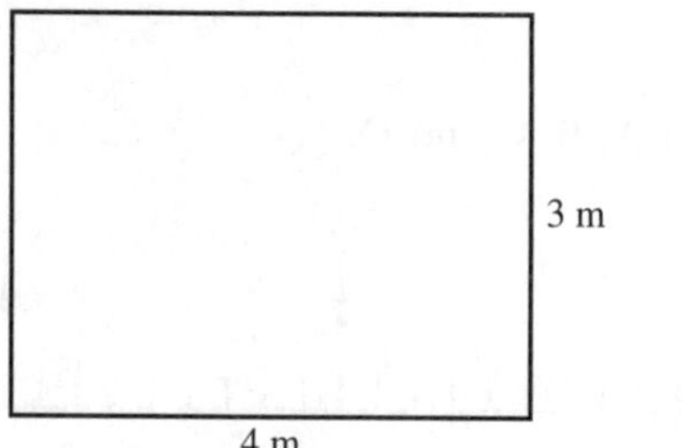

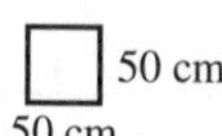

Exercise 22

1. Write down each calculation and find the missing digits.

(a)
```
    5 □ 3
  + 3 4 □
  -------
    □ 5 9
```

(b)
```
    3 3 4
  + □ 4 □
  -------
    6 □ 0
```

(c) □□□ ÷ 5 = 32

2. The fourteenth number in the sequence 1, 2, 4, 8, 16 ... is 8192.
What is:
(a) the fifteenth number
(b) the thirteenth number?

3. The manager of a toy shop bought 10 000 model cars for £4950.

The models were sold at 95p each.
What was the total profit made?

4. Work out, without using a calculator.

(a) 0·6 + 2·72 (b) 3·21 − 1·6
(c) 2·8 − 1·34 (d) 8 − 3·6
(e) 100 × 0·062 (f) 27·4 ÷ 10

5. Six people can travel in one car and there are altogether 106 people to transport. How many cars are needed?

6. Copy and complete these 'magic squares'.

(a)

−1	−2	
	0	
		1

(b)

		−1
	2	
5		0

(c)

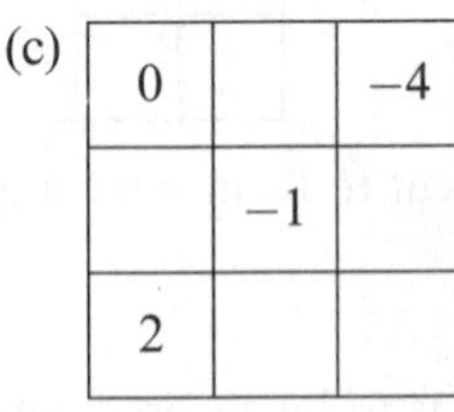

0		−4
	−1	
2		

7. Write these numbers in order of size, smallest first.

0·2 0·5 0·05 0·11 0·201 0·21

8. The scale below shows temperatures in °C.
Write down the temperatures for the arrows marked A, B, C and D.

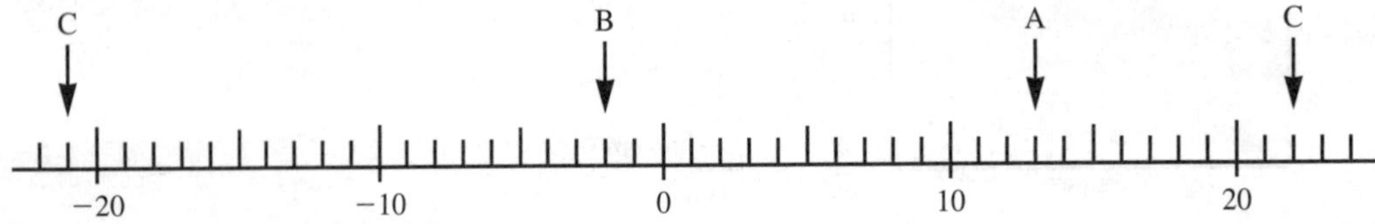

9. A baby falls asleep at 20.55 on Monday night and wakes up at 06.10 on Tuesday morning. For how long was the baby asleep?

10. Here are five number cards 

What is the largest odd number you can make with these five cards?

Exercise 23

1. Copy and complete the following bill.

$6\frac{1}{2}$ lb of potatoes at 12p per lb	=	£
4 lb of beef at per lb	=	£7·20
jars of coffee at 95p per jar	=	£6·65
Total	=	£

2. Write in index form [e.g. $2 \times 2 \times 2 = 2^3$].
(a) $3 \times 3 \times 3 \times 3$
(b) $1 \times 1 \times 1 \times 1 \times 1 \times 1 \times 1$
(c) $3 \times 3 \times 3 \times 7 \times 7$
(d) half of 2^5
(e) 10 times 10^5
(f) 1% of 1 million

3. Work out.
(a) $(-3) \times (-3)$
(b) $-7 + 2$
(c) $12 \div (-2)$
(d) $8 - 18$
(e) $5 - (-2)$
(f) $5 \times (-2)$

4. How many 50 ml bottles can be filled from a jar containing one litre of liquid?

5. (a) Which four coins make a total of 77p?
(b) Which five coins make a total of 86p?
(c) Which five coins make a total of £1·57?

6. Two numbers *m* and *z* are such that *z* is greater than 10 and *m* is less than 8. Arrange the numbers 9, *z* and *m* in order of size, starting with the smallest.

7. One day a third of the class is absent and 16 children are present. How many children are in the class when no one is away?

8. A train leaves Manchester at 09.00 and travels towards London at 100 mph. Another train leaves London for Manchester, also at 09.00, and travels at 80 mph. Which train is nearer to London when they meet?

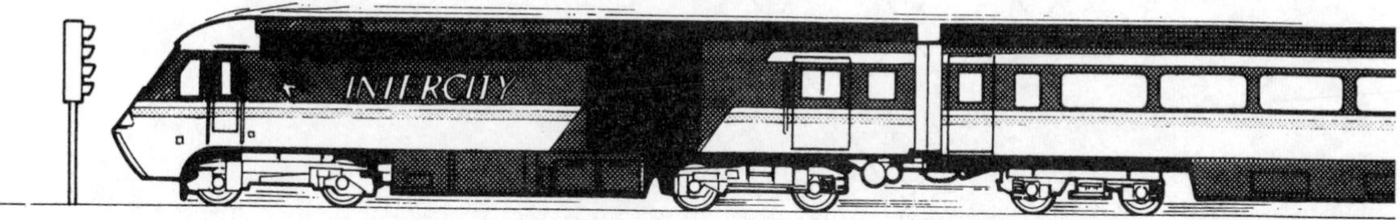

9. A man is 35 cm taller than his daughter, who is 5 cm shorter than her mother. The man was born in 1949 and is 1·80 m tall.
How tall is the wife?

10. In a simple code A = 1, B = 2, C = 3, ... Z = 26.
Decode the following messages.

(a) 23, 8, 1, 20
20, 9, 13, 5
4, 15
23, 5
6, 9, 14, 9, 19, 8.

(b) 19, 4^2, (3×7), 18, $(90 - 71)$
1^3, (9×2), $(2^2 + 1^2)$
18, $(\frac{1}{5}$ of $105)$, 2, $(1 \div \frac{1}{2})$, 3^2, 19, 2^3.

(c) 23, $(100 \div 20)$
1, $(2 \times 3 \times 3)$, $(2^2 + 1^2)$
21, $(100 - 86)$, $(100 \div 25)$, 5, $(2^4 + 2)$
1, (5×4), $(10 \div \frac{1}{2})$, 1, $(27 \div 9)$, $(99 \div 9)$.

Exercise 24

1. A special new cheese is on offer at £3·48 per kilogram. Mrs Mann buys half a kilogram. How much change does she receive if she pays with a £5 note?

2. A cup and a saucer together cost £2·80. The cup costs 60p more than the saucer. How much does the cup cost?

3. A garden 9 m by 12 m is to be treated with fertilizer. One cup of fertilizer covers an area of 2 m^2 and one bag of fertilizer is sufficient for 18 cups.
(a) Find the area of the garden.
(b) Find the number of bags of fertilizer needed.

4. Copy and complete the pattern below.

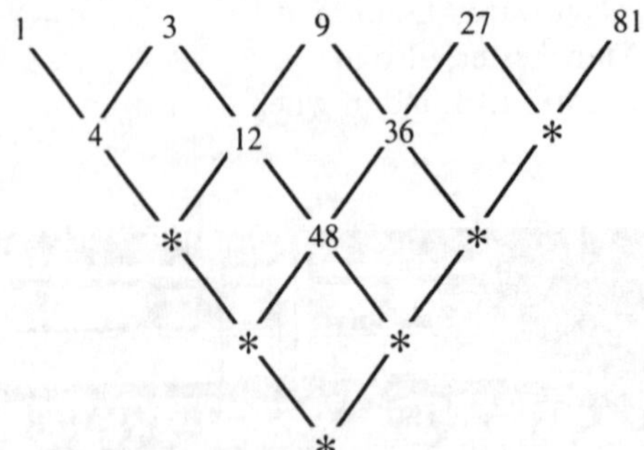

5. Six lamp posts lie at equal distances from each other along a straight road. If the distance between each pair of lamp posts is 20 m, how far is it from the first lamp post to the sixth?

6. Here is a list of numbers.

   2 5 8 22 25 27 44 49

   Write down the numbers which are:
   (a) factors of 15 (b) multiples of 9 (c) prime numbers
   (d) square numbers (e) cube numbers

7. A ship's voyage started at 20 30 on Tuesday and finished at 07 00 on the next day.
   How long was the journey in hours and minutes?

8. Work out, without using a calculator.
   (a) 0·6 − 0·06 (b) 0·04 × 1000
   (c) 0·4 ÷ 100 (d) 7·2 − 5
   (e) 10% of £90 (f) 25% of £160.

9. Copy each line and find the missing number.
   (a) $9 - \square = -2$ (b) $(-2) \times \square = 8$ (c) $-6 - 8 = \square$

10. Find two numbers which:
   (a) multiply to give 12 and add up to 7
   (b) multiply to give 42 and add up to 13
   (c) multiply to give 32 and add up to 12
   (d) multiply to give 48 and add up to 26.

Exercise 25

1. In a simple code A = 1, B = 2, C = 3 and so on. When the word 'BAT' is written in code its total score is (2 + 1 + 20) = 23.
   (a) Find the score for the word 'ZOOM'.
   (b) Find the score for the word 'ALPHABET'.
   (c) Find a word with a score of 40.

2. How many cubes, each of edge 1 cm, are required to fill a box with internal dimensions 5 cm by 8 cm by 3 cm?

3. A swimming pool 20 m by 12 m contains water to a uniform depth of $1\frac{1}{2}$ m. 1 m^3 of water weighs 1000 kg. What is the weight of the water in the pool?

4. The houses in a street are numbered from 1 to 60.
   How many times does the number '2' appear?

5. Draw a large copy of the square below.

1	2	3	4

Your task is to fill up all 16 squares using four 1's, four 2's, four 3's and four 4's. Each number may appear only once in any row (↔) or column (↕). The first row has been drawn already.

6. Between the times 11 57 and 12 27 the mileometer of a car changes from 23793 miles to 23825 miles.
At what average speed is the car travelling?

7. Which of the shapes below can be drawn without going over any line twice and without taking the pencil from the paper?
Write 'yes' or 'no' for each shape.

(a)
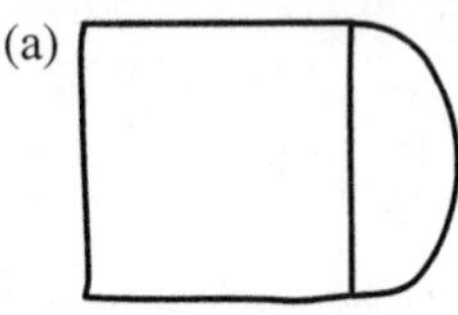

(b)

(c)

(d)
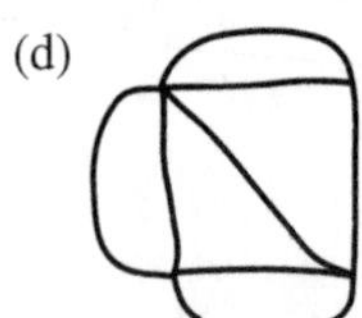

(e)
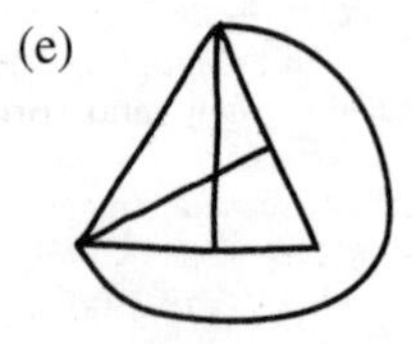

(f)
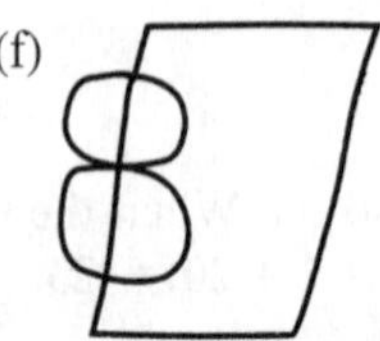

(g)

(h)
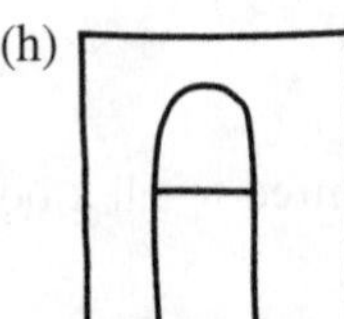

8. A generous, but not very bright, teacher decides to award 1p to the person coming 10th in a test, 2p to the person coming 9th, 4p to the person coming 8th and so on, doubling the amount each time. How much does the teacher award to the person who came top?

Timetables

Exercise 26

1. For how many minutes do each of the following programmes last:
   (a) 'The Money Programme'
   (b) 'Fawlty Towers'
   (c) 'Face the Press'
   (d) '100 Great Sporting Moments'?
2. How much of a video tape would be used if 'The Jewel in the Crown' and 'The Writing on the Wall' were recorded?
3. At what time does 'Comrades' start on the 24-hour clock?
4. There were four films on the two channels. What was the title of the shortest film?
5. A video tape is 3 hours long. How much of the tape is not used after taping the two films in the afternoon on Channel 4?
6. How much time is devoted to sport on BBC 2? [Include 'Under Sail'.]
7. For how many hours and minutes does Channel 4 broadcast programmes?
8. What is the starting time on the 24-hour clock of the programme in which 'Basil' appears?
9. How many programmes were repeats?
10. For how long are 'Pages from Ceefax' broadcast?
11. What is the starting time on the 24-hour clock of the programme in which the 'Redskins' appear?
12. How much of a two hour video tape is not used after taping 'Windmill' and 'The Natural World'?
13. For how many hours and minutes does BBC 2 broadcast programmes?

BBC 2

9.0	**PAGES FROM CEEFAX.**
10.20	**OPEN UNIVERSITY.**
11.25	**PAGES FROM CEEFAX.**
11.50	**CHAMPION THE WONDER HORSE*:** Lost River (rpt). A drought brings danger.
12.15	**WINDMILL:** Archive film on animals.
1.10	**STATES OF MIND:** Jonathan Miller talks to Professor Richard Gregory (rpt.).
2.0	**RUGBY SPECIAL:** Highlights of a County Championship match and a Welsh Cup match.
2.30	**TENNIS:** Benson and Hedges Final.
4.15	**UNDER SAIL:** New series.
4.35	**RACHMANINOV MASTERCLASS.**
5.20	**THINKING ALOUD:** Denis Healey joins a discussion on espionage.
6.0	**NEWS REVIEW,** with Moira Stewart.
6.30	**THE MONEY PROGRAMME:** Guns for Sale. A look at Britain's defence industry.
7.15	**THE NATURAL WORLD:** City of Coral. A voyage beneath the Caribbean.
8.5	**COMRADES:** Educating Rita. The first of 12 films about life in the Soviet Union profiles a young trainee teacher.
8.50	**100 GREAT SPORTING MOMENTS:** Daley Thompson's Gold in the Moscow Olympics.
9.10	**FAWLTY TOWERS:** Basil and Sybil fall out over alterations to the hotel (rpt.).
9.40	**FILM:** A Dangerous Summer (see Film Guide).
11.5	**TENNIS:** Benson and Hedges Final.
11.55	**MUSIC AT NIGHT. 12.10 CLOSE.**

CHANNEL 4

1.5	**IRISH ANGLE — HANDS:** Basket Maker.
1.30	**FACE THE PRESS:** Graham Kelly, Secretary of the Football League, questioned by Ian Wooldridge of the Daily Mail and Brian Glanville of the Sunday Times.
2.0	**POB'S PROGRAMME,** with Patricia Hodge.
2.30	**FILM*:** Journey Together (see Film Guide).
4.15	**FILM*:** The London Blackout Murders, with John Abbot (see Film Guide).
5.15	**NEWS; WEATHER,** followed by **THE BUSINESS PROGRAMME.**
6.0	**AMERICAN FOOTBALL:** Dallas Cowboys at Washington Redskins.
7.15	**THE HEART OF THE DRAGON:** Understanding (rpt.).
8.15	**THE JEWEL IN THE CROWN (T):** The Towers of Silence (rpt.).
9.15	**THE WRITING ON THE WALL:** Who Governs? The political events of 1974 recalled by Robert Kee.
10.25	**FILM*:** Seven Days to Noon (see Film Guide). **12.10 CLOSE.**

2 ALGEBRA 1

2.1 Basic algebra

Using letters for numbers

Many problems in mathematics are made easier to solve when letters are used instead of numbers. It is important to remember that *letters stand for numbers*.

Find what number I am left with.

(a) I start with x, multiply by 7 and then add 10.	$x \longrightarrow 7x \longrightarrow 7x + 10$
(b) I start with y, subtract 5 and then add t.	$y \longrightarrow y - 5 \longrightarrow y - 5 + t$
(c) I start with a, subtract 3 and then multiply the result by 5.	$a \longrightarrow a - 3 \longrightarrow 5(a - 3)$
(d) I start with x, add 7 and then square the result.	$x \longrightarrow x + 7 \longrightarrow (x + 7)^2$

Notice that *brackets* have been used in parts (c) and (d).

Exercise 1

In each question, find what number I am left with.

1. I start with x, multiply it by 3 and then add 6. $3x+6$
2. I start with x, multiply it by 5 and then add 7. $5x+7$
3. I start with x, double it and then subtract 4. $2x-4$
4. I start with x, multiply it by 6 and then subtract y. $6x-y$
5. I start with y, treble it and then add t. $3y+t$
6. I start with x, add 4 and then multiply the result by 3. $3(x+4)$
   [Hint: use brackets]
7. I start with x, add 3 and then multiply the result by 5. $5(x+3)$
8. I start with y, add 11 and then multiply the result by 6. $6(y+11)$
9. I start with x, add 3 and then divide the result by 4. $\frac{x+3}{4}$
   [Hint: If you divide m by 5, write $\frac{m}{5}$ rather than $m \div 5$.]
10. I start with x, subtract 7 and then divide the result by 3. $\frac{x-7}{3}$
11. I start with y, subtract 8 and then divide the result by 5. $\frac{y-8}{5}$
12. I start with $4a$, add 3, multiply the result by 2 and then divide the final result by 4. $\frac{2(4a+3)}{4}$
13. I start with m, subtract 6, multiply the result by 3 and the divide the final result by 4. $\frac{3(m-6)}{4}$

14. I start with x, square it and then subtract 6.
15. I start with x, square it, add 3 and then divide the result by 4.
16. I start with n, add 2 and then square the result. [Use brackets.]
17. I start with w, subtract x and then square the result.
18. I start with x, square it, subtract 7 and then divide the result by 3.
19. I start with x, subtract 9, square the result and then add 10.
20. I start with y, add 7, square the result and then divide by x.
21. I start with a, subtract x, cube the result and then divide by y.
22. A piece of wood is l cm long. If I cut off a piece 3 cm long, how much wood remains?
23. A piece of string is 15 cm long. How much remains after I cut off a piece of length x cm?
24. A delivery van weighs l kg. At a depot it picks up goods weighing 200 kg and later delivers goods weighing m kg. How much does it weigh after making the delivery?
25. A box usually contains n chocolates. The shopkeeper puts an extra 2 chocolates into each box. A girl buys 4 boxes. How many chocolates does she have?
26. A brick weighs w kg. How much do six bricks weigh?
27. A sack weighs l kg. How much do x sacks weigh?
28. A man shares a sum of n pence equally between six children. How much does each child receive?
29. A sum of £p is shared equally between you and four others. How much does each person receive?
30. A cake weighing 12 kg is cut into n equal pieces. How much does each piece weigh?

Collecting terms

- '$3x + 4$' is an *expression*. It is *not* an equation because there is no equals sign. $3x$ and 4 are two *terms* in the expression.
- The expression $7x + 2x$ consists of two *like terms*, $7x$ and $2x$. Like terms can be added or subtracted. So $7x + 2x = 9x$.
- The expression $5x - 3y$ consists of two *unlike* terms, $5x$ and $3y$. Unlike terms cannot be added or subtracted.

(a) $8a + 7a - 3a = 12a$ (b) $3x + y + 2x = 5x + y$

(c) $x^2 + 3x^2 + 2x = 4x^2 + 2x$ (d) $5 + 3y + 6 + y^2 = 11 + 3y + y^2$

Exercise 2

Collect like terms together.

1. $2x + 3 + 3x + 5$
2. $4x + 8 + 5x - 3$
3. $5x - 3 + 2x + 7$
4. $6x + 1 + x + 3$
5. $4x - 3 + 2x + 10 + x$
6. $5x + 8 + x + 4 + 2x$
7. $7x - 9 + 2x + 3 + 3x$
8. $5x + 7 - 3x - 2$
9. $4x - 6 - 2x + 1$
10. $10x + 5 - 9x - 10 + x$
11. $4a + 6b + 3 + 9a - 3b - 4$
12. $8m - 3n + 1 + 6n + 2m + 7$
13. $6p - 4 + 5q - 3p - 4 - 7q$
14. $12s - 3t + 2 - 10s - 4t + 12$
15. $a - 2b - 7 + a + 2b + 8$
16. $3x + 2y + 5z - 2x - y + 2z$
17. $6x - 5y + 3z - x + y + z$
18. $2k - 3m + n + 3k - m - n$
19. $12a - 3 + 2b - 6 - 8a + 3b$
20. $3a + x + e - 2a - 5x - 6e$
21. $x^2 + 3x + 2 + 4x + 1$
22. $x^2 + 4x + 3 + 3x + 5$
23. $x^2 + 5x + 2 - 2x + 1$
24. $x^2 + 2x + 2x^2 + 4x + 5$
25. $x^2 + 5x + x^2 + x - 7$
26. $2x^2 - 3x + 8 + x^2 + 4x + 4$
27. $3x^2 + 4x + 6 - x^2 - 3x - 3$
28. $5x^2 - 3x + 2 - 3x^2 + 2x - 2$
29. $2x^2 - 2x + 3 - x^2 - 2x - 5$
30. $6x^2 - 7x + 8 - 3x^2 + 5x - 10$
31. $3y^2 - 6x + y^2 + x^2 + 7x + 4x^2$
32. $8 - 5x - 2x^2 + 4 + 6x + 2x^2$
33. $5 + 2y + 3y^2 - 8y - 6 + 2y^2 + 3$
34. $ab + a^2 - 3b + 2ab - a^2$
35. $3c^2 - d^2 + 2cd - 3c^2 - d^2$
36. $ab + 2a^2 + 3ab - 4a^2 + 2a$
37. $x^3 + 2x^2 - x + 3x^2 + x^3 + x$
38. $5 - x^2 - 2x^3 + 6 + 2x^2 + 3x^3$
39. $xy + ab - cd + 2xy - ab + dc$
40. $pq - 3qp + p^2 + 2qp - q^2$

In questions **41** to **46** find the perimeter of each shape. Give the answers in the simplest form.

41.

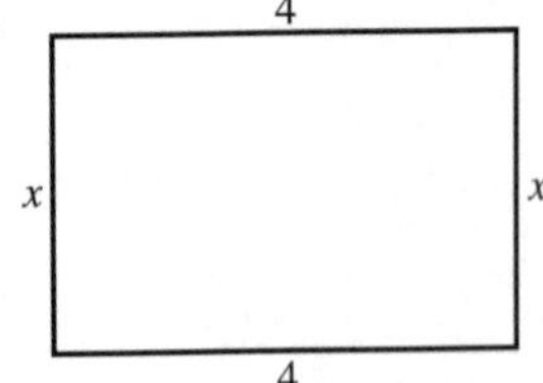

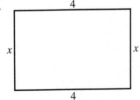

42.

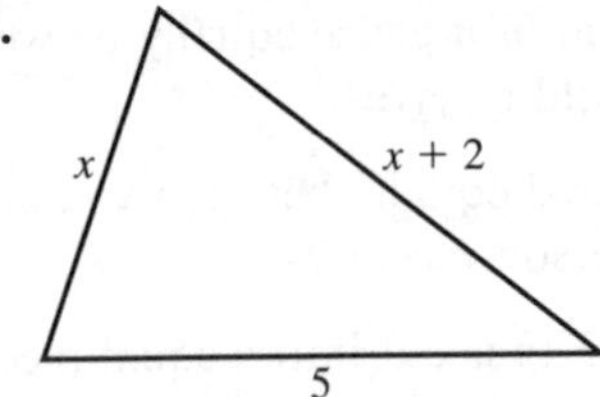

43.

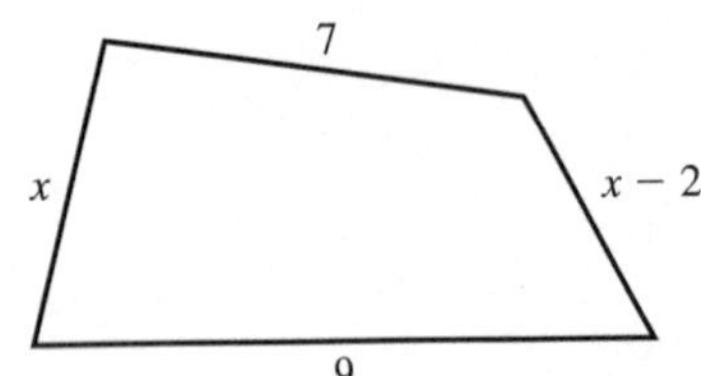

44.

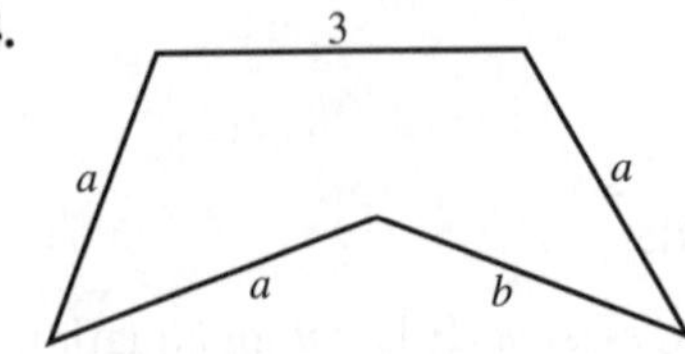

45.

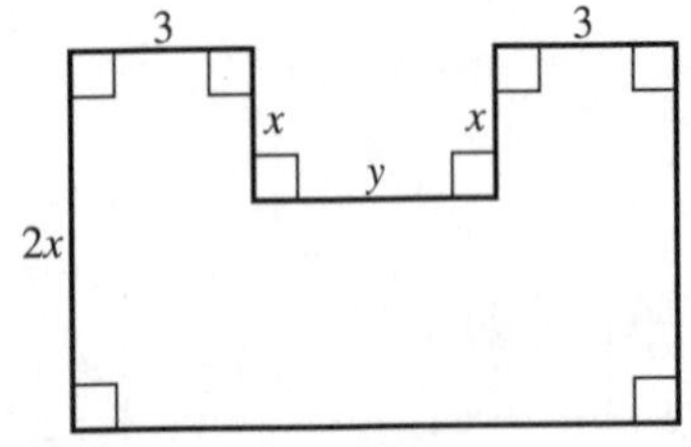

46.

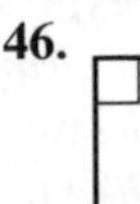

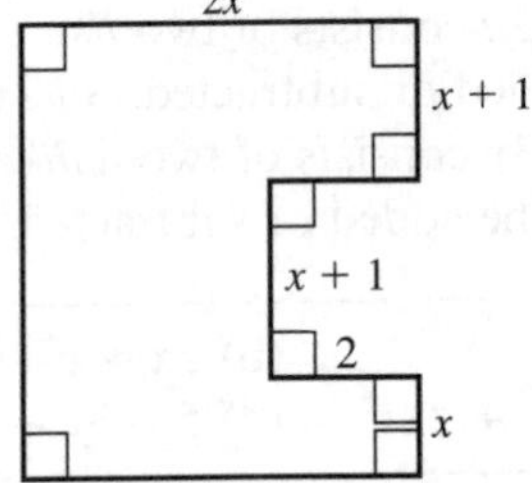

Simplifying terms and brackets

(a) $3 \times 4x = 12x$ (b) $5x \times 4x = 20x^2$ (c) $-3 \times 2x = -6x$
(d) $5(2a \times 3a) = 30a^2$ (e) $3m \times 2n = 6mn$ (f) $5b \times 2bc = 10b^2c$

(g) $3(2x - 1) = 6x - 3$ (h) $x(3x + 4) = 3x^2 + 4x$
(i) $a(a + 2b) = a^2 + 2ab$ (j) $t^2(3t - 2) = 3t^3 - 2t^2$

(k) $2(x + 3) + 5(x - 1)$
$= 2x + 6 + 5x - 5$
$= 7x + 1$

(l) $5(a - b) - 2(2a - b)$
$= 5a - 5b - 4a + 2b$
$= a - 3b$

Exercise 3

Write in a more simple form.

1. $2 \times 3x$ **2.** $4 \times 2x$ **3.** $3 \times 2x$ **4.** $3a \times 5$
5. $5 \times 3x$ **6.** $3 \times 2y$ **7.** $4 \times 5y$ **8.** $5t \times (-2)$
9. $7 \times 3x$ **10.** $-2 \times 3x$ **11.** $-5 \times 4x$ **12.** $2y \times 10$
13. $-2 \times 5x$ **14.** $7 \times 4a$ **15.** $5 \times 3a$ **16.** $100 \times 10a$

17. $x \times 2x$ **18.** $x \times 4x$ **19.** $y \times 3y$ **20.** $2x \times 3x$
21. $4x \times 2x$ **22.** $5y \times 2y$ **23.** $4t \times 6t$ **24.** $6a \times a$
25. $x \times 2x^2$ **26.** $2x \times 3x^2$ **27.** $4y^2 \times 2y$ **28.** $3a \times 2a^2$
29. $7p \times 3p$ **30.** $2(3x \times 2x)$ **31.** $4(3x \times 5x)$ **32.** $5(2x \times 3x)$

33. $2a \times 3b$ **34.** $x \times 3x^3$ **35.** $y \times 2x$ **36.** $2p \times 5q$
37. $3x \times 5y$ **38.** $6x \times 3x^2$ **39.** $3a \times 8a^3$ **40.** $ab \times 2a$
41. $xy \times 3y$ **42.** $cd \times 5c$ **43.** $ab \times ab$ **44.** $2xy \times xy$
45. $3d \times d \times d$ **46.** $5(2x \times xy)$ **47.** $3a \times (-2a)$ **48.** $-a \times (-2ab)$

Exercise 4

Remove the brackets.

1. $2(x + 3)$ **2.** $3(x + 5)$ **3.** $4(x + 6)$
4. $2(2x + 1)$ **5.** $5(2x + 3)$ **6.** $4(3x - 1)$
7. $6(2x - 2)$ **8.** $3(5x - 2)$ **9.** $5(3x - 4)$
10. $7(2x - 3)$ **11.** $2(2x + 3)$ **12.** $3(2x + 1)$
13. $5(x + 4)$ **14.** $6(2x + 2)$ **15.** $-2(4x - 1)$

16. $-5(2x - 2)$ **17.** $-3(2x + 1)$ **18.** $-(2x + 1)$
19. $-(3x + 2)$ **20.** $-(4x - 5)$ **21.** $x(x + 3)$
22. $x(x + 5)$ **23.** $x(x - 2)$ **24.** $x(x - 3)$
25. $x(2x + 1)$ **26.** $x(3x - 2)$ **27.** $x(3x + 5)$
28. $2x(x - 1)$ **29.** $2x(x + 2)$ **30.** $3x(2x + 3)$

31. A solid rectangular block measures x cm by x cm by $(x + 3)$ cm. Find a simplified expression for its surface area in cm^2.

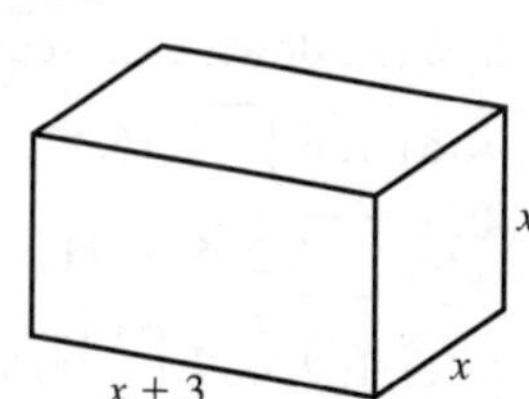

Exercise 5

Remove the brackets and simplify.

1. $3(x+2)+4(x+1)$
2. $5(x-2)+3(x+4)$
3. $2(a-3)+3(a+1)$
4. $5(a+1)+6(a+2)$
5. $7(a-2)+(a+4)$
6. $3(t-2)+5(2+t)$
7. $3(x+2)-2(x+1)$
8. $4(x+3)-3(x+2)$
9. $5(x-2)-3(x-2)$
10. $4(a-2)-2(2a+1)$
11. $x(2x+1)+3(x+2)$
12. $x(2x-3)+5(x+1)$
13. $a(3a+2)+2(2a-2)$
14. $y(5y+1)+3(y-1)$
15. $x(2x+1)+x(3x+1)$
16. $a(2a+3)-a(a+1)$
17. Three rods A, B and C have lengths of x, $(x+1)$ and $(x-2)$ cm respectively, as shown.

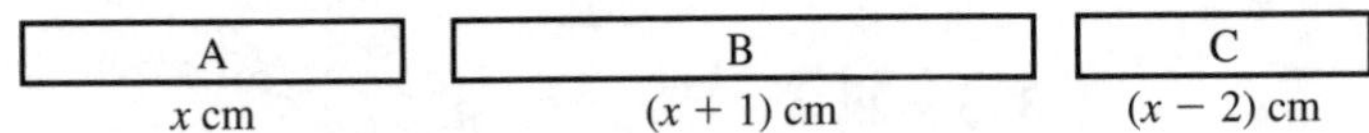

In the diagrams below express the length l in terms of x. Give your answers in their simplest form.

(a) 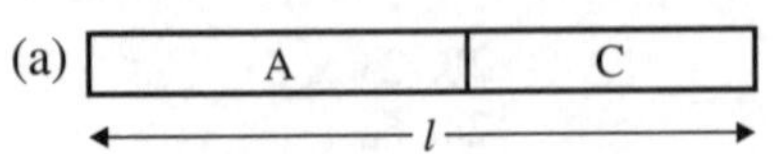

(b) 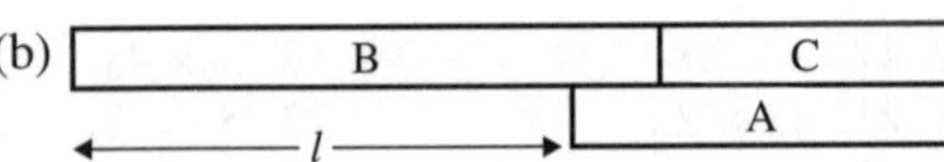

(c) 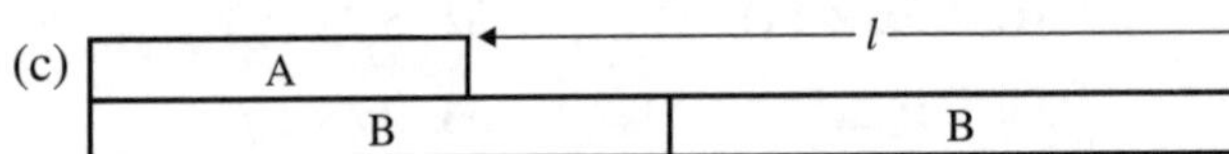

(d) 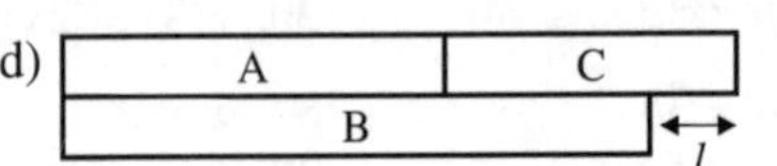

(e) 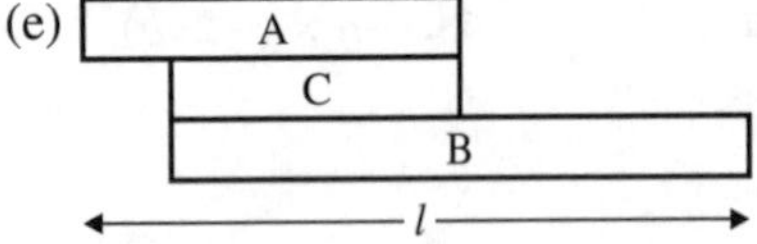

(f) 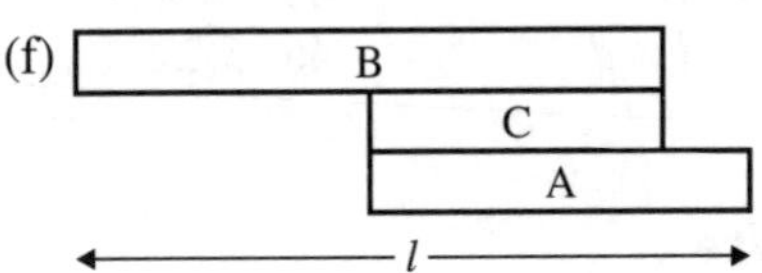

2.2 Sequences

Exercise 6

1. Find the next number in each sequence.

(a) 1, 5, 9, 13, ...
(b) 39, 36, 33, 30, ...
(c) 3, 6, 12, 24, ...
(d) 4, 9, 15, 22, ...
(e) 200, 100, 50, 25, ...
(f) 88, 99, 110, ...

2. Write down each sequence and find the missing number.

(a) 1, 6, ☐, 16, ...
(b) 1, 2, 4, 8, ☐, ...
(c) ☐, 2, 5, 8, 11, ...
(d) 2400, 240, 24, ☐, ...
(e) 1, 2, 4, 7, ☐, 16, ...
(f) 12, 8, 4, ☐, −4, ...

3. Here is the start of a sequence: 1, 3, 4, ...
Each new term is found by adding the last two terms.
For example $4 = 1 + 3$.
The next term will be 7.
(a) Write down the next six terms.
(b) Use the same rule to write down the next four terms of the sequence which starts 2, 5, 7, ...

2. (a) Write down the next two lines of the sequence.
$3 \times 4 = 3 + 3^2$
$4 \times 5 = 4 + 4^2$
$5 \times 6 = 5 + 5^2$
=
=
(b) Complete the lines below.
$10 \times 11 =$
$30 \times 31 =$

5. Copy the pattern and write down the next three lines.
$1 + 9 \times 0 = 1$
$2 + 9 \times 1 = 11$
$3 + 9 \times 12 = 111$
$4 + 9 \times 123 = 1111$
$5 + 9 \times 1234 =$

6. For the sequence 2, 3, 8, ... each new term is found by squaring the last term and then subtracting one.
Write down the next two terms.

7. The sequence 3, 3, 5, 4, 4 is obtained by counting the letters in 'one, two, three, four, five, ...'.
Write down the next three terms.

8. The odd numbers 1, 3, 5, 7, 9, ... can be added to give an interesting sequence.

$$1 = 1 = 1 \times 1 \times 1$$
$$3 + 5 = 8 = 2 \times 2 \times 2$$
$$7 + 9 + 11 = 27 = 3 \times 3 \times 3$$
$$13 + 15 + 17 + 19 = 64 = 4 \times 4 \times 4$$

1, 8, 27, 64 are *cube* numbers.
We write $2^3 = 8$ ['two cubed equals eight']
$4^3 = 64$
Or the other way round:
$\sqrt[3]{8} = 2$ ['the cube root of eight equals two']
$\sqrt[3]{27} = 3$

(a) Continue adding the odd numbers in the same way as before.
Do we *always* get a cube number?
(b) Write down
(i) $\sqrt[3]{125}$ (ii) $\sqrt[3]{1000}$ (iii) 11^3.

9. (a) Write down the next three lines of this pattern.

$$1^3 = 1^2 = 1$$
$$1^3 + 2^3 = (1+2)^2 = 9$$
$$1^3 + 2^3 + 3^3 = (1+2+3)^2 = 36$$

(b) Work out as simply as possible:

$$1^3 + 2^3 + 3^3 + 4^3 + 5^3 + 6^3 + 7^3 + 8^3 + 9^3 + 10^3:$$

10. Here is the sequence of the first six odd and even numbers.

	1st	2nd	3rd	4th	5th	6th
odd	1	3	5	7	9	11
even	2	4	6	8	10	12

Find (a) the 8th even number
(b) the 8th odd number
(c) the 13th even number
(d) the 13th odd number.

11. You can use a rule to work out the answers.
(a) If the 57th even number is 114, what is the 57th odd number?
(b) Write down
(i) the 45th even number
(ii) the 53rd odd number
(iii) the 100th odd number
(iv) the 219th odd number.

12. Here we have written the numbers in three columns.

left	middle	right	Line
1	2	3	1
4	5	6	2
7	8	9	3
10	11	12	4
13	14	15	5
16	17	18	6
19	20	21	7

(a) What number will you get on the right of
(i) line 8 (ii) line 12 (iii) line 25?

(b) Write down the number in the middle of
(i) line 8 (ii) line 12 (iii) line 20.

(c) What number will you get in
(i) line 10 on the left
(ii) line 13 on the right
(iii) line 17 in the middle
(iv) line 30 on the left?

(d) Find the missing number:
(i) 120 is on the right of line ____.
(ii) 61 is on the left of line ____.
(iii) 92 is in the middle of line ____.
(iv) 148 is on the left of line ____.

Differences in sequences

In the sequence of diagrams below, we will count the points p on the circle and the number of lines l that have been drawn. Each point is joined to every other point on the circle.

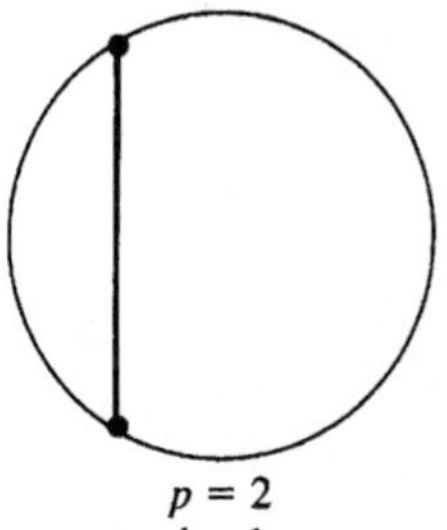

$p = 2$
$l = 1$

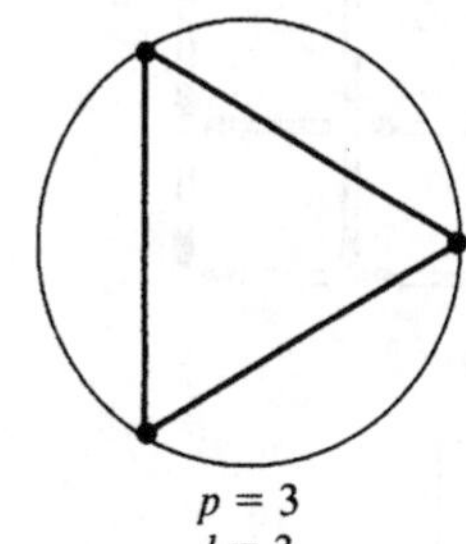

$p = 3$
$l = 3$

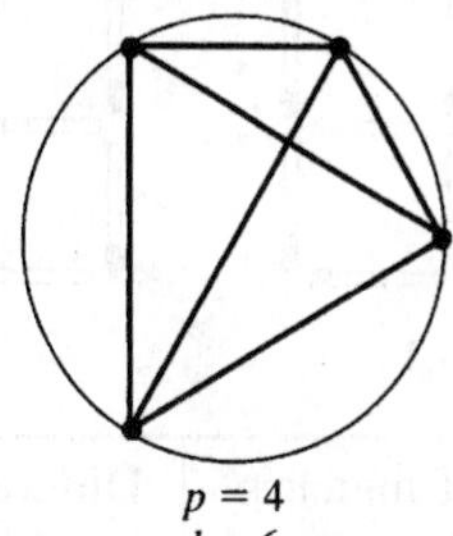

$p = 4$
$l = 6$

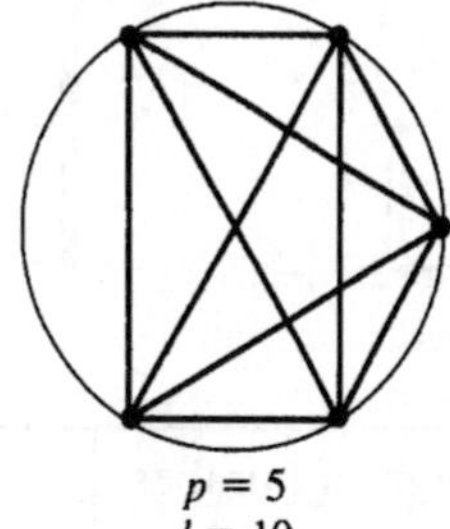

$p = 5$
$l = 10$

Here is a table.

p	l
2	1
3	3
4	6
5	10
6	15

(a) The *differences* in the l column form a pattern.

p	l	Difference
2	1	
		2
3	3	
		3
4	6	
		4
5	10	
		5
6	15	

(b) We can use the differences to predict the next values for l.

p	l	Difference
2	1	
		2
3	3	
		3
4	6	
		4
5	10	
		5
6	15	
		6
7	(21)	
		7
8	(28)	

↑ These two are predictions.

This technique is useful for making predictions in many investigations. We can easily confirm that the predictions work by drawing a circle with 7 points and then 8 points.

Exercise 7

1. Here is a sequence of matchstick squares.

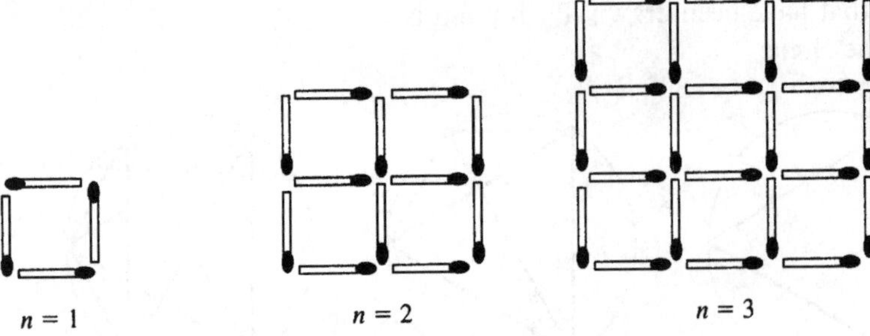

Diagram number n	No. of matches m	Difference
1	4	
		8
2	12	
		12
3	24	
		16
4	40	
5	?	

Use the differences to predict the number of matches in diagram number 5.

2. Here we have matchstick triangles.

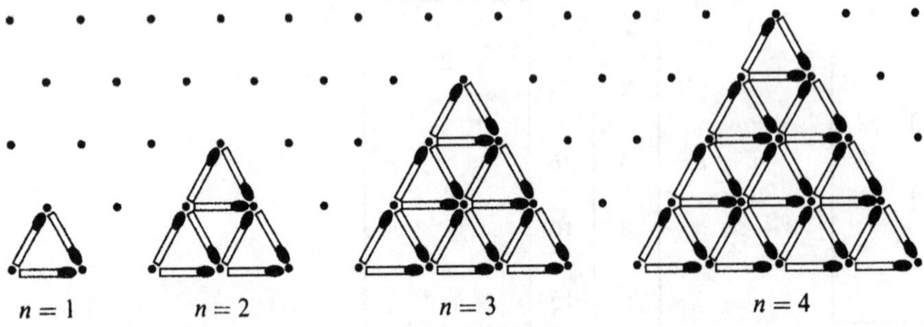

Count the number of matches m in each diagram and make a table.

n	m	Difference
1	3	
2	9	
3		
4		

(a) Use differences to predict the number of matches in diagram number 5 ($n = 5$).

(b) Now draw diagram 5 to see if your prediction is correct.

3. Look at the coordinates of the points on this curve.
The x-coordinates form an obvious pattern but what about the y-coordinates?
Write the y-coordinates in a column.

3
8
15
24
35

Use differences to work out the next number in this sequence.

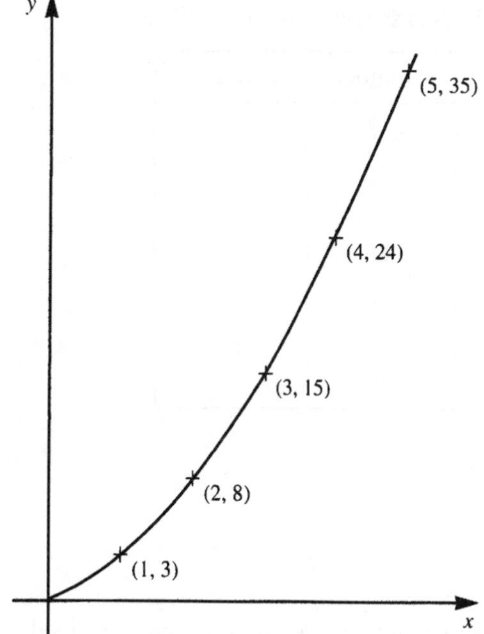

4. Here is a quadrilateral, a pentagon and a hexagon.

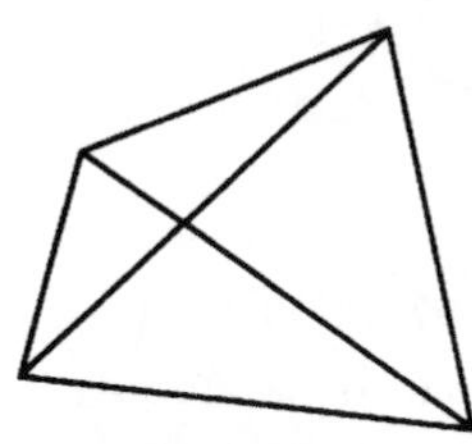

2 diagonals

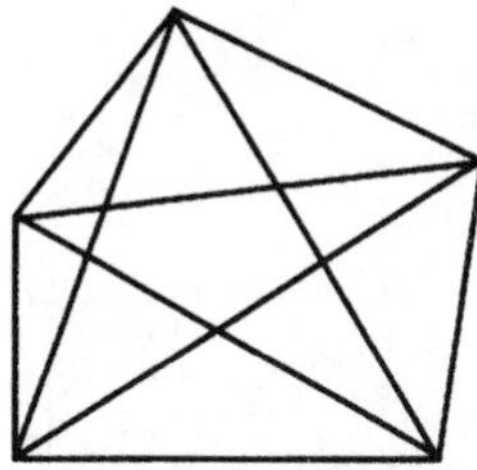

5 diagonals

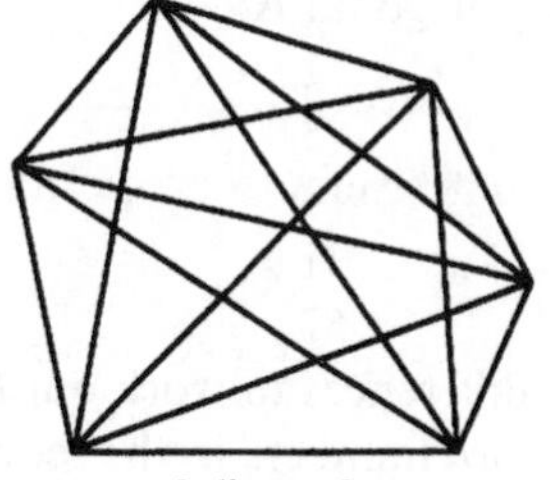

9 diagonals

(a) How many diagonals are there in a polygon with seven sides?
(b) Use the sequence to predict the number of diagonals in a polygon with 10 sides.

5. Look at the tables and use differences to find the missing number.

(a)

n	r
2	10
3	18
4	28
5	40
6	?

(b)

n	t
2	3
3	6
4	10
5	15
6	?

(c)

n	r
1	4
2	9
3	16
4	25
5	?

6. Find the next two numbers in each sequence.
(a) 4, 9, 17, 28
(b) 7, 15, 25, 37
(c) 2, 5, 10, 17, 26

7. This sequence is more difficult.

Number	Difference
2	
	3
5	
	6
11	
	10
21	
	15
36	

The first differences make no obvious pattern. Try the next set of differences.

Number	Difference	Second difference
2		
	3	
5		3
	6	
11		4
	10	
21		5
	15	
36		?
	?	
?		

Find the missing numbers.

8. The number square opposite is formed by writing numbers in a spiral.

(a) Look at the sequence of numbers along diagonal A.

1
3
13
31
57

Use differences to work out the next *two* numbers in the sequence.

(b) The numbers in diagonal B form the sequence 1 5 17 37 65. Find the next two numbers in this sequence.

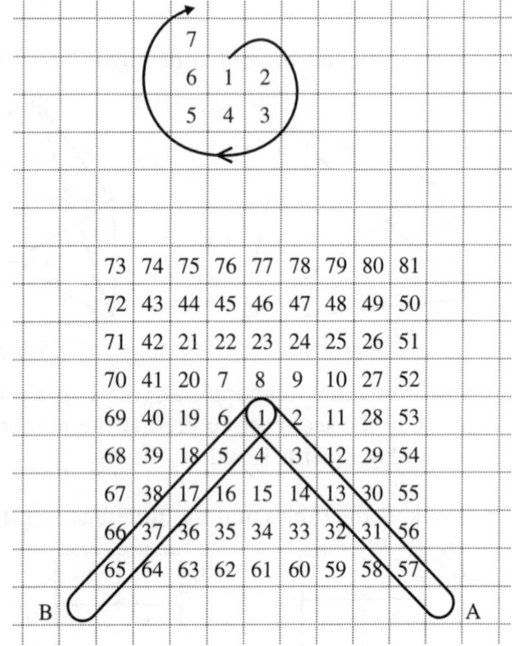

9. Use the method of Question **7** to find the missing numbers.

(a)	(b)	(c)
2	2	2
8	9	9
20	28	20
40	65	36
70	126	58
?	?	?

10. This is a harder sequence. Find the first differences, second differences, third differences and so on until you find a pattern.
Use the differences to find the next number in the sequence.

15
39
119
315
711
1415

The nth term in a sequence

(a) For the sequence 3, 6, 9, 12, 15, ... the rule is 'add 3'.

Here is the *mapping diagram* for the sequence.

Term number (n)		Term
1	⟶	3
2	⟶	6
3	⟶	9
4	⟶	12
⋮		⋮
10	⟶	30
⋮		⋮
n	⟶	$3n$

The terms are found by multiplying the term number by 3.
So the 10th number is 30, the 33rd term is 99.

A *general* term in the sequence is the nth term, where n stands for any number.
The nth term of this sequence is $3n$.

(b) Here is a more difficult sequence: 5, 9, 13, 17, ...

The rule is 'add 4' so, in the mapping diagram, we have written a column for 4 times the term number [i.e. $4n$].

Term number (n)		$4n$		Term
1	⟶	4	⟶	5
2	⟶	8	⟶	9
3	⟶	12	⟶	13
4	⟶	16	⟶	17

We see that each term is 1 more than $4n$.
So, the 10th term is $(4 \times 10) + 1 = 41$
the 15th term is $(4 \times 15) + 1 = 61$
the nth term is $(4 \times n) + 1 = 4n + 1$

Exercise 8

1. Write down each sequence and select the correct formula for the nth term from the list given.

(a) 2, 4, 6, 8, ...
(b) 10, 20, 30, 40, ...
(c) 3, 6, 9, 12, ...
(d) 11, 22, 33, 44, ...
(e) 100, 200, 300, 400, ...
(f) 6, 12, 18, 24, ...
(g) 22, 44, 66, 88, ...
(h) 30, 60, 90, 120, ...

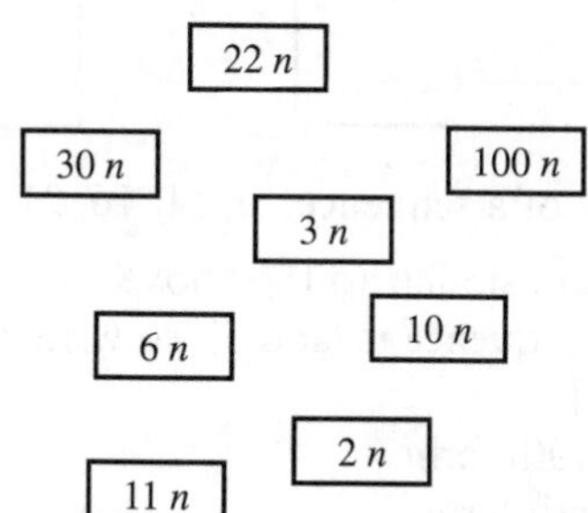

2. Copy and complete these mapping diagrams.

(a)

Term number (n)		Term
1	$\longrightarrow$	5
2	$\longrightarrow$	10
3	$\longrightarrow$	15
4	$\longrightarrow$	20
⋮		⋮
11	$\longrightarrow$	☐
⋮		⋮
n	$\longrightarrow$	☐

(b)

Term number (n)		Term
1	$\longrightarrow$	9
2	$\longrightarrow$	18
3	$\longrightarrow$	27
4	$\longrightarrow$	36
⋮		⋮
20	$\longrightarrow$	☐
⋮		⋮
n	$\longrightarrow$	☐

(c)

Term number (n)		Term
1	$\longrightarrow$	100
2	$\longrightarrow$	200
3	$\longrightarrow$	300
⋮		⋮
12	$\longrightarrow$	☐
⋮		⋮
n	$\longrightarrow$	☐

3. Copy and complete these mapping diagrams. Notice that an extra column has been written.

(a)

Term number (n)		$2n$		Term
1	$\longrightarrow$	2	$\longrightarrow$	5
2	$\longrightarrow$	4	$\longrightarrow$	7
3	$\longrightarrow$	6	$\longrightarrow$	9
4	$\longrightarrow$	8	$\longrightarrow$	11
⋮		⋮		⋮
10	$\longrightarrow$	☐	$\longrightarrow$	☐
⋮		⋮		⋮
n	$\longrightarrow$	☐	$\longrightarrow$	☐

(b)

Term number (n)		$3n$		Term
1	$\longrightarrow$	3	$\longrightarrow$	4
2	$\longrightarrow$	6	$\longrightarrow$	7
3	$\longrightarrow$	9	$\longrightarrow$	10
4	$\longrightarrow$	12	$\longrightarrow$	13
⋮		⋮		⋮
20	$\longrightarrow$	☐	$\longrightarrow$	☐
⋮		⋮		⋮
n	$\longrightarrow$	☐	$\longrightarrow$	☐

4. Here you are given the nth term. Copy and complete the diagrams.

(a)

Term number (n)		$6n$		Term
1	$\longrightarrow$	6	$\longrightarrow$	8
2	$\longrightarrow$	12	$\longrightarrow$	14
3	$\longrightarrow$	☐	$\longrightarrow$	☐
4	$\longrightarrow$	☐	$\longrightarrow$	☐
⋮		⋮		⋮
n	$\longrightarrow$	$6n$	$\longrightarrow$	$6n + 2$

(b)

Term number (n)		$5n$		Term
1	$\longrightarrow$	5	$\longrightarrow$	3
2	$\longrightarrow$	10	$\longrightarrow$	8
3	$\longrightarrow$	☐	$\longrightarrow$	☐
4	$\longrightarrow$	☐	$\longrightarrow$	☐
⋮		⋮		⋮
n	$\longrightarrow$	$5n$	$\longrightarrow$	$5n - 2$

5. Here are the first five terms of a sequence: 6, 11, 16, 21, 26, ...

(a) Draw a mapping diagram similar to the above.
[Hint: The rule for the sequence is 'add 5', so write a column for '$5n$' in the diagram.]

(b) Write down: (i) the 10th term
(ii) the nth term.

6. Here are three sequences.

A : 1, 4, 7, 10, 13, . . .
B : 6, 10, 14, 18, 22, . . .
C : 5, 12, 19, 26, 33, . . .

For each sequence: (a) draw a mapping diagram
(b) find the nth term.

7.

Look at the sequence A1, A2, A3, A4, . . . and B1, B2, B3, B4, . . .
Write down:

(a) A10 (b) B10
(c) the nth term in the 'A' sequence
(d) the nth term in the 'B' sequence.

8.

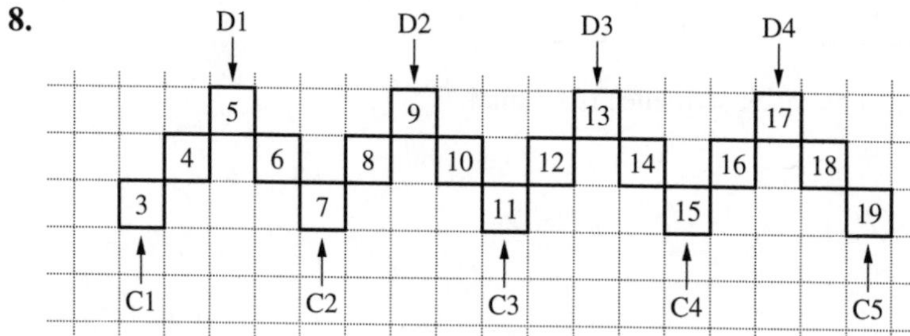

Look at the sequence C1, C2, C3, C4, . . . and D1, D2, D3, D4, . . .
Write down:

(a) C20 (b) D20
(c) the nth term in the 'C' sequence
(d) the nth term in the 'D' sequence.

9.

(a) Find the nth term in the 'P' sequence
(b) Find the nth term in the 'Q' sequence.

10. Here are two more difficult sequences. Copy and complete the mapping diagrams.

(a)

Term number (n)				Term
1	$\longrightarrow$	1×2	$\longrightarrow$	2
2	$\longrightarrow$	2×3	$\longrightarrow$	6
3	$\longrightarrow$	3×4	$\longrightarrow$	12
4	$\longrightarrow$	4×5	$\longrightarrow$	20
⋮		⋮		⋮
10	$\longrightarrow$	□	$\longrightarrow$	□
⋮		⋮		⋮
n	$\longrightarrow$	□	$\longrightarrow$	□

(b)

Term number (n)				Term
1	$\longrightarrow$	$1^2 + 1$	$\longrightarrow$	2
2	$\longrightarrow$	$2^2 + 1$	$\longrightarrow$	5
3	$\longrightarrow$	$3^2 + 1$	$\longrightarrow$	10
4	$\longrightarrow$	$4^2 + 1$	$\longrightarrow$	17
⋮		⋮		⋮
10	$\longrightarrow$	□	$\longrightarrow$	□
⋮		⋮		⋮
n	$\longrightarrow$	□	$\longrightarrow$	□

11. Look at the sequence 5, 8, 13, 20, ...

Decide which of the following is the correct expression for the nth term of the sequence.

$4n + 1$ $\quad$ $3n + 2$ $\quad$ $n^2 + 4$

In Questions **12** to **16** look carefully at how each sequence is formed.
Write down: (a) the 10th term
(b) The nth term.

12. $1^2, 2^2, 3^2, 4^2, \ldots$

13. $(1 \times 2), (2 \times 3), (3 \times 4), (4 \times 5), \ldots$

14. $\frac{1}{2}, \frac{2}{3}, \frac{3}{4}, \frac{4}{5}, \ldots$

15. $\frac{5}{1^2}, \frac{5}{2^2}, \frac{5}{3^2}, \frac{5}{4^2}, \ldots$

16. $(1 \times 3), (2 \times 4), (3 \times 5), (4 \times 6), \ldots$

17. Here are three sequences and three expressions. Write down each sequence and select the correct expression for its nth term.

A: $-1, 2, 5, 8, 11, \ldots$
B: $-1, 2, 7, 14, 23, \ldots$
C: $3, 8, 15, 24, 35, \ldots$

$n(n + 2)$

$n^2 - 2$

$3n - 4$

2.3 Solving equations

We can think of equations as weighing scales which are balanced. The scales stay balanced so long as you add or take away the same weight from both sides.
The same is true of equations.

Exercise 9

The scales are balanced. Work out the weight of the object x in each case. Each small weight □ is 1 kg.

1. 

2. 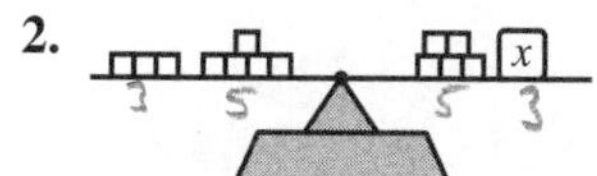

3. 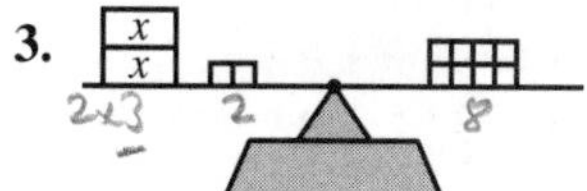

4. 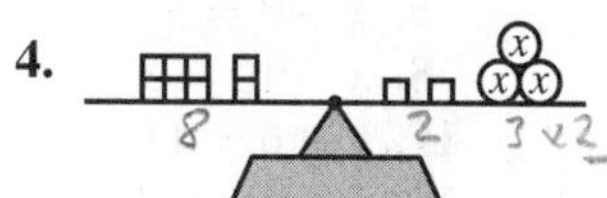

5. 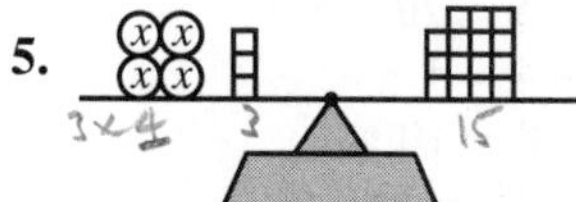

6. 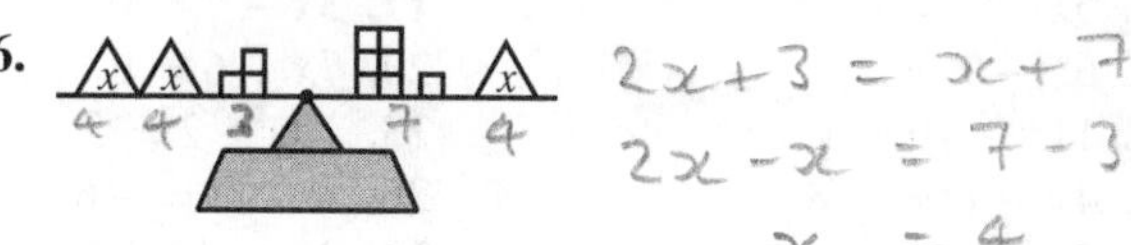

7. 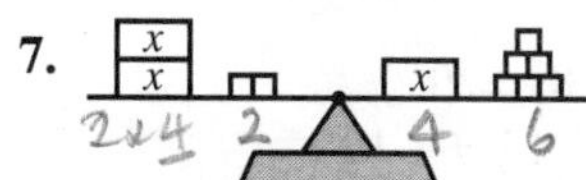

8. 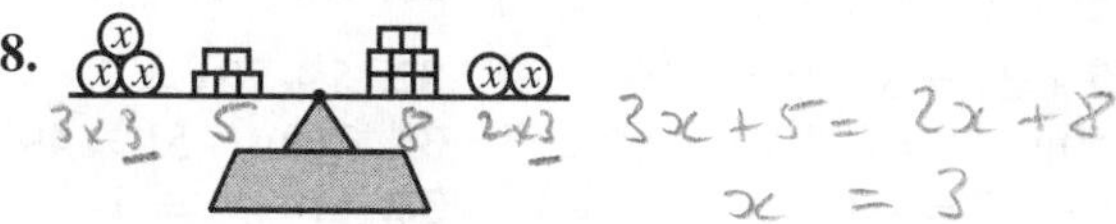

9. 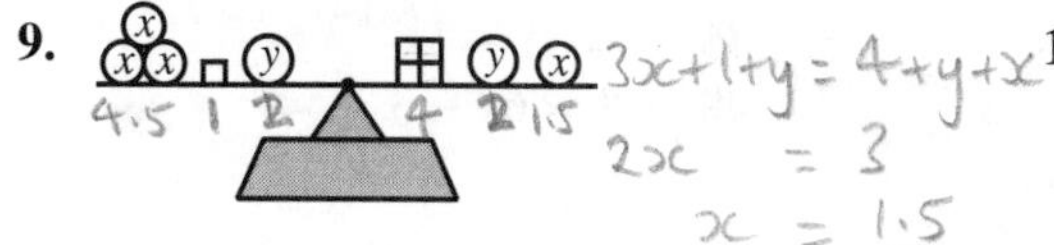

10. 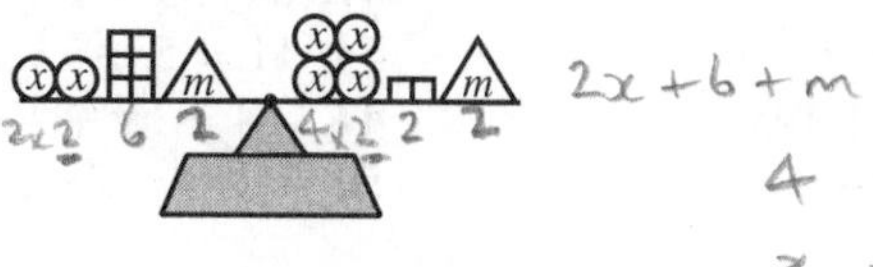

In Questions **11** to **14** ○, △ and □ are weights.

11. If □ = 8, find △ and ○

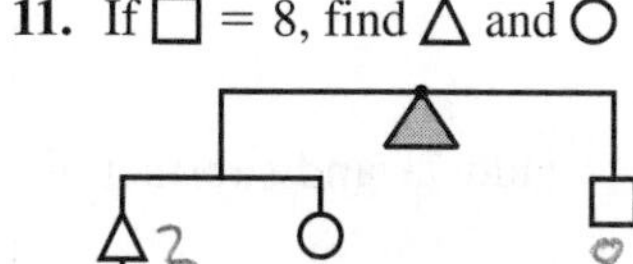

12. If ○ = 6, find △ and □

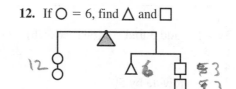

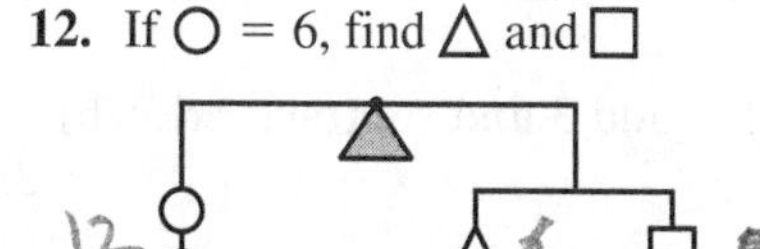

13. △ = 6, find ○ and □

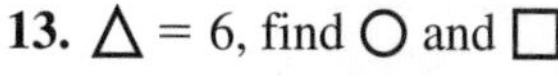

14. △ = 8, find □ and ○

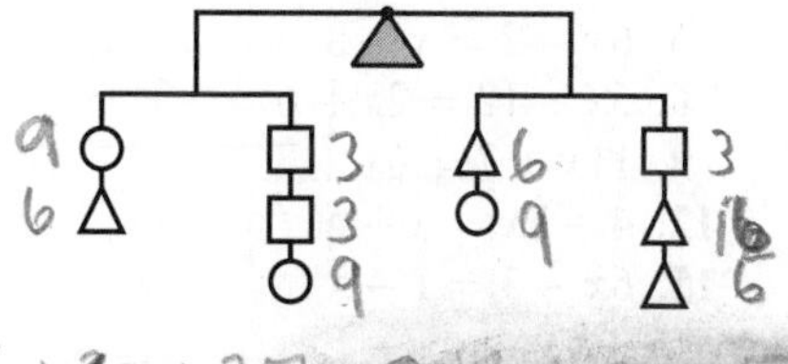

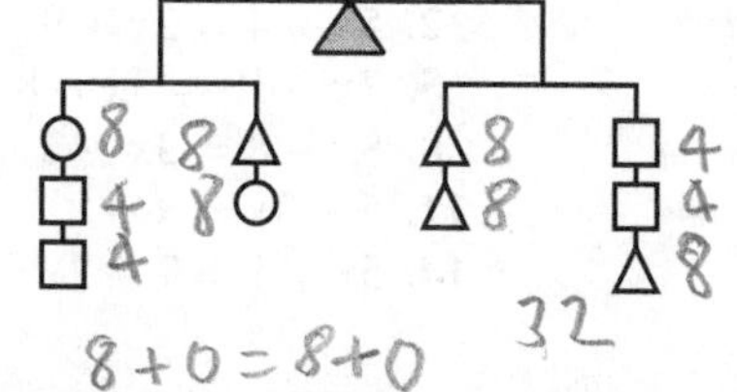

- We solve equations by doing the same thing to both sides.

(a)
$$\begin{aligned} x+6 &= 11 \\ x &= 11-6 \quad \text{[take away 6]} \\ x &= 5 \end{aligned}$$

(b)
$$\begin{aligned} 3x+14 &= 16 \\ 3x &= 16-14 \quad \text{[take away 14]} \\ 3x &= 2 \\ x &= \tfrac{2}{3} \quad \text{[divide by 3]} \end{aligned}$$

(c)
$$\begin{aligned} 4x-5 &= -2 \\ 4x &= -2+5 \quad \text{[add 5]} \\ 4x &= 3 \\ x &= \tfrac{3}{4} \quad \text{[divide by 4]} \end{aligned}$$

(d)
$$\begin{aligned} 7 &= 2x+15 \\ -15+7 &= 2x \quad \text{[take away 15]} \\ -8 &= 2x \\ -4 &= x \quad \text{[divide by 2]} \end{aligned}$$

Exercise 10

Solve the equations.

1. $x-7=5$
2. $x+11=20$
3. $x+12=30$
4. $x-6=-2$
5. $x-8=9$
6. $x+5=0$
7. $x-13=-7$
8. $x+10=3$
9. $5+x=9$
10. $9+x=17$
11. $y-6=11$
12. $y+8=3$
13. $3x+1=16$
14. $4x+3=27$
15. $2x-3=1$
16. $5x-3=1$
17. $3x-7=0$
18. $2x+5=20$
19. $6x-9=2$
20. $7x+6=6$
21. $9x-4=1$
22. $11x-10=1$
23. $15y+2=5$
24. $7y+8=10$
25. $4y-11=-8$
26. $3z-8=-6$
27. $4p+25=30$
28. $5t-6=0$
29. $9m-13=1$
30. $4+3x=5$
31. $7+2x=8$
32. $5+20x=7$
33. $3+8x=0$
34. $50y-7=2$
35. $200y-51=49$
36. $5u-13=-10$
37. $9x-7=-11$
38. $11t+1=1$
39. $3+8y=40$
40. $12+7x=2$
41. $6=3x-1$
42. $8=4x+5$
43. $9=2x+7$
44. $11=5x-7$
45. $0=3x-1$
46. $40=11+14x$
47. $-4=5x+1$
48. $-8=6x-3$
49. $13=4x-20$
50. $-103=2x+7$

Equations with *x* on both sides

Solve the equations

(a)
$$\begin{aligned} 8x-3 &= 3x+1 \quad \text{[add 3 and subtract } 3x\text{]} \\ 8x-3x &= 1+3 \\ 5x &= 4 \\ x &= \tfrac{4}{5} \quad \text{[divide by 5]} \end{aligned}$$

(b)
$$\begin{aligned} 3x+9 &= 18-7x \\ 3x+7x &= 18-9 \quad \text{[add } 7x \text{ and subtract 9]} \\ 10x &= 9 \\ x &= \tfrac{9}{10} \quad \text{[divide by 2]} \end{aligned}$$

Exercise 11

1. $7x-3=3x+8$
2. $5x+4=2x+9$
3. $6x-2=x+8$
4. $8x+1=3x+2$
5. $7x-10=3x-8$
6. $5x-12=2x-6$
7. $4x-23=x-7$
8. $8x-8=3x-2$
9. $11x+7=6x+7$
10. $9x+8=10$
11. $5+3x=x+8$
12. $4+7x=x+5$
13. $6x-8=4-3x$
14. $5x+1=7-2x$
15. $6x-3=1-x$

16. $3x - 10 = 2x - 3$ **17.** $5x + 1 = 6 - 3x$ **18.** $11x - 20 = 10x - 15$
19. $6 + 2x = 8 - 3x$ **20.** $7 + x = 9 - 5x$ **21.** $3y - 7 = y + 1$
22. $8y + 9 = 7y + 8$ **23.** $7y - 5 = 2y$ **24.** $3z - 1 = 5 - 4z$
25. $8 = 13 - 4x$ **26.** $10 = 12 - 2x$ **27.** $13 = 20 - 9x$
28. $8 = 5 - 2x$ **29.** $5 + x = 7 - 8x$ **30.** $3x + 11 = 2 - 3x$

(a)
$$\begin{aligned} 3(x-1) &= 2(x+7) \\ 3x - 3 &= 2x + 14 \\ 3x - 2x &= 14 + 3 \\ x &= 17 \end{aligned}$$

(b)
$$\begin{aligned} 5(2x+1) &= 3(x-2) + 20 \\ 10x + 5 &= 3x - 6 + 20 \\ 10x - 3x &= -6 + 20 - 5 \\ 7x &= 9 \\ x &= 1\tfrac{2}{7} \end{aligned}$$

Exercise 12

Solve the equations.

1. $2(x+1) = x + 5$ **2.** $4(x-2) = 2(x+1)$ **3.** $5(x-3) = 3(x+2)$
4. $3(x+2) = 2(x-1)$ **5.** $5(x-3) = 2(x-7)$ **6.** $6(x+2) = 2(x-3)$
7. $10(x-3) = x$ **8.** $3(2x-1) = 4(x+1)$ **9.** $4(2x+1) = 5(x+3)$
10. $3(x-1) + 7 = 2(x+1)$ **11.** $5(x+1) + 3 = 3(x-1)$ **12.** $7(x-2) - 3 = 2(x+2)$
13. $5(2x+1) - 5 = 3(x+1)$ **14.** $3(4x-1) - 3 = x + 1$ **15.** $2(x-10) = 4 - 3x$
16. $3x + 2(x+1) = 3x + 12$ **17.** $4x - 2(x+4) = x + 1$ **18.** $2x - 3(x+2) = 2x + 1$
19. $5x - 2(x-2) = 6 - 2x$ **20.** $3(x+1) + 2(x+2) = 10$ **21.** $4(x+3) + 2(x-1) = 4$
22. $3(x-2) - 2(x+1) = 5$ **23.** $5(x-3) + 3(x+2) = 7x$ **24.** $3(2x+1) - 2(2x+1) = 10$
25. $4(3x-1) - 3(3x+2) = 0$

Equations with fractions

Solve the equations

(a)
$$\begin{aligned} \frac{7}{x} &= 8 \\ 7 &= 8x \quad \text{[multiply by } x\text{]} \\ \frac{7}{8} &= x \end{aligned}$$

(b)
$$\begin{aligned} \frac{3x}{4} &= 2 \\ 3x &= 8 \quad \text{[multiply by 4]} \\ x &= \frac{8}{3} \\ x &= 2\tfrac{2}{3} \end{aligned}$$

Exercise 13

Solve the equations.

1. $\frac{3}{x} = 5$ **2.** $\frac{4}{x} = 7$ **3.** $\frac{11}{x} = 12$ **4.** $\frac{6}{x} = 11$ **5.** $\frac{2}{x} = 3$

6. $\frac{5}{y} = 9$ **7.** $\frac{7}{y} = 9$ **8.** $\frac{4}{t} = 3$ **9.** $\frac{3}{a} = 6$ **10.** $\frac{8}{x} = 12$

11. $\frac{3}{p} = 1$ **12.** $\frac{15}{q} = 10$ **13.** $\frac{x}{4} = 6$ **14.** $\frac{x}{5} = 3$ **15.** $\frac{y}{5} = -2$

16. $\frac{a}{7} = 3$ **17.** $\frac{t}{3} = 7$ **18.** $\frac{m}{4} = \frac{2}{3}$ **19.** $\frac{x}{7} = \frac{5}{8}$ **20.** $\frac{2x}{3} = 1$

21. $\frac{4x}{5} = 3$ **22.** $\frac{x+1}{4} = 3$ **23.** $\frac{x-3}{2} = 5$ **24.** $\frac{4+x}{7} = 2$ **25.** $\frac{4}{x+1} = 3$

26. $3 = \frac{9}{x+2}$ **27.** $\frac{5}{x-2} = 3$ **28.** $\frac{7}{x} = \frac{1}{4}$ **29.** $\frac{3}{x} = \frac{2}{3}$ **30.** $\frac{2x+1}{3} = 1$

31. $\frac{x}{2} = 110$ **32.** $\frac{500}{y} = -1$ **33.** $-99 = \frac{98}{f}$ **34.** $\frac{x}{3} + 5 = 7$ **35.** $\frac{x}{5} - 2 = 4$

36. $\frac{2x}{3} + 4 = 5$ **37.** $\frac{x}{6} - 10 = 4$ **38.** $\frac{6}{x} + 1 = 2$ **39.** $\frac{5}{x} - 7 = 0$ **40.** $5 + \frac{3}{x} = 10$

Exercise 14

In this exercise □, △, ○ and ∗ represent weights which are always balanced.

1. (a) ∗△∗ □○

(b)

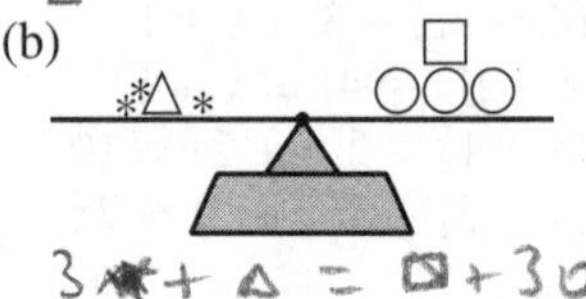

(c)

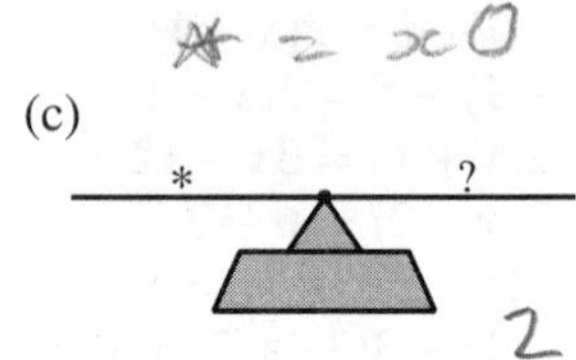

How many ○'s?

2. (a)

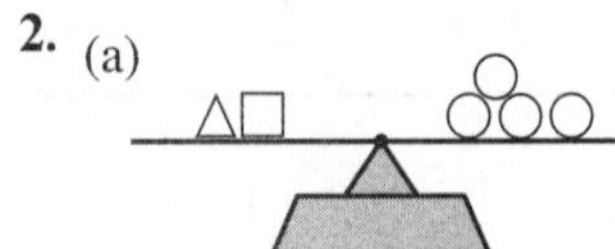

(b)

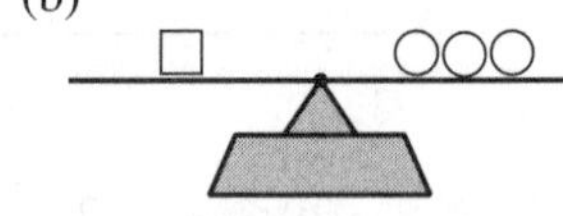

(c)

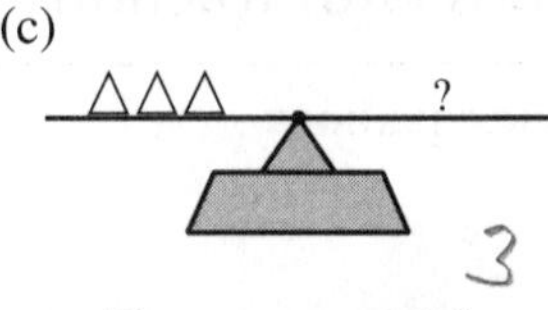

How many ○'s?

3. (a) ○ ○ □ = ∗ ∗
(b) □ □ ○ = ∗ ∗ ○
(c) □ = How many ○'s?

4. (a) □ ○ ○ = △ □ □ □
(b) □ □ □ ○ = △ △ □
(c) □ ○ = △ □
(d) ○ = How many □'s?

5. (a) □ □ = ○ △
(b) ○ ○ ○ □ = □ △
(c) ○ □ □ □ = △ △ ○
(d) □ = How many ○'s?

6. (a) ○ ○ □ = ∗ ○
(b) ∗ ∗ = ○ ○ ○
(c) □ ∗ = ○ ○
(d) ∗ = How many □'s?

7. (a) ○ □ □ = △ ∗
(b) ∗ ∗ ∗ = △ △
(c) ○ □ = △
(d) △ △ △ △ = How many □'s ?

8. (a) ○ □ = △
(b) ○ = □ ∗
(c) ○ ○ □ = △ ∗ ∗
(d) □ = How many ∗'s?

Solving problems with equations

If I multiply a 'mystery' number by 2 and then add 3 the answer is 14. Find the 'mystery' number.

Let the mystery number be x.

Then $2x + 3 = 14$

$2x = 11$

$x = 5\frac{1}{2}$

The 'mystery' number is $5\frac{1}{2}$.

Exercise 15

Find the 'mystery' number in each question by forming an equation and then solving it.

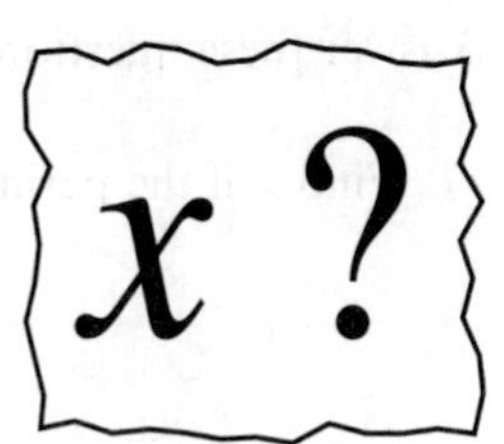

1. If I multiply the number by 3 and then add 4, the answer is 13.

2. If I multiply the number by 4 and then add 5, the answer is 8.

3. If I multiply the number by 2 and then subtract 5, the answer is 4.

4. If I multiply the number by 10 and then add 19, the answer is 16.

5. If I add 3 to the number and then multiply the result by 4, the answer is 10.

6. If we subtract 11 from the number and then treble the result, the answer is 20.

7. If we double the number, add 4 and then multiply the result by 3, the answer is 13.

8. If we treble the number, take away 6 and then multiply the result by 2, the answer is 18.

9. If we double the number and subtract 7 we get the same answer as when we add 5 to the number.

10. If we multiply the number by 5 and subtract 4, we get the same answer as when we add 3 to the number and then double the result.

11. If we multiply the number by 6 and add 1, we get the same answer as when we add 5 to the number and then treble the result.

12. If I add 5 to the number and then multiply the result by 4, I get the same answer as when I add 1 to the number and then multiply the result by 2.

The length of a rectangle is twice the width. If the perimeter is 36 cm, find the width.

(a) Let the width of the rectangle be x cm.
Then the length of the rectangle is $2x$ cm.

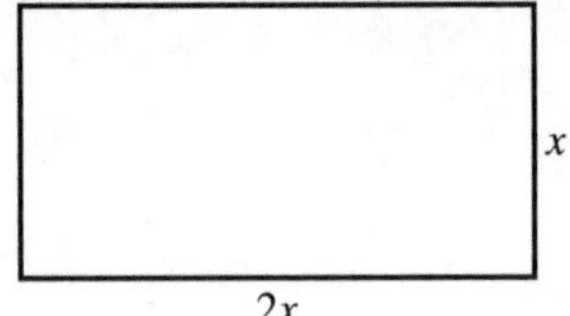

(b) Form an equation.
$x + 2x + x + 2x = 36$

(c) Solve $6x = 36$
$x = 6$
The width of the rectangle is 6 cm.

Exercise 16

Answer these questions by forming an equation and then solving it.

1. Find x if the perimeter is 7 cm.

2. Find x if the perimeter is 10 cm.

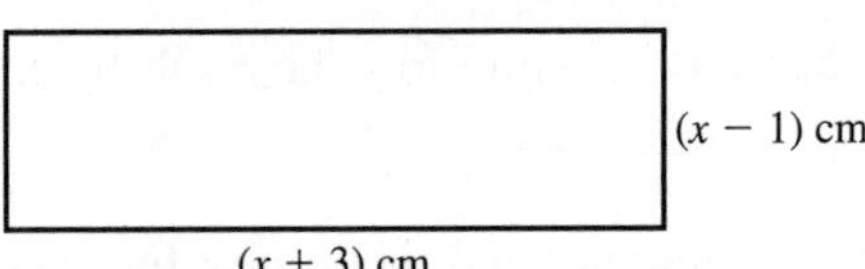

3. The length of a rectangle is 3 times its width. If the perimeter of the rectangle is 11 cm, find its width.
[Hint: Let the width be x cm.]

4. The length of a rectangle is 4 cm more than its width. If its perimeter is 13 cm, find its width.

5. The width of a rectangle is 5 cm less than its length. If the perimeter of the rectangle is 18 cm, find its length.

6. Find x in the following shapes.

(a)

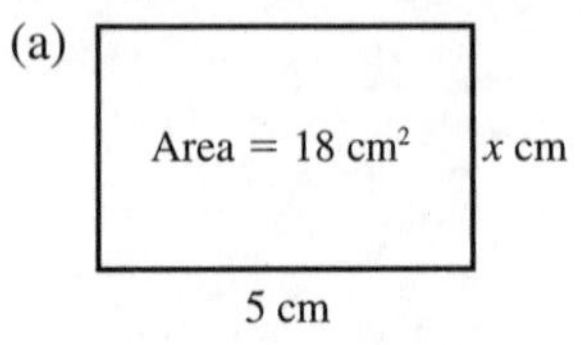

(b)

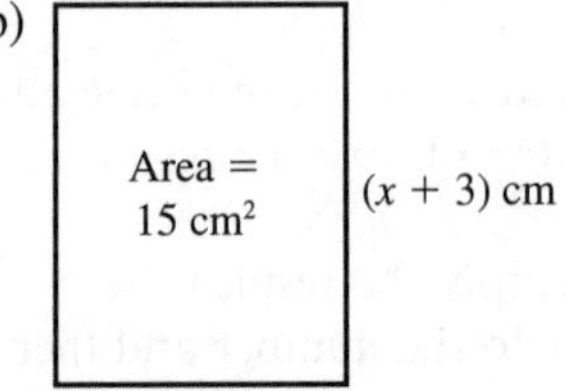

(c)

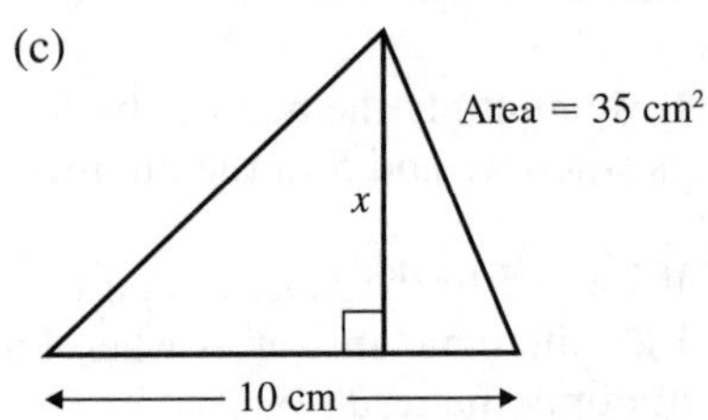

7. Find x in the following triangles.

(a)

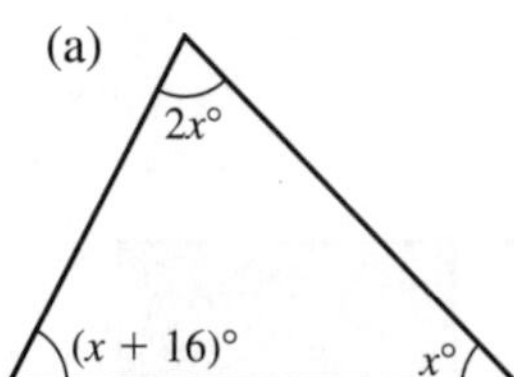

(b)

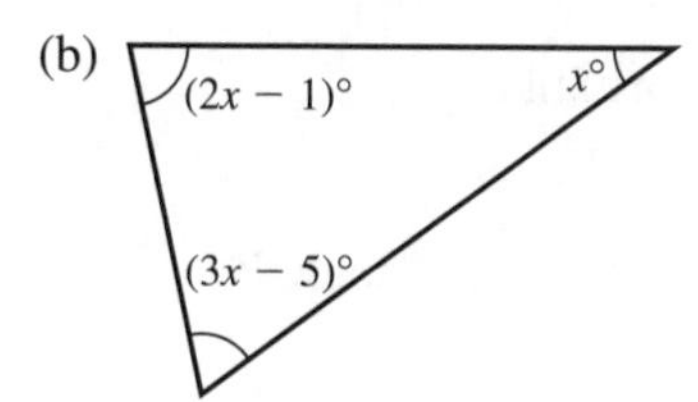

(c)

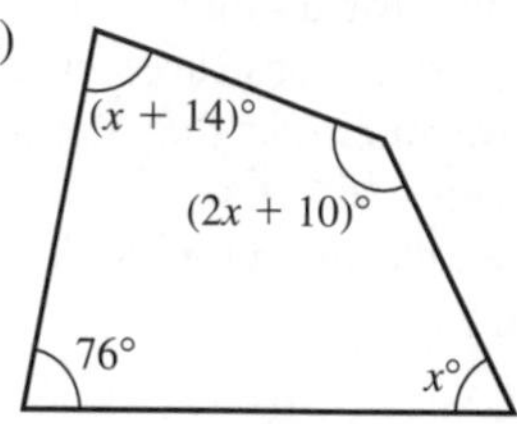

8. The angles of a triangle are 32°, $x°$ and $(4x + 3)°$. Find the value of x.

9. The sum of three consecutive whole numbers is 168. Let the first number be x. Form an equation and hence find the three numbers.

10. The sum of four consecutive whole numbers is 170. Find the numbers.

11. In this triangle AB $= x$ cm.
BC is 3 cm shorter than AB.
AC is twice as long as BC.
(a) Write down, in terms of x, the lengths of
(i) BC
(ii) AC.
The perimeter of the triangle is 41 cm.
(b) Write down an equation in x and solve it to find x.

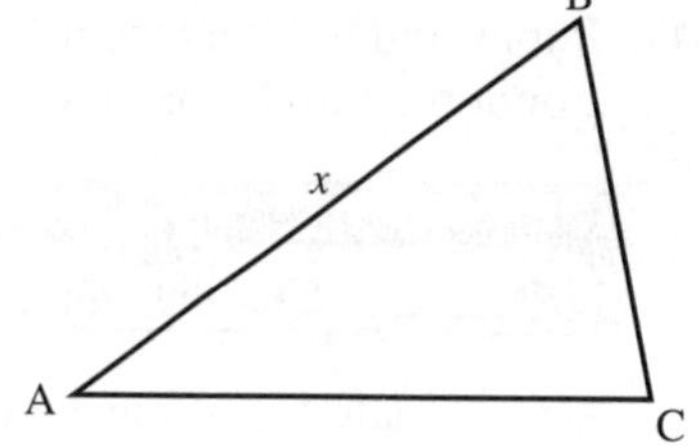

12. This is a rectangle. Work out x and hence find the perimeter of the rectangle.

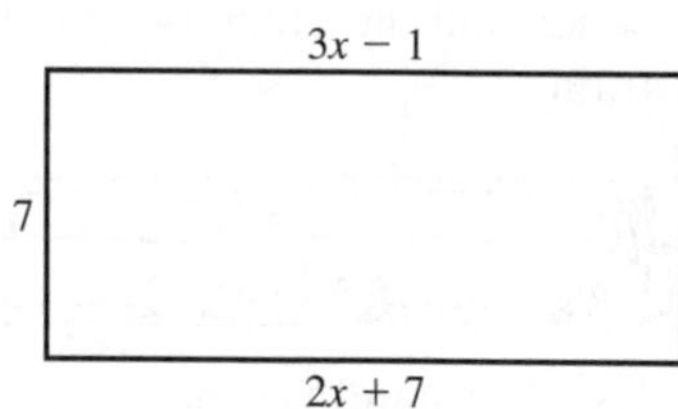

13. Here are four expressions involving an unknown number n.

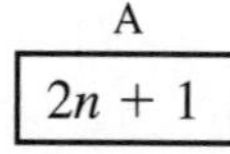

A	B	C	D
$2n + 1$	$n - 5$	$2n + 3$	$3n + 1$

(a) Find the value of n if the expressions A and B are equal.
(b) Find the value of n if the expressions C and D are equal.
(c) Which two expressions could never be equal for *any* value of n?

14. Find the length of the sides of this equilateral triangle.

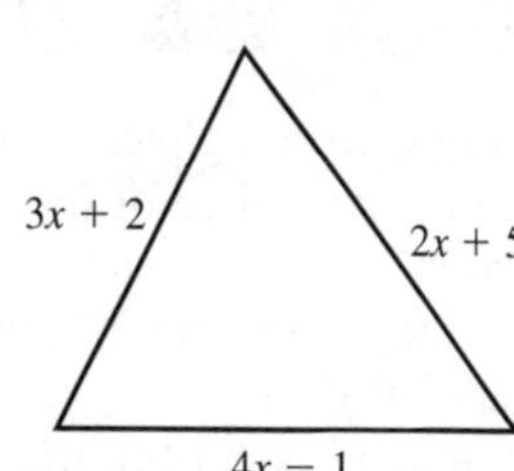

15. Petra has £12 and Suki has nothing. They both receive the same money for doing a delivery job.
Now Petra has three times as much as Suki.
How much did they get for the job?

16. The area of rectangle A is twice the area of rectangle B.
Find x.

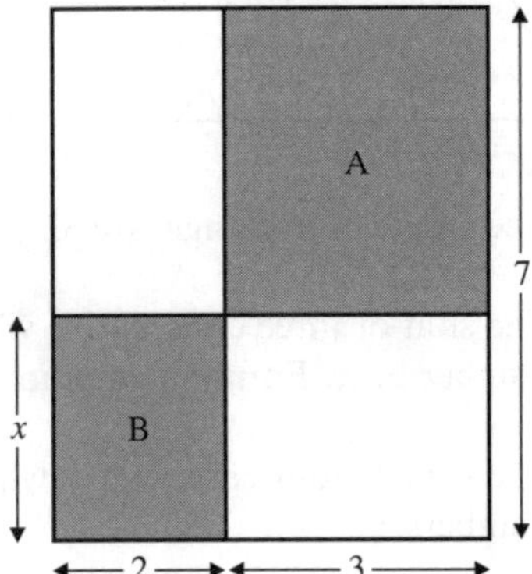

17. Pupils and teachers from Gibson College went on an outing to London in 4 full coaches. Two teachers had to go by train.

Unfortunately 3 of the coaches were parked illegally in London and their wheels were clamped. For the return journey there was one full coach and the other 143 pupils and teachers had to go back by train.

Use x to stand for the number of people in one full coach.
Make an equation involving x and solve it to find the number of people on a coach.

18. Cory has nine teddy bears and she decides they each need a new ribbon.

She buys two long pieces of material to cut into nine equal ribbons.
From the first piece of material she cuts 7 ribbons and has 11 cm left over.
From the second piece of material she cuts 2 ribbons and has 146 cm left over.
How long is each ribbon?

2.4 Drawing graphs

Draw the graph of $y = 4 - 2x$ for values of x from -2 to $+3$.

(a)

x	-2	-1	0	1	2	3
4	4	4	4	4	4	4
$-2x$	4	2	0	-2	-4	-6
y	8	6	4	2	0	-2

(b) Plot the values of x and y from the table.

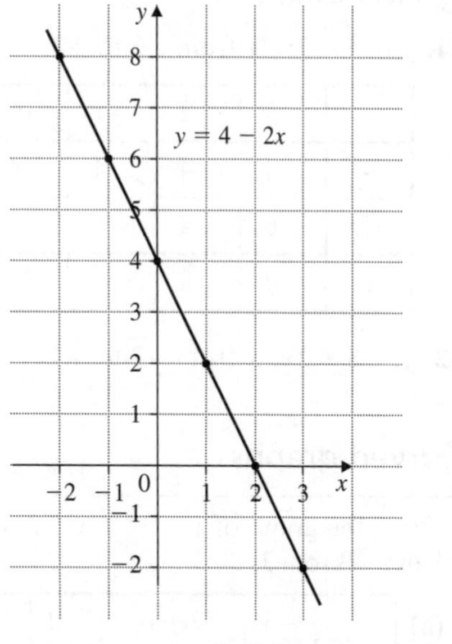

Exercise 17

For each question make a table of values and then draw the graph.
Suggested scales: 1 cm to 1 unit on both axes, unless otherwise stated.

1. $y = 2x + 1$; x from -3 to $+3$.

x	-3	-2	-1	0	1	2	3
$2x$	-6	-4					
$+1$	1	1	1				
y	-5	-3					

2. $y = 3x - 5$; x from -2 to $+3$.

3. $y = x + 2$; x from -4 to $+4$.

4. $y = 2x - 7$; x from -2 to $+5$.

5. $y = 4x + 1$; x from -3 to $+3$.
(Use scales of 1 cm to 1 unit on the x-axis and 1 cm to 2 units on the y-axis.)

6. $y = x - 3$; x from -2 to $+5$.

7. $y = 2x + 4$; x from -4 to $+2$.

8. $y = 3x + 2$; x from -3 to $+3$.

9. $y = x + 7$; x from -5 to $+3$.

10. $y = 4x - 3$; x from -3 to $+3$.
(Use scales of 1 cm to 1 unit on the x-axis and 1 cm to 2 units on the y-axis.)

11. $y = 4 - 2x$; x from -3 to $+3$.

x	-3	-2	-1	0	1	2	3
4	4	4	4	4			4
$-2x$	6	4					-6
y	10	8					-2

12. $y = 8 - 2x$; x from -2 to $+4$.

Curved graphs

Draw the graph of $y = x^2 + x - 2$ for values of x from -3 to $+3$.

(a)

x	-3	-2	-1	0	1	2	3
x^2	9	4	1	0	1	4	9
$+x$	-3	-2	-1	0	1	2	3
-2	-2	-2	-2	-2	-2	-2	-2
y	4	0	-2	-2	0	4	10

(b) Plot the x and y values from the table.

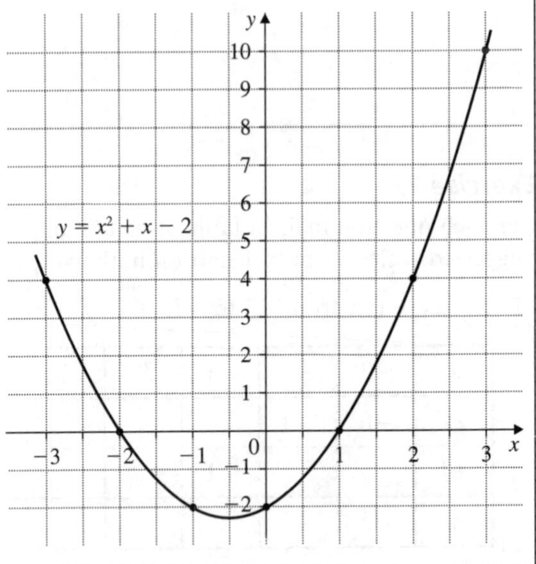

Exercise 18

For each question make a table of values and then draw the graph. Suggested scales: 2 cm to 1 unit on the x-axis and 1 cm to 1 unit on the y-axis.

1. $y = x^2 + 2$; x from -3 to $+3$.

x	-3	-2	-1	0	1	2	3
x^2	9	4	1	0	1		
$+2$	2	2	2				
y	11	6	3				

2. $y = x^2 + 5$; x from -3 to $+3$.

3. $y = x^2 - 4$; x from -3 to $+3$.

4. $y = x^2 - 8$; x from -3 to $+3$.

5. $y = x^2 + 2x$; x from -4 to $+2$.

x	-4	-3	-2	-1	0	1	2
x^2	16	9					4
$+2x$	-8	-6					4
y	8	3					8

6. $y = x^2 + 4x$; x from -5 to $+1$.

7. $y = x^2 + 4x - 1$; x from -2 to $+4$.

8. $y = x^2 + 2x - 5$; x from -4 to $+2$.

9. $y = x^2 + 3x + 1$; x from -4 to $+2$.

These graphs are more difficult.

10. $y = x^3 + 1$; x from -3 to $+3$.
Scales: 2 cm to 1 unit for x;
1 cm to 5 units for y.

11. $y = \frac{12}{x}$; x from 1 to 12.

12. $y = 2x^2 + 3x - 1$; x from -4 to $+2$.
Scales: 2 cm to 1 unit for x;
1 cm to 1 unit for y.
[Remember $2x^2 = 2(x^2)$. Work out x^2 and then multiply by 2.]

13. $y = \frac{16}{x}$; x from 1 to 10.

Scales: 1 cm to 1 unit for x;
1 cm to 1 unit for y.

14. A rectangle has a perimeter of 14 cm and length x cm. Show that the width of the rectangle is $(7 - x)$ cm and hence that the area A of the rectangle is given by the formula $A = x(7 - x)$.
Draw the graph, plotting x on the horizontal axis with a scale of 2 cm to 1 unit, and A on the vertical axis with a scale of 1 cm to 1 unit. Take x from 0 to 7. From the graph find:

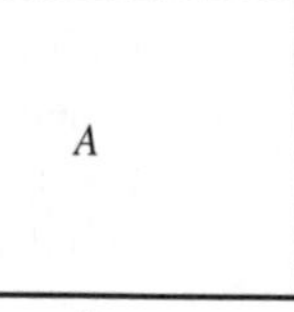

(a) the area of the rectangle when $x = 2{\cdot}25$ cm
(b) the dimensions of the rectangle when its area is 9 cm^2
(c) the maximum area of the rectangle
(d) the length and width of the rectangle corresponding to the maximum area.

15. The diagram shows the net of an open box, with the base shaded.

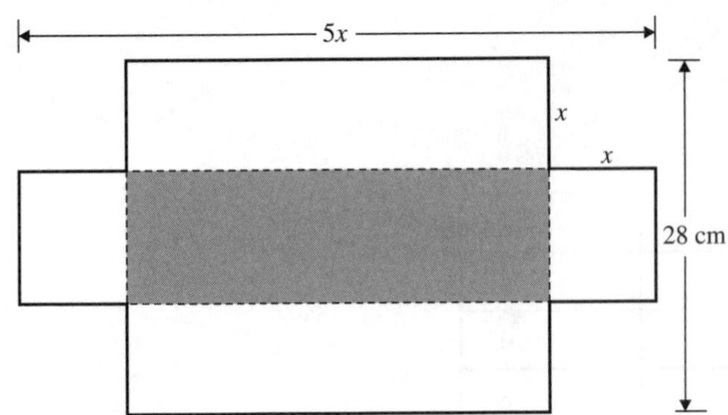

(a) Explain why the area, A cm^2, of the base of the box is given by the formula

$$A = 3x(28 - 2x)$$

(b) Plot the graph of A against x for values of x from 4 to 10. Use a scale of 2 cm to 1 unit for x and a scale of 2 cm to 10 units for A. Draw the A-axis with values from 240 to 300.

(c) From your graph, find the value of x which gives the maximum value of A.

(d) For this value of x, calculate the volume of the box.

16. A ball is thrown upwards at 35 m/s. After t seconds its height in metres is given by the equation

$$h = 35t - 5t^2$$

(a) Copy and complete this table.

Time t	0	1	2	3	4	5	6	7
Height h								

(b) Draw a graph, using a scale of 2 cm to 1 second across the page and 2 cm to 10 m up the page.

(c) A second ball is thrown and its height is given by

$$h = 20t - 5t^2.$$

On the same page draw a graph for this ball, taking t from 0 to 4.

(d) When is the first ball at its highest point?

(e) For how long is the first ball above 50 m?

(f) What is the greatest height reached by the second ball?

Graphical solution of equations

Accurately drawn graphs enable approximate solutions to be found for a wide range of equations, many of which are impossible to solve exactly by other methods.

Draw the graph of the function $y = 2x^2 - x - 3$ for $-2 \leqslant x \leqslant 3$.

(a) To solve the equation

$2x^2 - x - 3 = 6$,

the line $y = 6$ is drawn.

At the points of intersection (A and B), y simultaneously equals both 6 and $(2x^2 - x - 3)$.

So we may write

$2x^2 - x - 3 = 6$

The solutions are the x-values of the points A and B,
i.e. $x = -1{\cdot}9$ and $x = 2{\cdot}4$ approx.

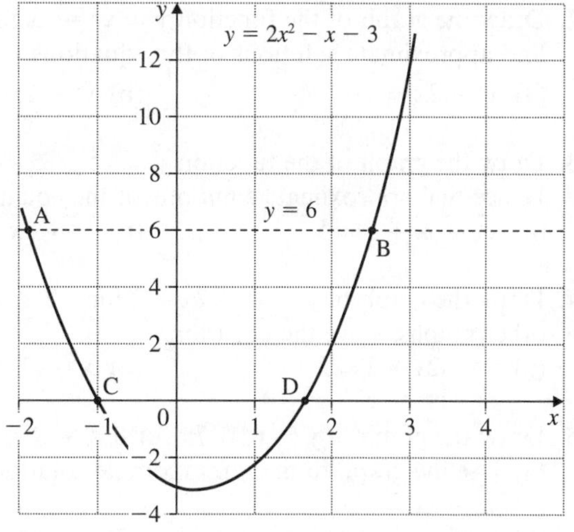

(b) To solve the equation $2x^2 - x - 3 = 0$,

the line $y = 0$ is drawn.

[The line $y = 0$ is the x-axis.]

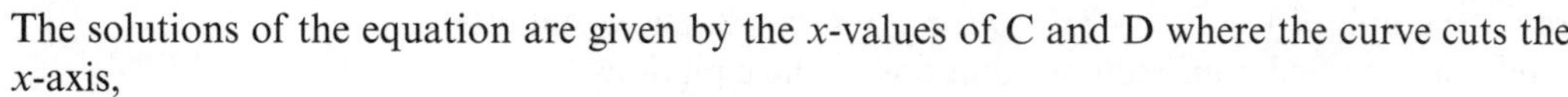

The solutions of the equation are given by the x-values of C and D where the curve cuts the x-axis,

i.e. $x = -1$ and $x = 1{\cdot}5$ approximately.

Exercise 19

1. In the diagram shown, the graphs of $y = x^2 - 2x - 3$, $y = 3$ and $y = -2$ have been drawn.

   Use the graphs to find approximate solutions to the following equations.

   (a) $x^2 - 2x - 3 = 3$
   (b) $x^2 - 2x - 3 = -2$
   (c) $x^2 - 2x - 3 = 0$

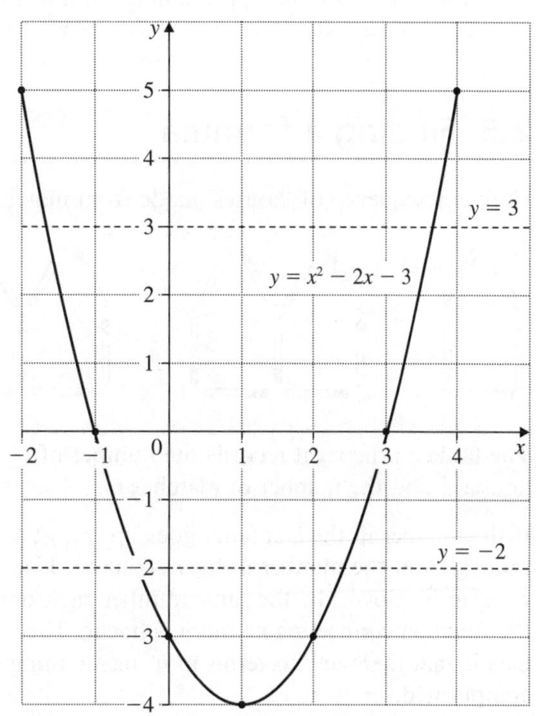

In Questions **2** to **6** use a scale of 2 cm to 1 unit for x and 1 cm to 1 unit for y.

2. Draw the graph of the function $y = x^2 - 2x$ for $-1 \leqslant x \leqslant 4$. Hence find approximate solutions of the equations
(a) $x^2 - 2x = 1$ (b) $x^2 - 2x = 0$

3. Draw the graph of the function $y = x^2 - 3x + 5$ for $-1 \leqslant x \leqslant 5$. Hence find approximate solutions of the equations
(a) $x^2 - 3x + 5 = 5$ (b) $x^2 - 3x + 5 = 8$

4. Draw the graph of $y = x^2 - 2x + 2$ for $-2 \leqslant x \leqslant 4$. By drawing other graphs, solve the equations
(a) $x^2 - 2x + 2 = 8$ (b) $x^2 - 2x + 2 = 3$

5. Draw the graph of $y = x^2 - 7x$ for $0 \leqslant x \leqslant 7$.
(a) Use the graph to find approximate solutions of the equation $x^2 - 7x = -3$.
(b) Explain why the equation $x^2 - 7x = -14$ does not have a solution.

6. Draw the graph of $y = 2x^2 + 3x - 9$ for $-3 \leqslant x \leqslant 2$. Draw suitable straight lines to find approximate solutions of the equations
(a) $2x^2 + 3x - 9 = 0$ (b) $2x^2 + 3x - 9 = x$

7. Draw the graph of $y = x^3 - 5x$ for $-3 \leqslant x \leqslant 3$. Draw suitable straight lines to find approximate solutions of the equations
(a) $x^3 - 5x = 0$ (b) $x^3 - 5x = x$

2.5 Finding a formula

Here is a sequence of 'houses' made from matches.

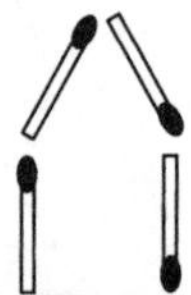
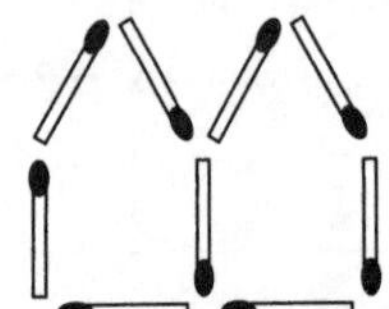
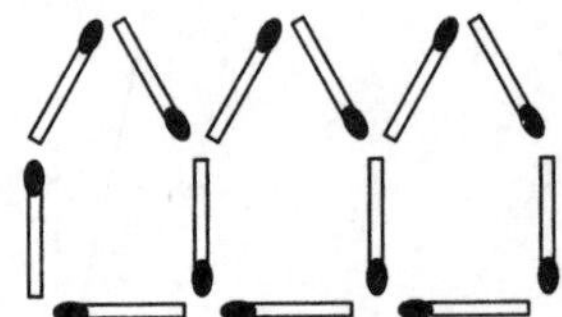
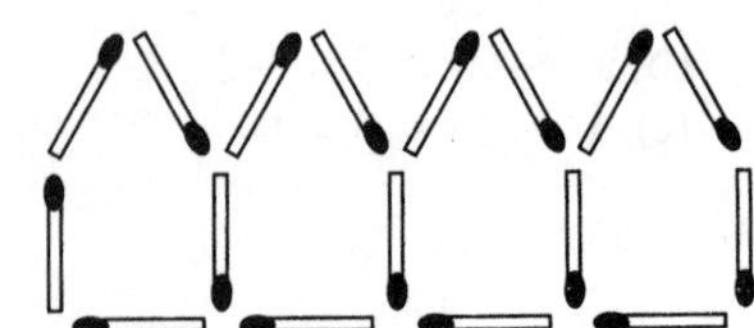

The table on the right records the number of houses h and the number of matches m.

h	m
1	5
2	9
3	13
4	17

If the number in the h column goes up one at a time, look at the number in the m column. If it goes up (or down) by the same number each time, the function connecting m and h is linear. This means that there are no terms in h^2 or anything more complicated.

In this case, the numbers in the m column go up by 4 each time. This suggests that a column for $4h$ might help.

Now it is fairly clear that m is one more than $4h$.

So the formula linking m and h is $m = 4h + 1$

h	$4h$	m
1	4	5
2	8	9
3	12	13
4	16	17

The table shows how r changes with n. What is the formula linking r with n?

n	r
2	3
3	8
4	13
5	18

Because r goes up by 5 each time, write another column for $5n$. The table shows that r is always 7 less than $5n$, so the formula linking r with n is $r = 5n - 7$.

n	$5n$	r
2	10	3
3	15	8
4	20	13
5	25	18

Unfortunately if the numbers on the left do not go up by one each time, this method does not work. In that case you have to think of something clever!

Exercise 20

1. Below is a sequence of diagrams showing black tiles b and white tiles w with the related table.

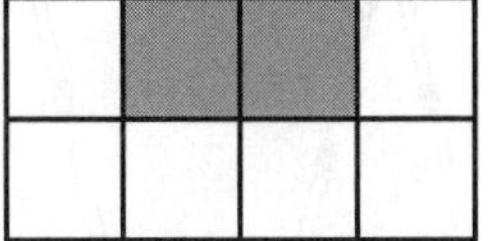

b	w
1	5
2	6
3	7
4	8

What is the formula for w in terms of b? [i.e. write '$w =$ ....']

2. This is a different sequence with black tiles b and white tiles w and the related table.

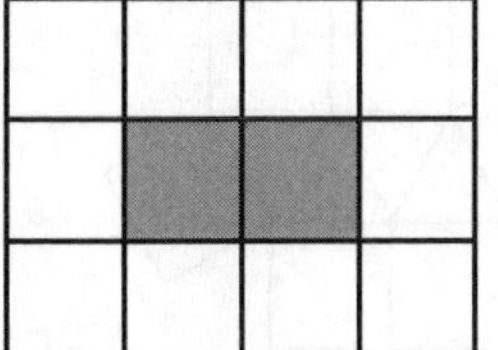

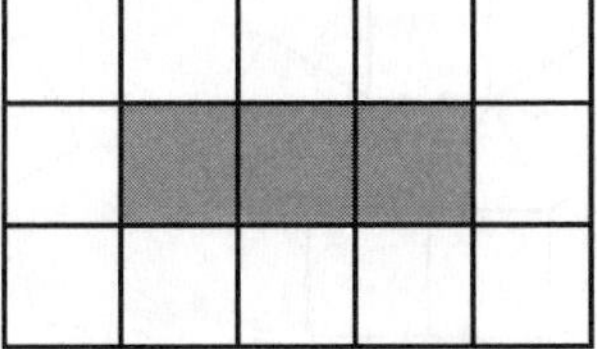

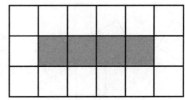

b	w
1	10
2	12
3	14
4	16

What is the formula? Write it as $w = \ldots$

3. Here is a sequence of I's.

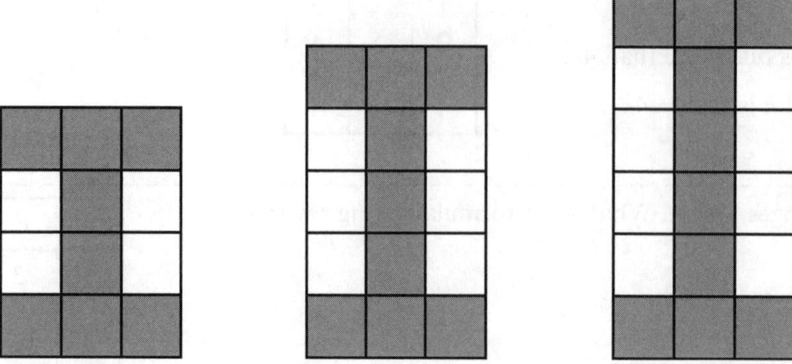

Make your own table for black tiles b and white tiles w. What is the formula for w in terms of b?

4. In this sequence we have matches (m) and triangles (t).

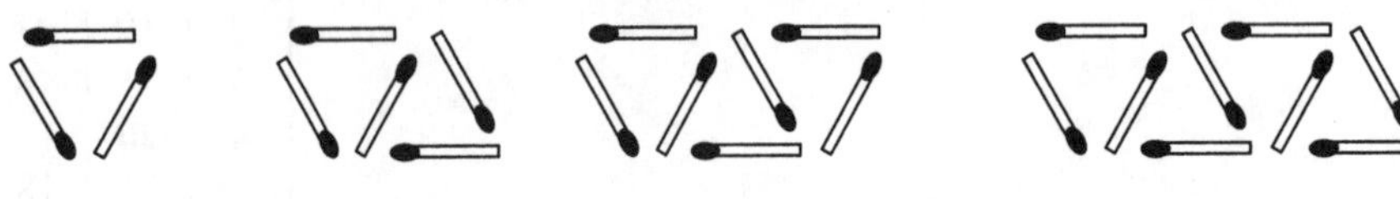

Make a table for t and m. It starts like this:

t	m
1	3
2	5
⋮	⋮

Continue the table and find a formula for m in terms of t.
Write '$m = \ldots\ldots$'.

5. Here is a different sequence of matches and triangles.

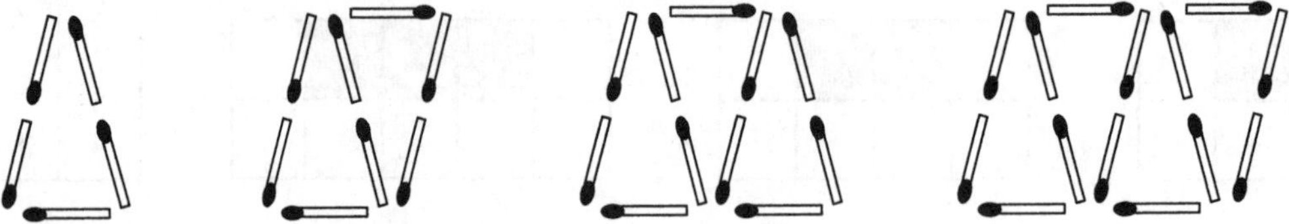

Make a table and find a formula connecting m and t.

6. In this sequence there are triangles (t) and squares (s) around the outside.

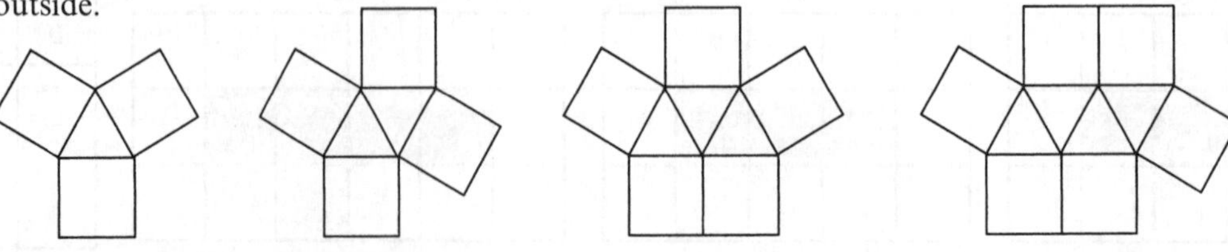

What is the formula connecting t and s?

7. Look at the tables below. In each case, find a formula connecting the two letters.

(a)

n	p
1	3
2	8
3	13
4	18

write '$p = \ldots$'

(b)

n	k
2	17
3	24
4	31
5	38

write '$k = \ldots$'

(c)

n	w
3	17
4	19
5	21
6	23

write '$w = \ldots$'

8. In these tables it is harder because the numbers on the left do not go up by one each time. Try to find a formula in each case.

(a)

n	y
1	4
3	10
7	22
8	25

(b)

n	h
2	5
3	9
6	21
10	37

(c)

n	k
3	14
7	26
9	32
12	41

9. This is one member of a sequence of cubes (c) made from matches (m).

Find a formula connecting m and c.

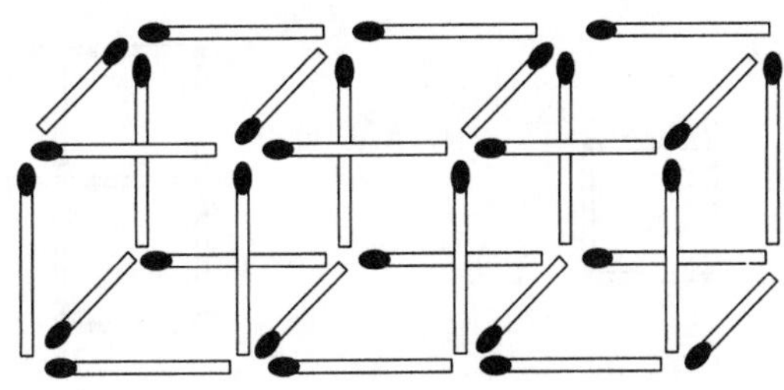

10. You can make some nice loops by fitting pentagon tiles together.

Diagram $n = 1$ | Diagram $n = 2$ | Diagram $n = 3$

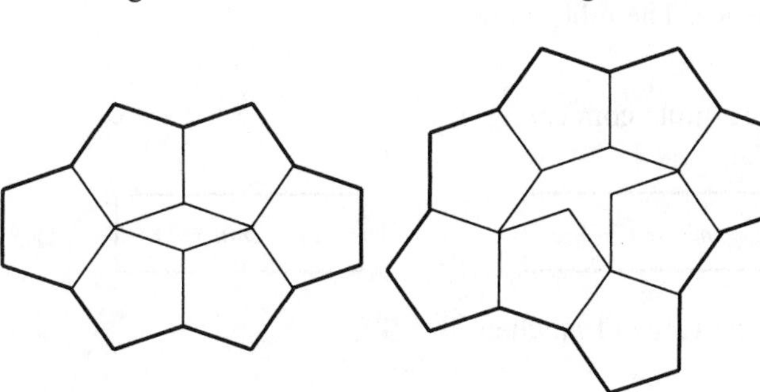

6 tiles (t)
14 external edges (e)

8 tiles (t)
17 external edges (e)

10 tiles (t)
20 external edges (e)

Make your own tables involving n, t and e.

(a) Find a formula connecting n and t.

(b) Find a formula connecting n and e.

(c) Find a formula connecting t and e.

11. In this sequence of diagrams we have shown the number of lines, n, and the maximum number of crossovers, c.

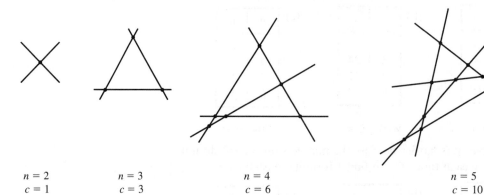

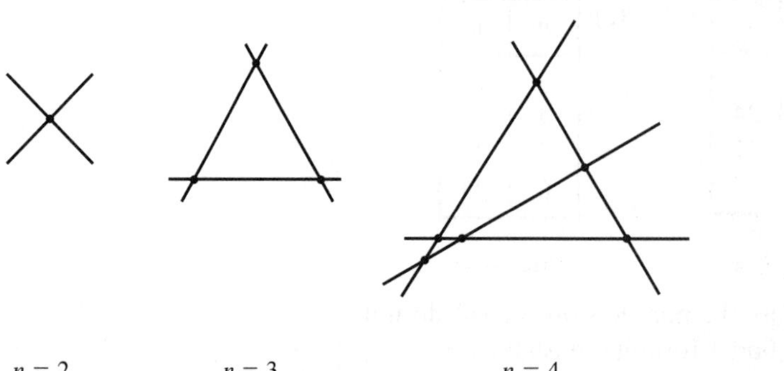

$n = 2$, $c = 1$ | $n = 3$, $c = 3$ | $n = 4$, $c = 6$ | $n = 5$, $c = 10$

Which of the following is the correct formula connecting n and c?

$c = 2n - 3$ | $c = \frac{n(n-1)}{2}$ | $c = n^2 - 2n - 1$

12.

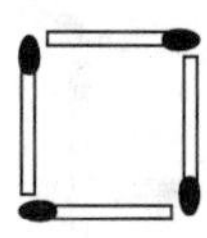

$n = 1$
$m = 4$

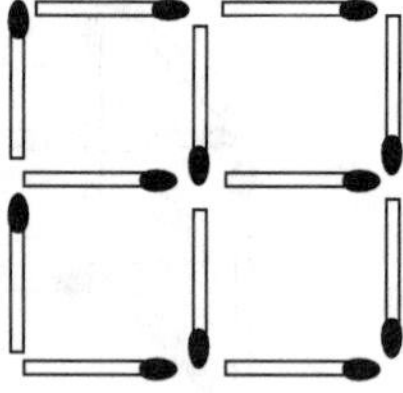

$n = 2$
$m = 12$

Diagram number n	Number of matches m
1	4
2	12
3	24
4	40

Here are the first two diagrams in a sequence. The table shows values of n and m.

(a) Which of the following is the correct formula connecting n and m?

$m = n^2 + 3n$ | $m = 8n - 4$ | $m = 2n(n + 1)$

(b) Use the correct formula to work out the value of m when $n = 10$.

3 Shape and Space 1

3.1 Accurate drawing

Some questions involving bearings or irregular shapes are easy to solve by drawing an accurate diagram.

Navigators on ships use scale drawings to work out their position or their course.

To improve the accuracy of your work, follow these guidelines.

- Use a *sharp* HB pencil.
- Don't press too hard.
- If drawing an *acute* angle make sure your angle is less than 90°.
- If you use a pair of compasses make sure they are fairly stiff so the radius does not change accidentally.

Exercise 1

Use a protractor and ruler to draw full size diagrams and measure the sides marked with letters.

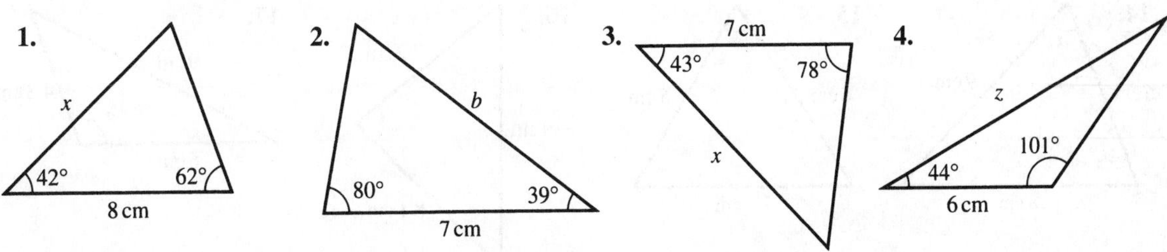

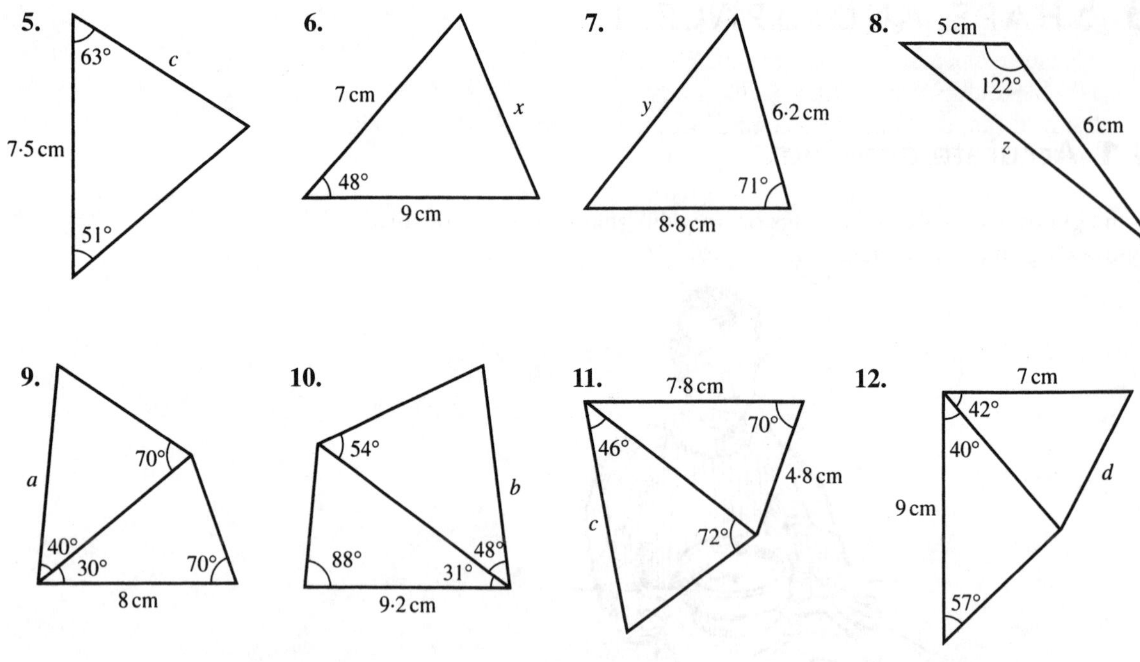

13 (a) Follow these steps to draw a triangle with sides 7 cm, 5 cm, 6 cm.

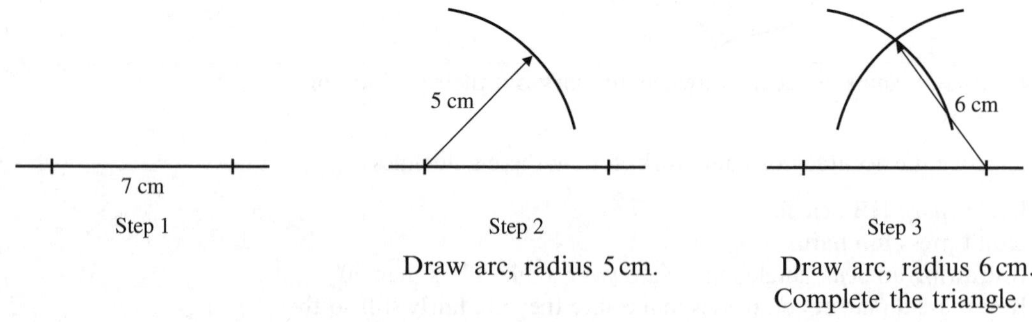

(b) Construct a triangle with sides 9 cm, 7 cm, 5 cm.

In Questions **14** to **17** construct the triangles using a pair of compasses.
Measure the angles marked with letters.

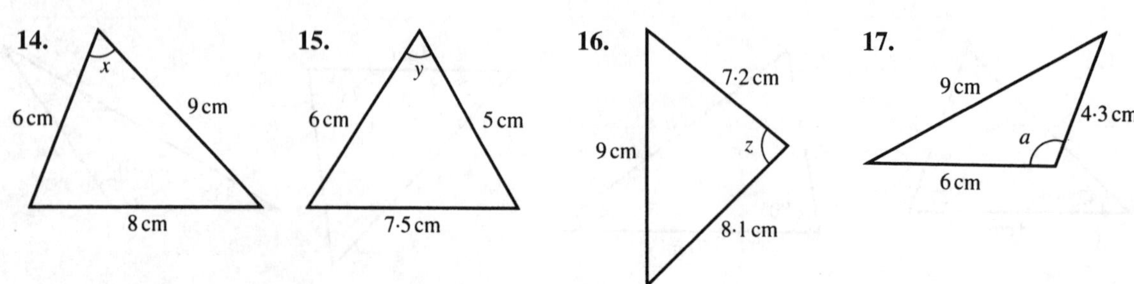

18. Farmer Gibson has to work out the area of his field to calculate his EC subsidy. The field is not a rectangle or parallelogram or any standard shape. He has measured the four sides of the field and one of the diagonals.

(a) Make a scale drawing of the field, using a scale of 1 cm to 10 m.

(b) Measure the lengths of the dotted lines and hence work out the total area of the field to the nearest 100 m^2.

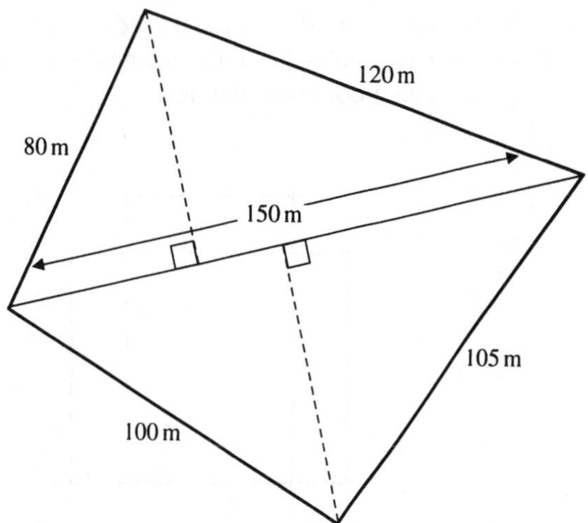

Nets

If the cube here was made of cardboard, and you cut along some of the edges and laid it out flat, you would have the *net* of the cube.

A cube has: 8 vertices
6 faces
12 edges.

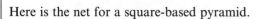

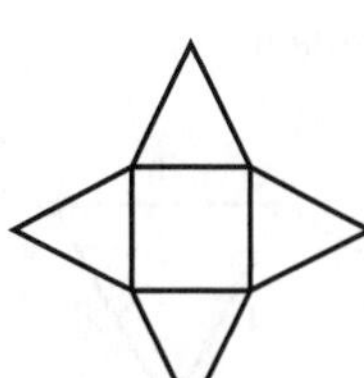

Here is the net for a square-based pyramid.

This pyramid has: 5 vertices
5 faces
8 edges.

Exercise 2

1. Which of the nets below can be used to make a cube?

(a)

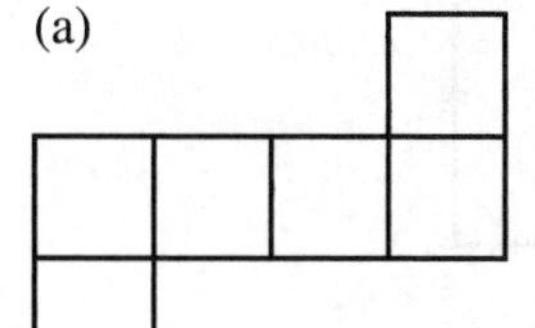

(b)

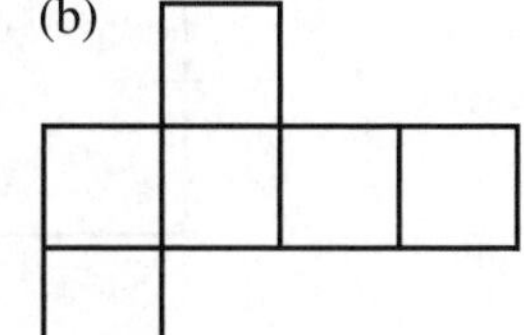

(c)

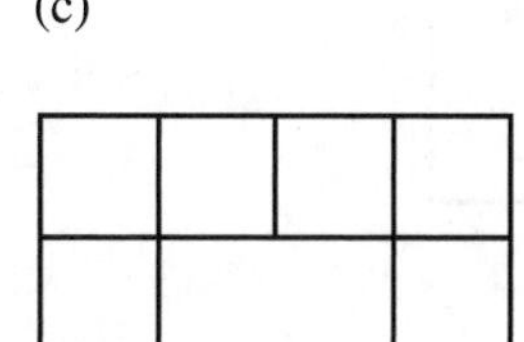

(d)

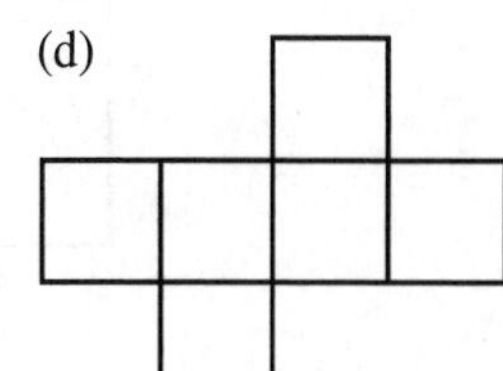

2. The numbers on opposite faces of a dice add up to 7. Take one of the possible nets for a cube from Question **1** and show the number of dots on each face.

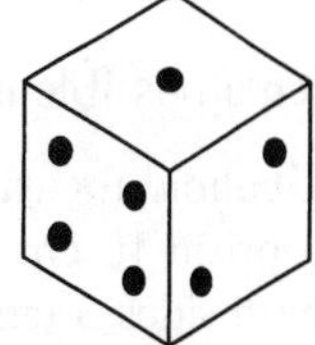

3. Here we have started to draw the net of a cuboid (a closed rectangular box) measuring 4 cm × 3 cm × 1 cm. Copy and then complete the net.

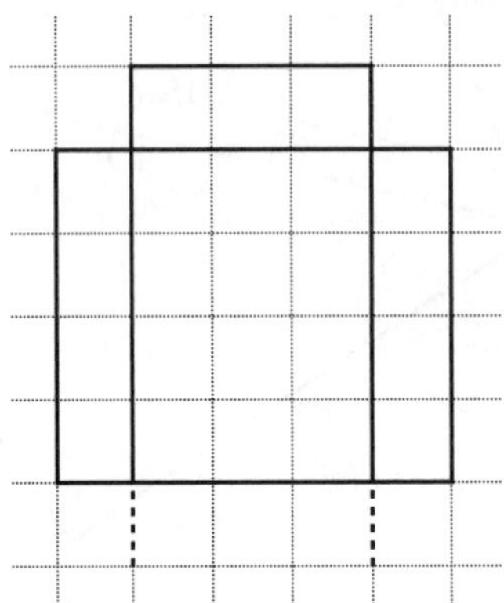

4. The diagram shown needs one more square to complete the net of a cube. Copy and cut out the shape and then draw the *four* possible nets which would make a cube.

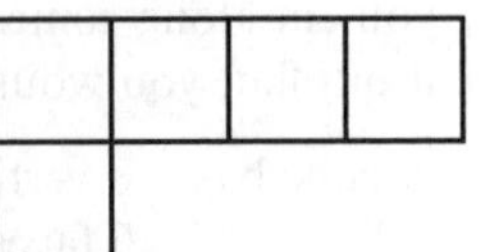

5. Describe the solid formed from each of these nets. State the number of vertices and faces for each object.

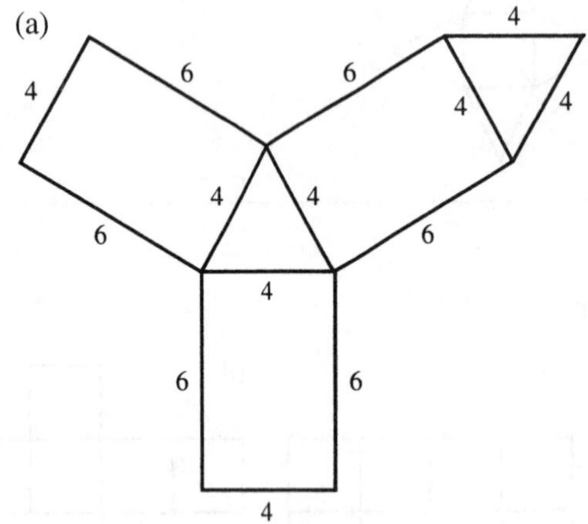

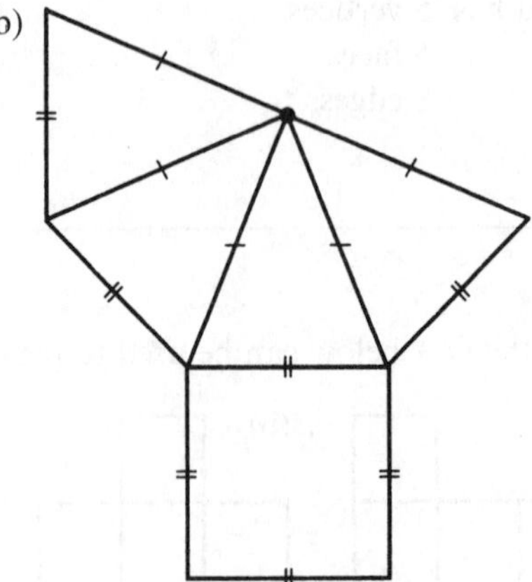

6. Sketch a possible net for each of the following:

(a) a cuboid measuring 5 cm by 2 cm by 8 cm
(b) a prism 10 cm long whose cross-section is a right-angled triangle with sides 3 cm, 4 cm and 5 cm.

7. A cube can be dissected into three equal pyramids. Make three solids from the net shown and fit them together to make a cube. All lengths are in cm.

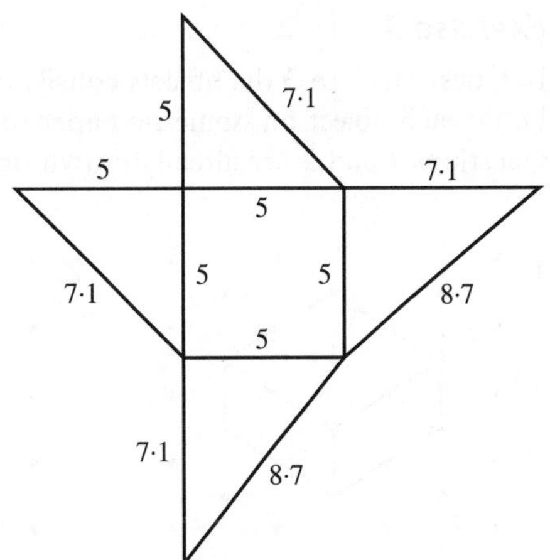

Isometric drawing

- When we draw a solid on paper we are making a 2-D representation of a 3-D object.

Here are two pictures of the same cuboid, measuring $4 \times 3 \times 2$ units.

(a) On ordinary squared paper

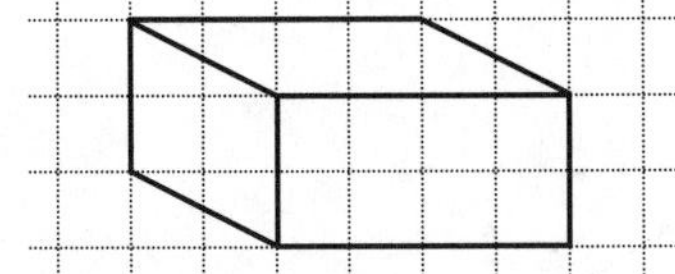

(b) On isometric paper
[a grid of equilateral triangles]

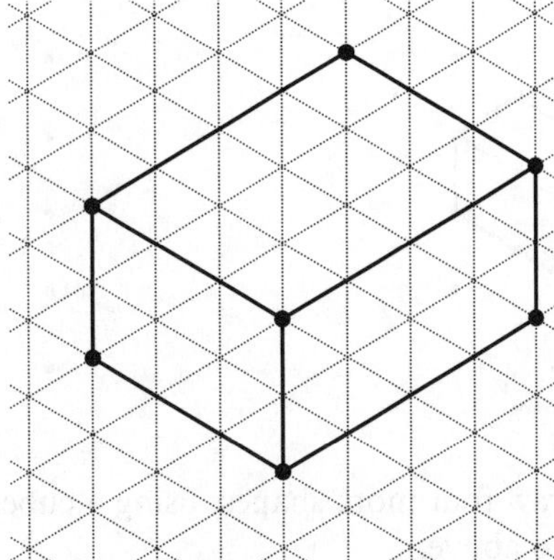

The dimensions of the cuboid cannot be taken from the first picture but they can be taken from the picture drawn on isometric paper.
Instead of isometric paper you can also use 'triangular dotty' paper like this:
Be careful to use it the right way round (as shown here).

Exercise 3

In Questions **1** to **3** the objects consist of 1 cm cubes joined together. Draw each object on isometric paper (or 'triangular dotty' paper). Questions **1** and **2** are already drawn on isometric paper.

1.

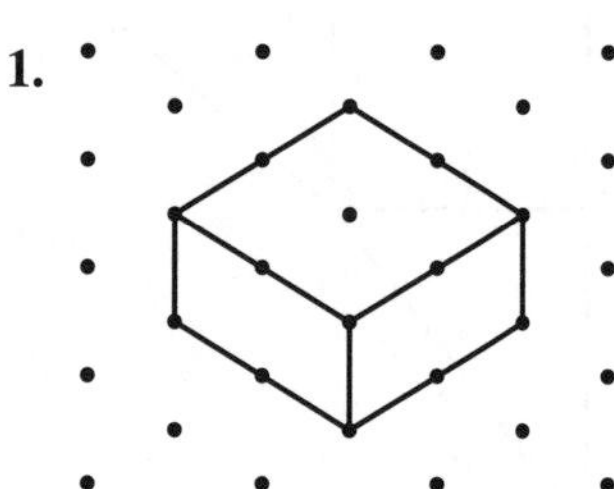

2.

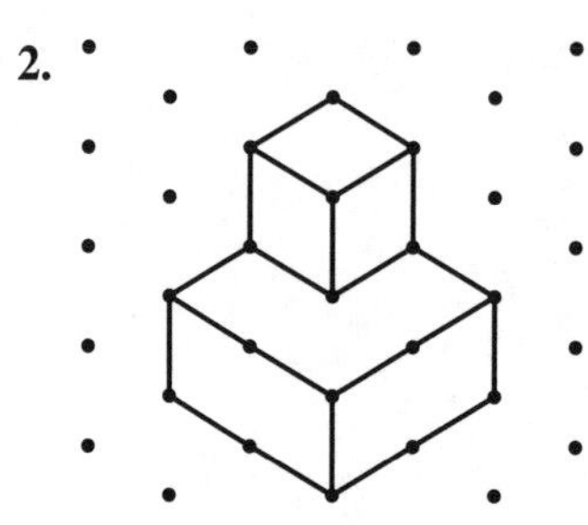

3.

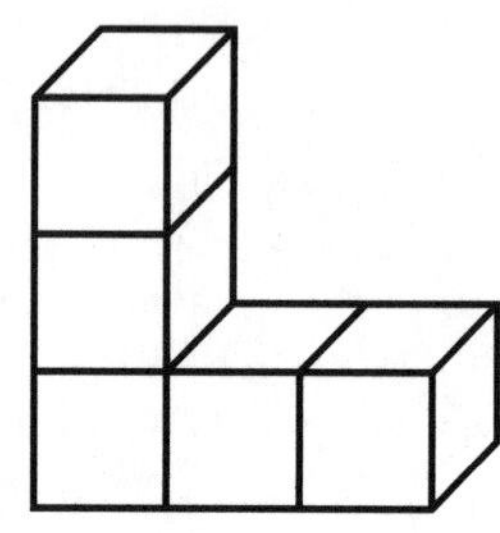

4. The diagram shows one edge of a cuboid. Complete the drawings of *two* possible cuboids, each with a volume of 12 cm^3.

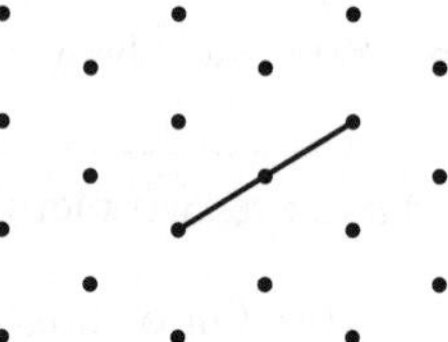

5. Here are two shapes made using 4 multilink cubes.

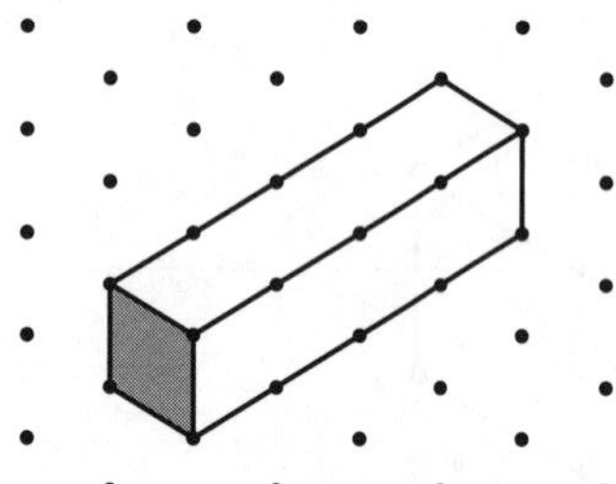

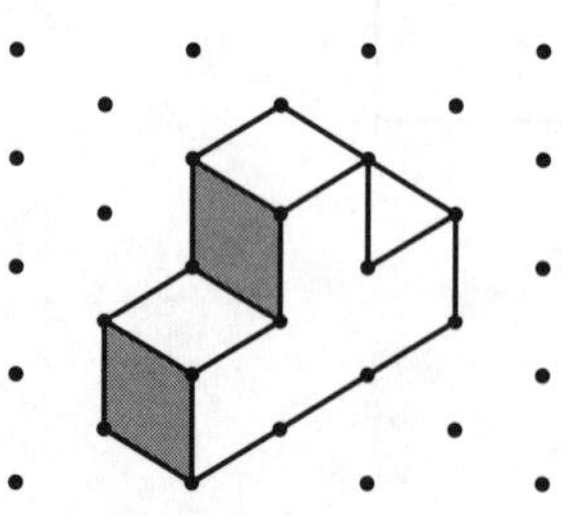

Make and then draw four more shapes, using 4 cubes, which are different to the two above.

6. The shape shown falls over on to the shaded face. Draw the shape after it has fallen over.

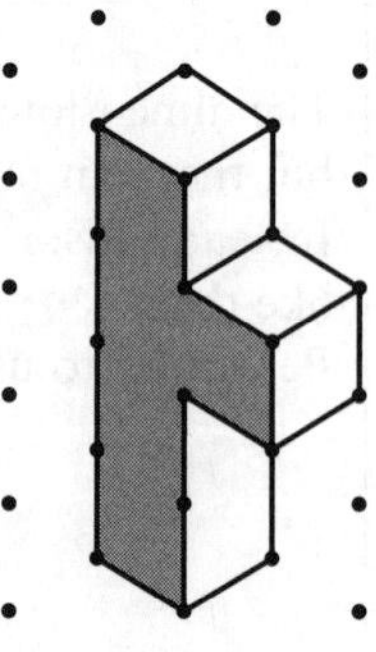

7. You need 16 small cubes.
Make the two shapes below and then arrange them into a $4 \times 4 \times 1$ cuboid by adding a third shape, which you have to find. Draw the third shape on isometric paper. There are *two* possible shapes.

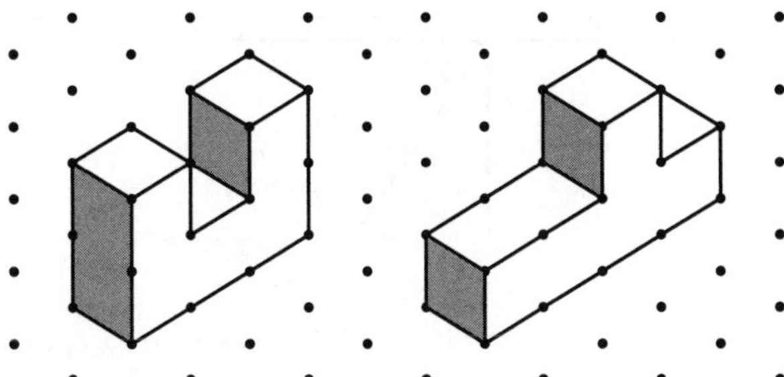

8 Make the letters of your initials and then draw them on isometric paper.

9. (a) The side view and plan view (from above) of object A are shown.

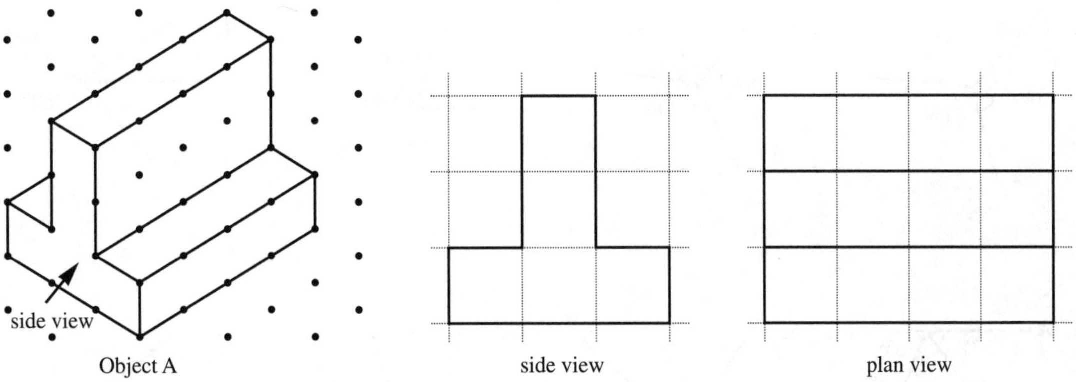

(b) Draw the side view and plan view of objects B and C.

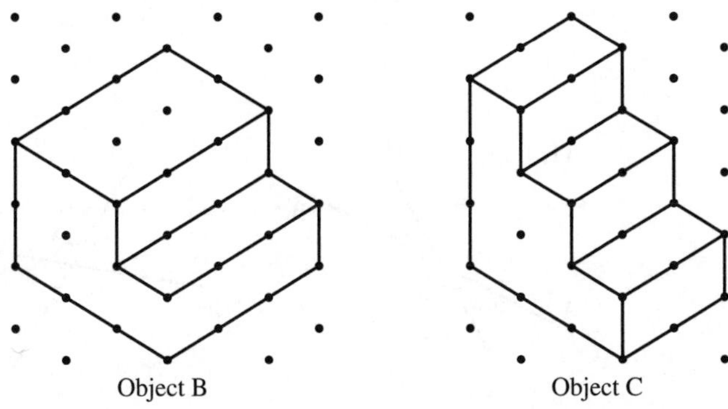

3.2 Angle facts

- The angles at a point add up to 360°.
- The angles on a straight line add up to 180°.

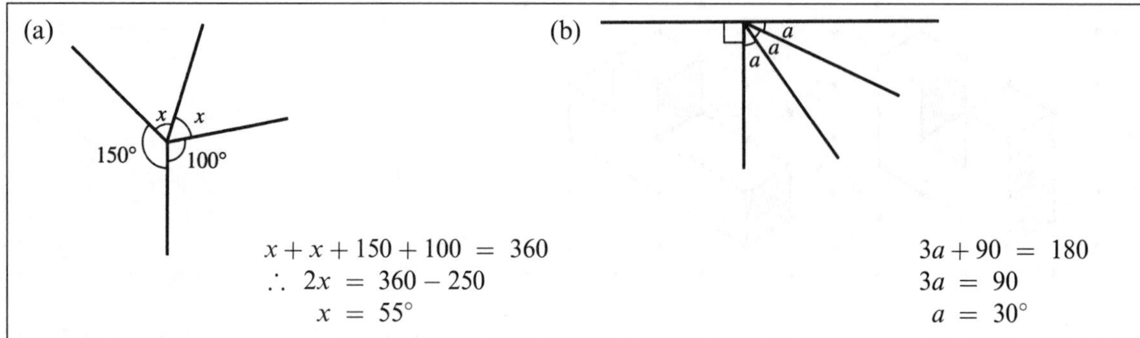

$$x + x + 150 + 100 = 360$$
$$\therefore\ 2x = 360 - 250$$
$$x = 55°$$

$$3a + 90 = 180$$
$$3a = 90$$
$$a = 30°$$

Exercise 4

Find the angles marked with letters. The lines AB and CD are straight.

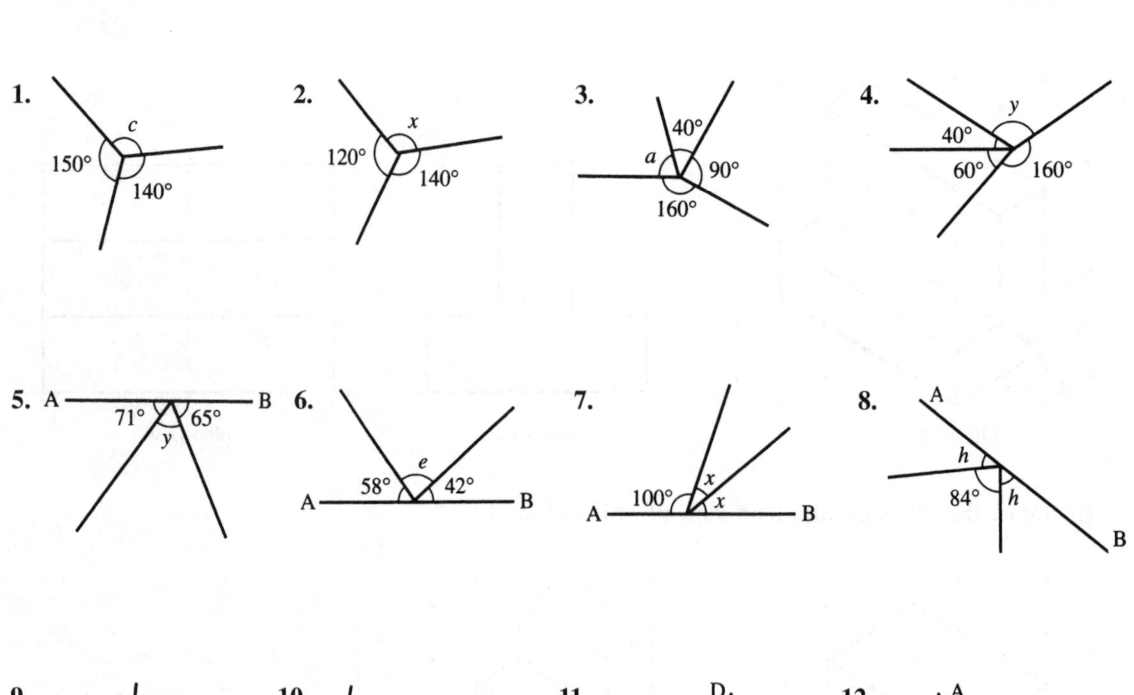

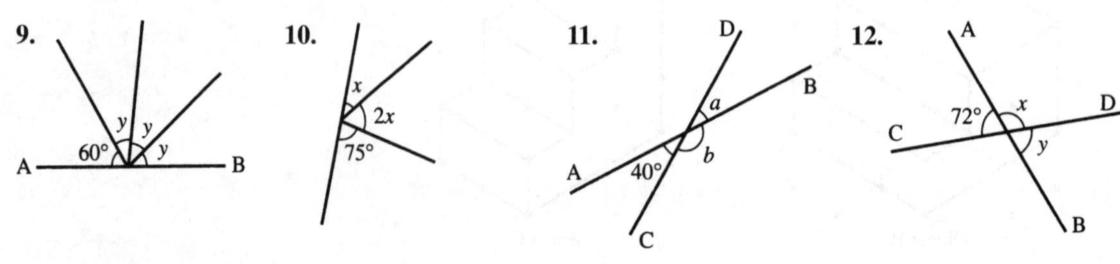

Triangles

- The angles in a triangle add up to 180°.

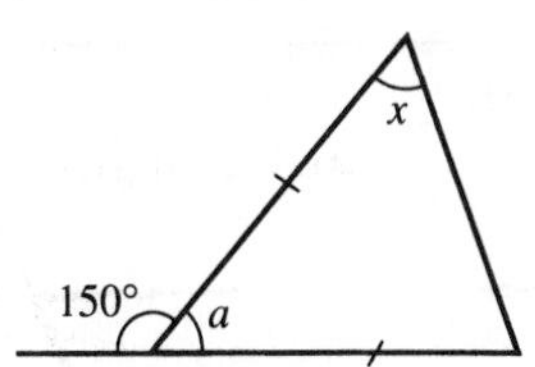

$a = 180 - 150° = 30°$

The triangle is isosceles $\therefore\ 2x + 30 = 180$

$2x = 150$

$x = 75°$

Exercise 5

Find the angles marked with letters. For the more difficult questions it is helpful to draw a diagram.

1.

2.

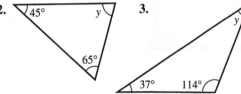

3.

4. 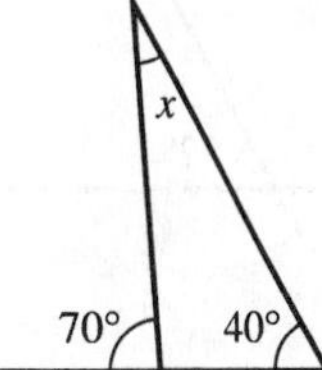

5. 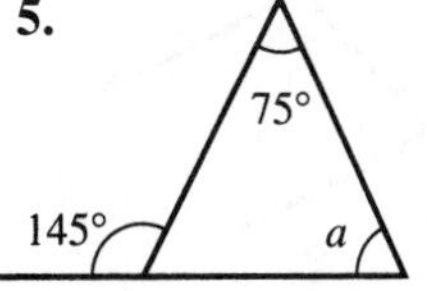

6. 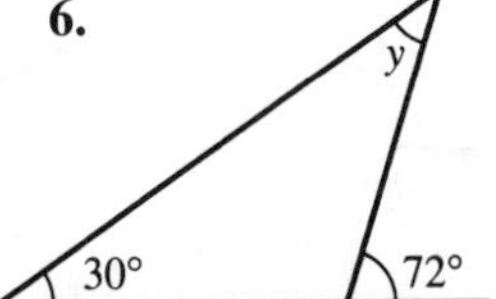

7. 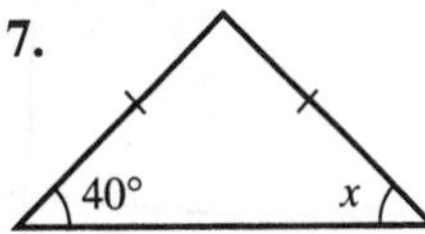

8. 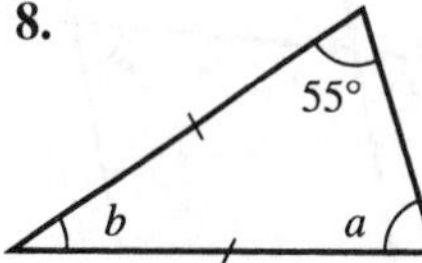

9. 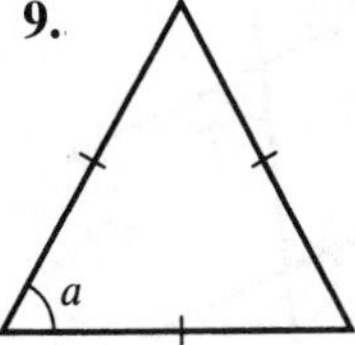

10. 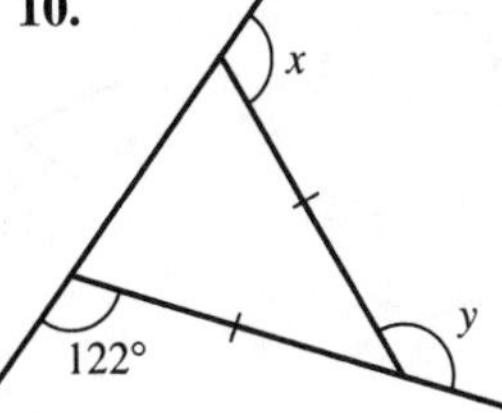

11. 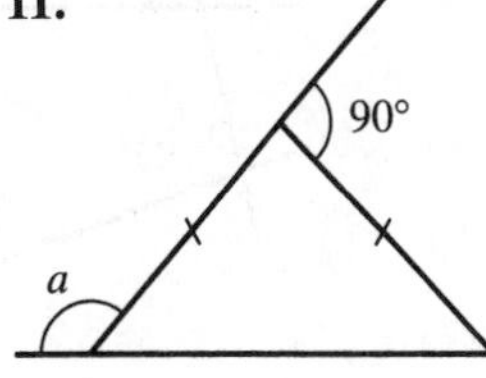

12. 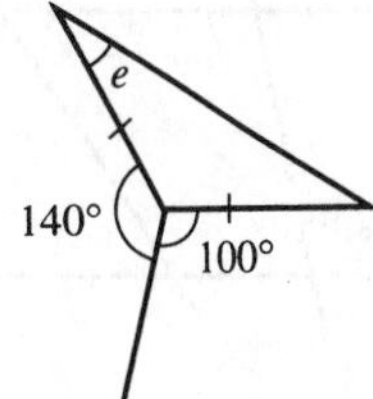

13. 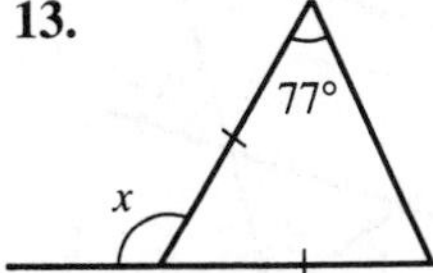

14. 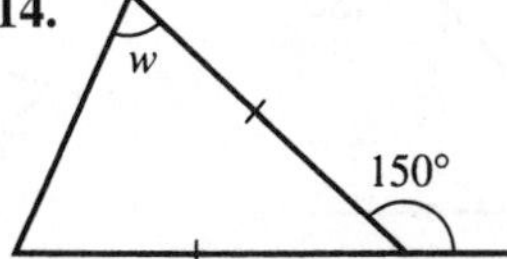

15. 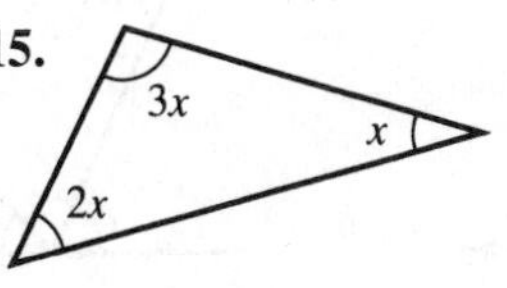

16. 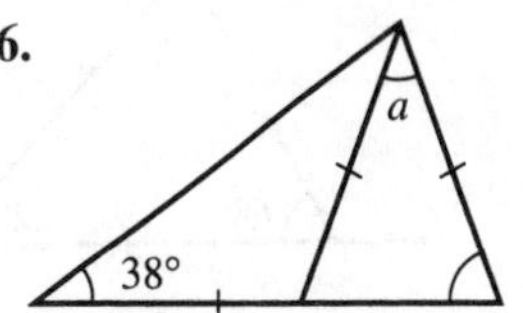

Parallel lines

- When a line cuts a pair of parallel lines all the acute angles are equal and all the obtuse angles are equal.

Some people remember:
'F angles' and 'Z angles'

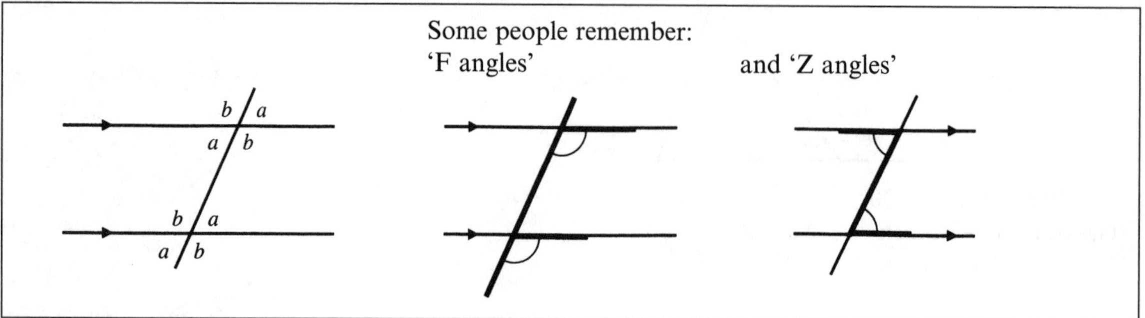

Exercise 6

Find the angles marked with letters.

1.

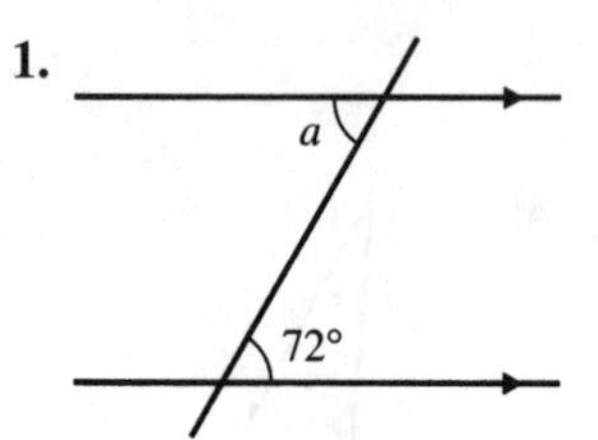

2.

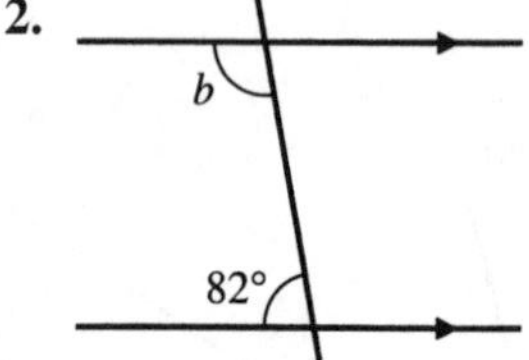

3.

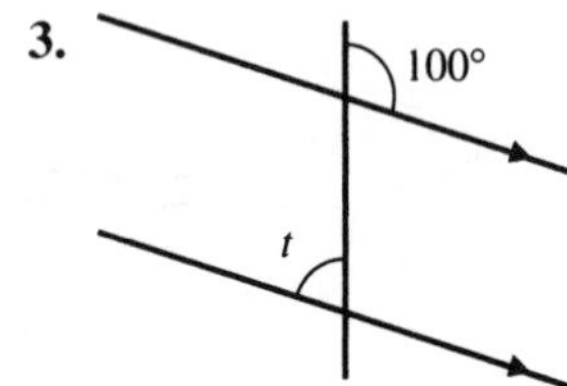

4.

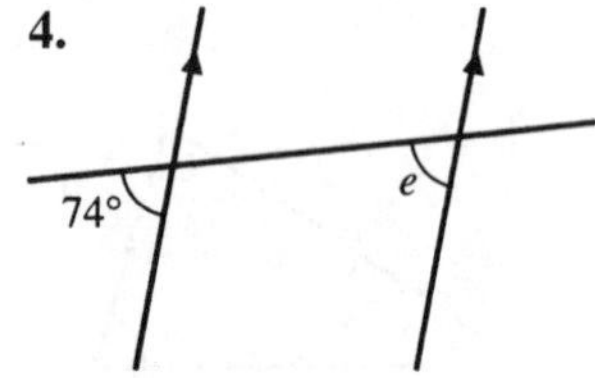

5.

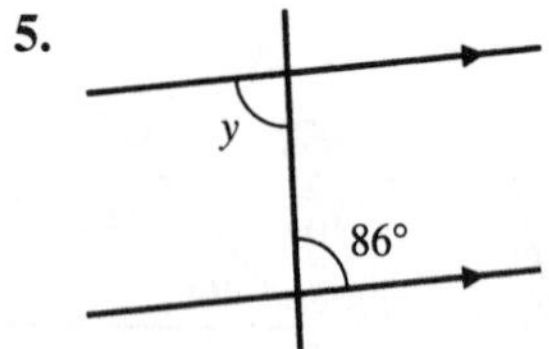

6.

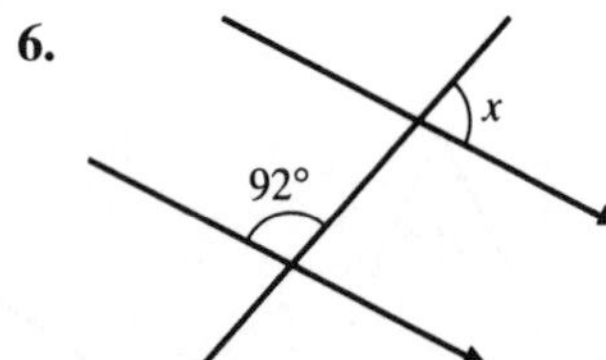

7.

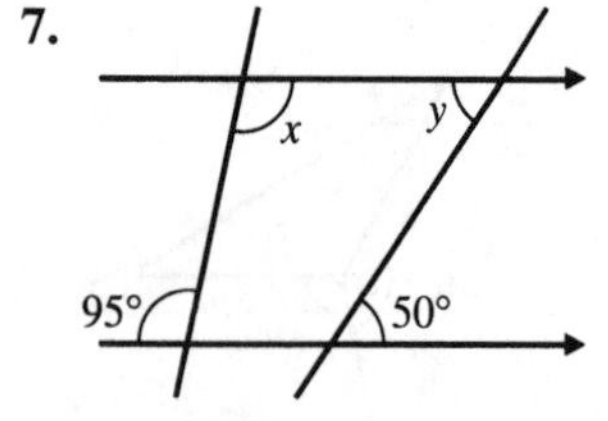

8.

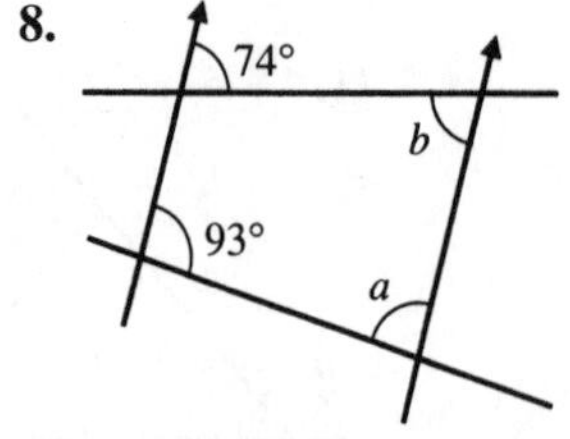

9.

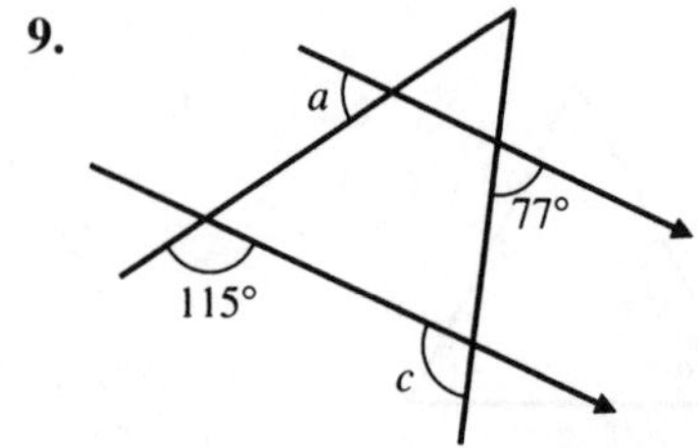

10.

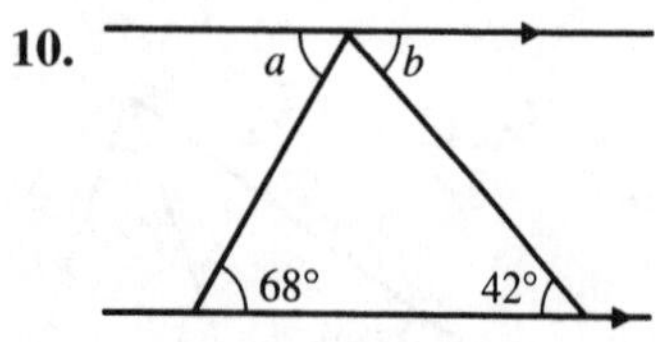

11.

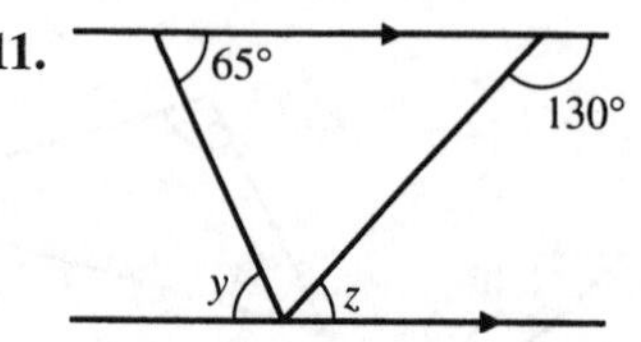

12.

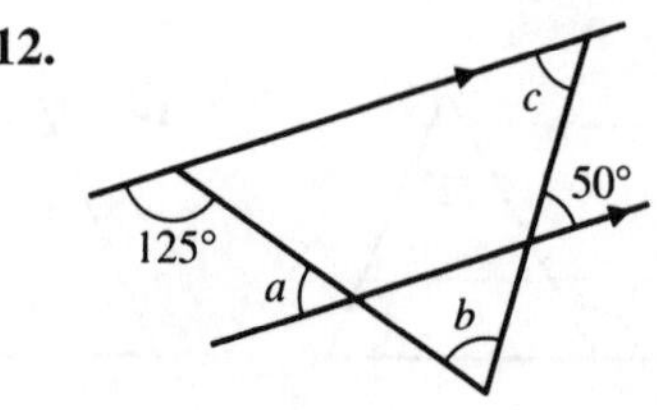

Mixed questions

The next exercise contains questions which summarise the work of the last three exercises.

Exercise 7

Find the angles marked with letters.

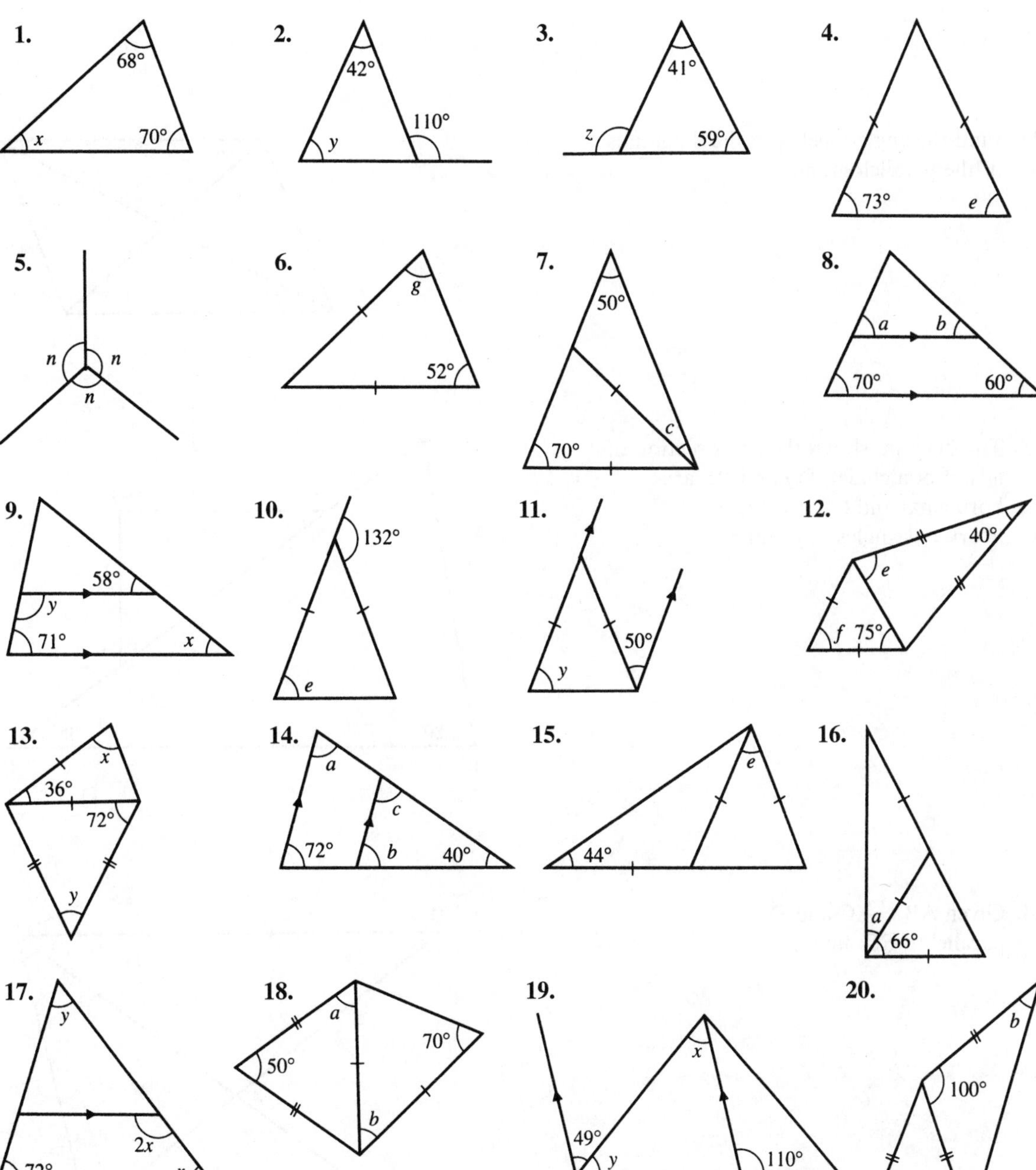

21. The diagram shows two equal squares joined to a triangle.
Find the angle x.

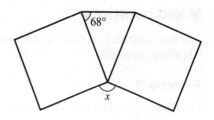

22. Find the angle a between the diagonals of the parallelogram.

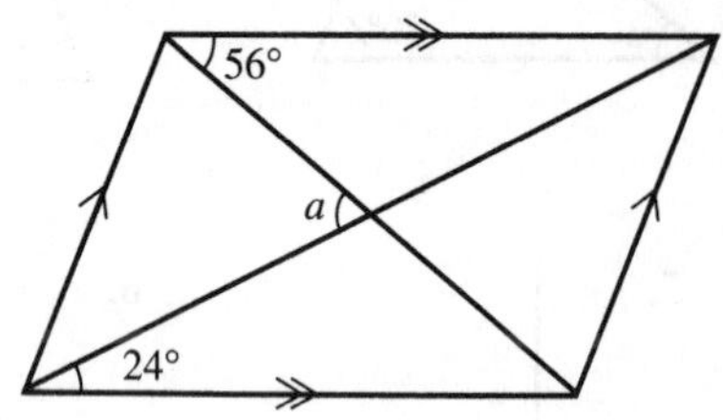

23. The diagram shows the cross section of a roof of a chalet. PQ and RS are horizontal and ST is vertical.
Work out angles x, y and z.

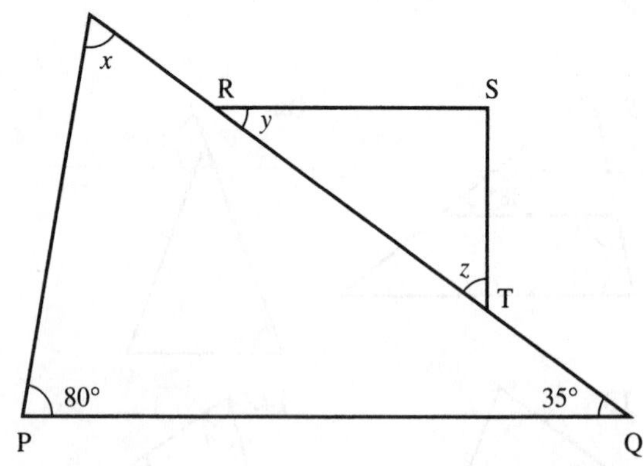

24. Given AB = AC and DA is parallel to EC, find x.

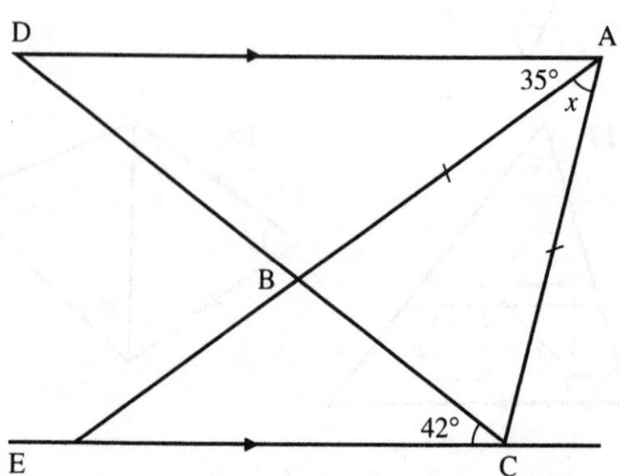

3.3 Symmetry

(a) Line symmetry

The letter M has one line of symmetry, shown dotted.

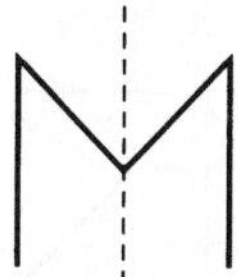

(b) Rotational symmetry

The shape may be turned about O into three identical positions. It has rotational symmetry of order three.

Exercise 8

For each shape state:
(a) the number of lines of symmetry
(b) the order of rotational symmetry.

1. 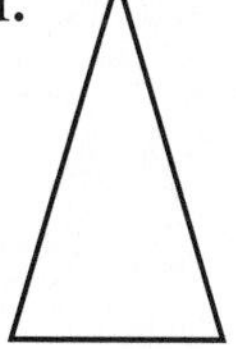

2. 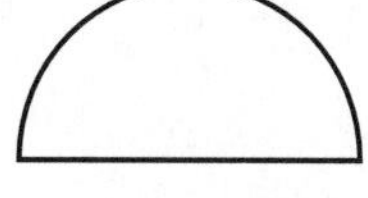

3. 

4. 

5. 

6. 

7. 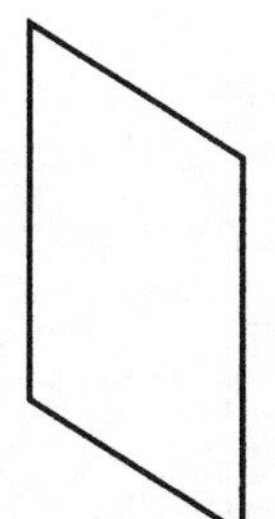

8. 

9. 

10. 

11. 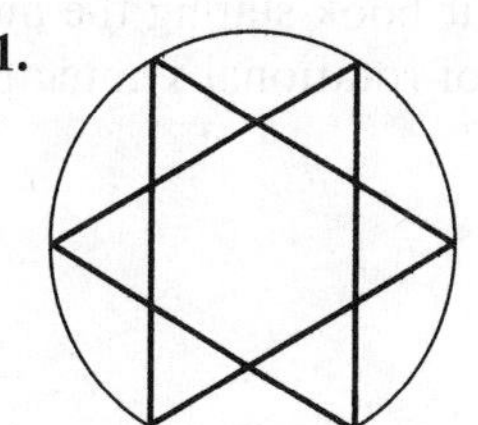

12. 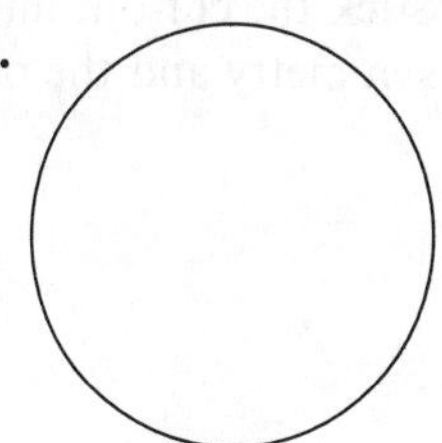

Exercise 9

In Questions **1** to **8**, the broken lines are axes of symmetry. In each question only *part of the shape* is given. Copy what is given onto squared paper and then carefully complete the shape.

1.

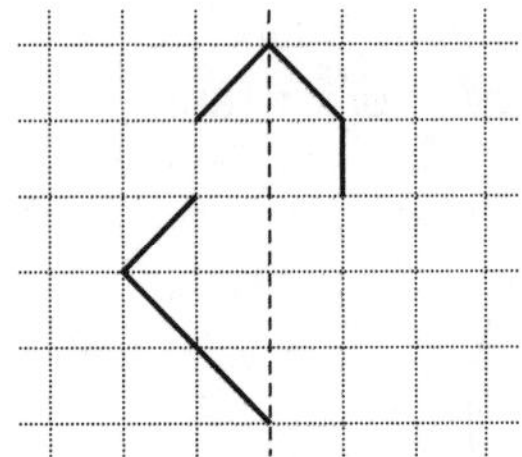

2.

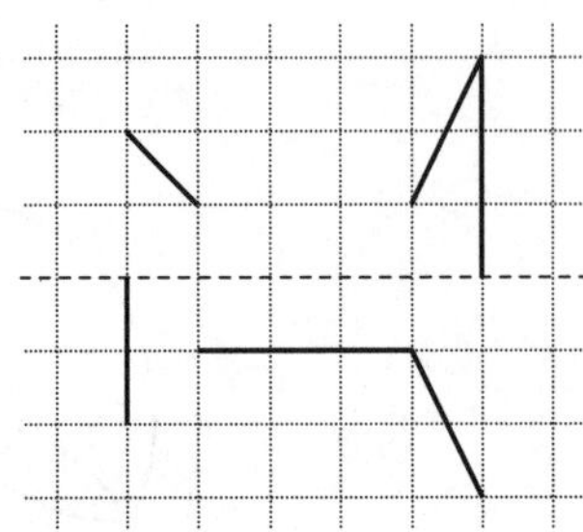

3.

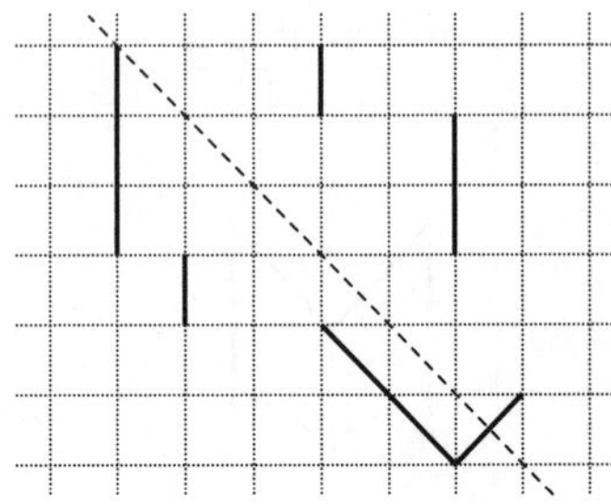

4.

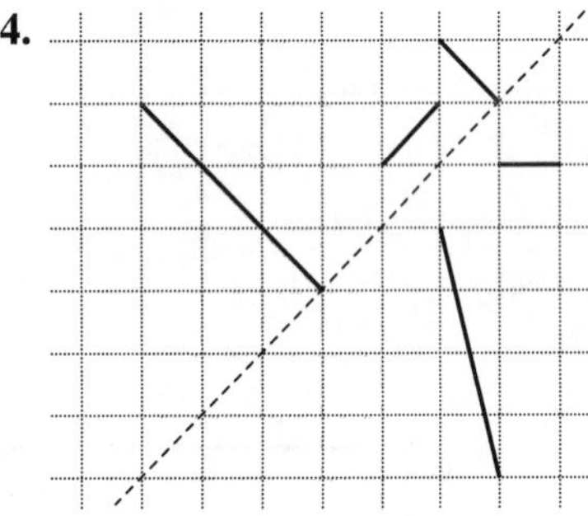

5.

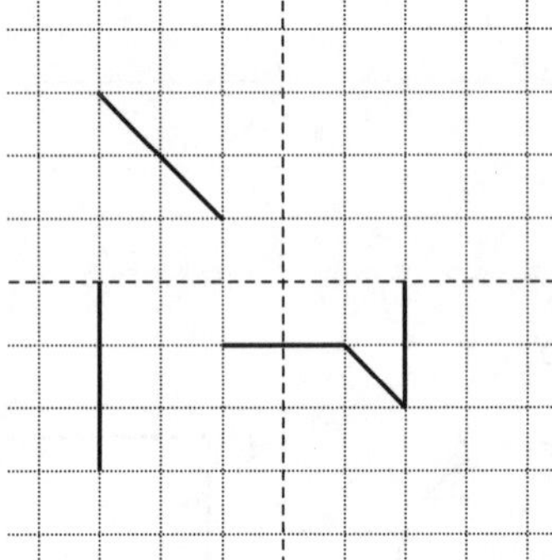

6.

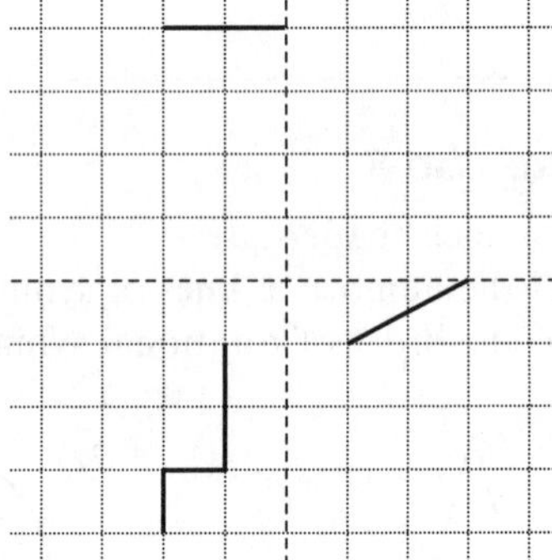

7.

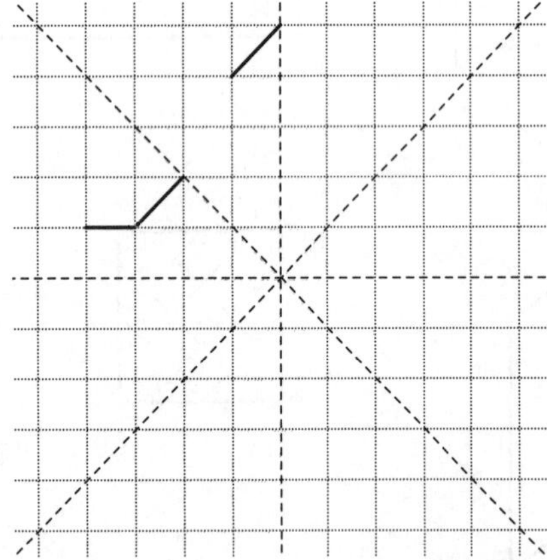

8.

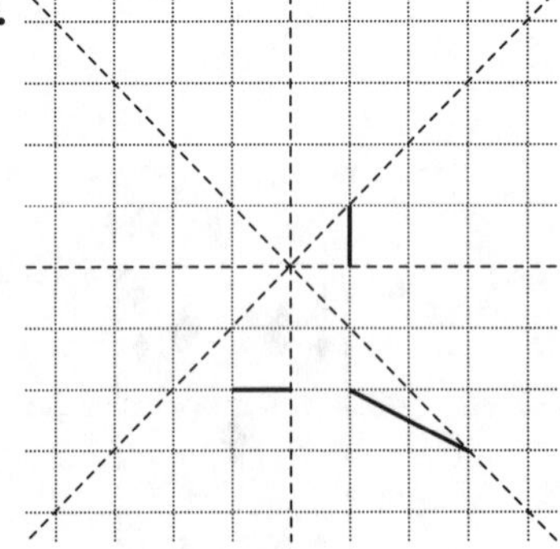

9. Fold a piece of paper twice and cut out any shape from the corner. Stick the cut-out into your book stating the number of lines of symmetry and the order of rotational symmetry.

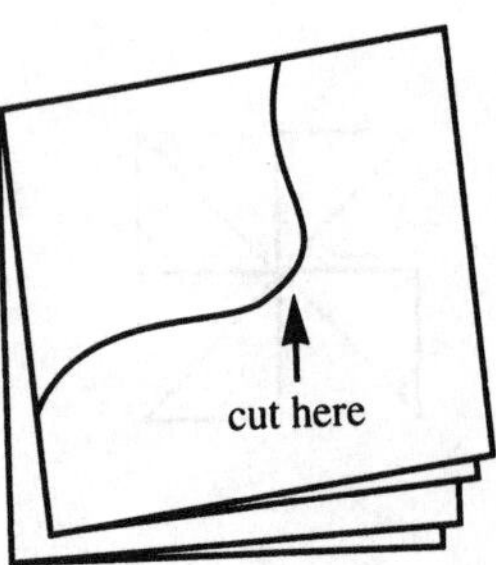

Planes of symmetry

- A plane of symmetry divides a 3-D shape into two congruent shapes. One shape must be a mirror image of the other shape.

The shaded plane is a plane of symmetry of the cube.

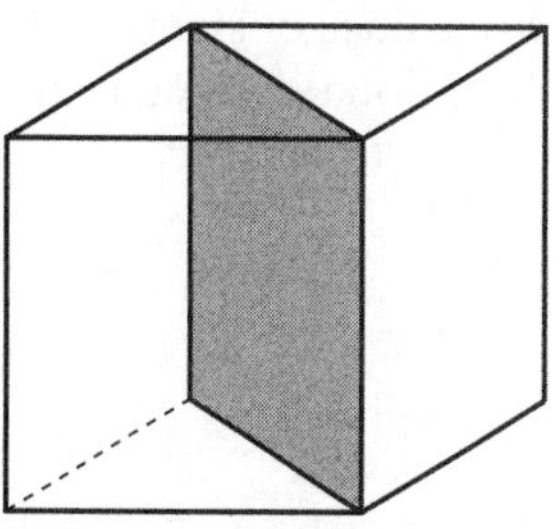

Exercise 10

1. How many planes of symmetry does this cuboid have?

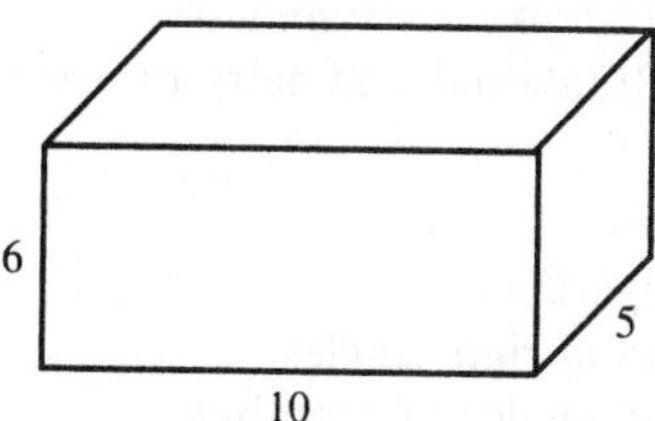

2. How many planes of symmetry do these shapes have?

(a)
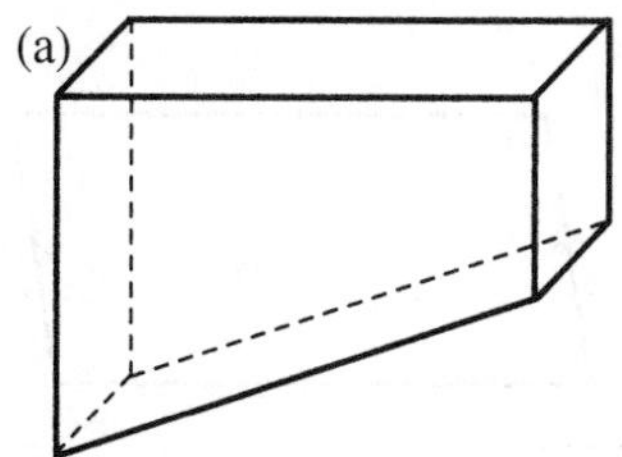

(b)
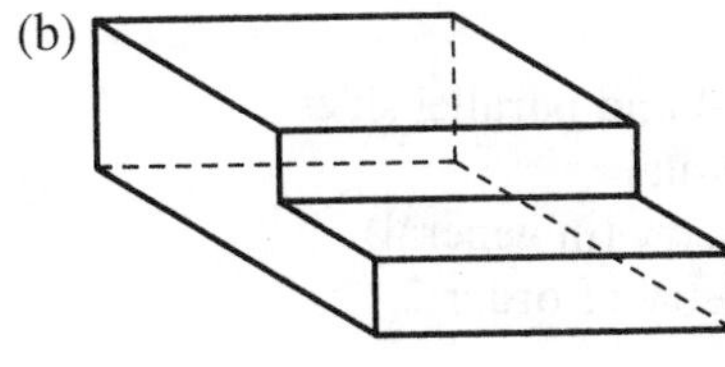

(c)
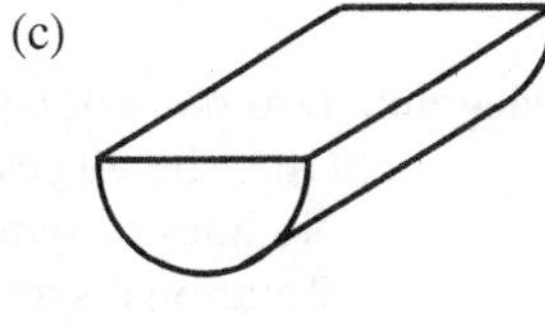

3. How many planes of symmetry does a cube have?

4. Draw a pyramid with a square base so that the vertex of the pyramid is vertically above the centre of the square base. Show any planes of symmetry by shading.

5. The diagrams show the plan view and the side view of an object.

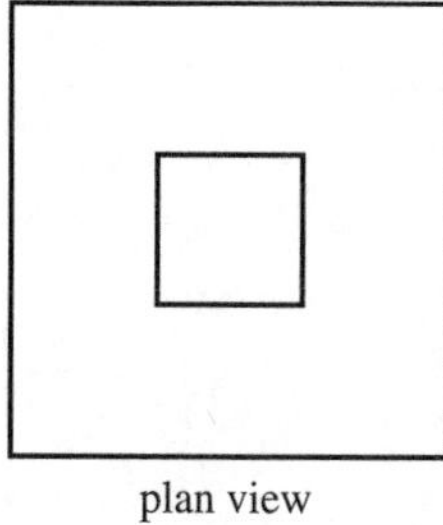
plan view

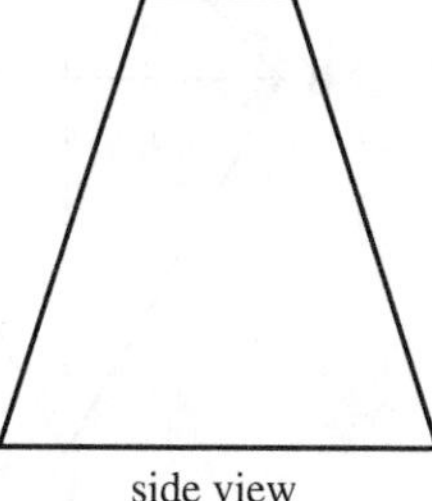
side view

How many planes of symmetry has this object?

3.4 Quadrilaterals

- **Square:** Four equal sides
  All angles 90°
  Four lines of symmetry
  Rotational symmetry of order 4.

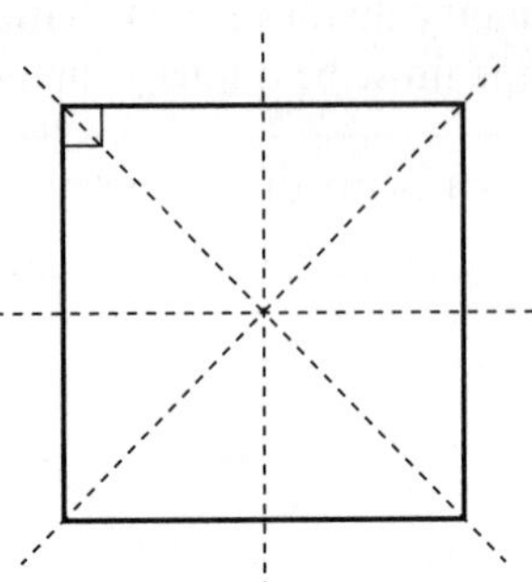

- **Rectangle** (not square): Two pairs of equal and parallel sides
  All angles 90°
  Two lines of symmetry
  Rotational symmetry of order 2.

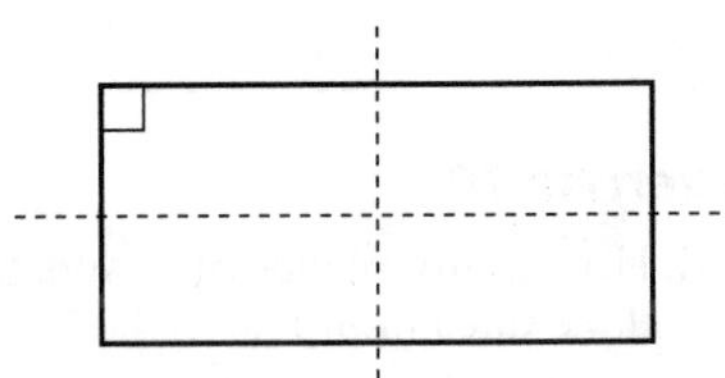

- **Rhombus:** Four equal sides
  Opposite sides parallel
  Diagonals bisect at right angles
  Diagonals bisect angles of rhombus
  Two lines of symmetry
  Rotational symmetry of order 4.

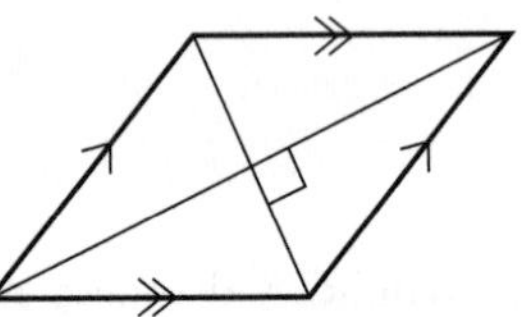

- **Parallelogram:** Two pairs of equal and parallel sides
  Opposite angles equal
  No lines of symmetry (in general)
  Rotational symmetry of order 2.

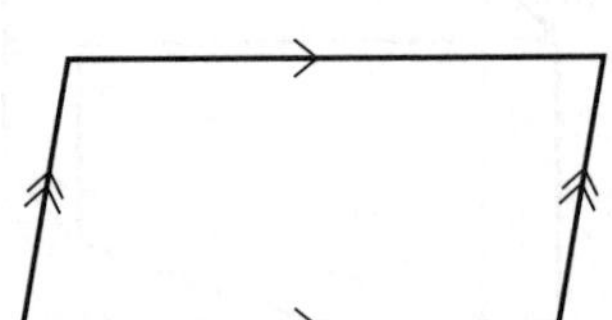

- **Trapezium:** One pair of parallel sides
  Rotational symmetry of order 1.

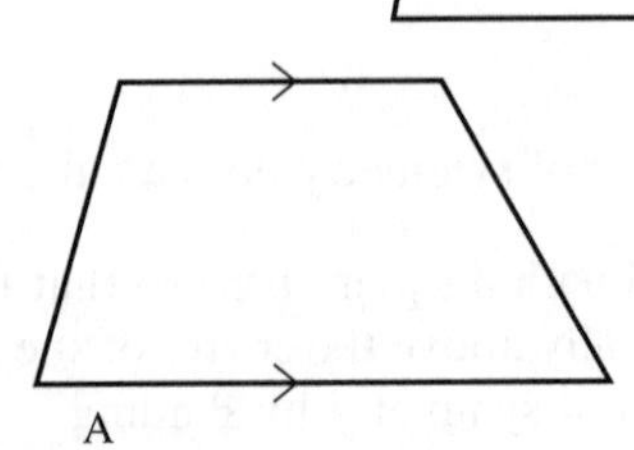

- **Kite:** AB = AD, CB = CD
  Diagonals meet at 90°
  One line of symmetry
  Rotational symmetry of order 1.

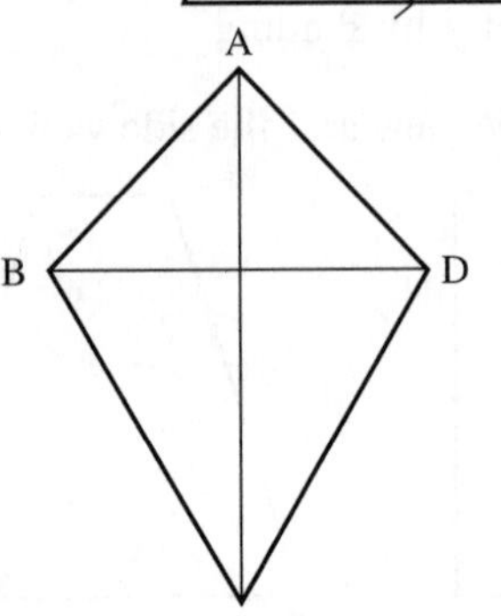

- For all quadrilaterals the sum of the interior angles is 360°.

Exercise 11

1. Write down the correct name for these five quadrilaterals which are drawn on isometric paper.

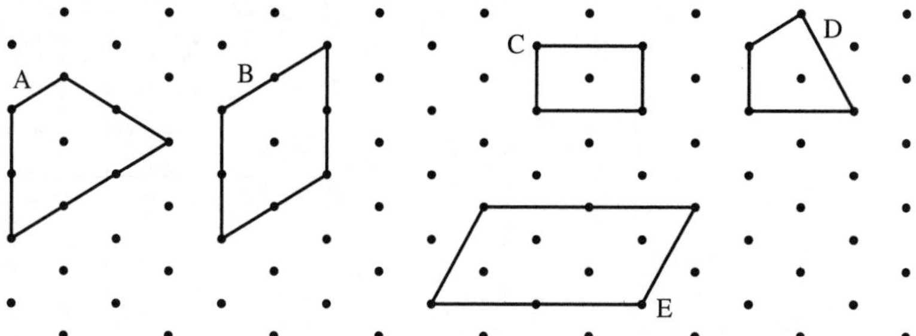

2. Copy the table and fill all the boxes with either ticks or crosses.

	Diagonals always equal	Diagonals always perpendicular	Diagonals always bisect the angles	Diagonals always bisect each other
Square				
Rectangle				
Parallelogram				
Rhombus				
Kite				

3. Find the angle x.

(a)
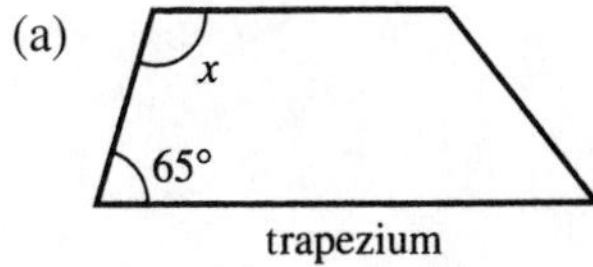

(b)
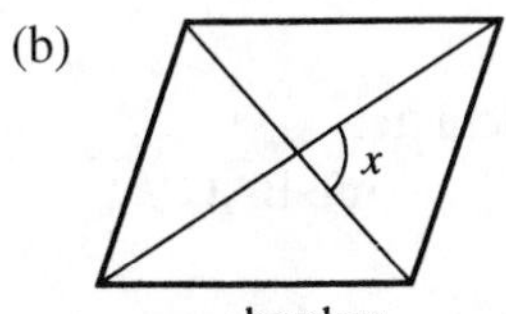

(c)
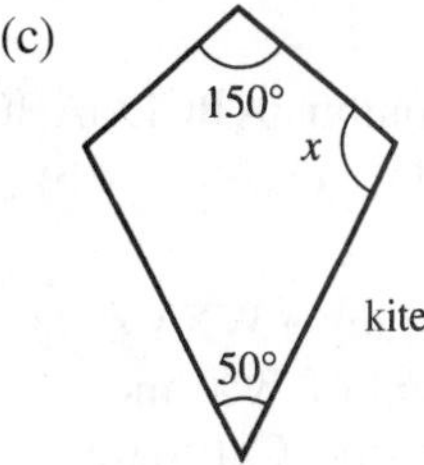

4. Copy each diagram on squared paper and mark with a cross the fourth vertex.

(a)
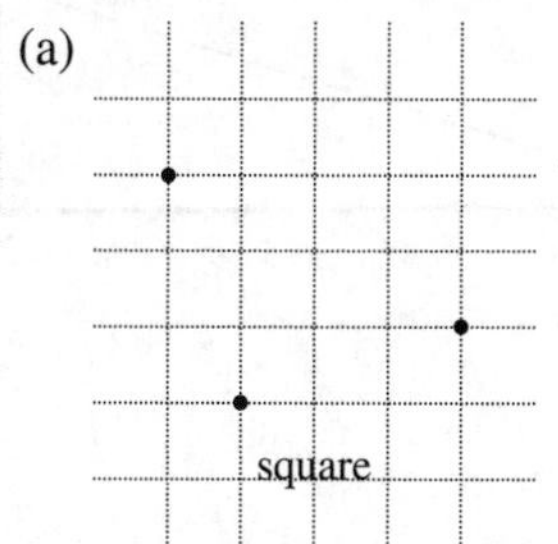

(b)
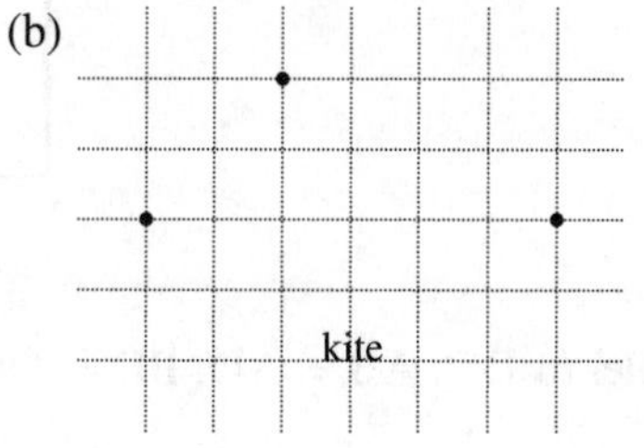

(c)
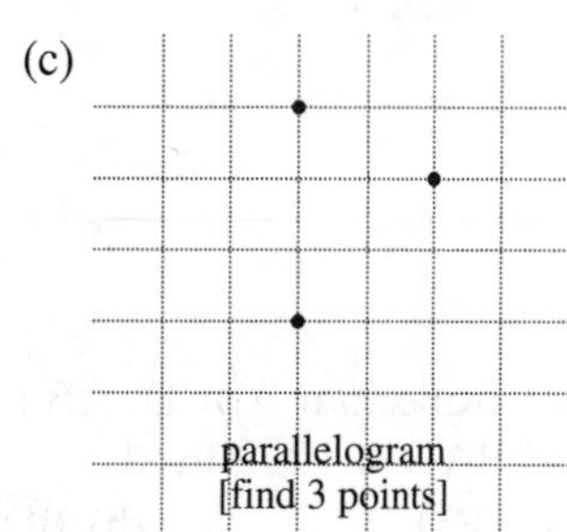

5. ABCD is a rhombus whose diagonals intersect at M.
Find the coordinates of C and D.

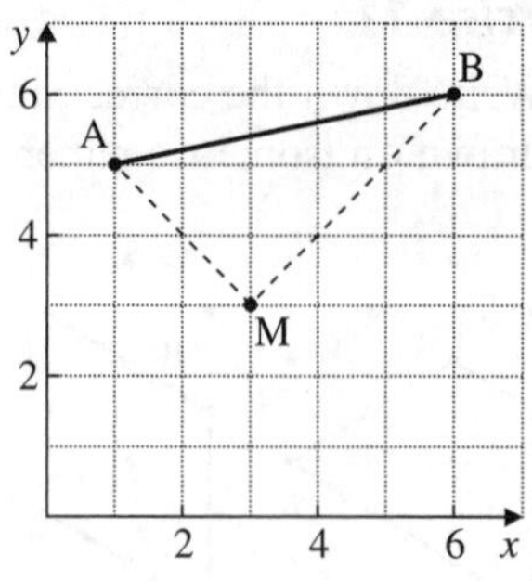

Exercise 12

In these questions begin by drawing a diagram and remember to put the letters around the shape in alphabetical order.

1. In a rectangle KLMN, $L\hat{N}M = 34°$. Calculate:
(a) $K\hat{L}N$ (b) $K\hat{M}L$

2. In a trapezium ABCD, $A\hat{B}D = 35°$, $B\hat{A}D = 110°$ and AB is parallel to DC. Calculate:
(a) $A\hat{D}B$ (b) $B\hat{D}C$

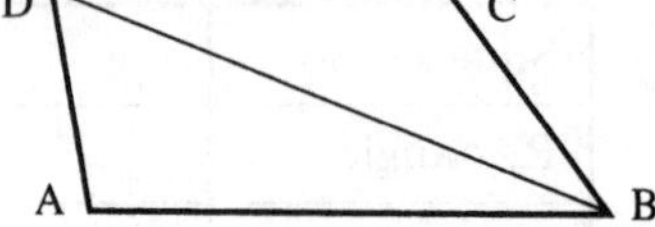

3. In a parallelogram WXYZ, $W\hat{X}Y = 72°$, $Z\hat{W}Y = 80°$. Calculate:
(a) $W\hat{Z}Y$ (b) $X\hat{W}Z$ (c) $W\hat{Y}X$

4. In a kite ABCD, AB = AD, BC = CD, $C\hat{A}D = 40°$ and $C\hat{B}D = 60°$. Calculate:
(a) $B\hat{A}C$ (b) $B\hat{C}A$ (c) $A\hat{D}C$

5. In a rhombus ABCD, $A\hat{B}C = 64°$. Calculate:
(a) $B\hat{C}D$ (b) $A\hat{D}B$ (c) $B\hat{A}C$

6. In a rectangle WXYZ, M is the mid-point of WX and $Z\hat{M}Y = 70°$. Calculate:
(a) $M\hat{Z}Y$ (b) $Y\hat{M}X$

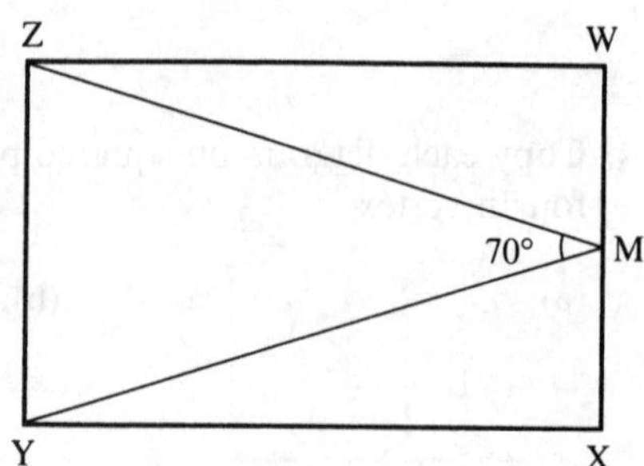

7. In a trapezium ABCD, AB is parallel to DC, AB = AD, BD = DC and $B\hat{A}D = 128°$. Find:
(a) $A\hat{B}D$ (b) $B\hat{D}C$ (c) $B\hat{C}D$

8. In a parallelogram KLMN,
KL = KM and $K\hat{M}L = 64°$.
Find:
(a) $M\hat{K}L$
(b) $K\hat{N}M$
(c) $L\hat{M}N$

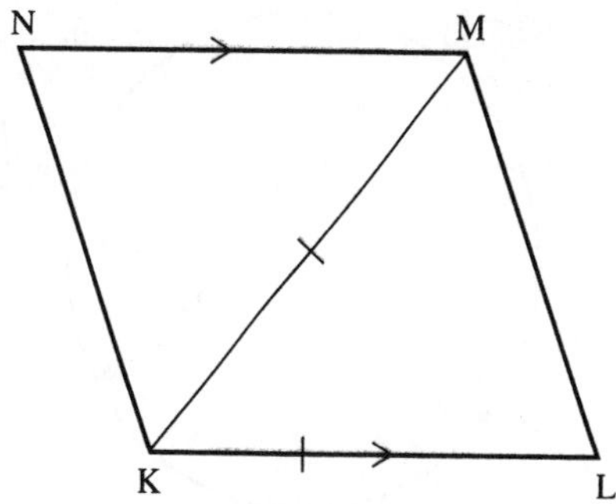

9. In a kite PQRS with PQ = PS and RQ = RS, $Q\hat{R}S = 40°$ and $Q\hat{P}S = 100°$. Find $P\hat{Q}R$.

10. In a rhombus PQRS, $R\hat{P}Q = 54°$. Find:
(a) $P\hat{R}Q$ (b) $P\hat{S}R$ (c) $R\hat{Q}S$

11. In a kite PQRS, $R\hat{P}S = 2P\hat{R}S$, PQ = QS = PS and QR = RS. Find:
(a) $Q\hat{P}S$ (b) $P\hat{R}S$ (c) $Q\hat{S}R$

3.5 Circle calculations

Circumference of a circle

- The circumference of a circle is given by $C = \pi d$.

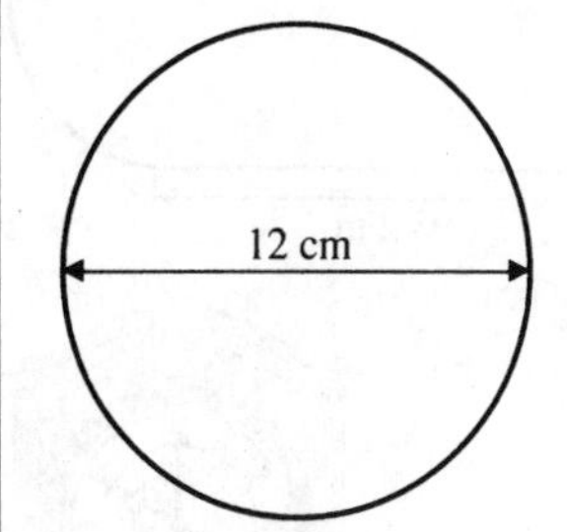

$C = \pi \times 12$ cm
$C = 37{\cdot}7$ cm (to 3 s.f.)
We have used the 'π' button on a calculator. The value of π (pi) is 3·142 approximately.

Exercise 13

Find the circumference. Use the 'π' button on a calculator or take $\pi = 3{\cdot}142$. Give the answers correct to 3 significant figures.

1.
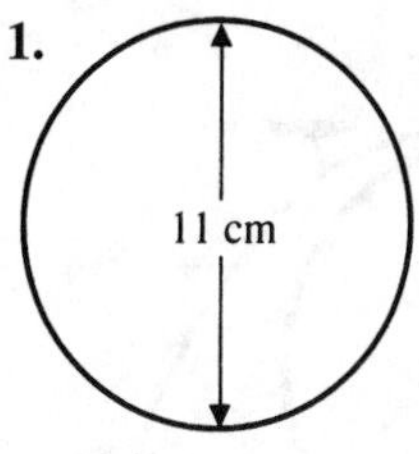

2.

3.
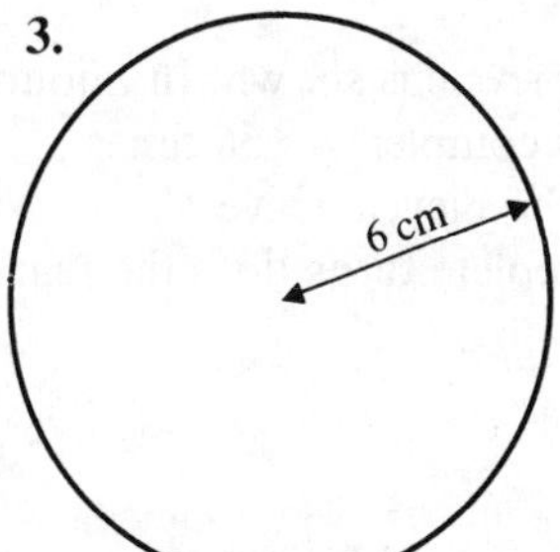

4.
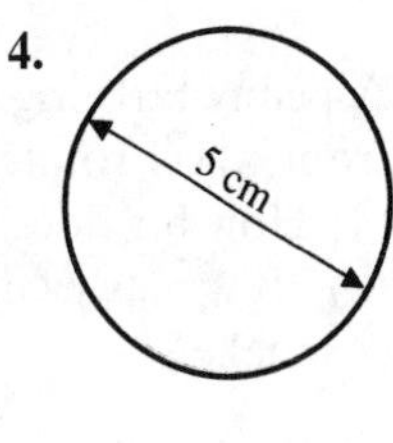

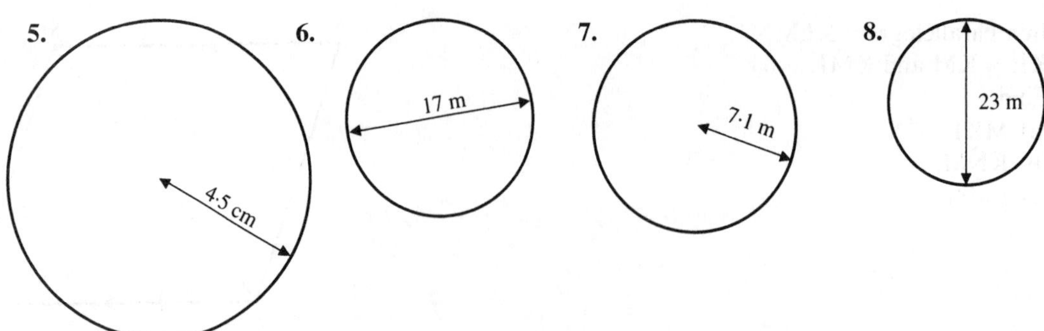

9. A ‘new’ 10p coin has a diameter of 2·4 cm and the ‘old’ 10p coin has a diameter of 2·8 cm.

How much longer, to the nearest mm, is the circumference of the old coin?

10. A circular pond has a diameter of 2·7 m. Calculate the length of the perimeter of the pond.

11. How many complete revolutions does a cycle wheel of diameter 60 cm make in travelling 400 m?

12. A running track has two semicircular ends of radius 34 m and two straights of 93·2 m as shown.

Calculate the total distance around the track to the nearest metre.

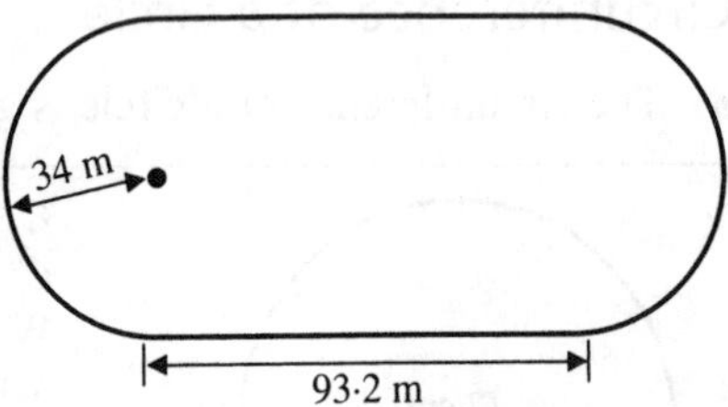

13. A fly, perched on the tip of the minute hand of a grandfather clock, is 14·4 cm from the centre of the clock face. How far does the fly move between 12:00 and 12:15?

14. A penny-farthing bicycle is shown. In a journey the front wheel rotates completely 156 times.
(a) How far does the bicycle travel?
(b) How many complete turns does the rear wheel make?

15. The diagram shows a framework for a target, consisting of 2 circles of wire and 6 straight pieces of wire. The radius of the outer circle is 30 cm and the radius of the inner circle is 15 cm.
Calculate the total length of wire needed for the whole framework.

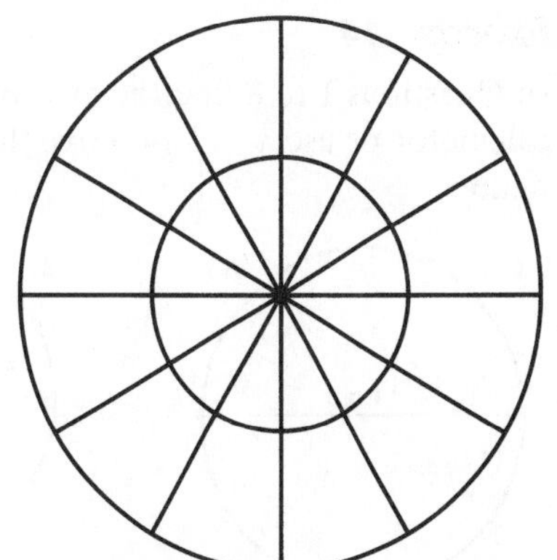

16. For a meeting, chairs are arranged in a large circle. The width of each chair is 40 cm.

How many chairs are needed to form a circle of diameter 3 m?

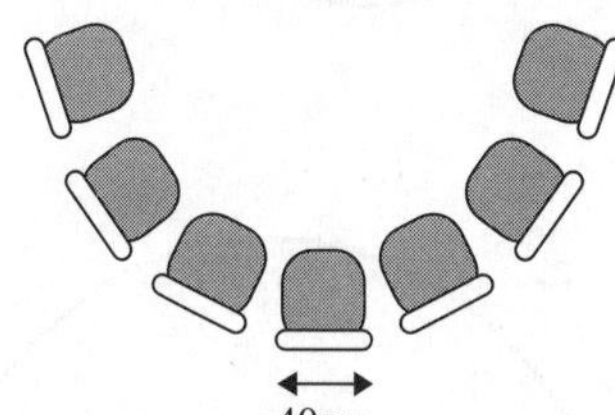

17. Lord Gibson decides to build a circular wall of radius 200 m around his stately home.

The diagram shows a section of the wall. Estimate, to the nearest thousand, the number of bricks required for the complete wall.

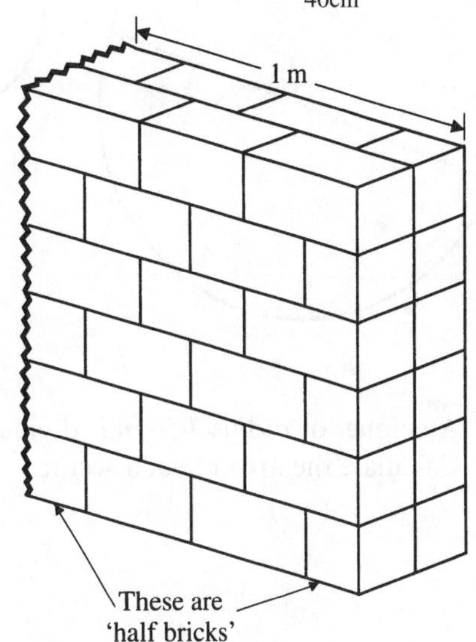

Area of a circle

- The area of a circle of radius r is given by $A = \pi r^2$.

Find the area of the circle shown.
In this circle $r = 4{\cdot}5$ cm
$\therefore$ Area of circle $= \pi \times 4{\cdot}5^2$
$= 63{\cdot}6\ \text{cm}^2$ (to 3 s.f.)

Remember the formula is $\pi(r^2)$ *not* $(\pi r)^2$.

On a calculator, work out the answer like this:

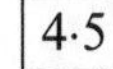  4·5 ×  =

4·5 × 4·5 × π =

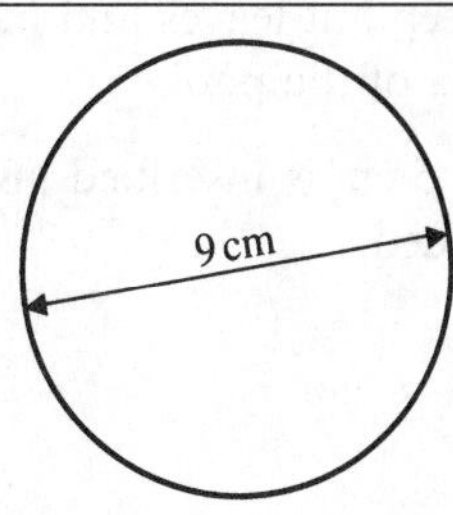

Exercise 14

In Questions **1** to **8** find the area of the circle. Use the 'π' button on a calculator or use $\pi = 3{\cdot}14$. Give the answers correct to three significant figures.

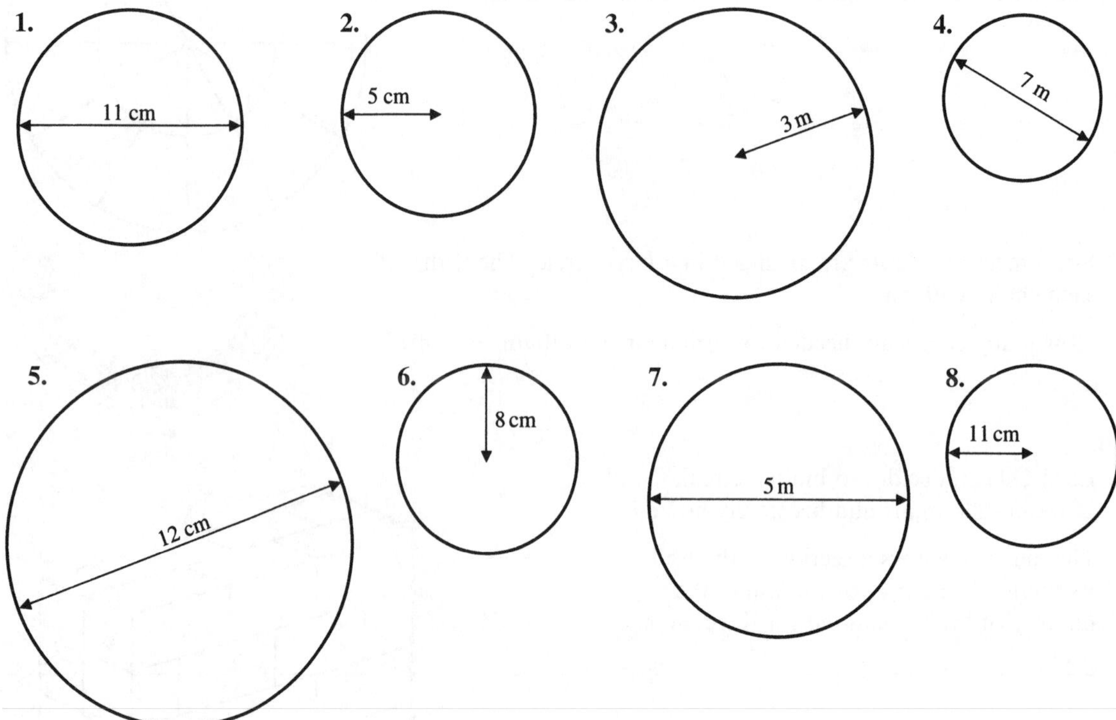

9. A spinner of radius 7·5 cm is divided into six equal sectors. Calculate the area of each sector.

10. A circular swimming pool of diameter 12·6 m is to be covered by a plastic sheet to keep out leaves and insects. Work out the area of the pool.

11. A circle of radius 5 cm is inscribed inside a square as shown. Find the area shaded.

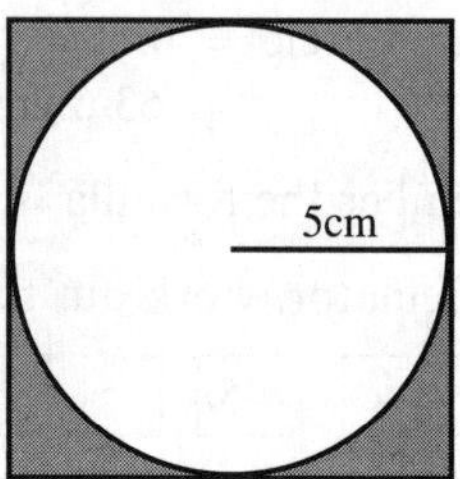

12. A large circular lawn is sprayed with weedkiller. Each square metre of grass requires 2 g of weedkiller. How much weedkiller is needed for a lawn of radius 27 m?

13. Discs of radius 4 cm are cut from a rectangular plastic sheet of length 84 cm and width 24 cm.

How many complete discs can be cut out? Find:
(a) the total area of the discs cut
(b) the area of the sheet wasted.

14. A circular pond of radius 6 m is surrounded by a path of width 1 m.
(a) Find the area of the path.
(b) The path is resurfaced with astroturf which is bought in packs each containing enough to cover an area of 7 m^2. How many containers are required?

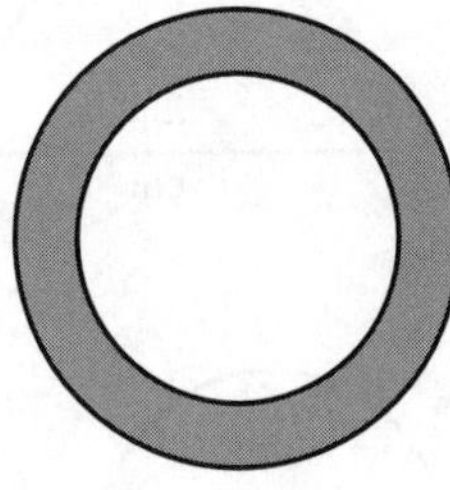

15. The diagram below shows a lawn (unshaded) surrounded by a path of uniform width (shaded). The curved end of the lawn is a semicircle of diameter 10 m.

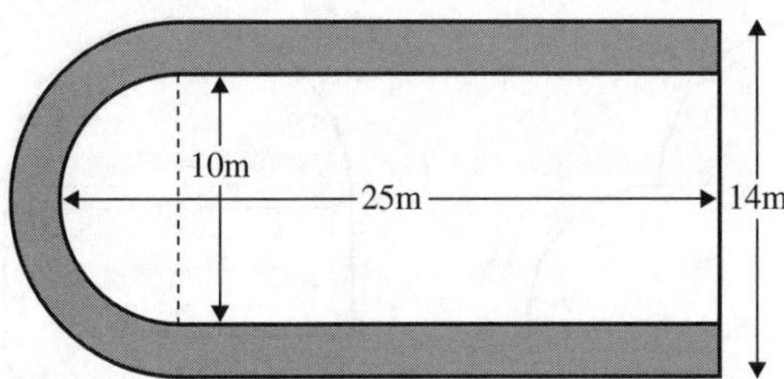

Calculate the total area of the path.

More complicated shapes

For the shape below find:

(a) the perimeter
(b) the area.

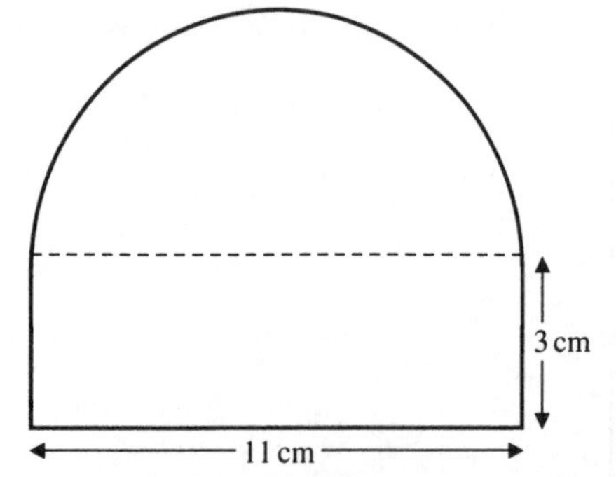

(a) Perimeter $= \left(\frac{\pi \times 11}{2}\right) + 11 + 3 + 3$

$= 34{\cdot}3$ cm (3 s.f.)

(b) Area $= \left(\frac{\pi \times 5{\cdot}5^2}{2}\right) + (11 \times 3)$

$= 80{\cdot}5\ \text{cm}^2$ (3 s.f.)

Exercise 15

Use the 'π' button on a calculator or take $\pi = 3{\cdot}14$. Give the answers correct to 3 s.f. For each shape find the perimeter.

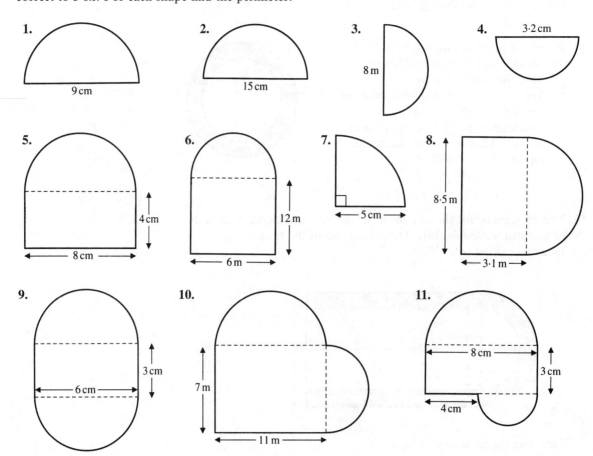

1. 9 cm

2. 15 cm

3. 8 m

4. 3·2 cm

5. 4 cm, 8 cm

6. 12 m, 6 m

7. 5 cm

8. 8·5 m, 3·1 m

9. 3 cm, 6 cm

10. 7 m, 11 m

11. 8 cm, 3 cm, 4 cm

Exercise 16

Find the area of each shape. All lengths are in cm.
In Questions **4, 5, 6** find the shaded area.

1.

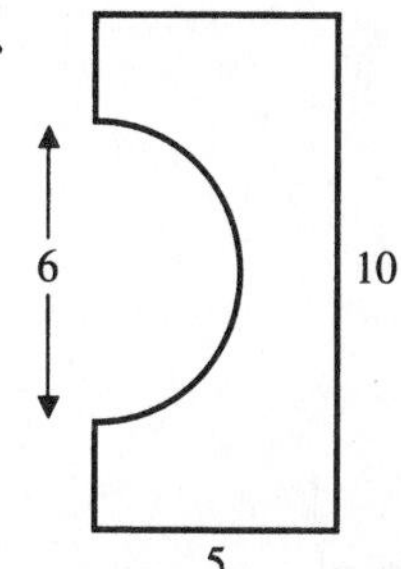

2.

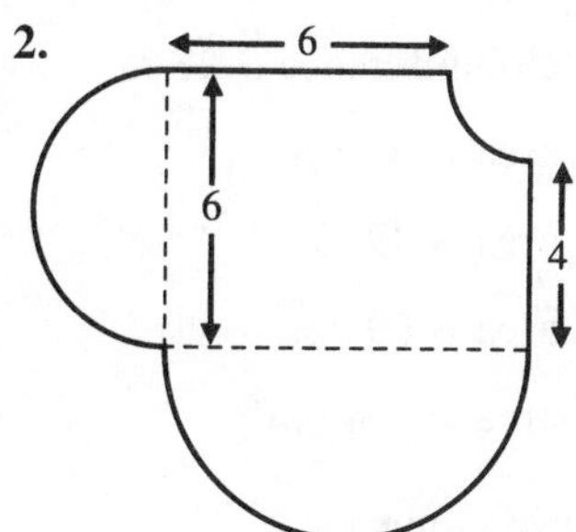

3.

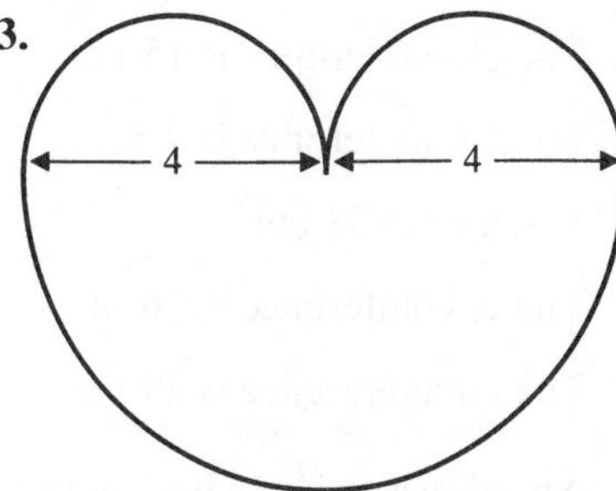

4.

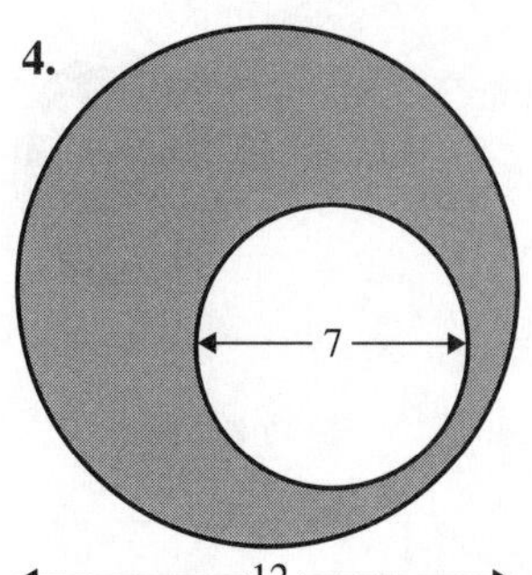

5.

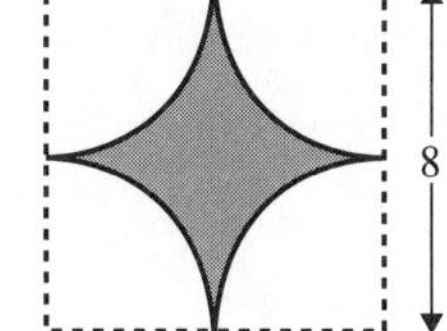

6.

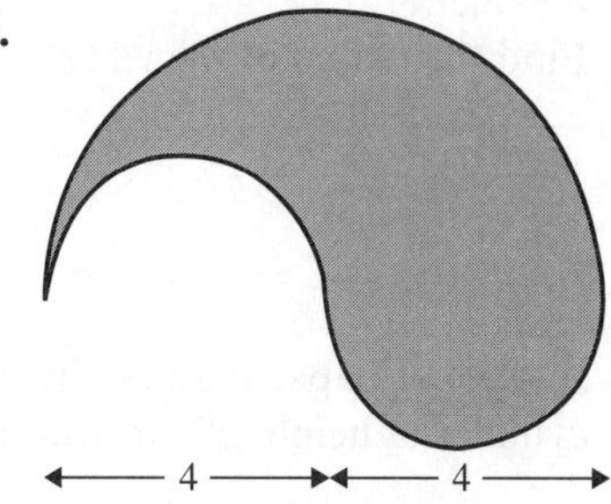

7. (a) Find the area of triangle OAD.
(b) Hence find the area of the square ABCD.
(c) Find the area of the circle.
(d) Hence find the shaded area.

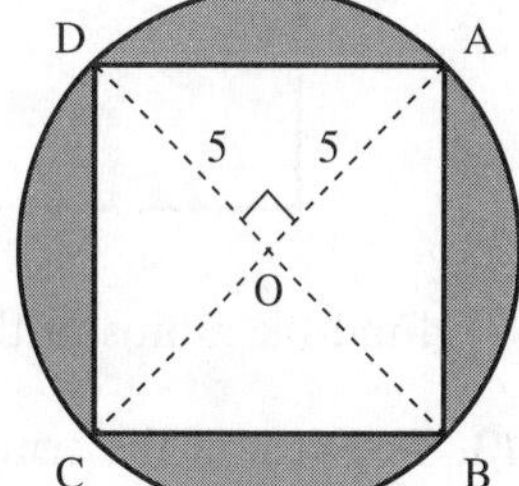

Finding the radius of a circle

Sometimes it is difficult to measure the diameter of a circle but it is fairly easy to measure the circumference.

(a) The circumference of a circle is 60 cm.
Find the radius of the circle.

$$C = \pi d$$
$$\therefore\ 60 = \pi d$$
$$\therefore\ \frac{60}{\pi} = d$$
$$\therefore\ r = \frac{(60/\pi)}{2} = 9{\cdot}55 \text{ cm (to 3 s.f.)}$$

(b) The area of a circle is 18 m^2.
Find the radius of the circle.

$$\pi r^2 = 18$$
$$r^2 = \frac{18}{\pi}$$
$$r = \sqrt{\left(\frac{18}{\pi}\right)} = 2{\cdot}39 \text{ m (to 3 s.f.)}$$

Exercise 17

In Questions **1** to **10** use the information given to calculate the radius of the circle. Use the 'π' button on a calculator or take $\pi = 3{\cdot}14$.

1. The circumference is 15 cm

2. The circumference is 28 m

3. The circumference is 7 m

4. The area is 54 cm^2

5. The area is 38 cm^2

6. The area is 49 m^2

7. The circumference is 16 m

8. The area is 60 cm^2

9. The circumference is 29 cm

10. The area is 104 cm^2

11. An odometer is a wheel used for measuring long distances. The circumference of the wheel is exactly one metre.
Find the radius of the wheel.

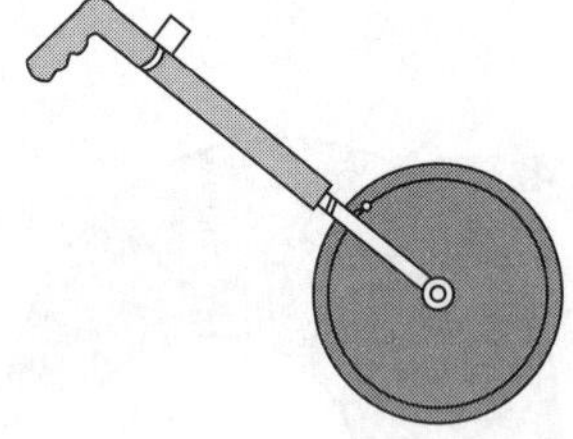

12. A sheet of paper is 32 cm by 20 cm. It is made into a hollow cylinder of height 20 cm with no overlap.

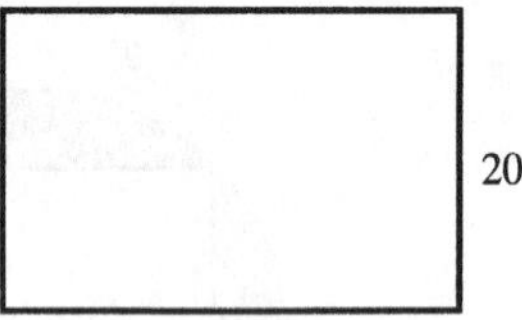

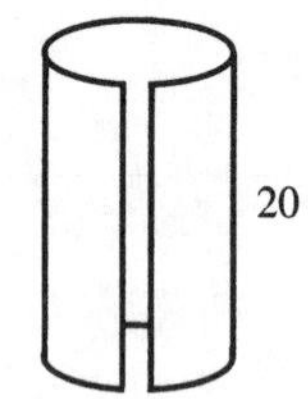

Find the radius of the cylinder.

13. The area of the centre circle on a football pitch is 265 m^2. Calculate the radius of the circle to the nearest 0·1 m.

14. Eight sections of curved railway track can be joined to make a circular track of circumference 184 cm.
Each section is 23 cm long.
Calculate the diameter of the circle.

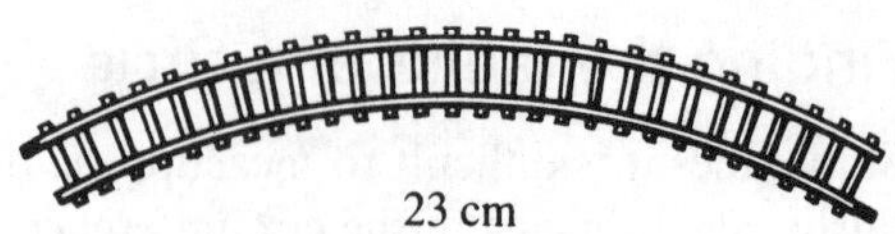

15. Calculate the radius of a circle whose area is equal to the sum of the areas of three circles of radii 2 cm, 3 cm and 4 cm.

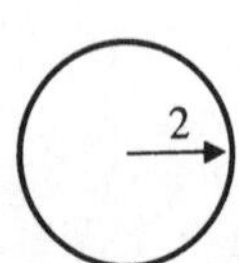

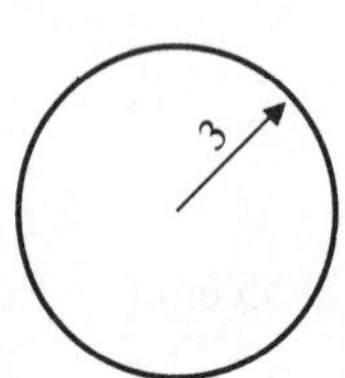

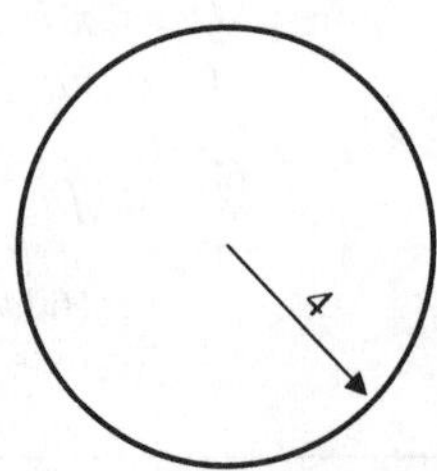

16. The handle of a paint tin is a semicircle of wire which is 28 cm long.
Calculate the diameter of the tin.

17. A television transmitter is designed so that people living inside a circle of area 120 000 km^2 can receive pictures.
What is the radius of this reception circle? Give your answer to the nearest km.

18. The circle and the square have the same area.
Find the radius of the circle.

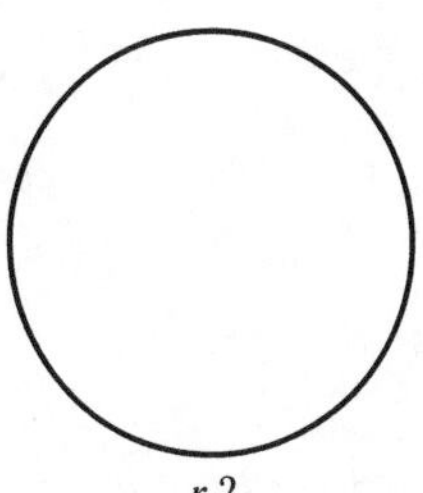

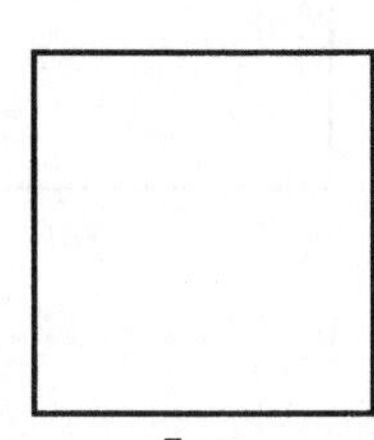

19. The circumference of this circle is 52 m.
Find its area.

20. The area of a circular target is 1·2 m^2. Find the circumference of the target.

21. The perimeter of a circular pond is 85 m long. Work out the area of the pond.

22. The sector shown is one-quarter of a circle and has an area of 23 cm^2.
Find the radius of the circle.

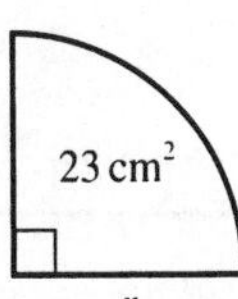

23. 'Muirfield' grass seed is sown at a rate of 40 grams per square metre and one box contains 2·5 kg. The seed is just enough to sow a circular lawn. Calculate the radius of this lawn to the nearest 0·1 metre.

3.6 Area and perimeter

Rectangle and triangle

- Rectangle:
  area $= l \times b$

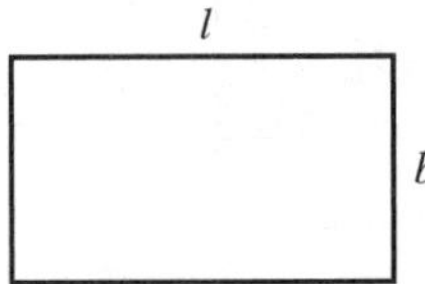

- Triangle:

  area $= \dfrac{b \times h}{2}$

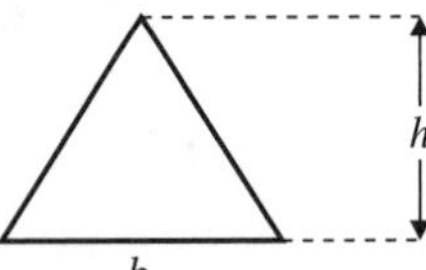

- The *perimeter* of a shape is the total length of its boundary.

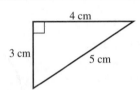

8 cm, 5 cm; 4 cm, 3 cm, 5 cm

Area $= 8 \times 5 = 40\ \text{cm}^2$

Perimeter $= 8 + 8 + 5 + 5 = 26\,\text{cm}$

Area $= \dfrac{3 \times 4}{2} = 60\ \text{cm}^2$

Perimeter $= 3 + 4 + 5 = 12\,\text{cm}$

Exercise 18

Work out the area. All lengths are in cm.

1. 6, 4

2.

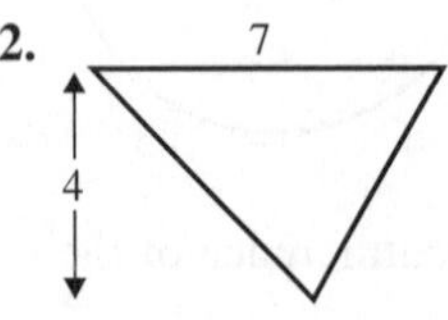

3.

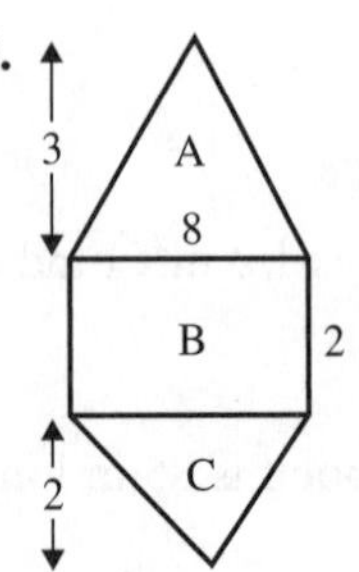

4.

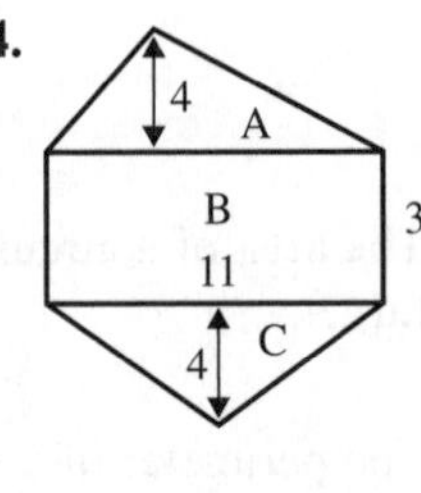

5.

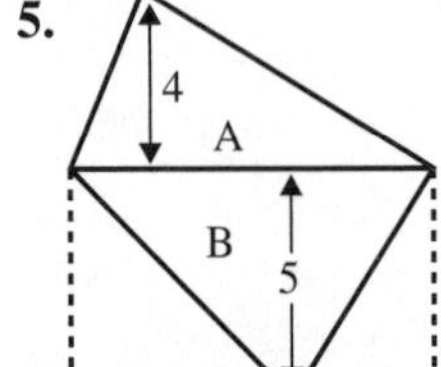

6.

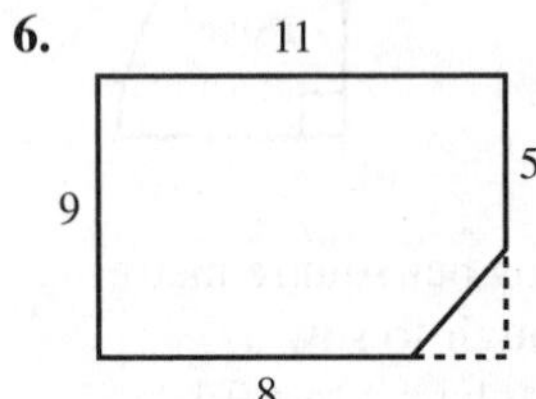

7. 6, A, 3, B, 6

8.

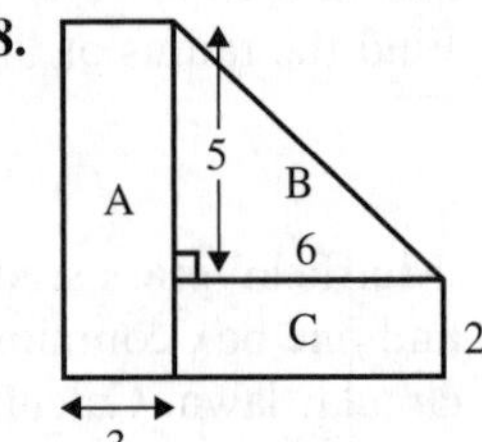

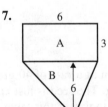

9. Here are three shapes made with centimetre squares.

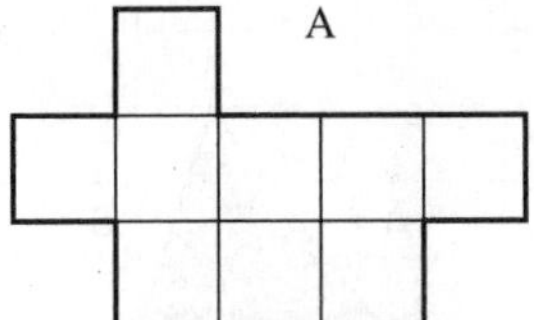

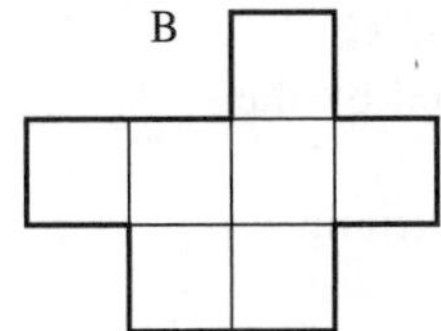

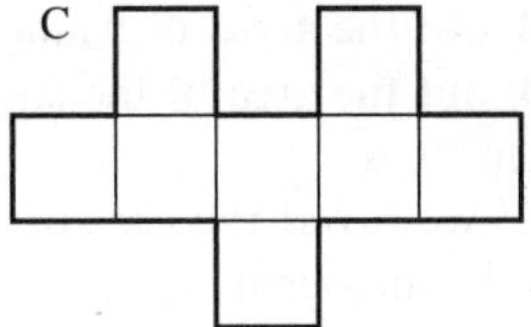

(a) Which shape has a perimeter of 18 cm?
(b) Which shape has the largest area?
(c) Draw a shape of your own design with area 8 cm^2 and perimeter 14 cm.

10. Use a ruler to find the perimeter of each picture.

(a) 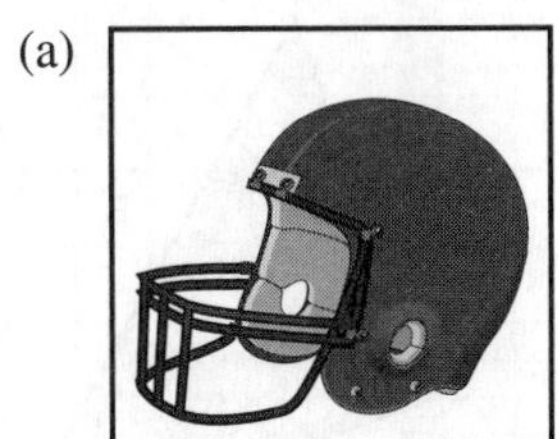

(b) 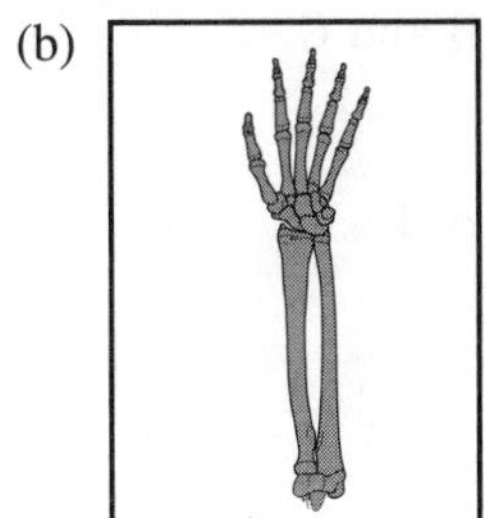

(c) 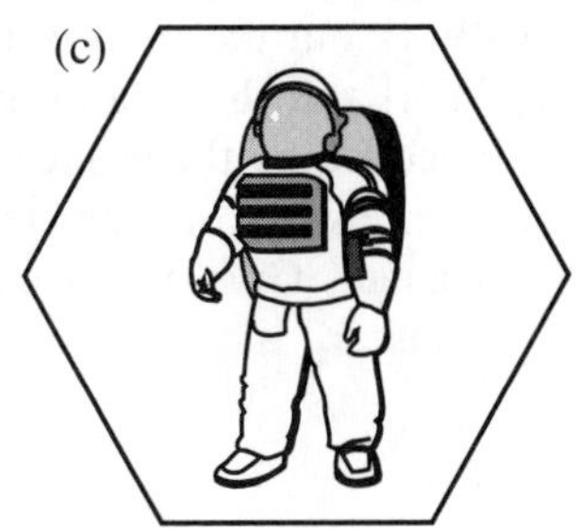

11. Farmland is sold at £2000 per hectare [1 hectare = 10 000 m^2]. How much would you pay for a rectangular field measuring 400 m by 600 m?

12. A rectangular pond, measuring 10 m by 6 m, is surrounded by a path which is 2 m wide.
Find the area of the path.

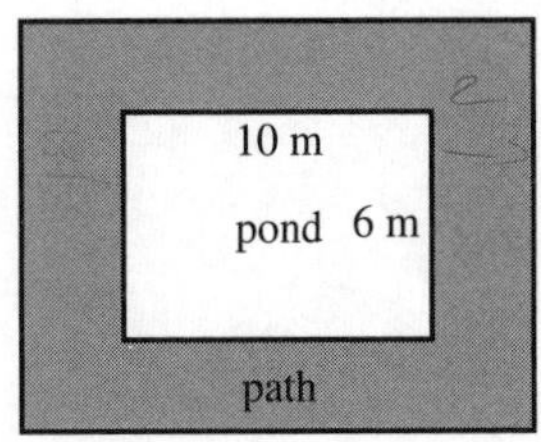

In Questions **13** to **16** find the perimeter of each shape.
All lengths are in cm.

13. 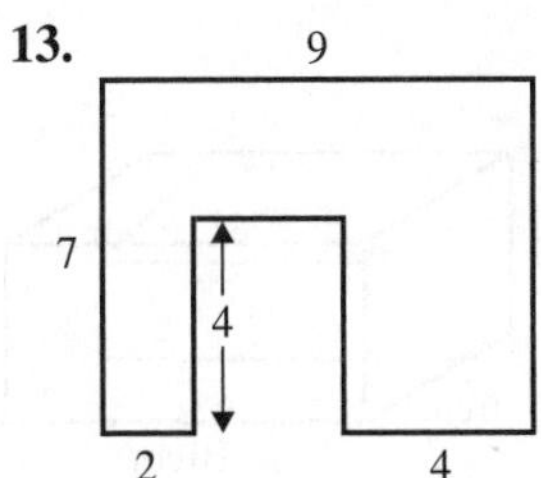

14. 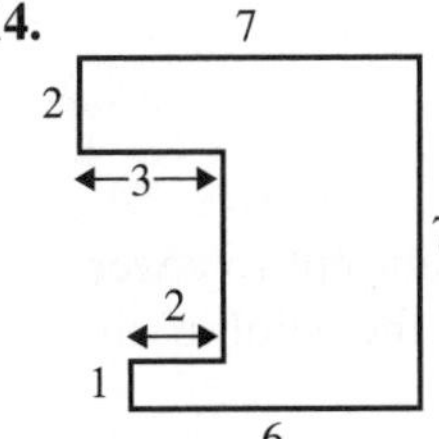

15. 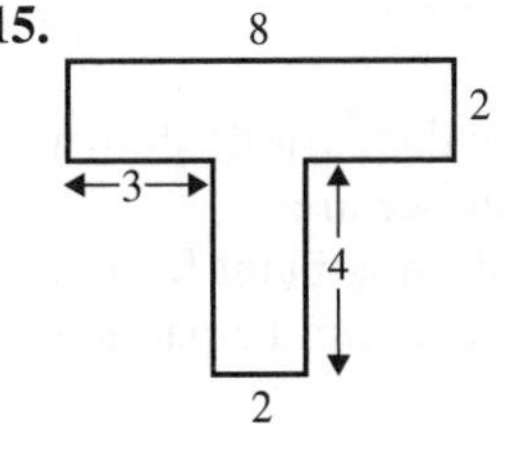

16. 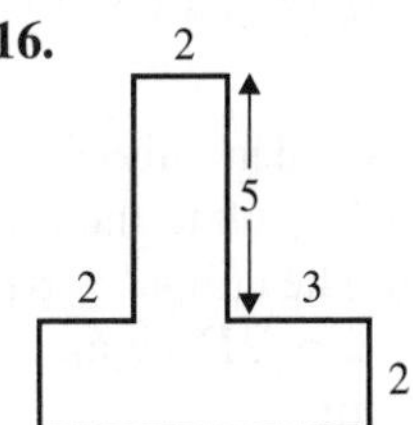

Exercise 19

1. (a) Copy the diagram.
   (b) Work out the areas of triangles A, B and C.
   (c) Work out the area of the square enclosed by the broken lines.
   (d) Hence work out the area of the shaded triangle. Give the answer in square units.

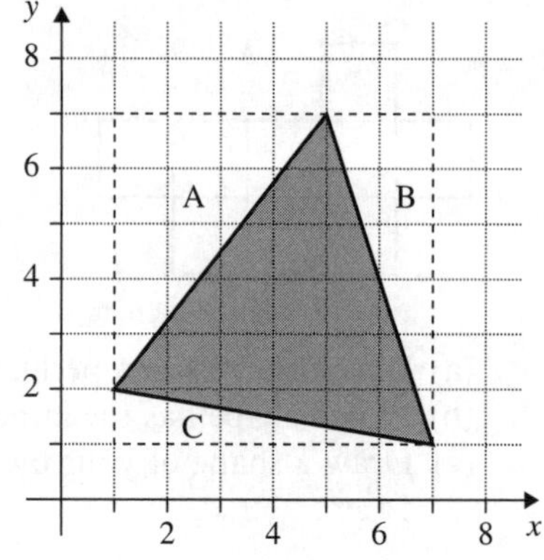

2. (a) Copy the diagram.
   (b) Work out the areas of triangles A, B and C.
   (c) Work out the area of the rectangle enclosed by the broken lines.
   (d) Hence work out the area of the shaded triangle. Give the answer in square units.

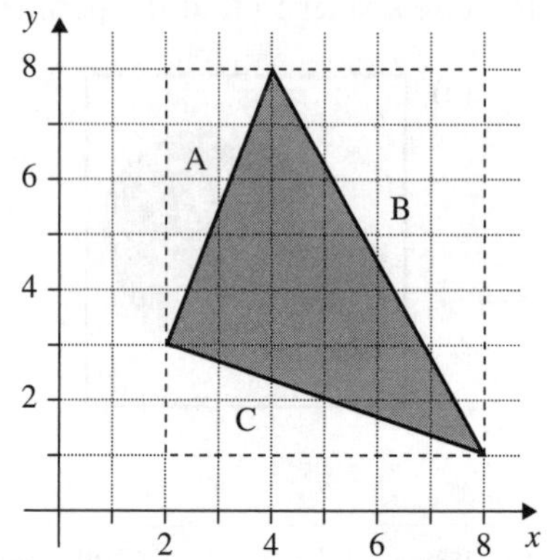

For Questions **3** to **7**, draw a pair of axes similar to those in Questions **1** and **2**. Plot the points in the order given and find the area of the shape enclosed.

3. (1,4), (6,8), (4,1)

4. (1,7), (8,5), (4,2)

5. (2,4), (6,1), (8,7), (4,8), (2,4)

6. (1,4), (5,1), (7,6), (4,8), (1,4)

7. (1,6), (2,2), (8,6), (6,8), (1,6)

8. A wooden cuboid has the dimensions shown.
   (a) Calculate the total surface area.
   (b) The cuboid is painted using paint from a tin sufficient to cover 3 m^2. How many cuboids can be painted using the paint in one tin?

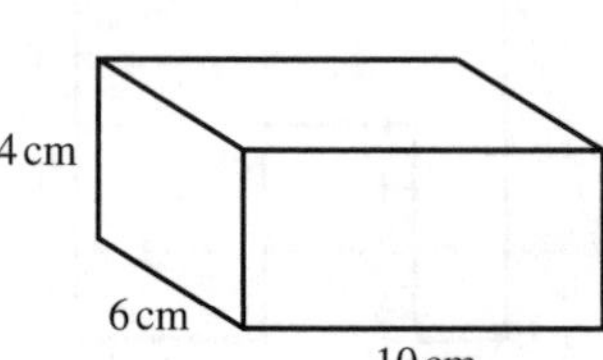

9. The total length of wood used in a picture frame is 160 cm. The length is 10 cm greater than the height.
Find the length of the frame.

10. A rectangular floor measuring 6 m by 4 m is covered by square tiles measuring 50 cm by 50 cm.
How many tiles are there?

11. A rectangular field 200 m long has an area of 10 000 m^2.
Calculate the perimeter of the field.

12. Find the length x. The area. is shown inside the shape.

(a) 85 m^2, x, 10 m

(b)
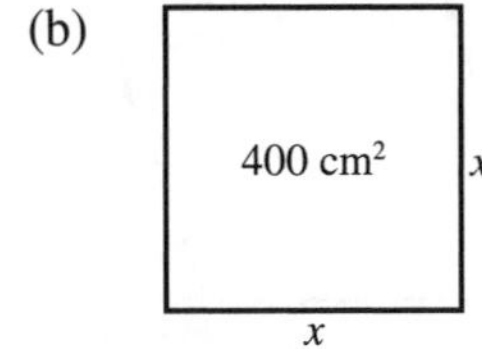

(c)
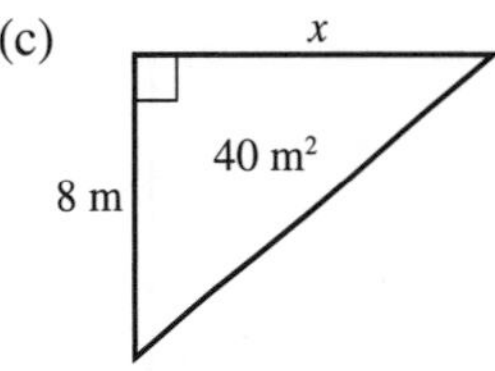

In Questions **13** to **16** find the area. The lengths are in cm.

13.
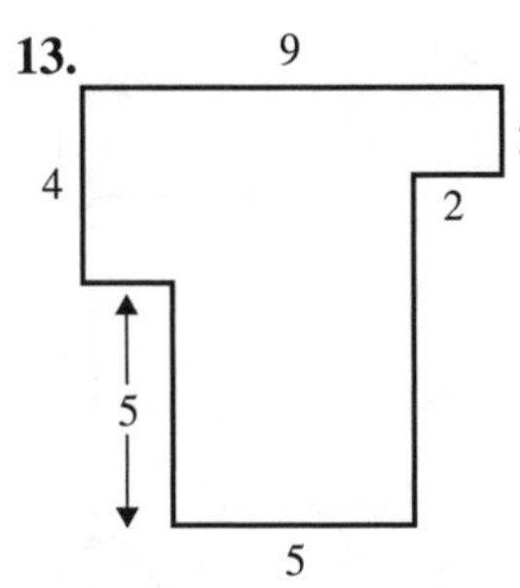

14.
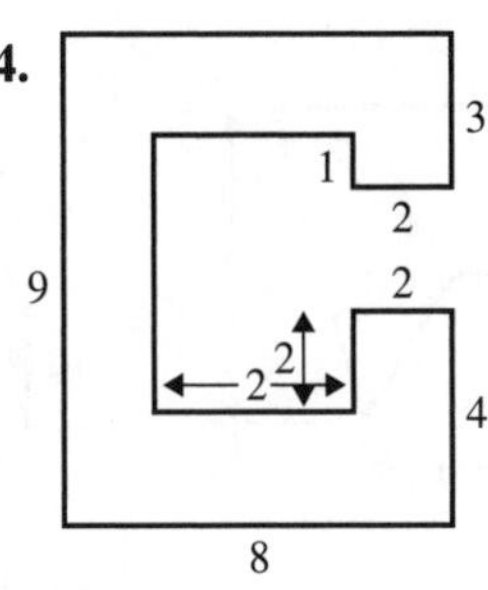

15.
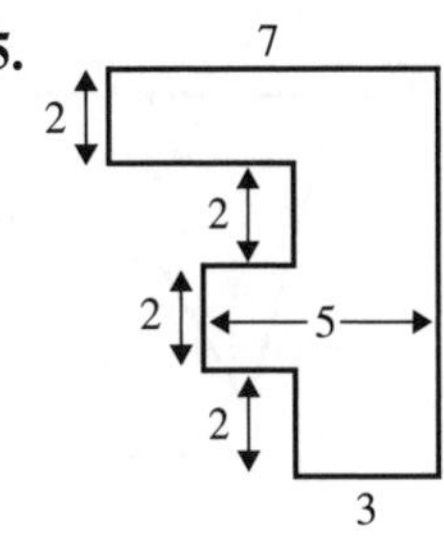

16.
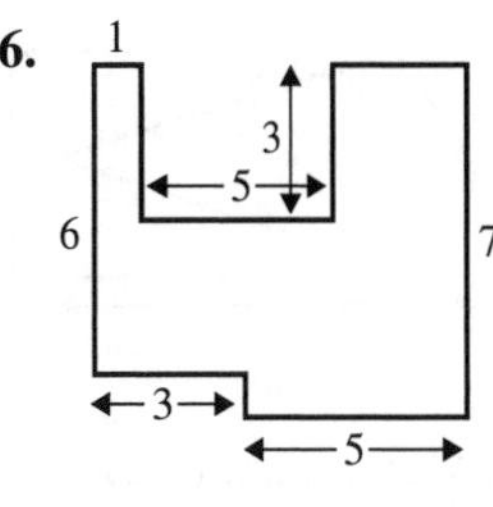

Trapezium and parallelogram

- Trapezium (two parallel sides)

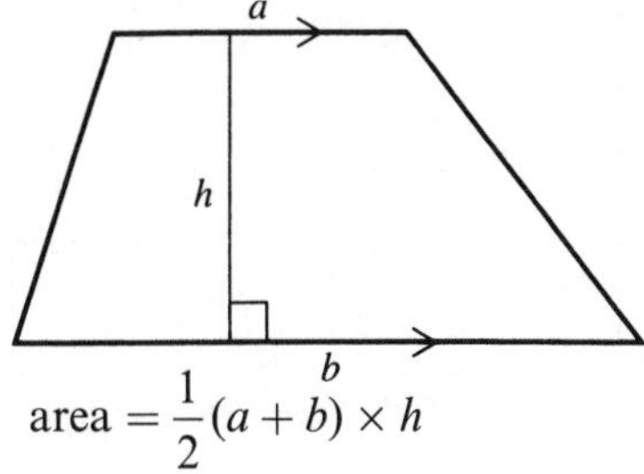

area $= \frac{1}{2}(a + b) \times h$

- Parallelogram

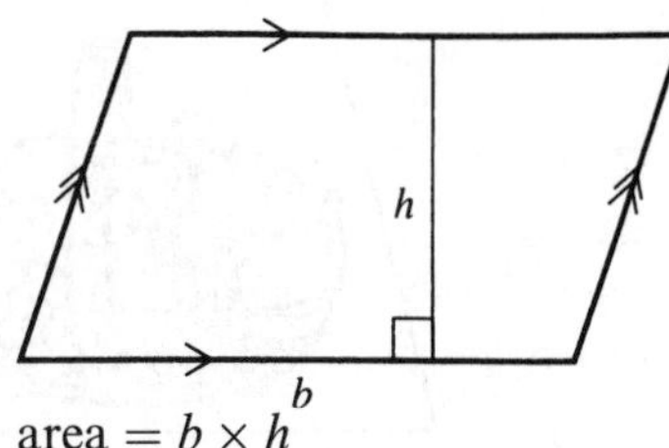

area $= b \times h$

Exercise 20

Find the area of each shape. All lengths are in cm.

1.
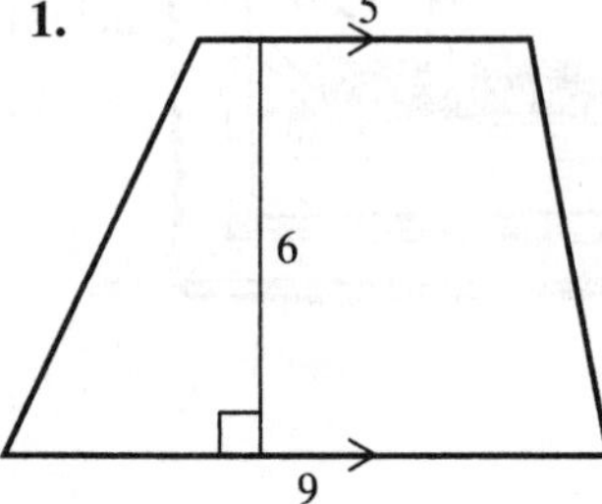

2.
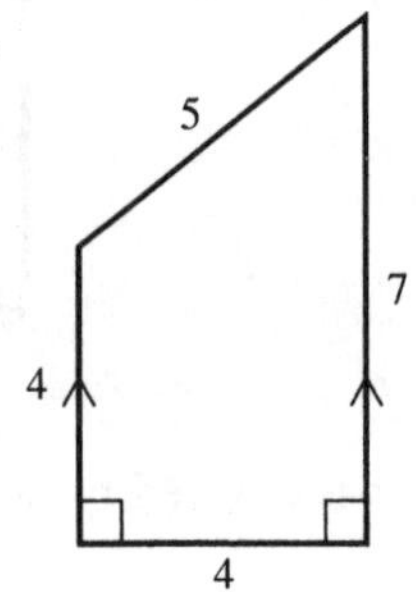

3.
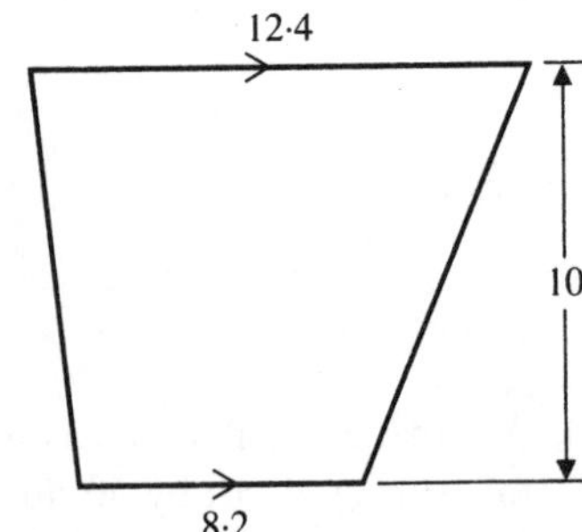

4.
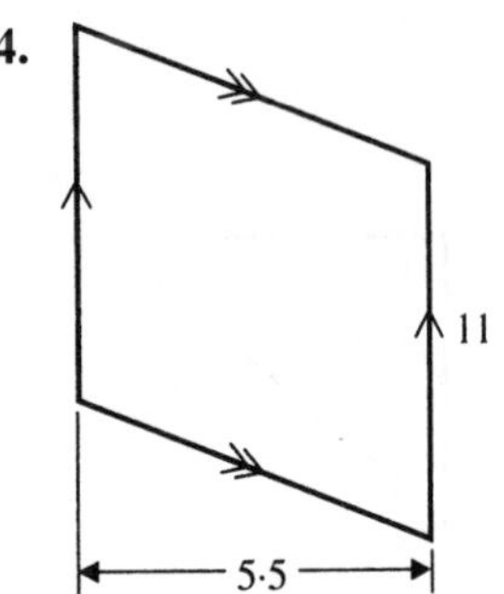

5.
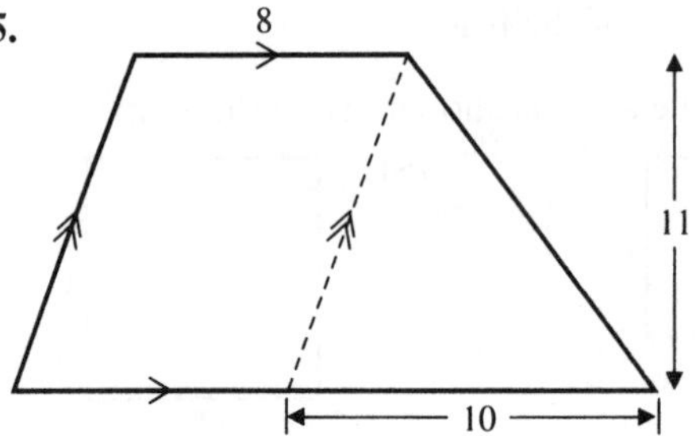

6.
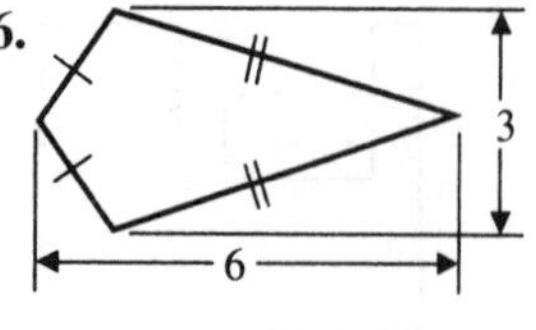

7.
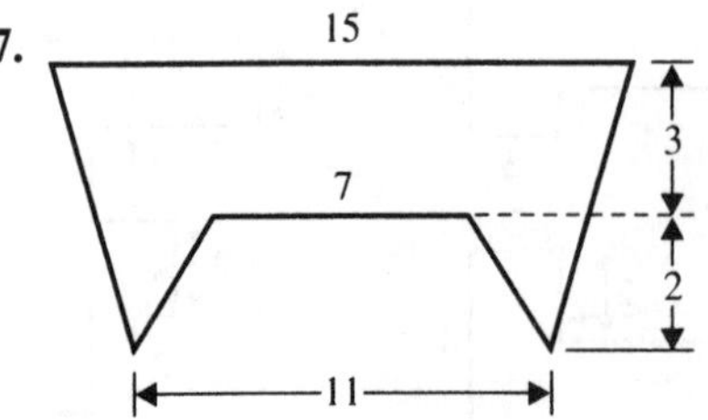

8.
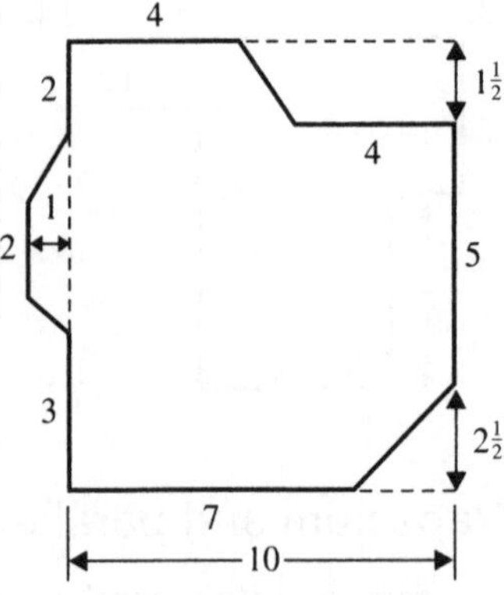

9. The picture shown has an area of $72\,cm^2$.
Find the height x.

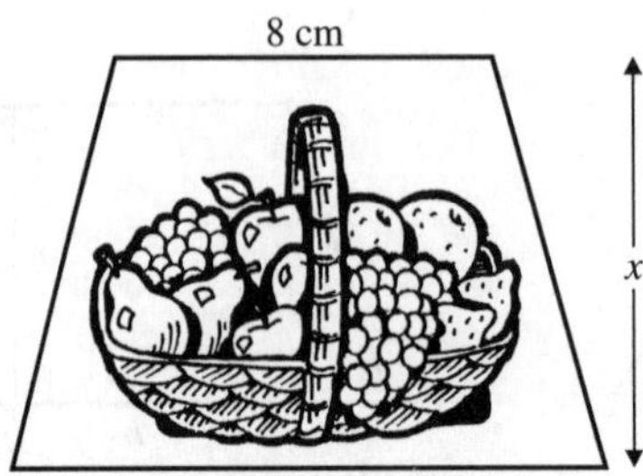

10. The field shown is sprayed at the rate of 2 litres per hectare. The cost of the spray is £25 for 100 litres.
How much will it cost to spray this field, to the nearest pound?

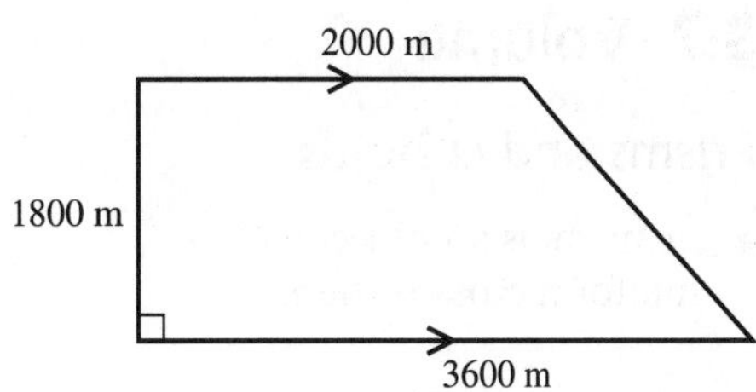

Designing square patterns

The object is to design square patterns of different sizes. The patterns are all to be made from smaller tiles all of which are themselves square.
Designs for a 4 × 4 square:

(a)

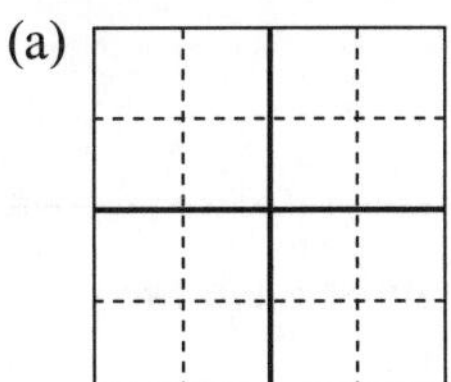

This design consists of four tiles each 2 × 2.
The pattern is rather dull.

(b) Suppose we say that the design must contain at least one 1 × 1 square.

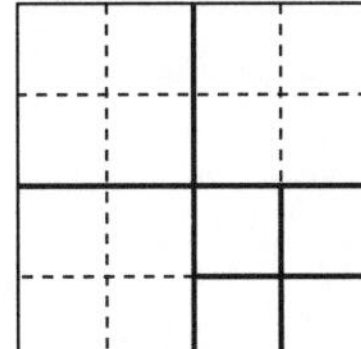

This design is more interesting and consists of seven tiles.

Exercise 21

1. Try the 5 × 5 square. Design a pattern which divides the 5 × 5 square into eight smaller squares.
2. Try the 6 × 6 square. Here you must include at least one 1 × 1 square. Design a pattern which divides the 6 × 6 square into nine smaller squares. Colour in the final design to make it look interesting.
3. The 7 × 7 square is more difficult. With no restrictions, design a pattern which divides the 7 × 7 square into nine smaller squares.
4. Design a pattern which divides an 8 × 8 square into ten smaller squares. You must not use a 4 × 4 square.
5. Design a pattern which divides a 9 × 9 square into ten smaller squares. You can use only one 3 × 3 square.
6. Design a pattern which divides a 10 × 10 square into eleven smaller squares. You must include a 3 × 3 square.
7. Design a pattern which divides an 11 × 11 square into eleven smaller squares. You must include a 6 × 6 square.

3.7 Volume

Prisms and cuboids

- A prism is an object with a uniform cross section.

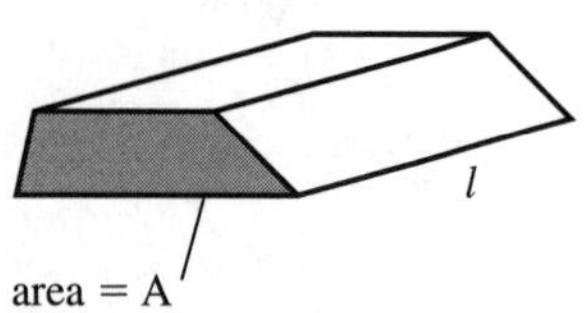

Volume $= A \times l$

- A cuboid is a prism whose cross section is a rectangle.

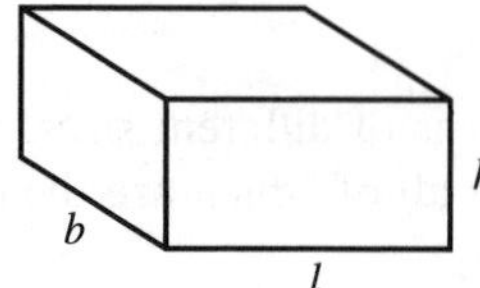

Volume $= l \times b \times h$

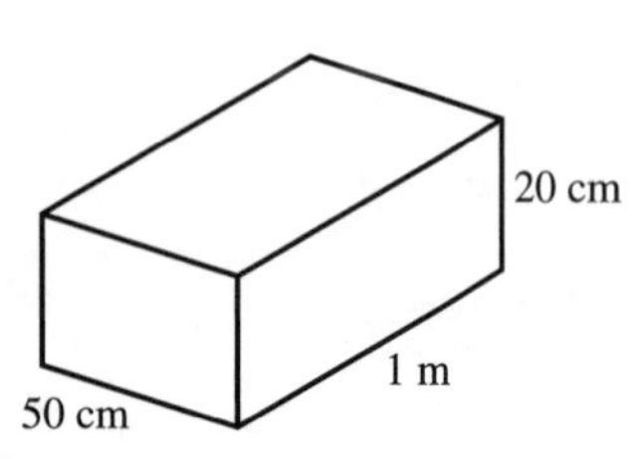

Notice that the length is in metres. We must have the same units for all dimensions.

Volume $= 50 \times 20 \times 100$
$= 100\,000\ \text{cm}^3$.

Exercise 22

Find the volume of each prism.

1. 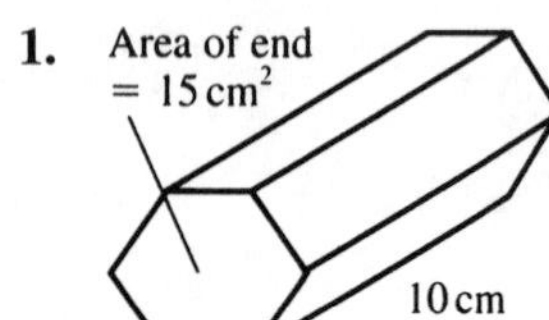

2. 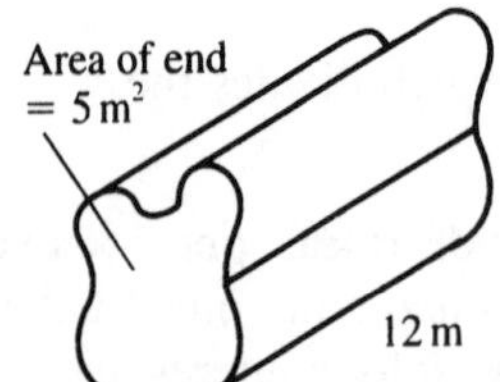

3. 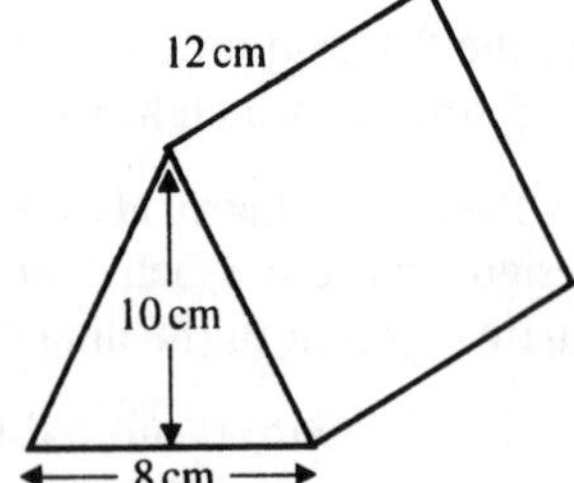

4. 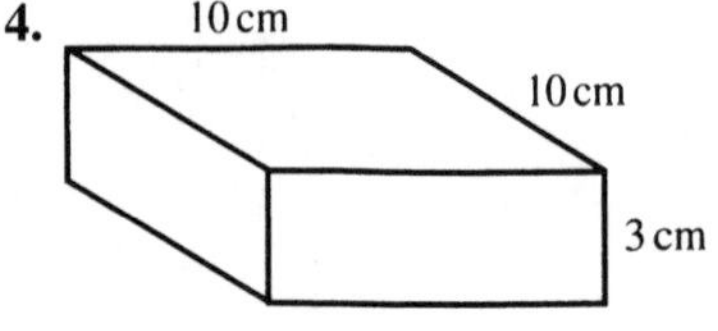

5. 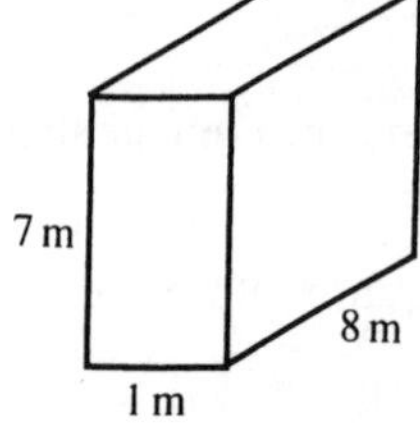

6. 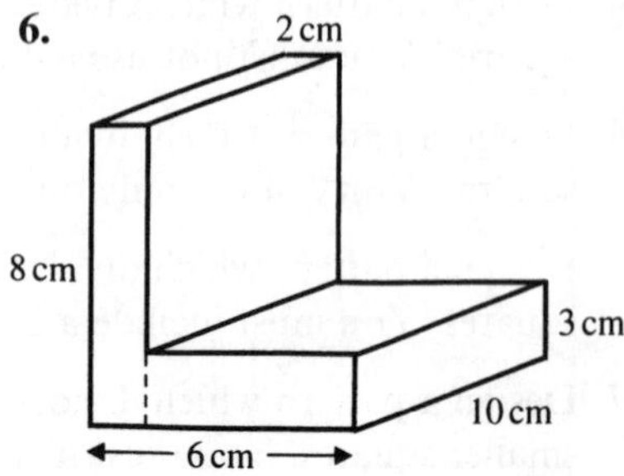

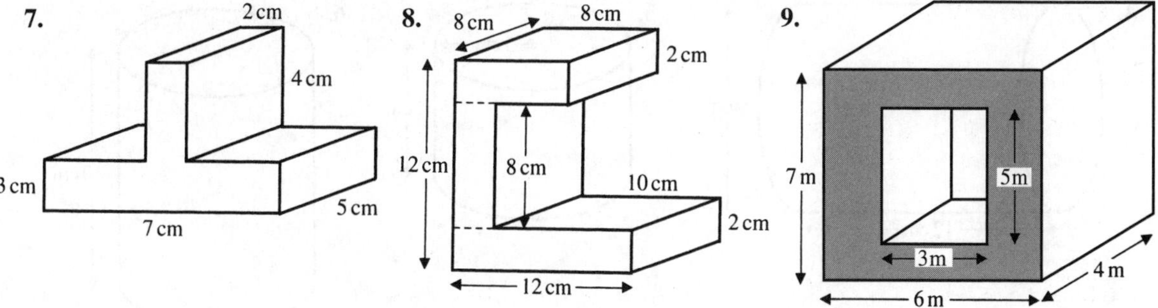

Cylinders

- A cylinder is a prism with a circular cross section.

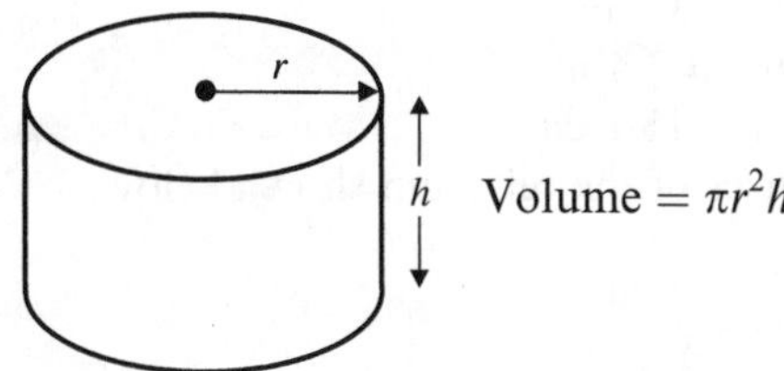

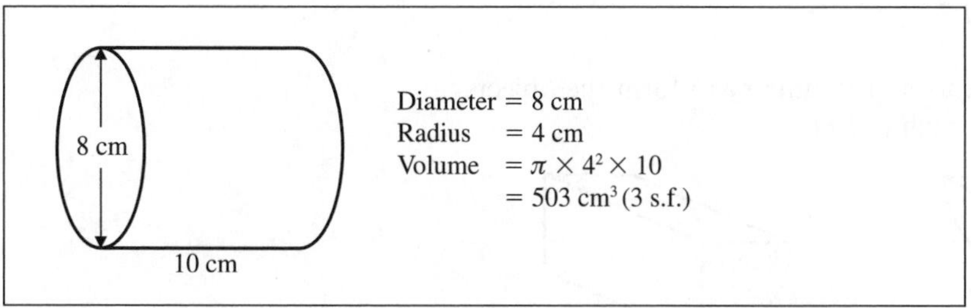

Diameter = 8 cm
Radius = 4 cm
Volume = $\pi \times 4^2 \times 10$
= 503 cm^3 (3 s.f.)

Exercise 23

Find the volume of each cylinder. Use the 'π' button on a calculator or use $\pi = 3{\cdot}14$. Give the answers correct to 3 s.f.

1.

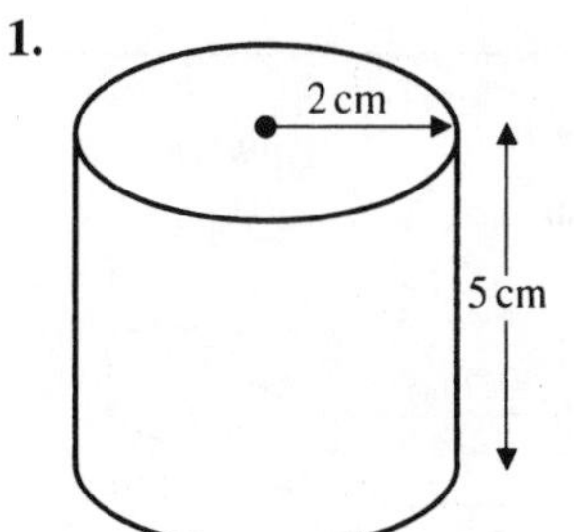

2.

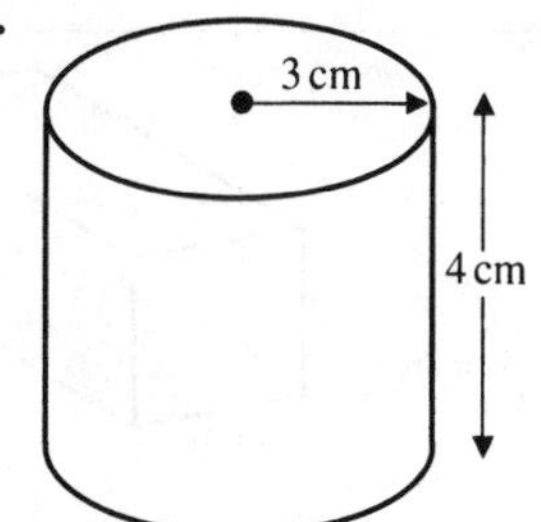

3.

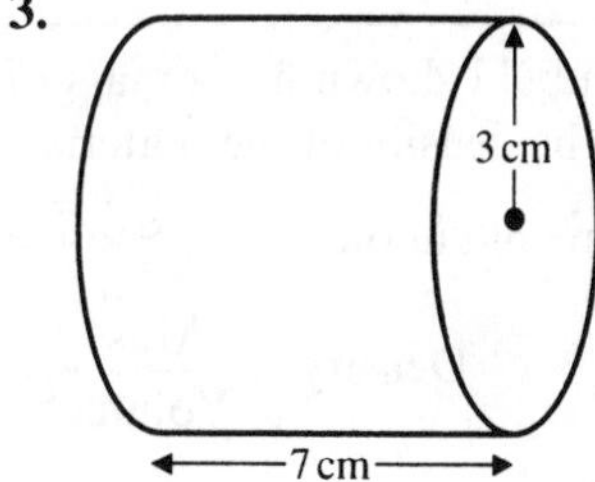

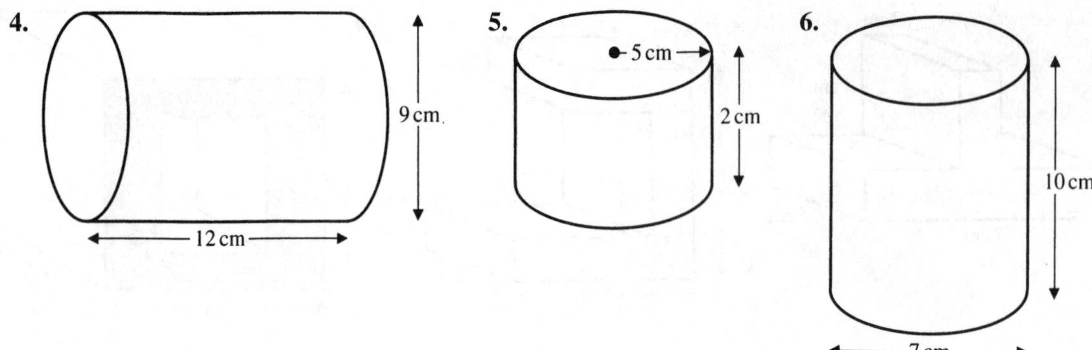

7. radius = 7 cm, height = 5 cm
8. diameter = 8 m, height = 3·5 m
9. diameter = 11 m, height = 2·4 m
10. radius = 3·2 cm, height = 15·1 cm
11. Find the capacity in litres of the oil drum shown below.
[1000 cm^3 = 1 litre]

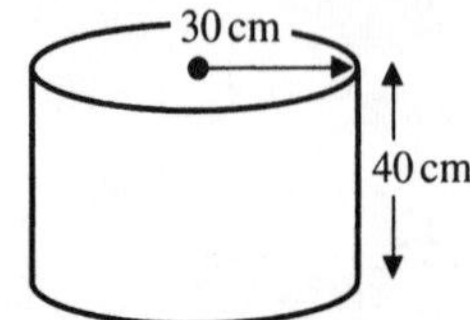

12. Cylinders are cut along the axis of symmetry to form the objects below. Find the volume of each object.

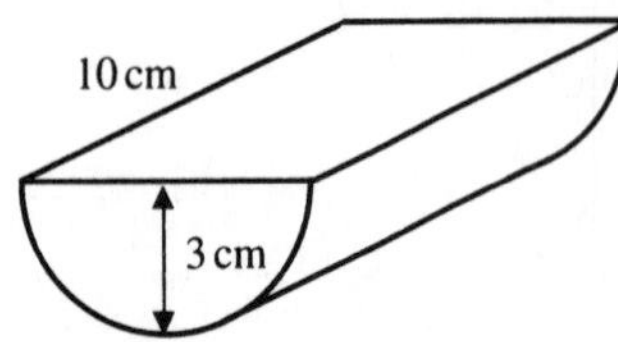

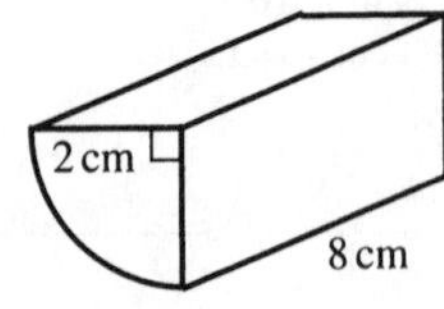

Mixed problems, density

- In some questions we use the *density* of a material.

$$\text{Density in g/cm}^3 = \frac{\text{Mass of object (in g)}}{\text{Volume of object (in cm}^3)}$$

The cuboid shown has a mass of 720 g.
Find the density of the material.

Volume of cuboid = $4 \times 5 \times 4 = 80\,\text{cm}^3$

$$\text{Density} = \frac{\text{Mass}}{\text{Volume}} = \frac{720}{80}$$
$$= 9\,\text{g/cm}^3$$

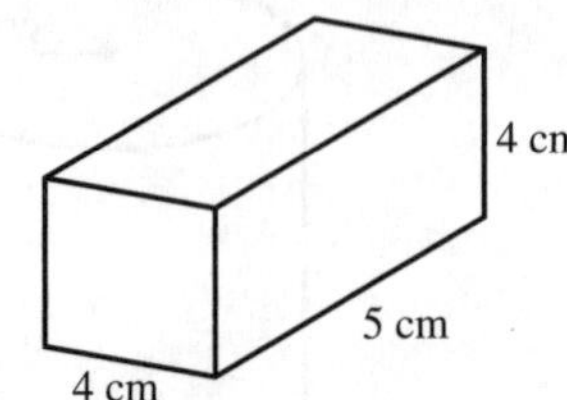

Exercise 24

Where necessary give answers correct to 3 s.f.

1. Find the density of each object.

(a)

mass = 150 g
volume = 100 cm³

(b)

mass = 1800 g
volume = 200 cm³

(c)

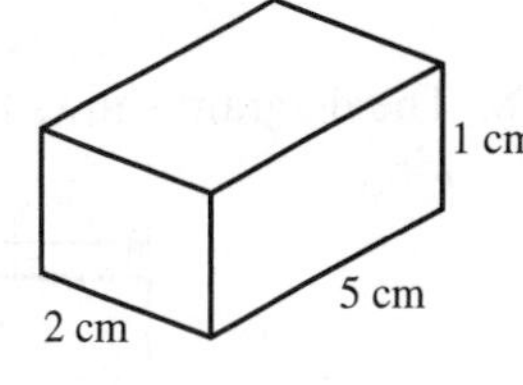

mass = 56 g

2. A steel ball has volume $1000\,cm^3$. The density of steel is $8\,g/cm^3$. Find the mass of the ball.

3. A cylindrical bar has a cross-sectional area of $12\,cm^2$ and a length of two *metres*. Calculate the volume of the bar in cm^3.

4. The diagram represents a building.

(a) Calculate the area of the shaded end.
(b) Calculate the volume of the building.

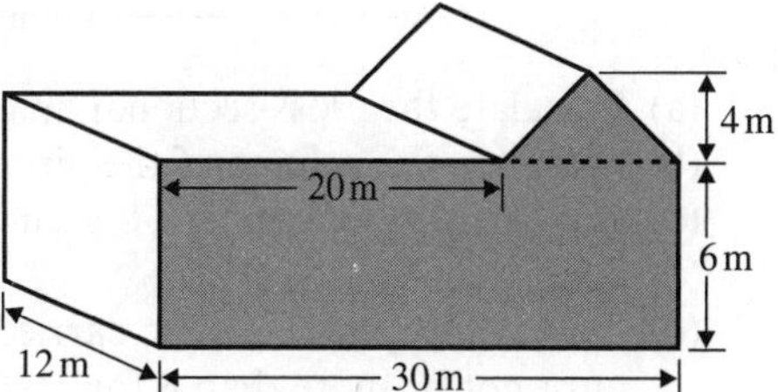

5. A rectangular block has dimensions 20 cm × 7 cm × 7 cm. Find the volume of the largest solid cylinder which can be cut from this block.

6. A washer is made by cutting a circle of metal from the centre of a metal disc. This washer is 2 mm thick.

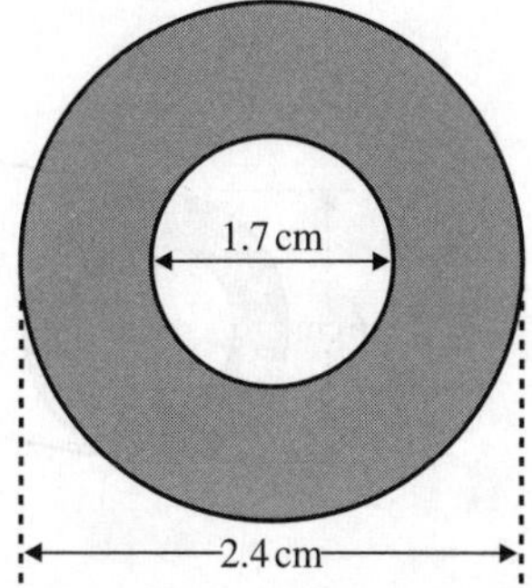

(a) Find the area of the flat surface of the washer.
(b) Calculate the volume of the washer.
(c) The metal has density $8\,g/cm^3$. Find the mass of the washer.

7. A cylindrical water tank has internal diameter 40 cm and height 50 cm and a cylindrical mug has internal diameter 8 cm and height 10 cm. If the tank is initially full, how many mugs can be filled from the tank?

8. The diagram shows the cross section of a steel girder which is 4 m long.

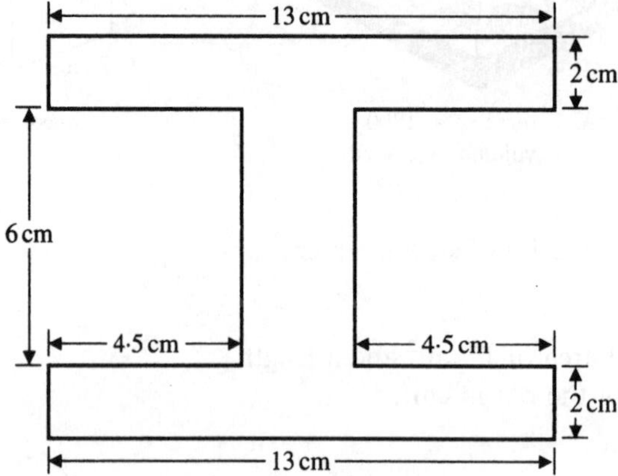

(a) Calculate the cross-sectional area in cm^2.
(b) Calculate the volume of the girder in cm^3.
(c) If the density of steel is 7·8 g/cm^3, find the mass of the girder in kg.
(d) How many girders can be carried on a lorry if its total load must not be more than 8 tonnes? (1 tonne = 1000 kg)

9. Mr Gibson decided to build a garage and began by calculating the number of bricks required. The garage was to be 6 m by 4 m and 2·5 m in height. Each brick measures 22 cm by 10 cm by 7 cm. Mr Gibson estimated that he would need about 40 000 bricks. Is this a reasonable estimate?

10. A cylindrical metal pipe has external diameter of 6 cm and internal diameter of 4 cm. Calculate the volume of metal in a pipe of length 1 m. If the density of the metal is 8 g/cm^3, find the mass of the pipe.

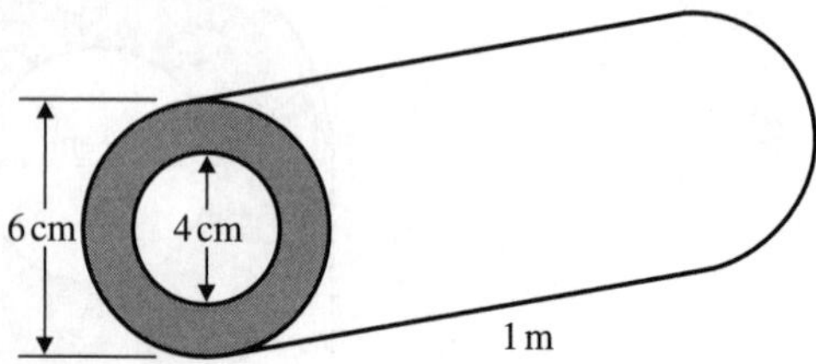

11. A cylindrical tin of height 15 cm and radius 4 cm is filled with sand from a rectangular box. How many times can the tin be filled if the dimensions of the box are 50 cm by 40 cm by 20 cm?

12. Rain which falls on to a flat rectangular surface of length 6 m and width 4 m is collected in a cylinder of internal radius 20 cm. What is the depth of water in the cylinder after a storm in which 1 cm of rain fell?

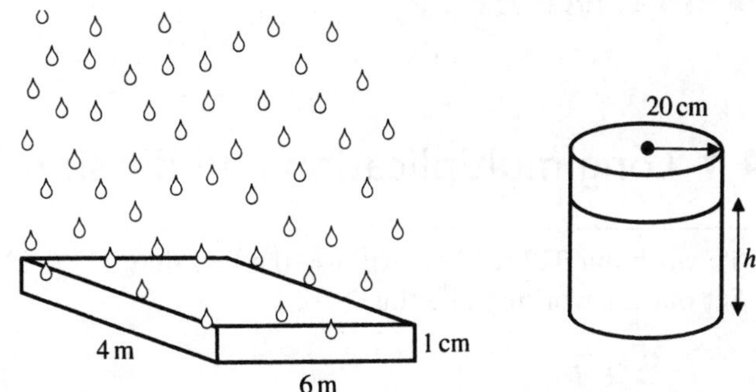

13. Water pours into the trough shown at a rate of 2 litres/min. How long, to the nearest minute, will it take to fill the trough?

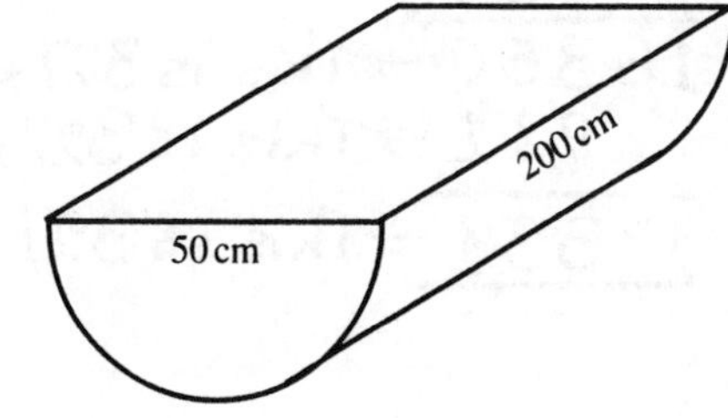

14. Water is poured from the cylindrical bottle shown into ice-cube moulds which are then put in a freezer. How many complete ice cubes of side 2·5 cm can be made?

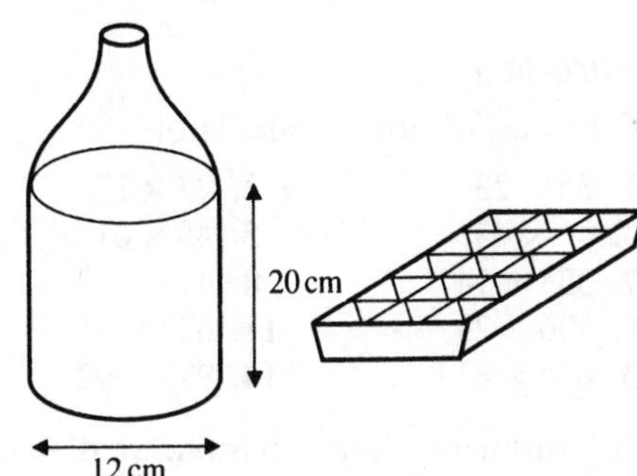

4 NUMBER 2

4.1 Long multiplication and division

To work out 327 × 53 we will use the fact that 327 × 53 = (327 × 50) + (327 × 3).
Set out the working like this.

```
   327
    53 ×
 16350 → This is 327 × 50
   981 → This is 327 × 3
 17331 → This is 327 × 53
```

Here is another example.

```
   541
    84 ×
 43280 → This is 541 × 80
  2164 → This is 541 × 4
 45444 → This is 541 × 84
```

Exercise 1

Work out, without a calculator.

1. 35 × 23 **2.** 27 × 17 **3.** 26 × 25
4. 31 × 43 **5.** 45 × 61 **6.** 52 × 24
7. 323 × 14 **8.** 416 × 73 **9.** 504 × 56
10. 306 × 28 **11.** 624 × 75 **12.** 839 × 79
13. 694 × 83 **14.** 973 × 92 **15.** 415 × 235

With ordinary 'short' division, we divide and find remainders. The method for 'long' division is really the same but we set it out so that the remainders are easier to find.

Work out 736 ÷ 32

```
     23
 32)736
    64↓
     96
     96
      0
```

(a) 32 into 73 goes 2 times
(b) 2 × 32 = 64
(c) 73 − 64 = 9
(d) 'bring down' 6
(e) 32 into 96 goes 3 times

Exercise 2

Work out, without a calculator.

1. 672 ÷ 21 **2.** 425 ÷ 17 **3.** 576 ÷ 32
4. 247 ÷ 19 **5.** 875 ÷ 25 **6.** 574 ÷ 26
7. 806 ÷ 34 **8.** 748 ÷ 41 **9.** 666 ÷ 24
10. 707 ÷ 52 **11.** 951 ÷ 27 **12.** 806 ÷ 34
13. 2917 ÷ 45 **14.** 2735 ÷ 18 **15.** 56 274 ÷ 19

Exercise 3

Solve each problem without a calculator.

1. A shop owner buys 56 tins of paint at 84p each. How much does he spend altogether?

2. Eggs are packed eighteen to a box.

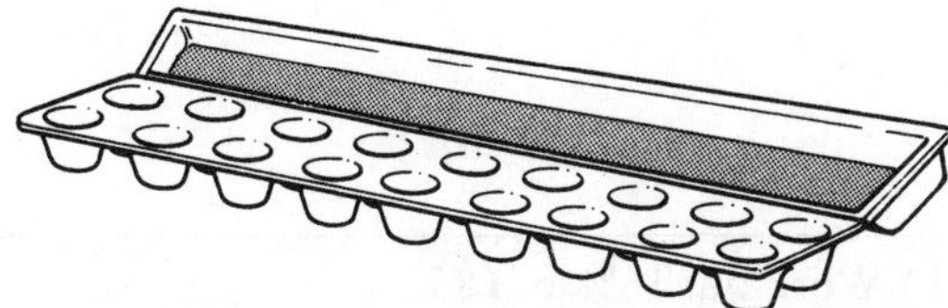

How many boxes are needed for 828 eggs?

3. On average a man smokes 146 cigarettes a week. How many does he smoke in a year?

4. Sally wants to buy as many 23p stamps as possible. She has £5 to buy them. How many can she buy and how much change is left?

5. How many 49-seater coaches will be needed for a school trip for a party of 366?

6. It costs £7905 to hire a plane for a day. A trip is organised for 93 people. How much does each person pay?

7. A lottery prize of £238 million was won by a syndicate of 17 people who shared the prize equally between them. How much did each person receive?

8. An office building has 24 windows on each of 8 floors. A window cleaner charges 42p for each window. How much is he paid for the whole building?

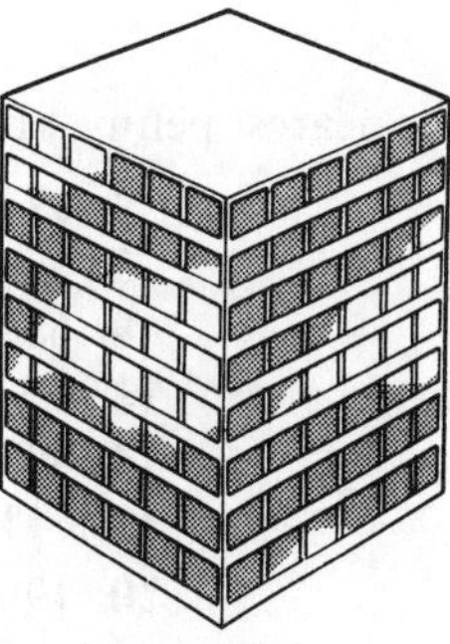

9. The headmaster of a school discovers an oil well in the school playground. As is the custom in such cases, he receives all the money from the oil. The oil comes out of the well at a rate of £15 for every minute of the day and night. How much does the headmaster receive in a 24-hour day?

10. Tins of peaches are packed 24 to a box. How many boxes are needed for 1285 tins?

4.2 Percentages

(a) Work out 22% of £40.

$$\frac{22}{100} \times \frac{40}{1} = \frac{880}{100}$$

Answer: £8·80

(b) Work out 16% of £85 [Alternative method].

Since $16\% = \frac{16}{100}$ we can replace 16% by 0·16

So 16% of £85 $= 0{\cdot}16 \times 85$
$= £13{\cdot}60$

Exercise 4

Work out.

1. 20% of £60
2. 10% of £80
3. 5% of £200
4. 6% of £50
5. 4% of £60
6. 30% of £80
7. 9% of £500
8. 18% of £400
9. 61% of £400
10. 12% of £80
11. 6% of $700
12. 11% of $800
13. 5% of 160 kg
14. 20% of 60 kg
15. 68% of 400 g
16. 15% of 300 m
17. 2% of 2000 km
18. 71% of $1000
19. 26% of 19 kg
20. 1% of 6000 g
21. 8·5% of £2400

Work out 6·5% of £17·50 correct to the nearest penny.

$$\frac{6{\cdot}5}{100} \times \frac{17{\cdot}5}{1} = \frac{113{\cdot}75}{100}$$
$$= £1{\cdot}1375$$

or ... $6{\cdot}5\% = \frac{6{\cdot}5}{100} = 0.065$

$0{\cdot}065 \times 17{\cdot}5 = 1{\cdot}1375$

Answer: £1·14 to the nearest penny.

Exercise 5

Give the answers to the nearest penny where necessary.

1. 4·5% of £6·22
2. 17% of £6·84
3. 15% of £8·11
4. 17% of £17·07
5. 37% of £9·64
6. 3·5% of £12·90
7. 8% of £11·64
8. 68% of £54·45
9. 73% of £23·24
10. 2·5% of £15·20
11. 6·3% of £12·50
12. 8·2% of £19·50
13. 87% of £15·40
14. 80% of £62·50
15. 12% of £24·50
16. $12\frac{1}{2}\%$ of £88·50
17. $7\frac{1}{2}\%$ of £16·40
18. $5\frac{1}{2}\%$ of £80
19. $12\frac{1}{2}\%$ of £90
20. 19% of £119·50
21. 8·35% of £110

A coat originally cost £24. Calculate the new price after a 5% reduction.

$$\begin{aligned}\text{Price reduction} &= 5\% \text{ of } £24\\ &= \frac{5}{100} \times \frac{24}{1} = £1{\cdot}20\\ \text{New price of coat} &= £24 - £1{\cdot}20\\ &= £22{\cdot}80\end{aligned}$$

A CD originally cost £11·60. Calculate the new price after a 7% increase.

We could work out 7% of £11·60 as in the example above. There is, however, a *quicker* way which many people prefer.
If we increase the price by 7% the final price is 107% of the old price.

$$\begin{aligned}\therefore \text{ new price} &= 107\% \text{ of } £11{\cdot}60\\ &= 1{\cdot}07 \times 11{\cdot}6\\ &= £12{\cdot}41 \text{ to the nearest penny.}\end{aligned}$$

For a 5% *reduction* as in the above example we would multiply by 0·95.

Exercise 6

1. Increase a price of £60 by 5%
2. Reduce a price of £800 by 8%
3. Reduce a price of £82·50 by 6%
4. Increase a price of £65 by 60%
5. Reduce a price of £2000 by 2%
6. Increase a price of £440 by 80%
7. Increase a price of £66 by 100%
8. Reduce a price of £91·50 by 50%
9. Increase a price of £88·24 by 25%
10. Reduce a price of £63 by $33\frac{1}{3}\%$

In the remaining questions give the answers to the nearest penny.

11. Increase a price of £8·24 by 46%
12. Increase a price of £7·65 by 24%
13. Increase a price of £5·61 by 31%
14. Reduce a price of £8·99 by 22%
15. Increase a price of £11·12 by 11%
16. Reduce a price of £17·62 by 4%
17. Increase a price of £28·20 by 13%
18. Increase a price of £8·55 by $5\frac{1}{2}\%$
19. Reduce a price of £9·60 by $7\frac{1}{2}\%$
20. Increase a price of £12·80 by $10\frac{1}{2}\%$

Exercise 7

1. In a closing-down sale a shop reduces all its prices by 20%. Find the sale price of a coat which previously cost £44.
2. The price of a car was £5400 but it is increased by 6%. What is the new price?
3. The price of a sideboard was £245 but, because the sideboard is scratched, the price is reduced by 30%. What is the new price?
4. A hi-fi shop offers a 7% discount for cash. How much does a cash-paying customer pay for an amplifier advertised at £95?

5. A rabbit weighs 2·8 kg. After being shot, its weight is increased by 1%. How much does it weigh now?

6. The insurance premium for a car is normally £90. With a 'no-claim bonus' the premium is reduced by 35%. What is the reduced premium?

7. Myxomatosis kills 92% of a colony of 300 rabbits. How many rabbits survive?

8. The population of a town increased by 32% between 1945 and 1985. If there were 45 000 people in 1945, what was the 1985 population?

9. A restaurant adds a 12% 'service charge' onto the basic price of meals. How much do I pay for a meal with a basic price of £8·50?

10. A new-born baby weighs 3·1 kg. Her weight increases by 8% over the next fortnight. What does she weigh then?

11. A large snake normally weighs 12·2 kg. After swallowing a rat, the weight of the snake is increased by 7%. How much does it weigh after dinner?

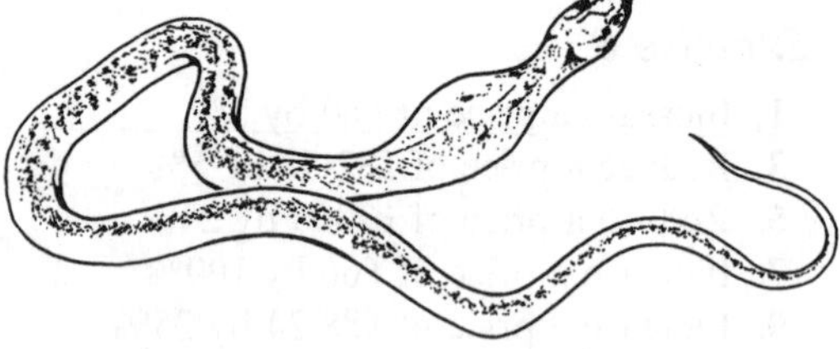

12. At the beginning of the year a car is valued at £3250. During the year its value falls by 15%. How much is it worth at the end of the year?

Exercise 8

In Questions **1** to **4** find the total bill.

1. 2 hammers at £5·30 each
   50 screws at 25p for 10
   5 bulbs at 38p each
   1 tape measure at £1·15
   VAT at 17·5% is added to the total cost.

2. 5 litres of oil at 85p per litre
   3 spanners at £1·25 each
   2 manuals at £4·30 each
   200 bolts at 90p for 10
   VAT at 17·5% is added to the total cost.

3. 12 rolls of wallpaper at £3·70 per roll
   3 packets of paste at £0·55 per packet
   2 brushes at £2·40 each
   1 step ladder at £15·50
   VAT at 17·5% is added to the total cost.

4. 5 golf clubs at £12·45 each
   48 golf balls at £15 per dozen
   100 tees at 1p each
   1 bag at £21·50
   1 umbrella at £12·99
   VAT at 17·5% is added to the total cost.

5. In a sale a dress priced at £35 is reduced by 20%. At the end of the week the *sale price* is reduced by a further 25%.
Calculate
(a) the price in the original sale
(b) the final price.

6. (a) In 2000 a club has 40 members who each pay £12 annual subscription. What is the total income from subscriptions?
(b) In 2001 the subscription is increased by 35% and the membership increases to 65.
(i) What is the 2001 subscription?
(ii) What is the total income from subscriptions in 2001?

Reverse percentages

After an increase of 6%, the price of a motor bike is £9010. What was the price before the increase?

A common mistake here is to work out 6% of £9010. This is wrong because the increase is 6% of the *old* price, not 6% of the new price.

106% of old price = £9010

$\therefore$ 1% of old price $= \dfrac{9010}{106}$

$\therefore$ 100% of old price $= \dfrac{9010}{106} \times 100$

The old price = £8500

To increase sales, the price of a magazine is reduced by 5%. Find the original price if the new price is 190p.

This is a reduction, so the new price is 95% of the old price.

95% of old price = 190p

1% of old price $= \dfrac{190}{95}$

100% of old price $= \dfrac{190}{95} \times 100$

Original price = 200p

Exercise 9

1. After an increase of 8%, the price of a car is £6696. Find the price of the car before the increase.

2. After a 12% pay rise, the salary of Mr Brown was £28 560. What was his salary before the increase?

3. Find the missing prices.

Item	Old price	New price	% change
(a) Jacket	?	£55	10% increase
(b) Dress	?	£212	6% increase
(c) CD player	?	£56·16	4% increase
(d) T.V.	?	£195	30% increase
(e) Car	?	£3960	65% increase

4. Between 1990 and 1997 the population of an island fell by 4%. The population in 1997 was 201 600. Find the population in 1990.

5. After being ill for 3 months, a man's weight went down by 12%. Find his original weight if he weighed 74·8 kg after the illness.

6. Find the missing prices.

Object	Old price	New price	% change
(a) Football	£9·50	?	3% increase
(b) Radio	?	£34·88	9% increase
(c) Roller blades	£52	?	15% decrease
(d) Golf club	?	£41·40	8% decrease

7. The diagram shows two rectangles. The width and height of rectangle B are both 20% greater than the width and height of rectangle A.

   Use the figures given to find the width and height of rectangle A.

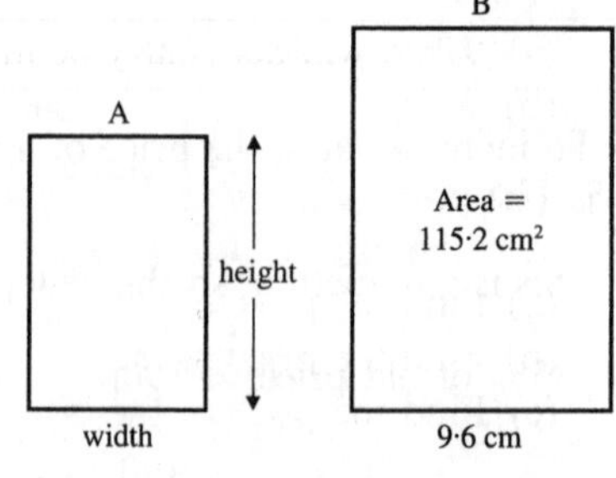

8. The label on a carton of yoghurt is shown. The figure on the right is smudged out. Work out what the figure should be.

Compound interest

Suppose a bank pays a fixed interest of 10% on money in deposit accounts. A man puts £500 in the bank.

After one year he has
$500 + 10\%$ of $500 = £550$

After two years he has
$550 + 10\%$ of $550 = £605$

[Check that this is $1{\cdot}10^2 \times 500$]

After three years he has
$605 + 10\%$ of $605 = £665{\cdot}50$

[Check that this is $1{\cdot}10^3 \times 500$]

In general after n years the money in the bank will be £$(1{\cdot}10^n \times 500)$.

Exercise 10

1. A bank pays interest of 10% on money in deposit accounts. Mrs Wells puts £2000 in the bank. How much has she after (a) one year, (b) two years, (c) three years?

2. A bank pays interest of 12%. Mr Olsen puts £5000 in the bank. How much has he after (a) one year, (b) three years?

3. A computer operator is paid £10 000 a year. Assuming her pay is increased by 7% each year, what will her salary be in four years time?

4. Mrs Bergkamp's salary in 2000 is £30 000 per year. Every year her salary is increased by 5%.
In 2001 her salary will be $30\,000 \times 1{\cdot}05 = £31\,500$
In 2002 her salary will be $30\,000 \times 1{\cdot}05 \times 1{\cdot}05 = £33\,075$
In 2003 her salary will be $30\,000 \times 1{\cdot}05 \times 1{\cdot}05 \times 1{\cdot}05 = £34\,728{\cdot}75$
And so on.
(a) What will her salary be in 2004?
(b) What will her salary be in 2006?

5. The price of a house was £90 000 in 1998. At the end of each year the price is increased by 6%.
(a) Find the price of the house after 1 year.
(b) Find the price of the house after 3 years.
(c) Find the price of the house after 10 years.

6. Assuming an average inflation rate of 8%, work out the probable cost of the following items in 10 years.
(a) car £6500 (b) T.V. £340 (c) house £50 000

7. A new car is valued at £15 000. At the end of each year its value is reduced by 15% of its value at the start of the year.
What will it be worth after 3 years?

8. Twenty years ago a bus driver was paid £50 a week. He is now paid £185 a week. Assuming an average rate of inflation of 7%, has his pay kept up with inflation?

9. The population of an island is 25 000 and it increases by 10% each year. After how many years will the original population be doubled?

10. A bank pays interest of 11% on £6000 in a deposit account. After how many years will the money have trebled?

Percentage change

Price changes are sometimes more significant when expressed as a percentage of the original price. For example if the price of a car goes up from £7000 to £7070, this is only a 1% increase. If the price of a jacket went up from £100 to £170 this would be a 70% increase! In both cases the actual increase is the same: £70.

- $\text{Percentage increase} = \dfrac{\text{actual increase}}{\text{original value}} \times \dfrac{100}{1}$

The price of a car is increased from £6400 to £6800.

$$\text{Percentage increase} = \frac{400}{6400} \times \frac{100}{1} = 6\tfrac{1}{4}\%$$

- $\text{Percentage decrease} = \dfrac{\text{actual decrease}}{\text{original value}} \times \dfrac{100}{1}$

Exercise 11

In Questions **1** to **10** calculate the percentage increase.

	Original price	Final price
1.	£50	£54
2.	£80	£88
3.	£180	£225
4.	£100	£102
5.	£75	£78
6.	£400	£410
7.	£5000	£6000
8.	£210	£315
9.	£600	£690
10.	$4000	$7200

In Questions **11** to **20** calculate the percentage decrease.

	Original price	Final price
11.	£800	£600
12.	£50	£40
13.	£120	£105
14.	£420	£280
15.	£6000	£1200
16.	$880	$836
17.	$15 000	$14 100
18.	$7·50	$6·00
19.	£8·20	£7·79
20.	£16 000	£15 600

Exercise 12

Find the percentage profit/loss using either of these formulae:

$$\text{percentage profit} = \frac{\text{actual profit}}{\text{cost price}} \times \frac{100}{1} \quad \text{or} \quad \text{percentage loss} = \frac{\text{actual loss}}{\text{cost price}} \times \frac{100}{1}$$

Give the answers correct to one decimal place.

	Cost price	Selling price
1.	£11	£15
2.	£21	£25
3.	£36	£43
4.	£41	£50
5.	£411	£461
6.	£5·32	£5·82
7.	£6·14	£7·00
8.	£2·13	£2·50
9.	£6·11	£8·11
10.	£18·15	£20

	Cost price	Selling price
11.	£20	£18·47
12.	£17	£11
13.	£13	£9
14.	£211	£200
15.	£8·15	£7
16.	£2·62	£3
17.	£1·52	£1·81
18.	$13·50	$13·98
19.	$3·05	$4·00
20.	$1705	$1816

Exercise 13

1. The number of people employed by a firm increased from 250 to 280. Calculate the percentage increase in the workforce.

2. During the first four weeks of her life a baby's weight increases from 3000 g to 3870 g. Calculate the percentage increase in the baby's weight.

3. Before cooking, a joint of meat weighs 2·5 kg. After cooking, the same joint of meat weighs only 2·1 kg. Calculate the percentage decrease in the weight of the joint.

4. When cold, an iron rod is 200 cm long. After being heated, the length increases to 200·5 cm. Calculate the percentage increase in the length of the rod.

5. A man buys a car for £4000 and sells it for £4600. Calculate the percentage profit.

6. A shopkeeper buys jumpers for £6·20 and sells them for £9·99. Calculate the percentage profit correct to one decimal place.

7. A grocer buys bananas at 20p per pound but after the fruit are spoiled he has to sell them at only 17p per pound. Calculate the percentage loss.

8. Before a service the petrol consumption of a car was 31 miles per gallon. After the service the consumption improved to 35·4 miles per gallon. Calculate the percentage improvement in the petrol consumption, correct to one decimal place.

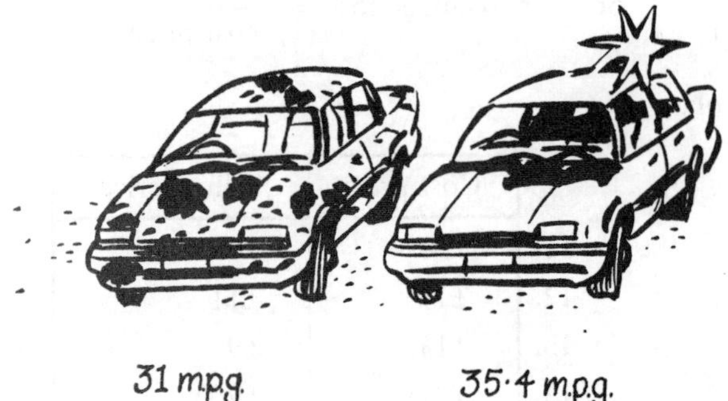

9. A shopkeeper bought 40 articles for £10 and sold them at 32p each. Calculate
   (a) the cost price of each article
   (b) the total selling price of the 40 articles
   (c) the total profit
   (d) the percentage profit.

10. A shopkeeper bought a crate of 40 tins of pears at 25p per tin.
    (a) Find the total cost of the crate of pears.
    (b) He sold 10 tins at 37p per tin, and the rest of the crate at 35p per tin.
        (i) How much profit did he make?
        (ii) Express this profit as a percentage of his total cost price.

11. ABCD is a square of side 100 cm. Side AB is increased by 20% and side AD is reduced by 25% to form rectangle APQR.
    (a) Calculate (i) the length of AP
        (ii) the length of AR
        (iii) the area of square ABCD
        (iv) the area of rectangle APQR.
    (b) By what percentage has the area of the square been reduced?

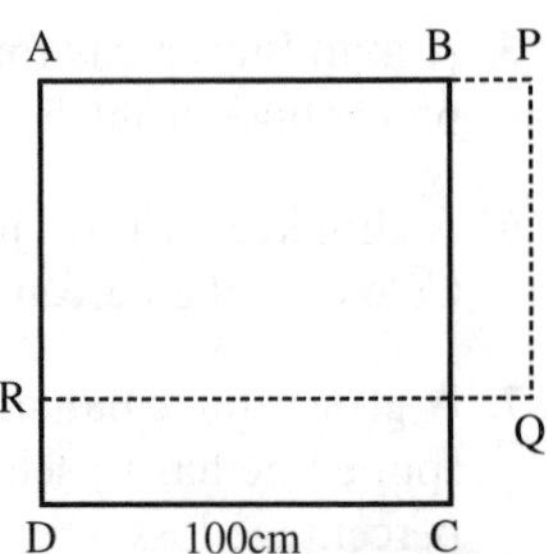

4.3 Map scales and ratio

The map below is drawn to a scale of 1 : 50 000. In other words 1 cm on the map represents 50 000 cm on the land.

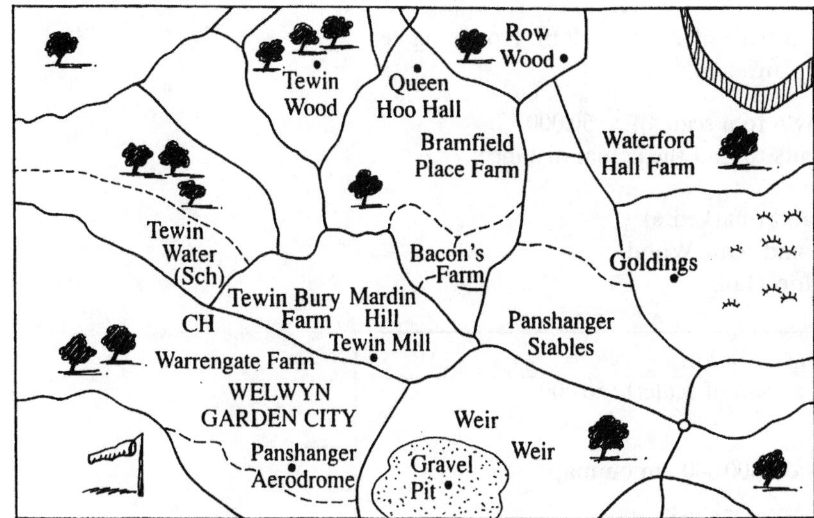

On a map of scale 1 : 25 000 two towns appear 10 cm apart. What is the actual distance between the towns in km?

1 cm on map = 25 000 cm on land
10 cm on map = 250 000 cm on land
250 000 cm = 2500 m
= 2·5 km

The towns are 2·5 km apart.

Exercise 14

1. The scale of a map is 1 : 1000. Find the actual length in metres represented on the map by 20 cm.
2. The scale of a map is 1 : 10 000. Find the actual length in metres represented on the map by 5 cm.
3. Copy and complete the table.

Map scale	Length on map	Actual length on land
(a) 1 : 10 000	10 cm	1 km
(b) 1 : 2000	10 cm	m
(c) 1 : 25 000	4 cm	km
(d) 1 : 10 000	6 cm	km

4. Find the actual distance in metres between two points which are 6·3 cm apart on a map whose scale is 1 : 1000.

5. On a map of scale 1 : 300 000 the distance between York and Harrogate is 8 cm. What is the actual distance in km?

6. A builder's plan is drawn to a scale of 1 cm to 10 m. How long is a road which is 12 cm on the plan?

7. The map on page 113 is drawn to a scale of 1 : 50 000. Make your own measurements to find the actual distance in km between:
   (a) Goldings and Tewin Wood (marked •)
   (b) Panshanger Aerodrome and Row Wood
   (c) Gravel Pit and Queen Hoo Hall.

The distance between two towns is 18 km.
How far apart will they be on a map of scale 1 : 50 000?

18 km = 1 800 000 cm
1 800 000 cm on land = $\frac{1}{50\,000} \times 1\,800\,000$ cm on map

Distance between towns on map = 36 cm

Exercise 15

1. The distance between two towns is 15 km. How far apart will they be on a map of scale 1 : 10 000?

2. The distance between two points is 25 km. How far apart will they be on a map of scale 1 : 20 000?

3. The length of a road is 2·8 km. How long will the road be on a map of scale 1 : 10 000?

4. The length of a reservoir is 5·9 km. How long will it be on a map of scale 1 : 100 000?

5. Copy and complete the table.

Map scale	Actual length on land	Length on map
(a) 1 : 20 000	12 km	cm
(b) 1 : 10 000	8·4 km	cm
(c) 1 : 50 000	28 km	cm
(d) 1 : 40 000	56 km	cm
(e) 1 : 5000	5 km	cm

6. The scale of a drawing is 1 cm to 10 m. The length of a wall is 25 m. What length will the wall be on the drawing?

Ratio

> Share £60 in the ratio 2 : 3.
>
> Total number of shares $= 2 + 3 = 5$
>
> ∴ One share $=$ £60 $\div 5 =$ £12
>
> ∴ The two amounts are £24 and £36.

Exercise 16

1. Share £30 in the ratio 1 : 2.
2. Share £60 in the ratio 3 : 1.
3. Divide 880 g of food between the cat and the dog in the ratio 3 : 5.
4. Divide $1080 between Sam and Chris in the ratio 4 : 5.
5. Share 126 gallons of petrol between Steven and Dave in the ratio 2 : 5.
6. Share £60 in the ratio 1 : 2 : 3.
7. Alan, Brian and Dawn divided £560 between them in the ratio 2 : 1 : 5. How much did Brian receive?
8. A sum of £120 is divided in the ratio 3 : 4 : 5. What is the largest share?
9. At an election 7800 people voted Labour, Conservative or Alliance in the ratio 4 : 3 : 5. How many people voted Alliance?
10. Find the ratio, 'shaded area' : 'unshaded area' for each diagram.

(a)
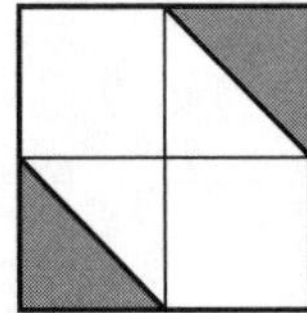

(b)

(c)
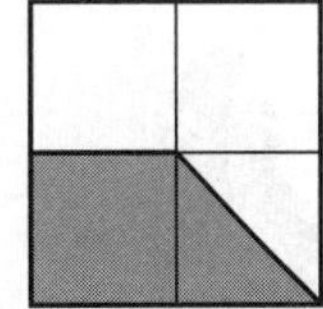

> In a class, the ratio of boys to girls is 3 : 4.
> If there are 9 boys, how many girls are there?
>
> Boys : Girls $= 3 : 4$
>
> Multiply both parts by 3.
>
> Boys : Girls $= 9 : 12$
>
> So there are 9 boys and 12 girls.

Exercise 17

1. In a room, the ratio of boys to girls is 3 : 2. If there are 12 boys, how many girls are there?

2. In a room, the ratio of men to women is 4 : 1. If there are 20 men, how many women are there?

3. In a box, the ratio of nails to screws is 5 : 3. If there are 15 nails, how many screws are there?

4. An alloy consists of copper, zinc and tin in the ratios 1 : 3 : 4. If there is 10 g of copper in the alloy, find the weights of zinc and tin.

5. In a shop the ratio of oranges to apples is 2 : 5. If there are 60 apples, how many oranges are there?

6. A recipe for 5 people calls for 1·5 kg of meat. How much meat is required if the recipe is adapted to feed 8 people?

7. A cake for 6 people requires 4 eggs. How many eggs are needed to make a cake big enough for 9 people?

8. A photocopier enlarges the original in the ratio 2 : 3. The height of a tree is 12 cm on the original. How tall is the tree on the enlarged copy?

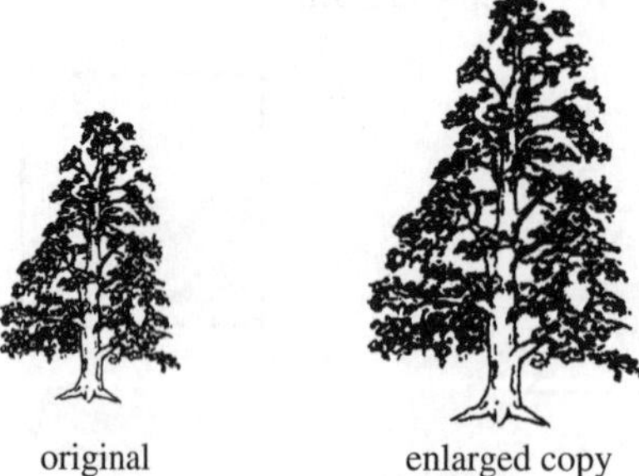

9. A photocopier enlarges copies in the ratio 4 : 5. The length of the headline 'BRIDGE COLLAPSES' is 18 cm on the original. How long is the headline on the enlarged copy?

10. A photocopier *reduces* in the ratio 5 : 3. The height of a church spire is 20 cm on the original. How tall is the church spire on the reduced copy?

11. A cake weighing 550 g has three ingredients: flour, sugar and raisins. There is twice as much flour as sugar and one and a half times as much sugar as raisins. How much flour is there?

12. If $\frac{5}{8}$ of the children in a school are boys, what is the ratio of boys to girls?

13. A man and a woman share a bingo prize of £1000 between them in the ratio 1 : 4. The woman shares her part between herself, her mother and her daughter in the ratio 2 : 1 : 1. How much does her daughter receive?

14. The number of pages in a newspaper is increased from 36 to 54. The price is increased in the same ratio. If the old price was 28p, what will the new price be?

15. Two friends bought a house for £220 000. Sam paid £140 000 and Joe paid the rest. Three years later they sold the house for £275 000. How much should Sam receive from the sale?

16. Concrete is made from 1 part cement, 2 parts sand and 5 parts aggregate (by volume). How much cement is needed to make 2 m^3 of concrete?

4.4 Approximations

A car travels a distance of 158 miles in $3\frac{1}{2}$ hours. What is the average speed?

$$\text{Speed} = \frac{\text{Distance}}{\text{Time}} = \frac{158}{3{\cdot}5}$$

On a calculator the answer is 45·142 857 14 mph.
It is not sensible to give all these figures in the answer. We have used a distance and a time which may not be all that accurate. It would be reasonable to give the answer as '45 mph'.

- We can approximate in two ways:
  (a) we can give *significant figures* (s.f.)
  (b) we can give *decimal places* (d.p.).

  Each type of approximation is described below.

Significant figures

Write the following numbers correct to three significant figures (3 s.f.).

(a) 2·6582 = 2·66 (to 3 s.f.)
↑

(b) 0·5142 = 0·514 (to 3 s.f.)
↑ [Ignore the zero before the '5']

(c) 84 660 = 84 700 (to 3 s.f.)
↑

(d) 0·04031 = 0·0403 (to 3 s.f.)
↑

In each case we look at the number marked with an arrow to see if it is 'five or more'.
Here we count figures from the left starting from the first non-zero figure.

Exercise 18

In Questions **1** to **8** write the numbers correct to three significant figures.

1. 2·3462 **2.** 0·81438 **3.** 26·241 **4.** 35·55
5. 112·74 **6.** 210·82 **7.** 0·8254 **8.** 0·031162

In Questions **9** to **16** write the numbers correct to two significant figures.

9. 5·894 **10.** 1·232 **11.** 0·5456 **12.** 0·7163
13. 0·1443 **14.** 1·831 **15.** 24·83 **16.** 31·37

In Questions **17** to **24** write the numbers correct to four significant figures.

17. 486·72 **18.** 500·36 **19.** 2·8888 **20.** 3·1125
21. 0·071542 **22.** 3·0405 **23.** 2463·5 **24.** 488 852

In Questions **25** to **36** write the numbers to the degree of accuracy indicated.

25. 0·5126 (3 s.f.) **26.** 5·821 (2 s.f.) **27.** 65·89 (2 s.f.) **28.** 587·55 (4 s.f.)
29. 0·581 (1 s.f.) **30.** 0·0713 (1 s.f.) **31.** 5·8354 (3 s.f.) **32.** 87·84 (2 s.f.)
33. 2482 (2 s.f.) **34.** 52 666 (3 s.f.) **35.** 0·0058 (1 s.f.) **36.** 6568 (1 s.f.)

Decimal places

Write the following numbers correct to two decimal places (2 d.p.).

(a) 8·358 = 8·36 (to 2 d.p.)
↑

(b) 0·0328 = 0·03 (to 2 d.p.)
↑

(c) 74·355 = 74·36 (to 2 d.p.)
↑

In each case we look at the number marked with an arrow to see if it is 'five or more'.
Here we count figures after the decimal point.

Exercise 19

In Questions **1** to **8** write the numbers correct to two decimal places (2 d.p.).

1. 5·381 **2.** 11·0482 **3.** 0·414 **4.** 0·3666
5. 8·015 **6.** 87·044 **7.** 9·0062 **8.** 0·0724

In Questions **9** to **16** write the numbers correct to one decimal place.

9. 8·424 **10.** 0·7413 **11.** 0·382 **12.** 0·095
13. 6·083 **14.** 19·53 **15.** 8·111 **16.** 7·071

In Questions **17** to **28** write the numbers to the degree of accuracy indicated.

17. 8·155 (2 d.p.)
18. 3·042 (1 d.p.)
19. 0·5454 (3 d.p.)
20. 0·005 55 (4 d.p.)
21. 0·7071 (2 d.p.)
22. 6·8271 (2 d.p.)
23. 0·8413 (1 d.p.)
24. 19·646 (2 d.p.)
25. 0·071 35 (4 d.p.)
26. 60·051 (1 d.p.)
27. −7·30 (1 d.p.)
28. −5·424 (2 d.p.)

29. Use a ruler to measure the dimensions of the rectangles below.
(a) Write down the length and width in cm correct to one d.p.
(b) Work out the area of each rectangle and give the answer in cm^2 correct to one d.p.

(i)

(ii)

Exercise 20

Write the answers to the degree of accuracy indicated.

1. $0{\cdot}153 \times 3{\cdot}74$ (2 d.p.)
2. $18{\cdot}09 \div 5{\cdot}24$ (3 s.f.)
3. $184 \times 2{\cdot}342$ (3 s.f.)
4. $17{\cdot}2 \div 0{\cdot}89$ (1 d.p.)
5. $58 \div 261$ (2 s.f.)
6. $88{\cdot}8 \times 44{\cdot}4$ (1 d.p.)
7. $(8{\cdot}4 - 1{\cdot}32) \times 7{\cdot}5$ (2 s.f.)
8. $(121 + 3758) \div 211$ (3 s.f.)
9. $(1{\cdot}24 - 1{\cdot}144) \times 0{\cdot}61$ (3 d.p.)
10. $1 \div 0{\cdot}935$ (1 d.p.)
11. $78{\cdot}3524^2$ (3 s.f.)
12. $(18{\cdot}25 - 6{\cdot}941)^2$ (2 d.p.)
13. $9{\cdot}245^2 - 65{\cdot}2$ (1 d.p.)
14. $(2 - 0{\cdot}666) \div 0{\cdot}028$ (3 s.f.)
15. $8{\cdot}43^3$ (1 d.p.)
16. $0{\cdot}924^2 - 0{\cdot}835^2$ (2 d.p.)

4.5 Metric and Imperial units

Years ago measurements were made using parts of the body. The inch was measured using the thumb and the foot by using the foot. Even today many people, when asked their height or weight, will say '5 feet 3' or '9 stone' rather than '1 metre 60' or '58 kg'.

Metric units

Length	Mass	Volume
10 mm = 1 cm	1000 g = 1 kg	1000 ml = 1 litre
100 cm = 1 m	1000 kg = 1 t	1000 l = 1 m^3
1000 m = 1 km	(t for tonne)	Also 1 ml = 1 cm^3

Exercise 21

Copy and complete.

1. 85 cm = m
2. 2·4 km = m
3. 0·63 m = cm
4. 25 cm = m
5. 7 mm = cm
6. 2 cm = mm
7. 1·2 km = m
8. 7 m = cm
9. 0·58 km = m
10. 815 mm = m
11. 650 m = km
12. 25 mm = cm
13. 5 kg = g
14. 4·2 kg = g
15. 6·4 kg = g
16. 3 kg = g
17. 0·8 kg = g
18. 400 g = kg
19. 2 t = kg
20. 250 g = kg
21. 0·5 t = kg
22. 0·62 t = kg
23. 7 kg = t
24. 1500 g = kg
25. 800 ml = l
26. 2 l = ml
27. 1000 ml = l
28. 4·5 l = ml
29. 6 l = ml
30. 3 l = cm^3
31. 2 m^3 = l
32. 5·5 m^3 = l

33. Write down the most appropriate metric unit for measuring:
(a) the distance between Glasgow and Leeds
(b) the capacity of a wine bottle
(c) the mass of raisins needed for a cake
(d) the diameter of a small drill
(e) the mass of a car
(f) the area of a football pitch.

Imperial units

Length	Mass	Volume
12 inches = 1 foot	16 ounces = 1 pound	8 pints = 1 gallon
3 feet = 1 yard	14 pounds = 1 stone	
1760 yards = 1 mile	2240 pounds = 1 ton	

Exercise 22

1. How many inches are there in two feet?
2. How many ounces are there in three pounds?
3. How many feet are there in ten yards?
4. How many pounds are there in two tons?
5. How many pints are there in six gallons?
6. How many yards are there in ten miles?
7. How many inches are there in one yard?
8. How many pounds are there in five stones?
9. How many pints are there in half a gallon?
10. How many yards are there in half a mile?

In Questions **11** to **20** copy each statement and fill in the missing numbers.

11. 9 feet = yards
12. 16 pints = gallons
13. 2 miles = yards
14. 5 pounds = ounces
15. 10 stones = pounds
16. 4 yards = feet
17. 4 feet = inches
18. 10 tons = pounds
19. 1 mile = feet
20. 6 feet = yards

Changing units

Although the metric system is generally replacing the Imperial system we still need to be able to convert from one set of units to the other.

- Try to remember the following approximate conversions.

1 inch $\approx$ 2·5 cm	1 gallon $\approx$ 5 litres
1 kg $\approx$ 2 pounds	1 km $\approx \frac{5}{8}$ mile
1 ounce $\approx$ 30 g	[or 8 km $\approx$ 5 miles]

(a) Change 16 km into miles.

$$1 \text{ km} \approx \tfrac{5}{8} \text{ mile}$$
$$\text{so } 16 \text{ km} \approx \tfrac{5}{8} \times 16$$
$$16 \text{ km} \approx 10 \text{ miles}$$

(b) Change 2 feet into cm.

$$2 \text{ feet} \approx 24 \text{ inches}$$
$$1 \text{ inch} \approx 2{\cdot}5 \text{ cm}$$
$$\therefore\ 2 \text{ feet} \approx 2.5 \times 24 \text{ cm}$$
$$\approx 60 \text{ cm}$$

Exercise 23

Copy each statement and fill in the missing numbers.

1. 10 inches = cm	**2.** 10 gallons = litres	**3.** 100 pounds = kg
4. 4 kg = pounds	**5.** 8 km = miles	**6.** 2 pounds = kg
7. 32 km = miles	**8.** 4 inches = cm	**9.** 5 pounds = kg
10. 8 pints = litres	**11.** 40 km = miles	**12.** 100 litres = gallons
13. 3 kg = pounds	**14.** $\frac{1}{2}$ km = mile	**15.** 400 litres = gallons
16. 60 g = ounces	**17.** 10 oz = g	**18.** 5 litres = gallons
19. 20 kg = pounds	**20.** 25 cm = inches	**21.** 1 foot = cm

22. A car handbook calls for the oil to be changed every 8000 km. How many miles is that?

23. On an Italian road the speed limit is 80 km/h. Convert this into a speed in mph.

24. Tomatoes are sold in Tesco at 85p per kilo and in Sainsburys at 30p per pound. Which supermarket has the lower price?

25. Here is the recipe for a pie.

Write the recipe with the correct metric quantities.

In Questions **26** to **30** copy each sentence and choose the number which is the best estimate.

26. A one pound coin has a mass of about [1 g, 10 g, 1 kg].

27. The width of the classroom is about [100 inches, 7 m, 50 m].

28. A can of Pepsi contains about [500 ml, $\frac{1}{2}$ gallon].

29. The distance from London to Birmingham is about [20 miles, 20 km, 100 miles].

30. The thickness of a one pound coin is about [3 mm, 6 mm, $\frac{1}{4}$ inch].

31. Here are scales for changing:
A kilograms and pounds,
B litres and gallons.
In this question give your answers to the *nearest whole number*.

(a) About how many kilograms are there in 6 pounds?
(b) About how many litres are there in 3·3 gallons?
(c) About how many pounds are there in 1·4 kilograms?

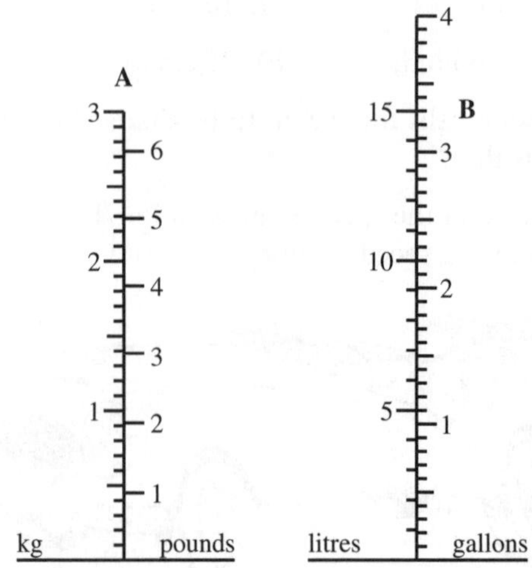

32. A fitter is doing a job which requires a 3 mm drill. He has no metric drills but he does have the following Imperial sizes (in inches): $\frac{1}{16}$, $\frac{1}{8}$, $\frac{3}{16}$. Which of these drills is the nearest in size to 3 mm?

4.6 Fractions

Equivalent fractions

- You can find equivalent fractions by multiplying or dividing the top and bottom of a fraction by the same number.

(a) $\frac{5}{6} = \frac{10}{12}$ (top ×2, bottom ×2)

(b) $\frac{15}{18} = \frac{5}{6}$ (top ÷3, bottom ÷3)

(c) $3\frac{1}{2} = 3 + \frac{1}{2}$

$= \frac{6}{2} + \frac{1}{2}$

$= \frac{7}{2}$ ← These are *improper* fractions.

(d) $5\frac{1}{4} = \frac{21}{4}$ $[21 = (5 \times 4) + 1]$

Exercise 24

1. Fill in the missing numbers to find the equivalent fractions.

(a) $\frac{3}{4} = \frac{\square}{8}$ (b) $\frac{2}{5} = \frac{\square}{10}$ (c) $\frac{1}{3} = \frac{\square}{9}$

(d) $\frac{1}{4} = \frac{\square}{20}$ (e) $\frac{2}{3} = \frac{6}{\square}$ (f) $\frac{1}{2} = \frac{5}{\square}$

(g) $\frac{9}{12} = \frac{\square}{4}$ (h) $\frac{15}{25} = \frac{\square}{5}$ (i) $\frac{8}{12} = \frac{2}{\square}$

2. Write the fraction shaded. Give the answer in its most simple form.

(a) (b) (c)

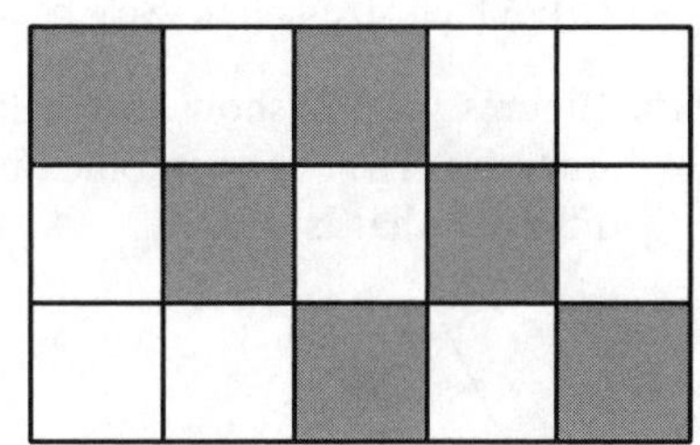

3. Write as improper fractions.

(a) $1\frac{1}{2}$ (b) $1\frac{3}{4}$ (c) $2\frac{1}{4}$ (d) $2\frac{2}{5}$

(e) $1\frac{4}{5}$ (f) $3\frac{1}{2}$ (g) $6\frac{3}{4}$ (h) $7\frac{2}{3}$

4. Write as mixed fractions.

(a) $\frac{7}{5}$ (b) $\frac{8}{3}$ (c) $\frac{5}{2}$ (d) $\frac{7}{3}$

(e) $\frac{9}{2}$ (f) $\frac{12}{7}$ (g) $\frac{20}{3}$ (h) $\frac{9}{4}$

5. The chart shows how the total price of a CD is made up.
(a) What fraction of the total price is tax?
(b) What fraction of the total price is advertising plus cost to make?
(c) What is the total profit made if 100 000 CDs are sold?

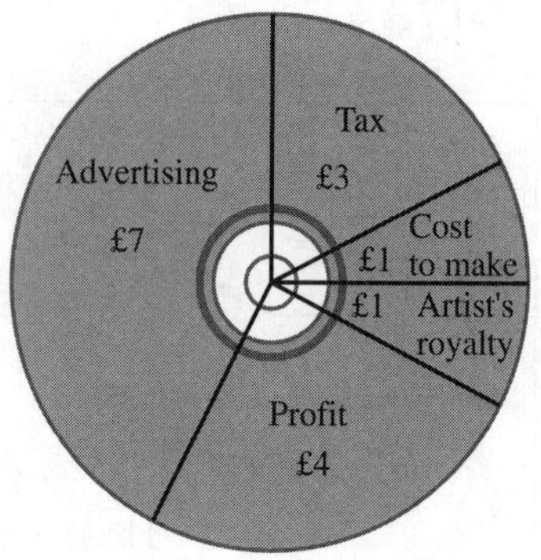

6. (a) Write all of these fractions with a denominator of 12.

$\frac{3}{4}$ $\frac{2}{3}$ $\frac{1}{2}$ $\frac{1}{4}$

(b) Write the fractions in order of size, smallest first.

7. Arrange the fractions in order of size.

(a) $\frac{7}{12}, \frac{1}{2}, \frac{2}{3}$ (b) $\frac{3}{4}, \frac{2}{3}, \frac{5}{6}$

(c) $\frac{1}{3}, \frac{17}{24}, \frac{5}{8}, \frac{3}{4}$ (d) $\frac{5}{6}, \frac{8}{9}, \frac{11}{12}$

8. Find the fraction which is mid-way between the two fractions given.

(a) $\frac{2}{5}, \frac{3}{5}$ (b) $\frac{5}{8}, \frac{7}{8}$

(c) $\frac{2}{3}, \frac{3}{4}$ (d) $\frac{1}{3}, \frac{4}{9}$

(e) $\frac{4}{15}, \frac{1}{3}$ (f) $\frac{3}{8}, \frac{11}{24}$

9. A set of drills starts at $\frac{1}{8}$ inch and goes up to $\frac{5}{8}$ inch in steps of $\frac{1}{16}$ inch.
(a) How many drills are there in the full set?
(b) Which size is half-way between $\frac{1}{4}$ inch and $\frac{3}{8}$ inch?

10. Figures 1 and 2 show an equilateral triangle divided into thirds and quarters. They are combined in Figure 3. Calculate the fraction of Figure 3 that is shaded.

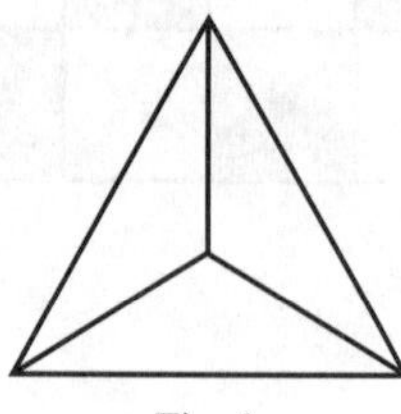
Fig. 1

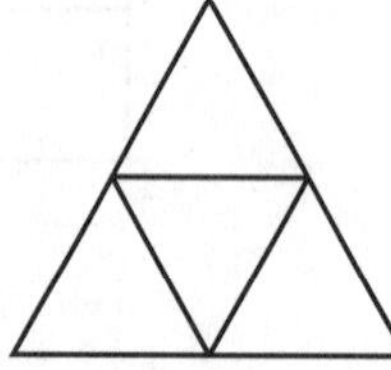
Fig. 2

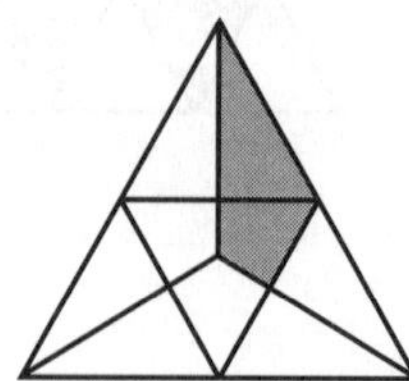
Fig. 3

11. A fraction is equivalent to $\frac{2}{3}$ and its denominator (bottom number) is 8 more than its numerator (top number). What is the fraction?

Adding and subtracting fractions

- Fractions can be added or subtracted when they have the same denominator.

(a) 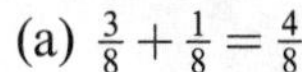 $\frac{3}{8} + \frac{1}{8} = \frac{4}{8}$

Notice that we add the numerators but not the denominators!

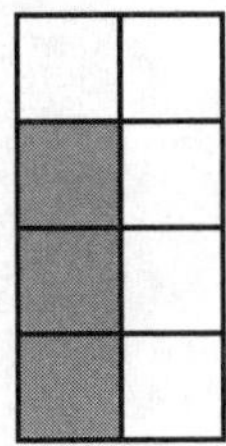 + 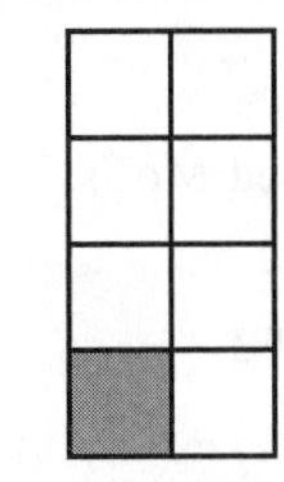 = 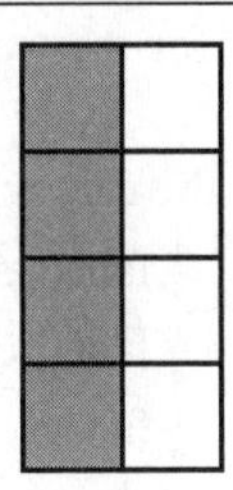

(b) $\frac{1}{2} + \frac{1}{5}$ Change $\frac{1}{2}$ and $\frac{1}{5}$ into equivalent fractions with the same denominator.

$\frac{5}{10} + \frac{2}{10} = \frac{7}{10}$ [The L.C.M. of 2 and 5 is 10.]

(c) $\frac{3}{4} - \frac{1}{3}$

$\frac{9}{12} - \frac{4}{12} = \frac{5}{12}$ [The L.C.M. of 4 and 3 is 12.]

(d) $2\frac{1}{2} - 1\frac{3}{4} = \frac{5}{2} - \frac{7}{4} = \frac{10}{4} - \frac{7}{4} = \frac{3}{4}$ [Change to improper fractions.]

Exercise 25

1. Work out.

(a) $\frac{5}{7} + \frac{1}{7}$ (b) $\frac{4}{9} + \frac{1}{9}$ (c) $\frac{7}{10} - \frac{1}{10}$ (d) $\frac{3}{5} + \frac{2}{5}$

2. Copy and complete.

(a) $\frac{1}{4} + \frac{1}{8} = \frac{\square}{8} + \frac{1}{8} =$ (b) $\frac{1}{2} + \frac{2}{5} = \frac{\square}{10} + \frac{\square}{10} =$ (c) $\frac{2}{5} + \frac{1}{3} = \frac{\square}{15} + \frac{\square}{15} =$

3. Work out.

(a) $\frac{1}{2} + \frac{1}{3}$ (b) $\frac{1}{4} + \frac{1}{6}$ (c) $\frac{1}{3} + \frac{1}{4}$ (d) $\frac{1}{4} + \frac{1}{5}$

(e) $\frac{2}{5} + \frac{2}{3}$ (f) $\frac{1}{4} + \frac{2}{5}$ (g) $\frac{1}{2} + \frac{2}{7}$ (h) $1\frac{1}{4} + 2\frac{1}{2}$

4. Work out.

(a) $\frac{2}{3} - \frac{1}{2}$ (b) $\frac{3}{4} - \frac{1}{3}$ (c) $\frac{4}{5} - \frac{1}{2}$ (d) $\frac{2}{3} - \frac{1}{4}$

(e) $\frac{1}{2} - \frac{2}{5}$ (f) $\frac{4}{5} - \frac{2}{3}$ (g) $2\frac{3}{4} - 1\frac{1}{8}$ (h) $1\frac{2}{3} - 1\frac{1}{2}$

5. Work out the perimeter of this drawing.

$3\frac{1}{8}$ inch

$2\frac{1}{4}$ inch

6. Here is a list of the number of hours for which a computer was used over 5 days: $6\frac{1}{2}$, $6\frac{1}{4}$, $5\frac{1}{2}$, $5\frac{3}{4}$, $6\frac{1}{2}$.
   (a) For how many hours was the computer used altogether?
   (b) The computer is rented at £10 per hour. What is the total rent for the week?

7. Of the cars which failed MoTs:
   $\frac{1}{4}$ failed on brakes
   $\frac{1}{3}$ failed on steering
   $\frac{1}{6}$ failed on lights
   the rest failed on worn tyres.
   What fraction of the cars failed on worn tyres?

8. In the equation on the right, all the asterisks stand for the same number. What is the number? $\left[\frac{*}{*} - \frac{*}{6} = \frac{*}{30}\right]$

9. The shaded rectangle is surrounded by a border $\frac{1}{16}''$ wide. Find the length and width marked.

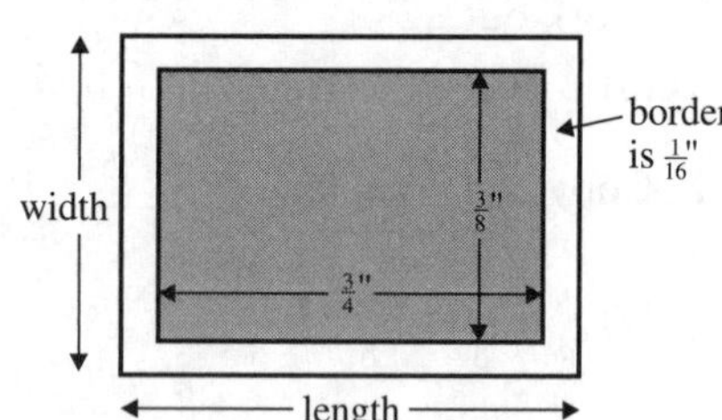

Multiplying and dividing fractions

(a) $\frac{2}{5} \times \frac{6}{7} = \frac{12}{35}$ (2 × 6) (5 × 7)

(b) $2\frac{2}{5} \times \frac{1}{5}$
$= \frac{12}{5} \times \frac{1}{5}$ [Change $2\frac{2}{5}$ to an improper fraction.]
$= \frac{12}{25}$

(c) $\frac{3}{8} \div \frac{4}{5} = \frac{3}{8} \times \frac{5}{4}$ [Invert $\frac{4}{5}$ and then multiply.]
$= \frac{15}{32}$

(d) $\frac{5}{11} \div \frac{1}{2} = \frac{5}{11} \times \frac{2}{1} = \frac{10}{11}$

Exercise 26

1. Work out.
   (a) $\frac{2}{3} \times \frac{1}{5}$ (b) $\frac{3}{4} \times \frac{5}{7}$ (c) $\frac{4}{5} \times \frac{2}{3}$ (d) $\frac{5}{6} \times \frac{5}{7}$
   (e) $\frac{5}{9} \times \frac{2}{3}$ (f) $\frac{4}{11} \times \frac{5}{6}$ (g) $\frac{7}{8} \times \frac{3}{4}$ (h) $\frac{8}{9} \times \frac{3}{4}$

2. (a) $\frac{3}{4} \div \frac{1}{2}$ (b) $\frac{3}{5} \div \frac{2}{3}$ (c) $\frac{5}{6} \div \frac{1}{4}$ (d) $\frac{2}{3} \div \frac{3}{4}$
(e) $\frac{5}{6} \div \frac{3}{4}$ (f) $\frac{5}{7} \div \frac{3}{4}$ (g) $1\frac{1}{4} \div 2$ (h) $3\frac{2}{9} \div \frac{1}{3}$

3. Copy and complete this multiplication square.

$\times$	$\frac{2}{3}$		
$\frac{1}{2}$		$\frac{3}{8}$	
		$\frac{3}{16}$	
$\frac{2}{5}$			$\frac{2}{25}$

4. Work out one-half of one-third of 65% of £360.

5. A rubber ball is dropped from a height of 300 cm. After each bounce, the ball rises to $\frac{4}{5}$ of its previous height.
How high, to the nearest cm, will it rise after the fourth bounce?

6. Steve Braindead spends his income as follows:
(a) $\frac{2}{5}$ of his income goes in tax
(b) $\frac{2}{3}$ of what is left goes on food, rent and transport
(c) he spends the rest on cigarettes, beer and betting.
What fraction of his income is spent on cigarettes, beer and betting?

7. Fill in the missing numbers so that the answer is always $\frac{3}{8}$.

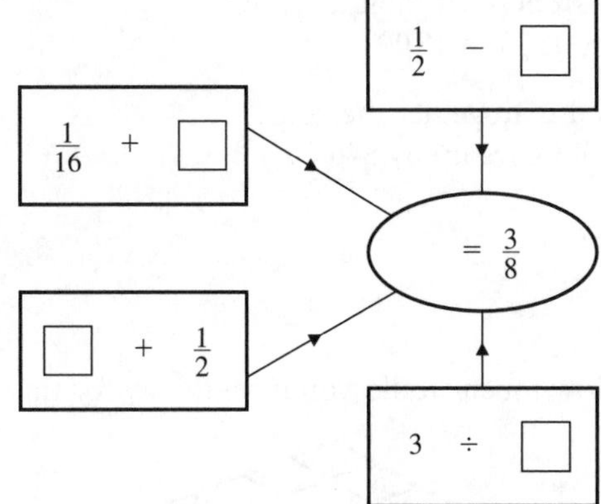

8. When it hatches from its egg, the shell of a certain crab is 1 cm across. When fully grown the shell is approximately 10 cm across. Each new shell is one-third bigger than the previous one. How many shells does a fully grown crab have during its life?

4.7 Mixed problems 2

Exercise 27

1. Four dozen bags of grain weigh 2016 kg. How much does each bag weigh?

2. An office building has twelve floors and each floor has twenty windows. A window cleaner charges 50p per window. How much will he charge to clean all the windows in the building?

3. Write the following to the degree of accuracy stated.
   (a) 7·243 (to 1 d.p.) (b) 11·275 (to 2 d.p.)
   (c) 0·115 (to 1 d.p.) (d) 0·0255 (to 3 d.p.)
   (e) 28·21 (to 1 d.p.) (f) 0·0072 (to 2 d.p.)

4. Write each statement and find the missing number.
   (a) $3^{\square} = 9$ (b) $\square^2 = 121$
   (c) $6^{\square} = 1$ (d) $5^3 \times 5^{\square} = 5^8$

5. A rectangular wheat field is 200 m by 400 m. One hectare is 10 000 m^2 and each hectare produces 3 tonnes of wheat.
   (a) What is the area of the field in hectares?
   (b) How much wheat is produced in this field?

6. A powerful computer is hired out at a rate of 50p per minute. How much will it cost to hire the computer from 06 30 to 18 00?

7. An old sailor keeps all of his savings in gold. Altogether the gold weighs ten pounds. One day the price of gold goes up by \$40 an ounce to \$520 an ounce.
   (a) By how much did his gold rise in value?
   (b) How much was it worth after the rise?
   (1 pound = 16 ounces)

8. This packet of sugar cubes costs 60p. How much would you have to pay for this packet?

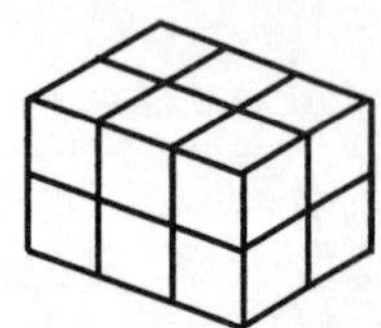

9. A wall measuring 3 m by 2 m is to be covered with square tiles of side 10 cm.
   (a) How many tiles are needed?
   (b) If the tiles cost £3·40 for ten, how much will it cost?

10. Draw the next member of the sequence.

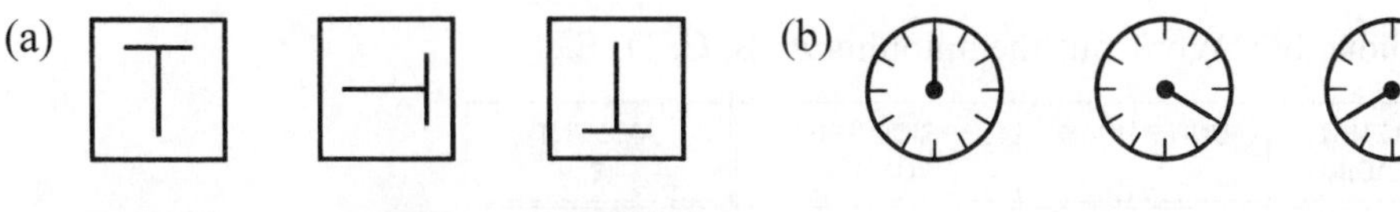

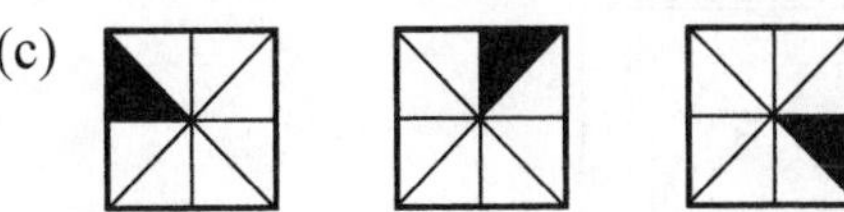

Exercise 28

1. The results of a test given to 50 children are shown below.

Mark	0	1	2	3	4	5
Number of pupils	1	4	10	12	15	8

   (a) How many pupils scored less than 3 marks?
   (b) Find the percentage of the pupils who scored
      (i) 2 marks (ii) 5 marks
      (iii) 3 marks or more (iv) no marks.

2. The thirteenth number in the sequence 1, 3, 9, 27, ... is 531 441. What is:
   (a) the twelfth number
   (b) the fourteenth number?

3. 6 sacks of corn will feed 80 hens for 12 days. Copy and complete the following.
   (a) 18 sacks of corn will feed 80 hens for ... days.
   (b) 6 sacks of corn will feed 40 hens for ... days.
   (c) 60 sacks of corn will feed 40 hens for ... days.
   (d) 30 sacks of corn will feed 80 hens for ... days.

4. Calculate the area of the shape below. Take $\pi = 3$.

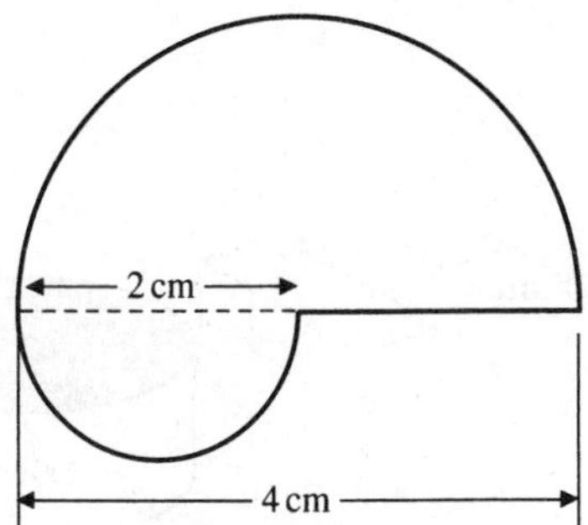

5. The mileometer of a car shows a reading of 14 941 miles. This number is called 'palindromic' because it reads the same backwards or forwards.
   (a) What will be the reading when the next palindromic number appears?
   (b) How far will the car have travelled by then?

6. Here is a telephone bill. Work out the amounts A, B, C, D, E.

DATE	METER READING	UNITS USED	PRICE PER UNIT	AMOUNT (£)
29/7/99	18714			
30/4/99	17956	A	3.80p	B
		Rental Charges		21.50
		Total Charges (excluding VAT)		C
		Value Added Tax at $17\frac{1}{2}$%		D
		Total Charges (including VAT)		E

7. A salesman is paid a basic salary of £5400 per year, plus commission of 5% on all his sales. Calculate his total salary if his sales totalled £40 000.

8. Petrol costs 69·2 pence per litre. How many litres can be bought for £8? Give your answer to one decimal place.

Exercise 29

1. A slimmer's calorie guide shows how many calories are contained in various foods:

   Bread 1·2 calories per g
   Cheese 2·5 calories per g
   Meat 1·6 calories per g
   Butter 6 calories per g

   Calculate the number of calories in the following meals.
   (a) 50 g bread, 40 g cheese, 100 g meat, 15 g butter.
   (b) 150 g bread, 85 g cheese, 120 g meat, 20 g butter.

2. Write as a single number.
   (a) 8^2 (b) 1^4 (c) 10^2
   (d) 3×10^3 (e) 2^5 (f) 3^4

3. A cylinder has a volume of 200 cm³ and a height of 10 cm. Calculate the area of its base.

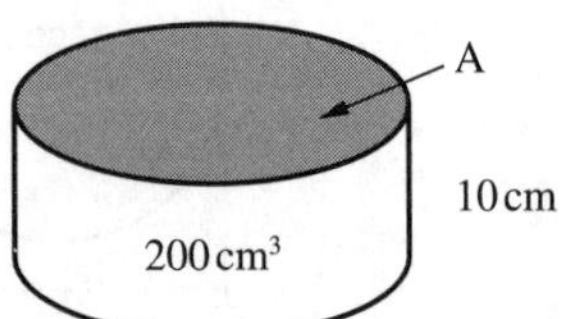

4. The diagram represents a railway siding. Each ● is a junction where a train can turn left or right. A turn to the left has a code 0 and a turn to the right has a code 1.

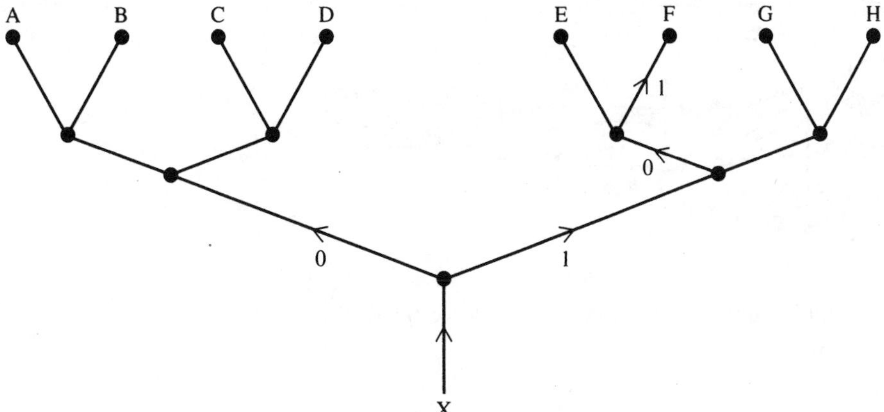

For example, a train starting at X would have code 101 in order to arrive at F.
Copy and complete the table below.

Point	A	B	C	D	E	F	G	H
Code						101		

5. A group of four adults are planning a holiday in France. The ferry costs, for the return journey, are:

Adult	£25
Car	£62

Travel around France is estimated at 2000 km and petrol costs 5 francs per litre. The car travels 10 km on one litre of petrol.

(a) Calculate the total cost of the return journey on the ferry.
(b) Calculate the number of litres of petrol to be used.
(c) Calculate the total cost, in francs, of the petrol.

6. A journey by boat takes 2 hours 47 minutes. How long will it take at half the speed?

7. Copy the following tables and write down the next *two* lines.

(a)
$$\begin{aligned} 2^2 &= 1^2 + 3 \\ 3^2 &= 2^2 + 5 \\ 4^2 &= 3^2 + 7 \\ 5^2 &= 4^2 + 9 \end{aligned}$$

(b)
$$\begin{aligned} 3^2 &= 4 + 1^2 + 2^2 \\ 5^2 &= 12 + 2^2 + 3^2 \\ 7^2 &= 24 + 3^2 + 4^2 \\ 9^2 &= 40 + 4^2 + 5^2 \end{aligned}$$

8. The area of a county is 6000 km^2. What volume of rain falls on the county during a day when there is 2 cm of rain? Give the answer in m^3.

9. Ten posts are equally spaced in a straight line. It is 450 m from the first to the tenth post. What is the distance between successive posts?

10. Find the smallest whole number that is exactly divisible by all the numbers 1 to 10 inclusive.

Exercise 30

1. Seven fig rolls together weigh 560 g. A calorie guide shows that 10 g of fig roll contains 52 calories.
   (a) How much does one fig roll weigh?
   (b) How many calories are there in 1 g of fig roll?
   (c) How many calories are there in one fig roll?

2. Two numbers x and t are such that t is greater than 6 and x is less than 4. Arrange the numbers 5, t and x in order of size, starting with the smallest.

3. To the nearest whole number 5·84, 16·23 and 7·781 are 6, 16 and 8 respectively.
   (a) Use these approximate values to obtain an approximate result for $\frac{5{\cdot}84 \times 16{\cdot}23}{7{\cdot}781}$.
   (b) Use the same approach to obtain approximate results for
   (i) $\frac{15{\cdot}72 \times 9{\cdot}78}{20{\cdot}24}$ (ii) $\frac{23{\cdot}85 \times 9{\cdot}892}{4{\cdot}867}$

4. King Richard is given three coins which look identical, but in fact one of them is an overweight fake.
   Describe how he could discover the fake using an ordinary balance and only *one* weighing operation.

5. A light aircraft flies 375 km on 150 litres of fuel. How much fuel is needed for a journey of 500 km?

6. A pile of 400 sheets of paper is 2·5 cm thick. What is the thickness in cm of one sheet of paper?

7. A map uses a scale of 1 to 100 000.
   (a) Calculate the actual length, in km, of a canal which is 5·4 cm long on the map.
   (b) A path is 600 m long. Calculate, in cm, the length this would be on the map.

8. Given the circumference C of a circle it is possible to estimate the area A by the following method:

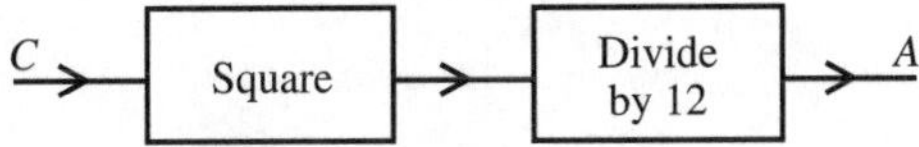

   (a) Find A when $C = 6$ cm.
   (b) Find A when $C = 18$ cm.
   (c) Write down the formula involving A and C.

9. I think of a number. If I subtract 4 and then divide the result by 4 the answer is 3. What number was I thinking of?

10. Try to draw four straight lines which pass through all of the 9 points below, without taking your pen from the paper and without going over any line twice.

[Hint: The lines may go outside the pattern of dots.]

Exercise 31

1. Twelve calculators cost £102. How many calculators could be bought for £76·50?

2. A car travels 35 m in 0·7 seconds. How far does it travel in
   (a) 0·1 s? (b) 1 s? (c) 2 minutes?

3. The outline of a 50p coin is shown below.

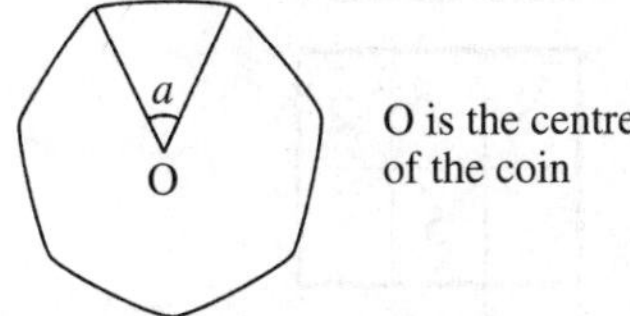

Calculate the size of the angle, a, to the nearest $\frac{1}{10}$ of a degree.

4. The diagram below shows the map of a farm which grows four different crops in the regions shown.

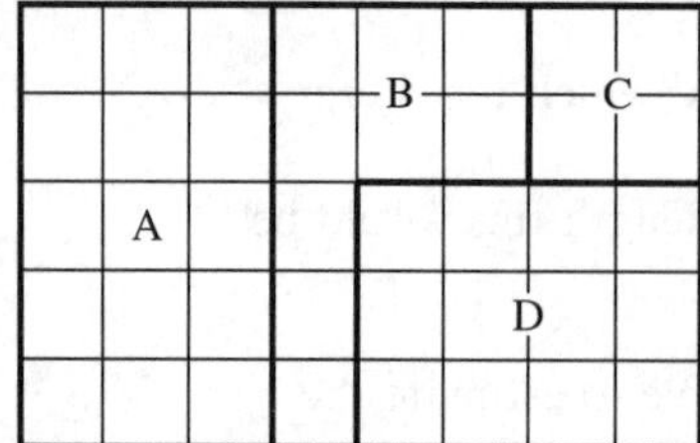

Each square represents one acre.
(a) What is the total area of the farm?
(b) What area is used for crop A?
(c) What percentage of the farm is used for
(i) crop C (ii) crop D
(iii) crop A (iv) crop B?

5. A man smokes 40 cigarettes a day and each packet of 20 cigarettes costs £3·80. How much does he spend on cigarettes in a whole year of 365 days?

6. A man worked 7 hours per day from Monday to Friday and 4 hours overtime on Saturday. The rate of pay from Monday to Friday is £4·50 per hour and the overtime rate is time and a half. How much did he earn during the week?

7. An examination is marked out of a total of 120 marks. How many marks did Alan get if he scored 65% of the marks?

8. A shopkeeper buys coffee at £3·65 per kg and sells it at 95p per 100 g. How much profit does he make per kg?

9. Five 2s can make 25: $22 + 2 + \frac{2}{2} = 25$.

(a) Use four 9s to make 100
(b) Use three 6s to make 7
(c) Use three 5s to make 60
(d) Use five 5s to make 61
(e) Use four 7s to make 1
(f) Use three 8s to make 11

10. Find the missing digits.

(a)

	2	
+	5	4
		7

(b)

	1	7
+		6
	6	

(c)

	5		2
+	1	3	
		1	8

(d)

	4		4
+		5	
	8	2	4

(e)

	8	
−		4
	5	2

(f)

	8		2
−		5	
	2	3	2

5 ALGEBRA 2

5.1 Substituting into formulae

(a) A formula connecting velocities with acceleration and time is $v = u + at$.
Find the value of v when $u = 3$
$a = 4$
$t = 6$.

$$v = u + at$$
$$v = 3 + (4 \times 6)$$
$$v = 27$$

(b) A formula for the tension in a spring is $T = \frac{kx}{a}$.
Find the value of T when $k = 13$
$x = 5$
$a = 2$.

$$T = \frac{kx}{a}$$
$$T = \frac{13 \times 5}{2}$$
$$T = 32\tfrac{1}{2}$$

Exercise 1

1. A formula involving force, mass and acceleration is $F = ma$. Find the value of F when $m = 12$ and $a = 3$.

2. The height of a growing tree is given by the formula $h = 2t + 15$. Find the value of h when $t = 7$.

3. The time required to cook a joint of meat is given by the formula $T =$ (mass of joint) $\times 3 + \frac{1}{2}$. Find the value of T when (mass of joint) $= 2\frac{1}{2}$.

4. An important formula in Physics states that $I = mu - mv$. Find the value of I when $m = 6$, $u = 8$, $v = 5$.

5. The distance travelled by an accelerating car is given by the formula $s = \left(\frac{u+v}{2}\right)t$. Find the value of s when $u = 17$, $v = 25$ and $t = 4$.

6. Einstein's famous formula states that $E = mc^2$. Find the value of E when $m = 0{\cdot}0001$ and $c = 3 \times 10^8$.

7. The height of a stone thrown upwards is given by $h = ut - 5t^2$. Find the value of h when $u = 70$ and $t = 3$.

8. The speed of an accelerating particle is given by the formula $v^2 = u^2 + 2as$. Find the value of v when $u = 11$, $a = 5$ and $s = 6$.

9. The time period T of a simple pendulum is given by the formula $T = 2\pi\sqrt{\left(\frac{\ell}{g}\right)}$, where ℓ is the length of the pendulum and g is the gravitational acceleration. Find T when $\ell = 0{\cdot}65$, $g = 9{\cdot}81$ and $\pi = 3{\cdot}142$.

10. The sum S of the squares of the integers from 1 to n is given by $S = \frac{1}{6}n(n+1)(2n+1)$. Find S when $n = 12$.

If $x = 3$, $y = -4$, work out the following.

(a) $2x + y$
$= 6 + -4$
$= 6 - 4$
$= 2$

(b) $xy - y$
$= -12 - -4$
$= -12 + 4$
$= -8$

(c) $5 + x + 3y$
$= 5 + 3 + -12$
$= 8 - 12$
$= -4$

Do some of the working in your head.

Exercise 2

If $a = -4$, $b = 5$, $c = -2$, work out:

1. $2a + 3$ **2.** $3b - 7$ **3.** $4a - 1$ **4.** $2b + c$ **5.** $5c - 2a$
6. $6a - 3$ **7.** $2c + b$ **8.** $3a - 2b$ **9.** $6c - 2b$ **10.** $3c + 4a$
11. $3c - 4$ **12.** $2a - 3c$ **13.** $7b + 3a$ **14.** $8a + 6c$ **15.** $2b - 4a$
16. $4b + 5$ **17.** $3a + 8$ **18.** $2c - a$ **19.** $5a - 2c$ **20.** $3b + 7$

If $n = 3$, $x = -1$, $y = 6$, work out:

21. $2x - 3$ **22.** $3y + 4n$ **23.** $5n + 2x$ **24.** $4y - x$ **25.** $7y - 2$
26. $3x + 2n$ **27.** $10x + 5$ **28.** $6x - y$ **29.** $4x - 5y$ **30.** $2y - 10$
31. $8n - 2y$ **32.** $7n + 3y$ **33.** $6y + 4$ **34.** $4n + 5x$ **35.** $2n + 3x$
36. $5y - 20$ **37.** $9y - n$ **38.** $8x + 2n$ **39.** $5x + 6$ **40.** $3n - 2x$

- $a^2 = a \times a$
  $a^3 = a \times a \times a$
  $2a^2 = 2(a^2)$
  $(2a)^2 = 2a \times 2a$
  $a(b - c)$: Work out the term in brackets first.
  $\frac{a+b}{c}$: The division line works like a bracket, so work out $a + b$ first.

If $y = -3$, $x = 2$, work out (a) y^2 (b) $3x^2$

(a) $y^2 = -3 \times -3 = 9$ (b) $3x^2 = 3 \times 4 = 12$

Exercise 3

If $m = 2$, $t = -2$, $x = -3$, $y = 4$, work out:

1. m^2 **2.** t^2 **3.** x^2 **4.** y^2

5. m^3 **6.** t^3 **7.** x^3 **8.** y^3

9. $2m^2$ **10.** $(2m)^2$ **11.** $2t^2$ **12.** $(2t)^2$

13. $2x^2$ **14.** $(2x)^2$ **15.** $3y^2$ **16.** $4m^2$

17. $5t^2$ **18.** $6x^2$ **19.** $(3y)^2$ **20.** $3m^3$

21. $x^2 + 4$ **22.** $y^2 - 6$ **23.** $t^2 - 3$ **24.** $m^3 + 10$

25. $x^2 + t^2$ **26.** $2x^2 + 1$ **27.** $m^2 + xt$ **28.** my^2

29. $(mt)^2$ **30.** $(xy)^2$ **31.** $(xt)^2$ **32.** yx^2

33. $m - t$ **34.** $t - x$ **35.** $y - m$ **36.** $m - y^2$

37. $t + x$ **38.** $2m + 3x$ **39.** $3t - y$ **40.** $xt + y$

41. $3(m + t)$ **42.** $4(x + y)$ **43.** $5(m + 2y)$ **44.** $2(y - m)$

45. $m(t + x)$ **46.** $y(m + x)$ **47.** $x(y - m)$ **48.** $t(2m + y)$

49. $m^2(y - x)$ **50.** $t^2(x^2 + m)$

Exercise 4

If $w = -2$, $x = 3$, $y = 0$, $z = 2$, work out:

1. $\frac{w}{z} + x$ **2.** $\frac{w + x}{z}$ **3.** $y\left(\frac{x + z}{w}\right)$ **4.** $x^2(z + wy)$

5. $x(x + wz)$ **6.** $w^2\sqrt{(z^2 + y^2)}$ **7.** $2(w^2 + x^2 + y^2)$ **8.** $2x(w - z)$

9. $\frac{z}{w} + x$ **10.** $\frac{z + w}{x}$ **11.** $\frac{x + w}{z^2}$ **12.** $\frac{y^2 - w^2}{xz}$

13. $z^2 + 4z + 5$ **14.** $\frac{1}{w} + \frac{1}{z} + \frac{1}{x}$ **15.** $\frac{4}{z} + \frac{10}{w}$ **16.** $\frac{yz - xw}{xz - w}$

17. Find $K = \sqrt{\left(\frac{a^2 + b^2 + c^2 - 2c}{a^2 + b^2 + 4c}\right)}$ if $a = 3$, $b = -2$, $c = -1$.

18. Find $W = \frac{kmn(k + m + n)}{(k + m)(k + n)}$ if $k = \frac{1}{2}$, $m = -\frac{1}{3}$, $n = \frac{1}{4}$.

5.2 Trial and improvement

Some problems cannot be solved using linear equations. In such cases, the method of 'trial and improvement' is often a help.

Exercise 5

1. Think of a rectangle having an area of $72\,\text{cm}^2$ whose base is twice its height.

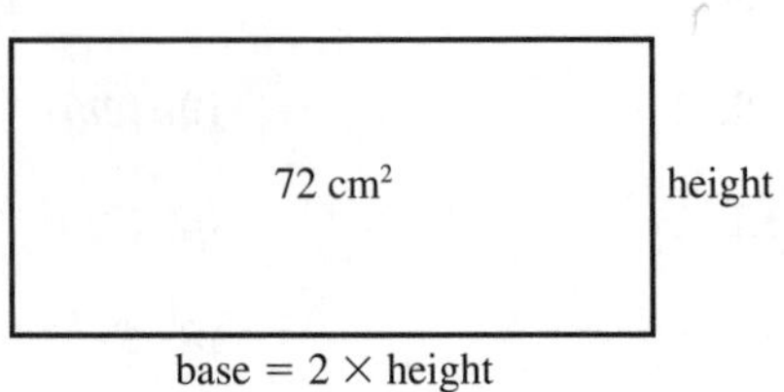

Write down the length of the base.

2. Find a rectangle of area $75\,\text{cm}^2$ so that its base is three times its height.

3. In each of the rectangles below, the base is twice the height. The area is shown inside the rectangle. Find the base and the height.

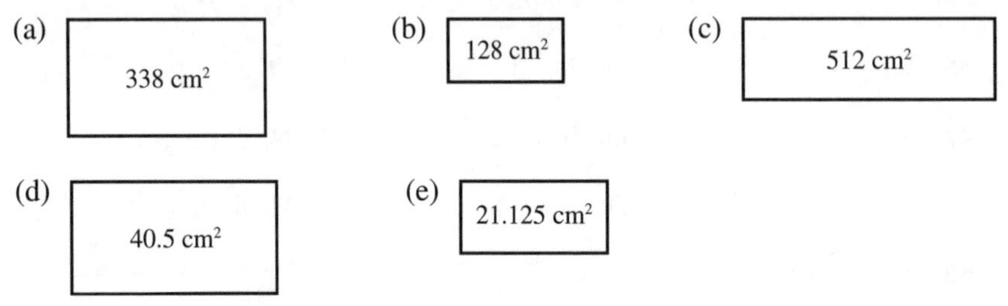

4. In this rectangle, the base is 1 cm more than the height and the area is $90\,\text{cm}^2$.

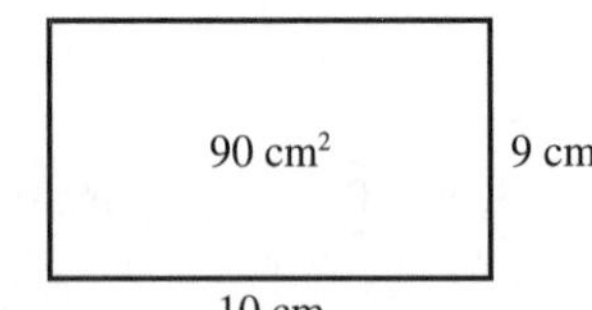

In each of the rectangles below, the base is 1 cm more than the height. Find each base and height.

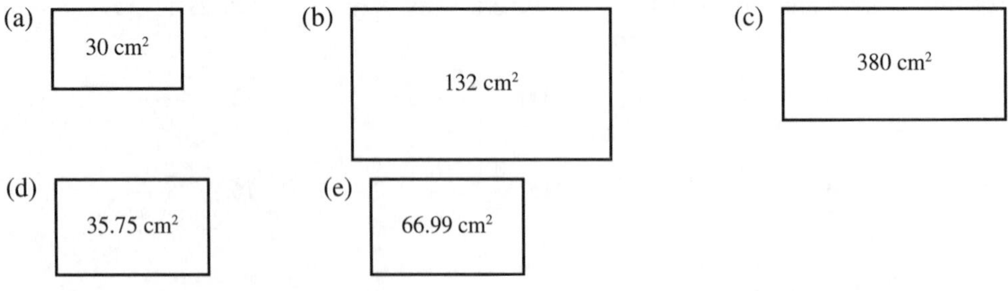

5. A problem! Once again the base of the rectangle is 1 cm more than the height. Try to find the base and the height of the rectangle.

75 cm²

Inexact answers

In some questions it is not possible ever to find an answer which is precisely correct. However, we can find answers which are nearer and nearer to the exact one, perhaps to the nearest 0·1 cm or even to the nearest 0·01 cm.

In this rectangle, the base is 1 cm more than the height h cm.
The area is $80\,\text{cm}^2$.
Find the height h, correct to 1 d.p.

80 cm² h $h + 1$

Here we are solving the equation $h(h+1) = 80$.

(a) Try different values for h. BE SYSTEMATIC.

$h = 8$:	$8(8+1)$	$= 72$	Too small
$h = 9$:	$9(9+1)$	$= 90$	Too large
$h = 8{\cdot}5$:	$8{\cdot}5(8{\cdot}5+1)$	$= 80{\cdot}75$	Too large
$h = 8{\cdot}4$:	$8{\cdot}4(8{\cdot}4+1)$	$= 78{\cdot}96$	Too small

(b) We now see that the answer is between 8·4 and 8·5. We also see that the value of $h = 8{\cdot}5$ gave the value *closest* to 80. We will take the answer as $h = 8{\cdot}5$, correct to 1 d.p.

Note: Strictly speaking, to ensure that our answer *is* correct to 1 decimal place, we should try $h = 8{\cdot}45$. This degree of complexity is unnecessary at this stage.

Solve the equation $x^3 + 2x = 90$, correct to 1 d.p.

Try $x = 4$:	$4^3 + (2 \times 4)$	$= 72$	Too small
$x = 5$:	$5^3 + (2 \times 5)$	$= 135$	Too large
$x = 4{\cdot}5$:	$4{\cdot}5^3 + (2 \times 4{\cdot}5)$	$= 100{\cdot}125$	Too large
$x = 4{\cdot}4$:	$4{\cdot}4^3 + (2 \times 4{\cdot}4)$	$= 93{\cdot}984$	Too large
$x = 4{\cdot}3$:	$4{\cdot}3^3 + (2 \times 4{\cdot}3)$	$= 88{\cdot}107$	Too small

Now 88·107 is closer to 90 than 93·984.

$\therefore$ The solution is $x = 4{\cdot}3$, correct to 1 decimal place.

Exercise 6

1. In these two rectangles, the base is 1 cm more than the height.

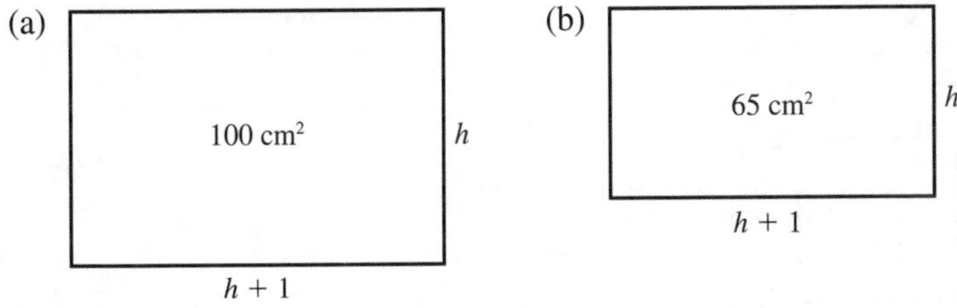

Find the value of h for each one, correct to 1 decimal place.

2. Find solutions to the following equations, giving the answer correct to 1 decimal place.

(a) $x(x-3) = 11$ (b) $x(x-2) = 7$

(c) $x^3 = 300$ (d) $x^2(x+1) = 50$

3. Here you need a calculator with a $\boxed{x^y}$ button.

Find x, correct to 1 decimal place.

(a) $x^5 = 313$ (b) $5^x = 77$ (c) $x^x = 100$

4. The number n has 2 digits after the decimal point and n to the power 10 is 2110 to the nearest whole number. Find n.

5. An engineer wants to make a solid metal cube of volume 526 cm^3. Call the edge of the cube x and write down an equation. Find x, giving your answer correct to 1 d.p.

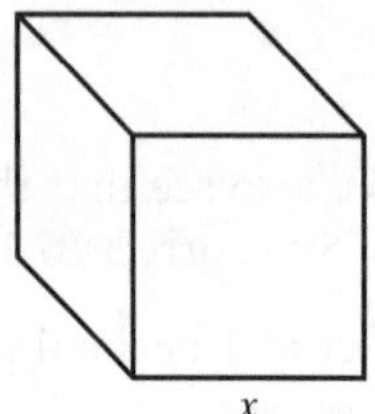

6. In this rectangle, the base is 2 cm more than the height. If the diagonal is 15 cm, find h correct to 2 d.p.

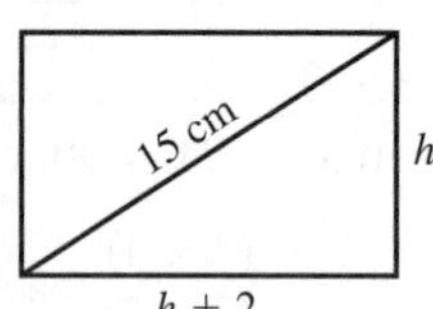

7. A designer for a supermarket chain wants to make a cardboard box of depth 6 cm. He has to make the length of the box 10 cm more than the width.

(a) What is the length of the box in terms of x? The box is designed so that its volume is to be 9000 cm^3.

(b) Form an equation involving x.

(c) Solve the equation and hence give the dimensions of the box to the nearest cm.

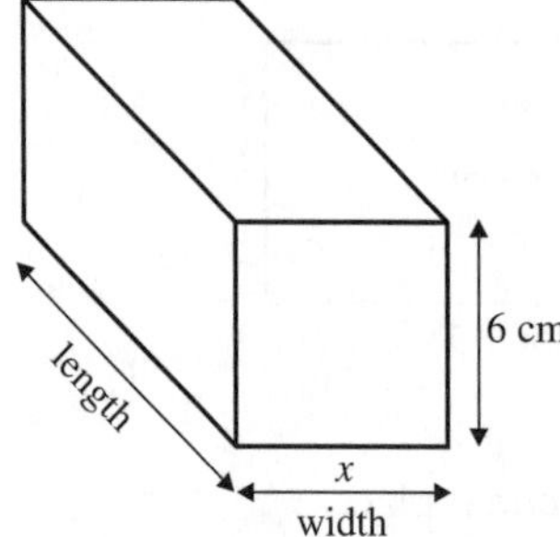

(b) Elimination method

Use this method when the first method is unsuitable (some prefer to use it for every question).

$$
\begin{array}{lrcll}
 & 2x + 3y & = & 5 & \ldots [1] \\
 & 5x - 2y & = & -16 & \ldots [2] \\
[1] \times 5 & 10x + 15y & = & 25 & \ldots [3] \\
[2] \times 2 & 10x - 4y & = & -32 & \ldots [4] \\
[3] - [4] & 15y - (-4y) & = & 25 - (-32) & \\
 & 19y & = & 57 & \\
 & y & = & 3 & \\
\text{Substitute in } [1] & 2x + 3 \times 3 & = & 5 & \\
 & 2x & = & 5 - 9 = -4 & \\
 & x & = & -2 &
\end{array}
$$

The solutions are $x = -2$, $y = 3$.

Exercise 9

Use the elimination method to solve the following.

1. $2x + 5y = 24$
$4x + 3y = 20$

2. $5x + 2y = 13$
$2x + 6y = 26$

3. $3x + y = 11$
$9x + 2y = 28$

4. $x + 2y = 17$
$8x + 3y = 45$

5. $3x + 2y = 19$
$x + 8y = 21$

6. $2a + 3b = 9$
$4a + b = 13$

7. $2x + 3y = 11$
$3x + 4y = 15$

8. $3x + 8y = 27$
$4x + 3y = 13$

9. $2x + 7y = 17$
$5x + 3y = -1$

10. $5x + 3y = 23$
$2x + 4y = 12$

11. $7x + 5y = 32$
$3x + 4y = 23$

12. $3x + 2y = 4$
$4x + 5y = 10$

13. $3x + 2y = 11$
$2x - y = -3$

14. $3x + 2y = 7$
$2x - 3y = -4$

15. $x - 2y = -4$
$3x + y = 9$

16. $5x - 7y = 27$
$3x - 4y = 16$

17. $3x - 2y = 7$
$4x + y = 13$

18. $x - y = -1$
$2x - y = 0$

19. $y - x = -1$
$3x - y = 5$

20. $x - 3y = -5$
$2y + 3x + 4 = 0$

Problems solved by simultaneous equations

Exercise 10

Solve each problem by forming a pair of simultaneous equations.

1. Find two numbers with a sum of 15 and a difference of 4. [Let the numbers be x and y.]

2. Twice one number added to three times another gives 21. Find the numbers, if the difference between them is 3.

3. The average of two numbers is 7, and three times the difference between them is 18. Find the numbers.

4. Here is a puzzle from a newspaper. The ? and * stand for numbers which are to be found. The totals for the rows and columns are given.

Write down two equations involving ? and * and solve them to find the values of ? and *.

?	*	?	*	36
?	*	*	?	36
*	?	*	*	33
?	*	?	*	36
39	33	36	33	

5. The line, with equation $y + ax = c$ passes through the points (1, 5) and (3, 1). Find a and c.
Hint: For the point (1, 5) put $x = 1$ and $y = 5$ into $y + ax = c$, etc.

6. The line $y = mx + c$ passes through (2, 5) and (4, 13).
Find m and c.

7. A stone is thrown into the air and its height, h metres above the ground, is given by the equation

$$h = at - bt^2.$$

From an experiment we know that $h = 40$ when $t = 2$ and that $h = 45$ when $t = 3$.
Show that $a - 2b = 20$
and $a - 3b = 15$.
Solve these equations to find a and b.

8. A television addict can buy either two televisions and three video-recorders for £1750 or four televisions and one video-recorder for £1250. Find the cost of one of each.

9. A pigeon can lay either white or brown eggs. Three white eggs and two brown eggs weigh 13 ounces, while five white eggs and four brown eggs weigh 24 ounces. Find the weight of a brown egg, b, and of a white egg, w.

10. A bag contains forty coins, all of them either 2p or 5p coins. Let there be x 2p coins and y 5p coins. If the value of the money in the bag is £1·55, find the number of each kind.

11. A slot machine takes only 10p and 50p coins and contains a total of twenty-one coins altogether. If the value of the coins is £4·90, find the number of coins of each value.

12. A turbo-charged tortoise makes a journey in two parts; it can either walk at 2 m/s or crawl at 1 m/s.

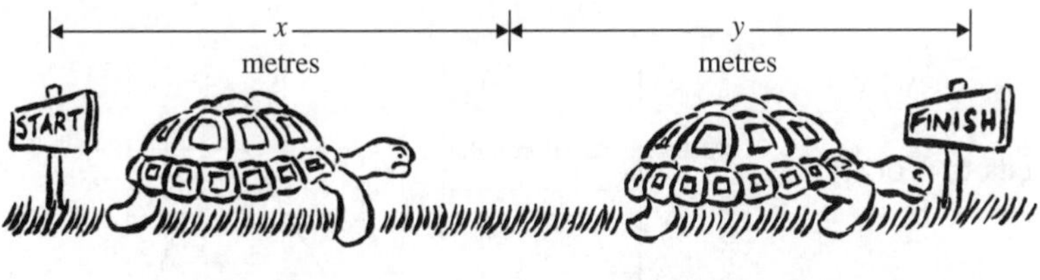

If the tortoise walks the first part and crawls the second, the journey takes 110 seconds.
If it crawls the first part and walks the second, the journey takes 100 seconds.
Let x metres be the length of the first part and y metres be the length of the second part.
Write down two simultaneous equations and solve them to find the lengths of the two parts of the journey.
[Use the formula Time = Distance ÷ Speed.]

13. The diagram shows segments of three straight lines.

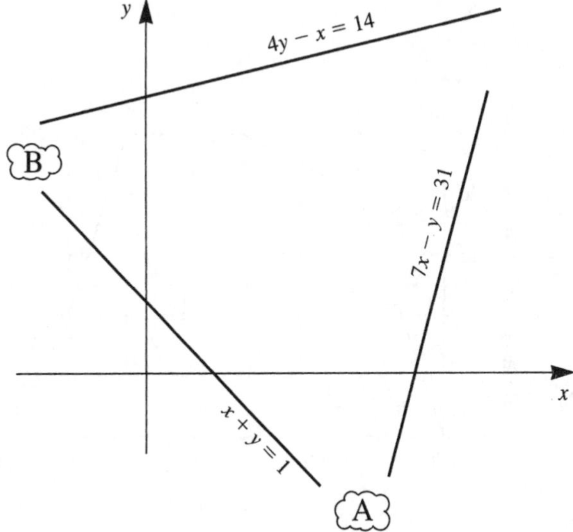

Find the coordinates of the points A and B where the lines cross.

14. The wage bill for five men and six women workers is £670, while the bill for eight men and three women is £610. Find the wage for a man and for a woman.

15. A kipper can swim at 14 m/s with the current and at 6 m/s against it. Find the speed of the current, c, and the speed of the kipper, k, in still water.

5.4 Interpreting graphs

Travel graphs

Exercise 11

1. The graph shows a return journey by car from Leeds to Scarborough.

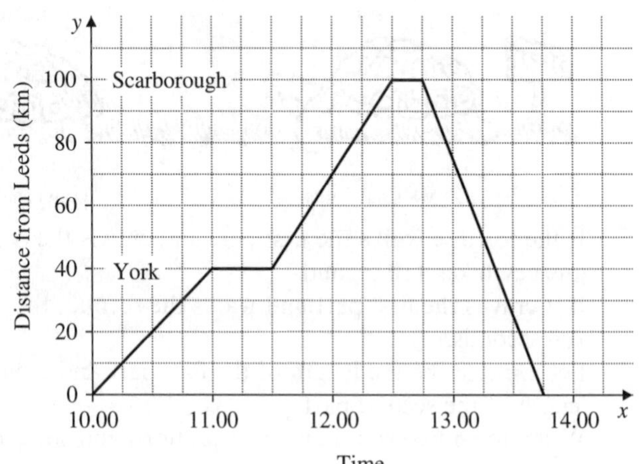

(a) How far is it from Leeds to York?
(b) How far is it from York to Scarborough?
(c) At which two places does the car stop?
(d) How long does the car stop at Scarborough?
(e) When does the car
  (i) arrive in York
  (ii) arrive back in Leeds?
(f) What is the speed of the car
  (i) from Leeds to York
  (ii) from York to Scarborough
  (iii) from Scarborough to Leeds?

2. Steve cycles to a friend's house but on the way his bike gets a puncture, and he has to walk the remaining distance. At his friend's house, he repairs the puncture, has a game of snooker and then returns home. On the way back, he stops at a shop to buy a book on how to play snooker.

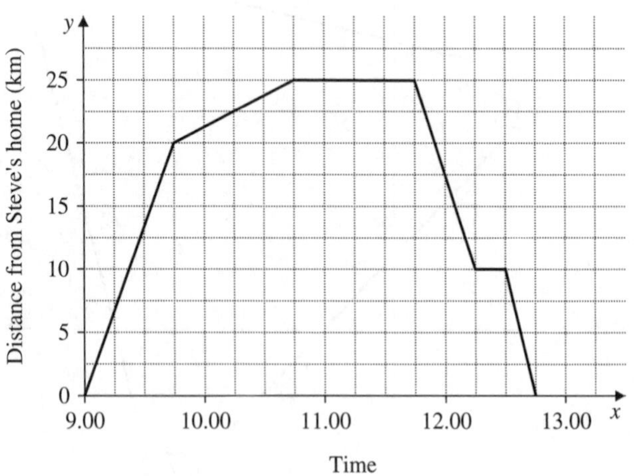

(a) How far is it to his friend's house?
(b) How far is it from his friend's house to the shop?
(c) At what time did his bike get a puncture?
(d) How long did he stay at his friend's house?
(e) At what speed did he travel
  (i) from home until he had the puncture
  (ii) after the puncture to his friend's house
  (iii) from his friend's house to the shop
  (iv) from the shop back to his own home?

3. Mr Berol and Mr Hale use the same road to travel between Aston and Borton.

(a) At what time did
   (i) Mr Berol arrive in Borton
   (ii) Mr Hale leave Aston?

(b) (i) When did Mr Berol and Mr Hale pass each other?
   (ii) In which direction was Mr Berol travelling?

(c) Find the following speeds:
   (i) Mr Hale from Aston to Stanley
   (ii) Mr Berol from Aston to Borton
   (iii) Mr Hale from Stanley to Borton
   (iv) Mr Berol from Borton back to Aston.

(d) (More difficult) When did Mr Hale arrive in Borton?

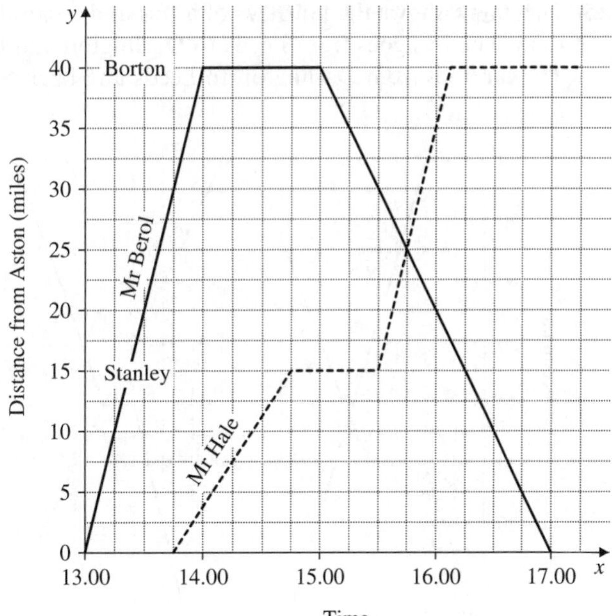

4. The graph shows the journeys made by a van and a car starting at York, travelling to Durham and returning to York.

(a) For how long was the van stationary during the journey?

(b) At what time did the car first overtake the van?

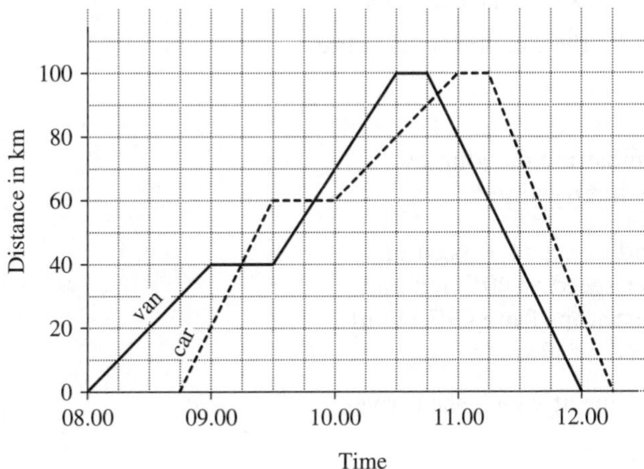

(c) At what speed was the van travelling between 09.30 and 10.00?

(d) What was the greatest speed attained by the car during the entire journey?

(e) What was the average speed of the car over its entire journey? [Average speed = (Distance travelled) ÷ (Total time taken).]

5. The graph shows the journeys of a bus and a car along the same road. The bus goes from Leeds to Darlington and back to Leeds. The car goes from Darlington to Leeds and back to Darlington.

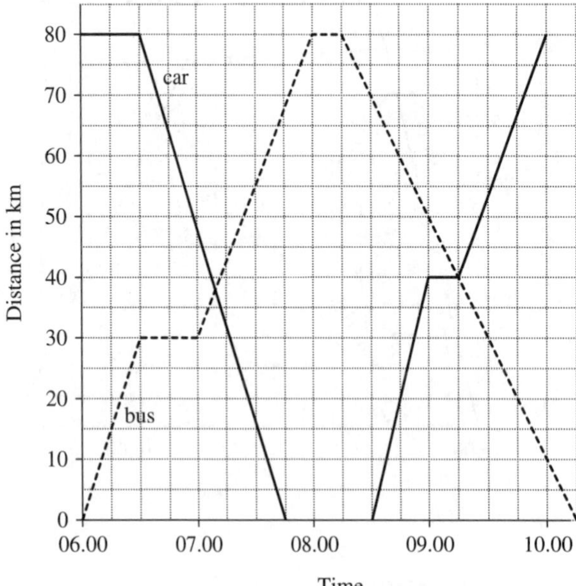

(a) When did the bus and the car meet for the second time?

(b) At what speed did the car travel from Darlington to Leeds?

(c) What was the average speed of the bus over its entire journey?

(d) Approximately how far apart were the bus and the car at 09.45?

(e) What was the greatest speed attained by the car during its entire journey?

In Questions **6, 7, 8,** draw a travel graph to illustrate the journey described. Draw axes with the same scales as in Question **5**.

6. (a) Mrs Chuong leaves home at 08.00 and drives at a speed of 50 km/h. After $\frac{1}{2}$ hour she reduces her speed to 40 km/h and continues at this speed until 09.30. She stops from 09.30 until 10.00 and then returns home at a speed of 60 km/h.

(b) Use a graph to find the approximate time at which she arrives home.

7. (a) Mr Coe leaves home at 09.00 and drives at a speed of 20 km/h. After $\frac{3}{4}$ hour he increases his speed to 45 km/h and continues at this speed until 10.45. He stops from 10.45 until 11.30 and then returns home at a speed of 50 km/h.

(b) Use the graph to find the approximate time at which he arrives home.

8. (a) At 10.00 Akram leaves home and cycles to his grandparents' house which is 70 km away. He cycles at a speed of 20 km/h until 11.15, at which time he stops for $\frac{1}{2}$ hour. He then completes the journey at a speed of 30 km/h. At 11.45 Akram's sister, Hameeda, leaves home and drives her car at 60 km/h. Hameeda also goes to her grandparents' house and uses the same road as Akram.

(b) At approximately what time does Hameeda overtake Akram?

Real life graphs

Exercise 12

1. The graph converts pounds into euros €.

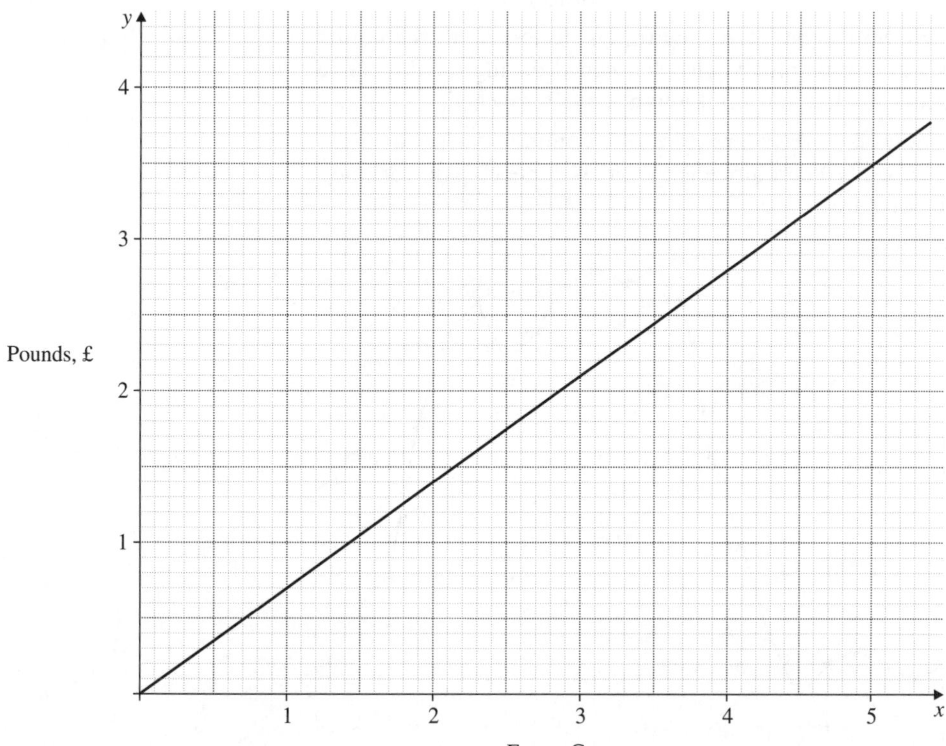

(a) Convert into pounds.
 (i) €4 (ii) €3·30

(b) Convert into euros.
 (i) £3 (ii) £1·40

(c) Henri, the highway robber, held up the Paris–Berlin stagecoach and got away with €50 000.
How much was that in pounds?

2. The graph shows the number of pupils on the premises of a school one day.

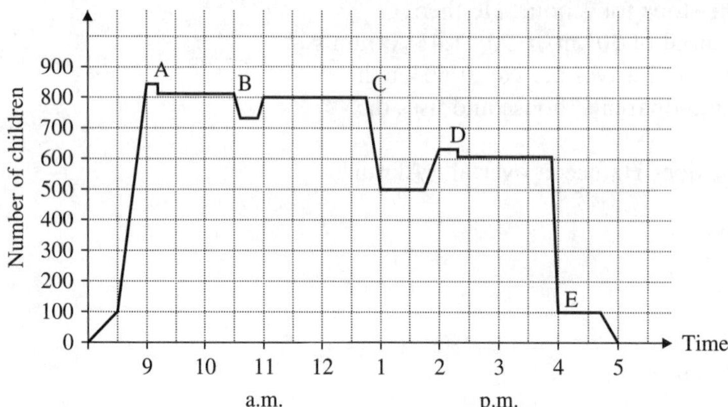

The graph tells you some interesting things. Referring to the points A, B, C, D, E, describe briefly what happened during the day. Give an explanation of what you think might have happened.

3. The graph shows how the share price of a company varied over a period of weeks. The share price is the price in pence paid for one share in the company.

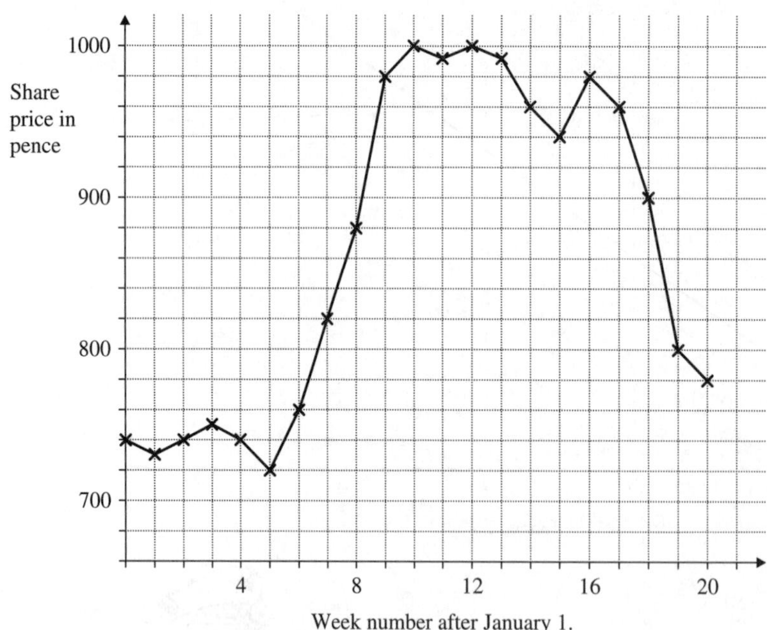

(a) What was the share price in Week 4?

(b) Naomi bought 200 shares in Week 6 and sold them all in week 18. How much profit did she make?

(c) Mr Gibson can buy (and then sell) 5000 shares. He consults a very accurate fortune teller who can predict the share price over coming weeks. What is the maximum profit he could make by buying and then selling shares?

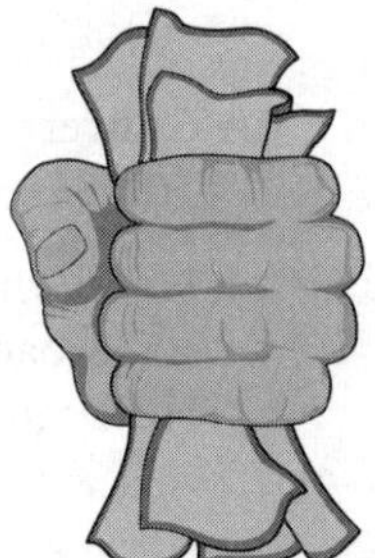

4. When listening to the weather forecast, you may have heard the expression 'wind chill'. Wind chill is a measure of how cold it will feel for a given air temperature and wind speed.

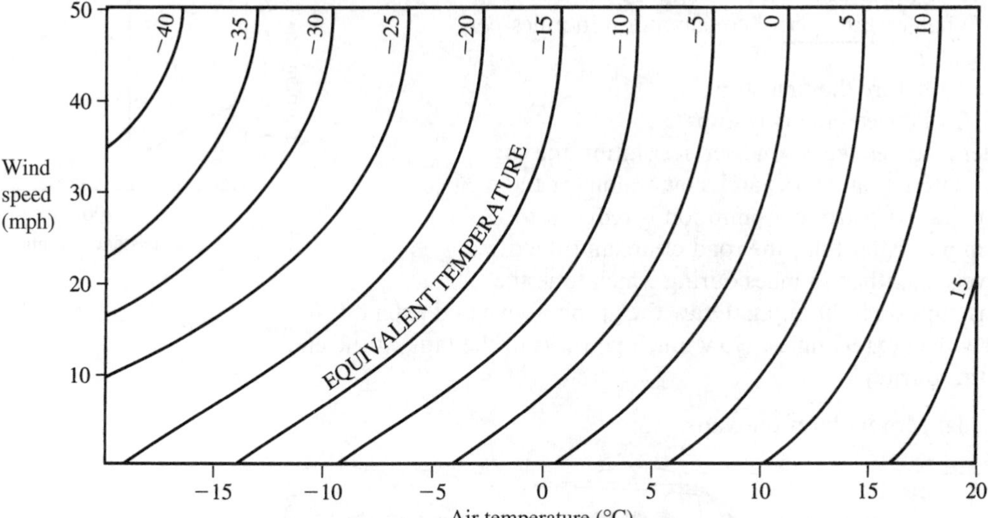

From the table, if the wind speed is 20 mph and the air temperature is 15 °C it will 'feel' like 10 °C. We call 10 °C the equivalent temperature or wind chill. The wind chill lines are drawn every 5° so you will have to estimate some answers.

(a) Find the wind chill if the wind speed is 40 mph and the air temperature is 14 °C.

(b) Find the wind chill if the wind speed is 18 mph and the air temperature is 0 °C.

(c) One day the wind chill was −15 °C and the wind speed was 40 mph. What was the air temperature?

(d) Does it feel colder when the air temperature is 0 °C and the wind speed is 30 mph, or when it is 5° below zero and the wind speed is 20 mph?

(e) Forecasters use the following terms as a guide to describe wind chills:

0° →	5 °C	Very Cool
−10° →	0 °C	Cold
−15° →	−10 °C	Very Cold
−25° →	−15 °C	Bitterly Cold
below −25 °C		Freezing cold (exposed flesh freezes).

(i) How would the forecaster describe the weather when the air temperature is −10 °C and the wind speed is 20 mph?

(ii) Would you go skiing if the air temperature was −8 °C and the wind speed was 35 mph?

5. A car travels along a motorway and the amount of petrol in its tank is monitored as shown on the graph.
   (a) How much petrol was bought at the first stop?
   (b) What was the petrol consumption in miles per gallon:
      (i) before the first stop
      (ii) between the two stops?

   After it leaves the second service station the car encounters road works and slow traffic for the next 20 miles. Its petrol consumption is reduced to 20 m.p.g. After that, the road clears and the car travels a further 75 miles during which time the consumption is 30 m.p.g. Draw the graph above and extend it to show the next 95 miles. How much petrol is in the tank at the end of the journey?

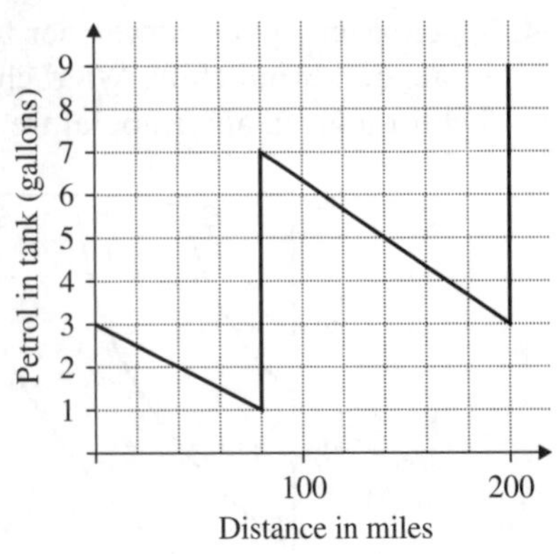

6. Kendal Motors hires out vans.

   Copy and complete the table where x is the number of miles travelled and C is the total cost in pounds.

x	0	50	100	150	200	250	300
C	35			65			95

   Draw a graph of C against x, using scales of 2 cm for 50 miles on the x-axis and 1 cm for £10 on the C-axis.
   Use the graph to find the number of miles travelled when the total cost was £71.

7. Jeff sets up his own business as a plumber.

24hr PLUMBING
0707 874561
call out 18
plus 15 per hour
NO VAT!

   Copy and complete the table where C stands for his total charge and h stands for the number of hours he works.
   Draw a graph with h across the page and C up the page.
   Use scales of 2 cm to 1 hour for h and 2 cm to £10 for C.
   Use your graph to find how long he worked if his charge was £55·50.

h	0	1	2	3
C		33		

Sketch graphs

Exercise 13

1. Which of the graphs A to D below best fits the following statement: 'Unemployment is still rising but by less each month.'

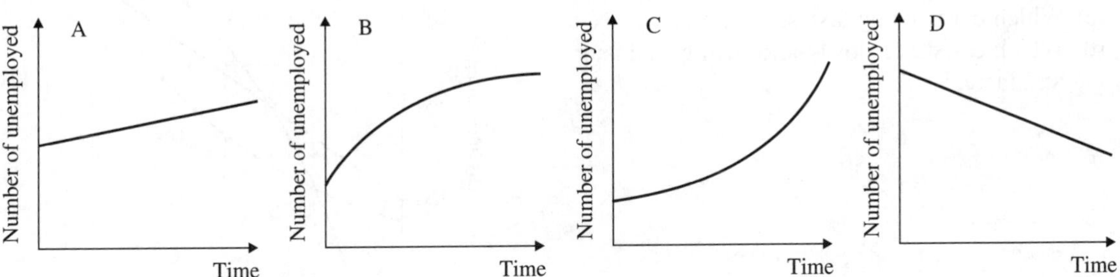

2. Which of the graphs A to D best fits the following statement: 'The price of oil was rising more rapidly in 1999 than at any time in the previous ten years.'

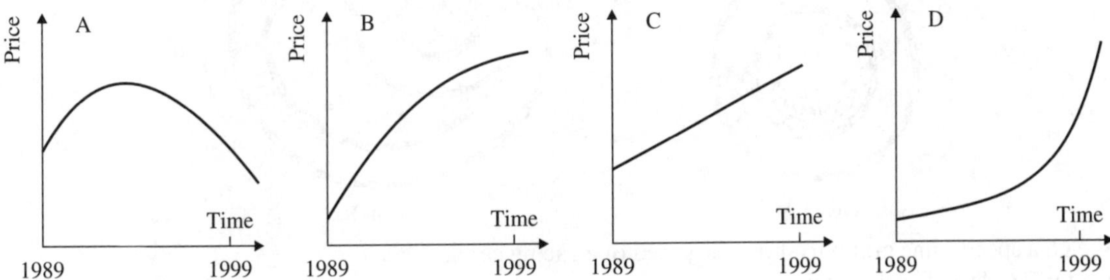

3. Which of the graphs A to D below best fits each of the following statements:
   (a) The birthrate was falling but is now steady.
   (b) Unemployment, which rose slowly until 1999, is now rising rapidly.
   (c) Inflation, which has been rising steadily, is now beginning to fall.
   (d) The price of gold has fallen steadily over the last year.

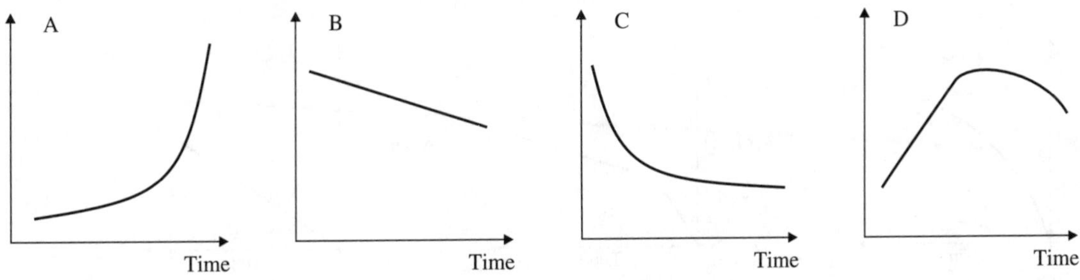

4. The graph shows the motion of three cars A, B and C along the same road.
Answer the following questions giving estimates where necessary.
(a) Which car is in front after
(i) 10 s (ii) 20 s?
(b) When is B in the front?
(c) Which car is going fastest after 5 s?
(d) Which car starts slowly and then goes faster and faster?

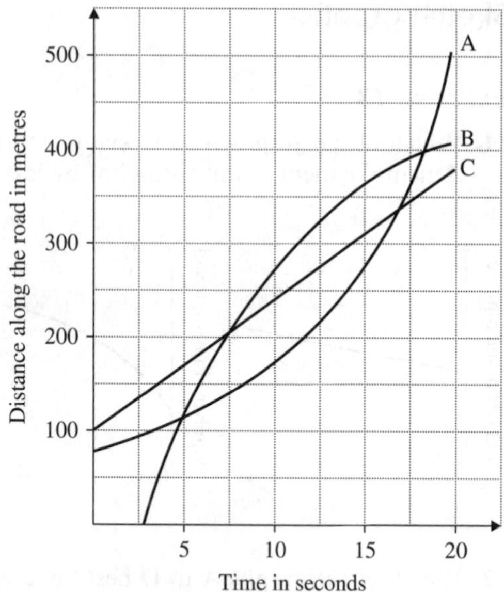

5. Here are two car racing circuits.

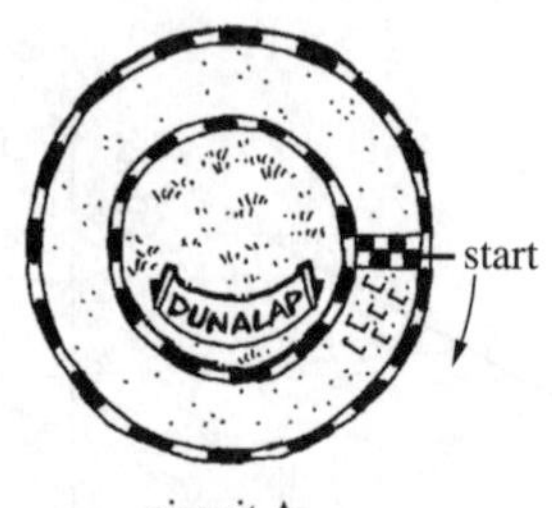

circuit A

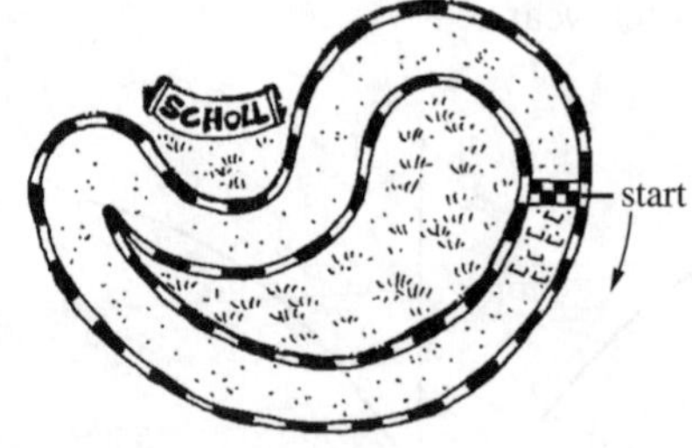

circuit B

Sketch a speed–time graph to show the speed of a racing car as it goes around one lap of each circuit.
[Not the first lap. Why?]

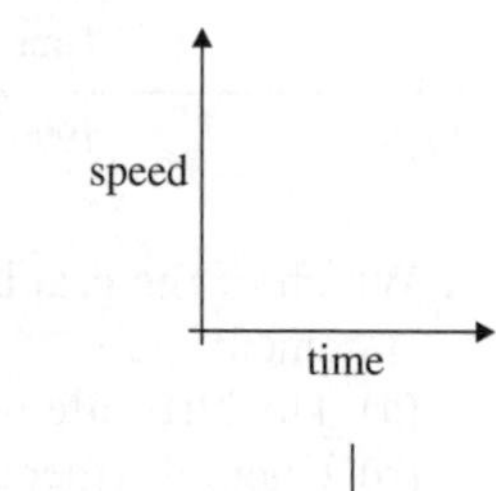

6. Water is poured at a constant rate into each of the containers A, B and C.
The graphs X, Y and Z show how the water level rises.
Decide which graph fits each container.

A 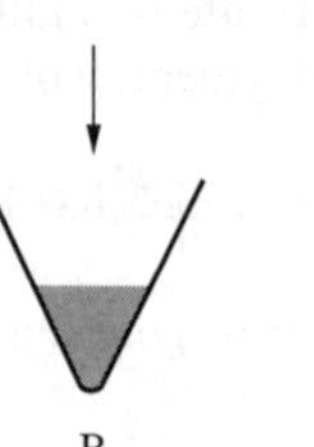 B 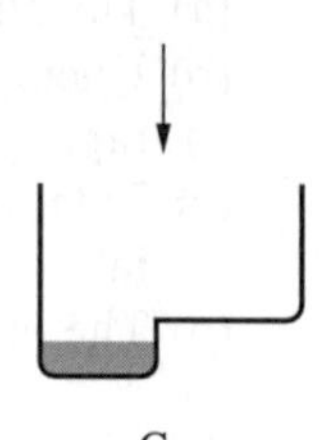 C

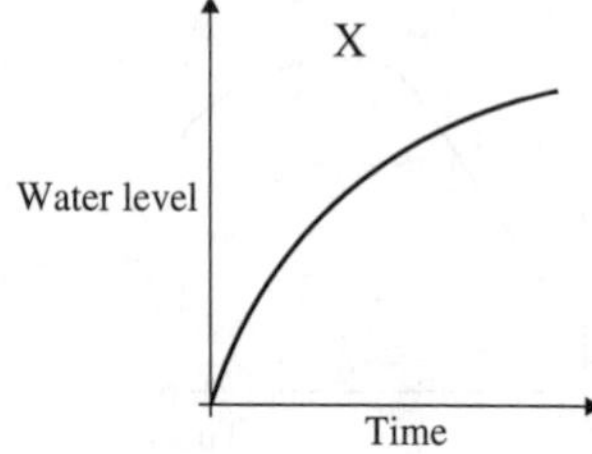

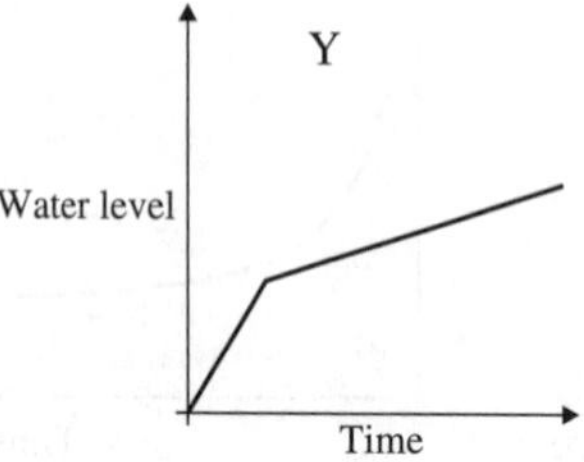

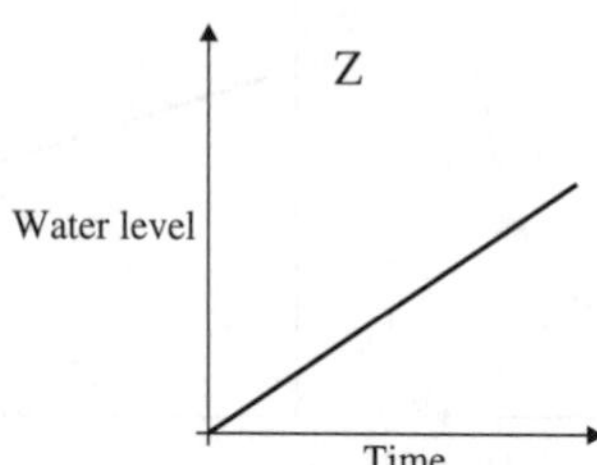

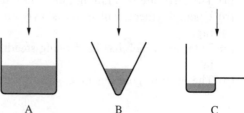

6 Shape and Space 2

6.1 Transforming shapes

Reflection

- With reflection the object and its image are *congruent* because they are the same size and shape.

(a) A′B′C′D′ is the image of ABCD after reflection in the broken line (the mirror line).

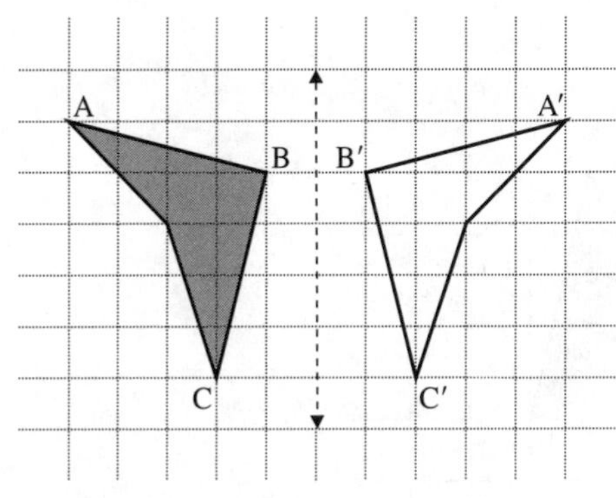

(b) △2 is the image of △1 after reflection in the diagonal mirror line.

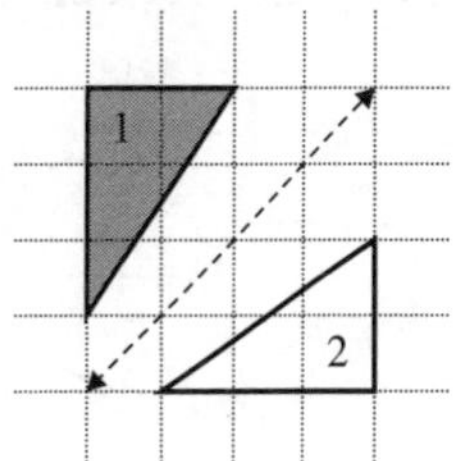

Exercise 1

On squared paper draw the object and its image after reflection in the broken line.

1.

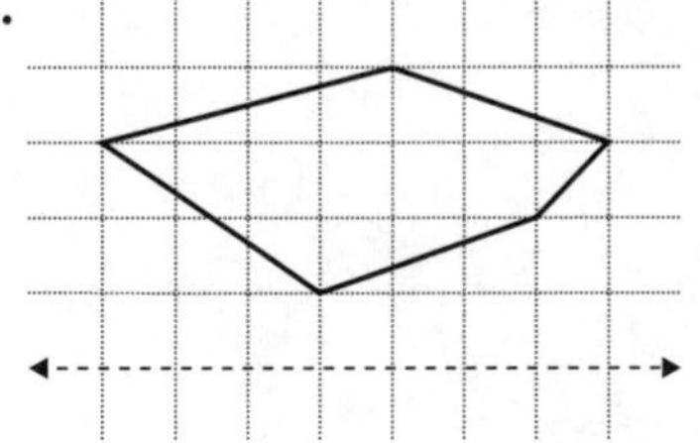

2.

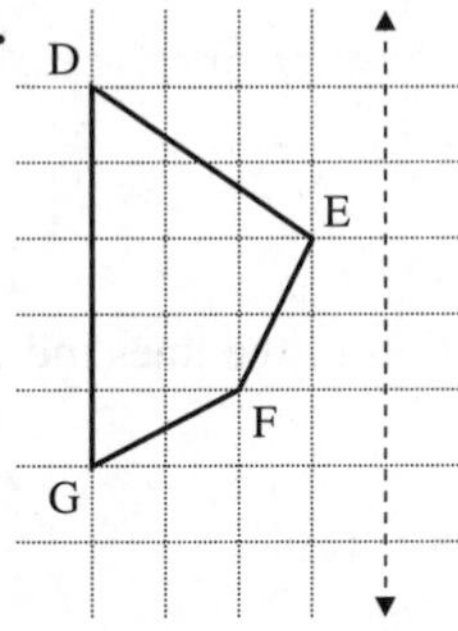

3.

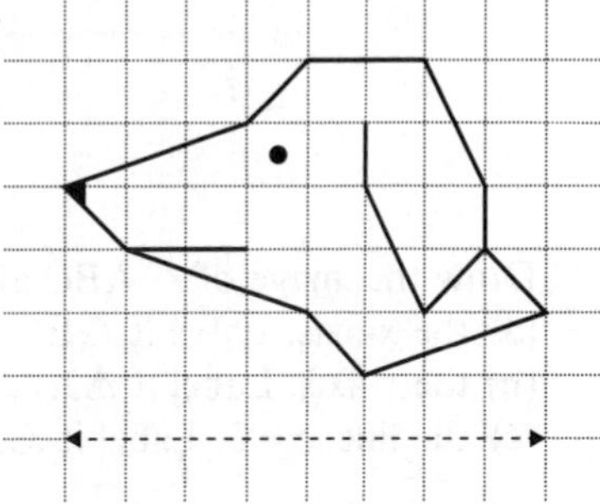

4.

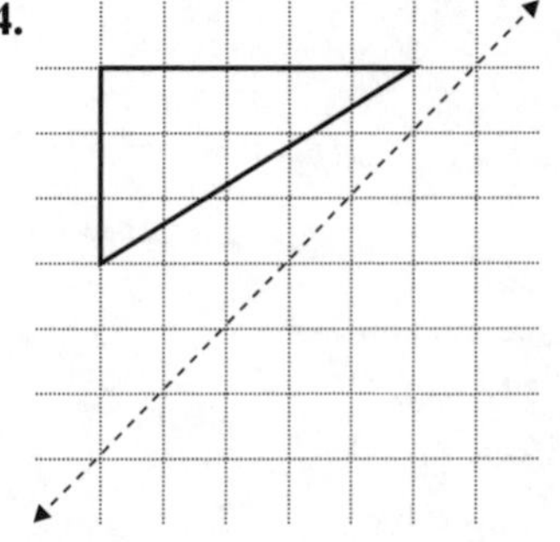

5.

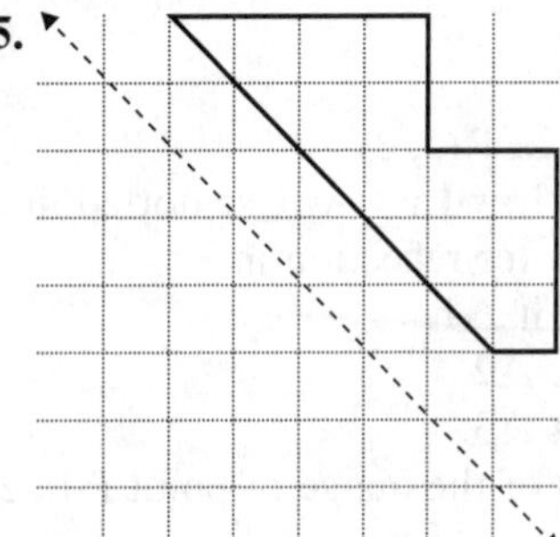

6.

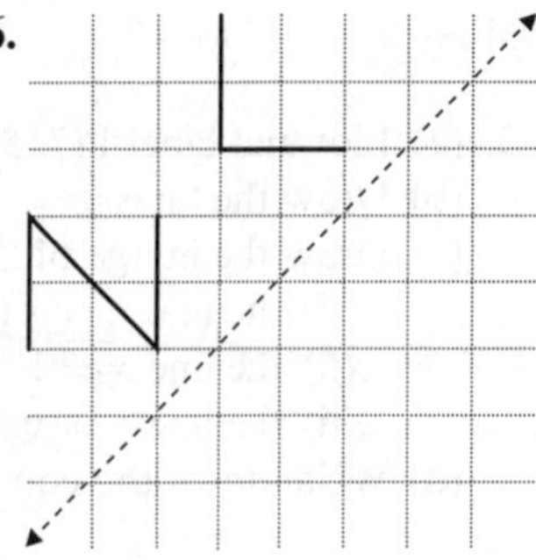

7. (a) Reflect $\triangle 1$ in the line AB.
   Label the image $\triangle 2$.
   (b) Reflect $\triangle 2$ in the line CD.
   Label the image $\triangle 3$.

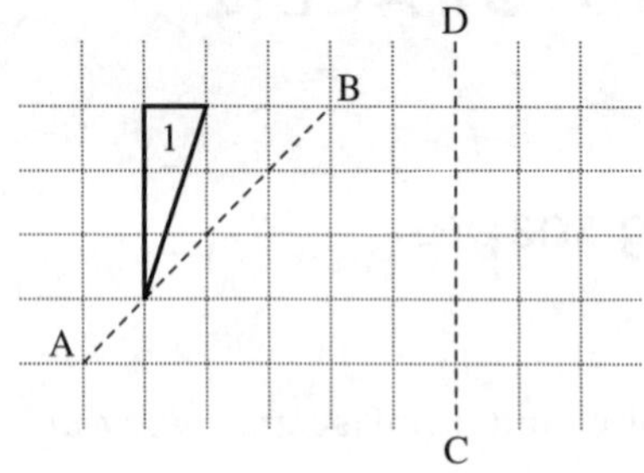

Exercise 2

1. Copy the diagram below.

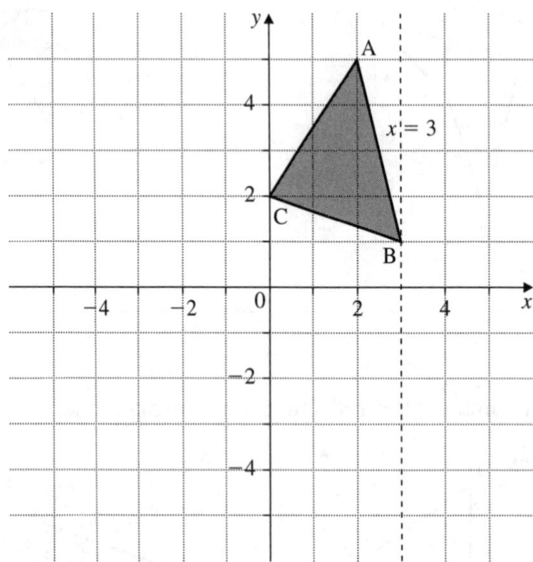

Draw the image of $\triangle$ ABC after reflection in the lines indicated.
(a) the x-axis. Label it $\triangle 1$.
(b) the y-axis. Label it $\triangle 2$.
(c) the line $x = 3$. Label it $\triangle 3$.

For Questions **2** to **5** draw a pair of axes so that both x and y can take values from -7 to $+7$.

2. (a) Plot and label P(7, 5), Q(7, 2), R(5, 2).
   (b) Draw the lines $y = -1$, $x = 1$ and $y = x$. Use dotted lines.
   (c) Draw the image of $\triangle$PQR after reflection in:
      (i) the line $y = -1$. Label it $\triangle 1$.
      (ii) the line $x = 1$. Label it $\triangle 2$.
      (iii) the line $y = x$. Label it $\triangle 3$.
   (d) Write down the coordinates of the image of point P in each case.

3. (a) Plot and label L(7, −5), M(7, −1), N(5, −1).
   (b) Draw the lines $y = x$ and $y = -x$. Use dotted lines.
   (c) Draw the image of △LMN after reflection in:
      (i) the x-axis. Label it △1.
      (ii) the line $y = x$. Label it △2.
      (iii) the line $y = -x$. Label it △3.
   (d) Write down the coordinates of the image of point L in each case.

4. (a) Draw the line $x + y = 7$. [It passes through (0, 7) and (7, 0).]
   (b) Draw △1 at (−3, −1), (−1, −1), (−1, −4).
   (c) Reflect △1 in the y-axis on to △2.
   (d) Reflect △2 in the x-axis on to △3.
   (e) Reflect △3 in the line $x + y = 7$ on to △4.
   (f) Reflect △4 in the y-axis on to △5.
   (g) Write down the coordinates of △5.

5. (a) Draw the lines $y = 2$, $x = -1$ and $y = x$.
   (b) Draw △1 at (1, −3), (−3, −3), (−3, −5).
   (c) Reflect △1 in the line $y = x$ on to △2.
   (d) Reflect △2 in the line $y = 2$ on to △3.
   (e) Reflect △3 in the line $x = -1$ on to △4.
   (f) Reflect △4 in the line $y = x$ on to △5.
   (g) Write down the coordinates of △5.

6. Find the equation of the mirror line for the reflection:
   (a) △1 on to △2
   (b) △1 on to △3
   (c) △1 on to △4
   (d) △1 on to △5.

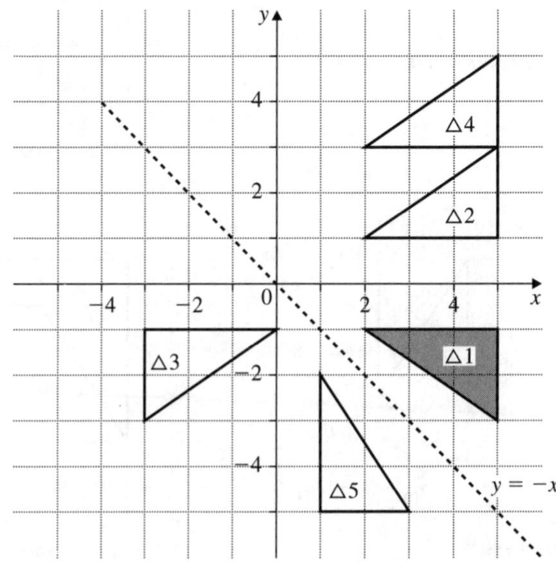

Rotation

- You need three things to describe a rotation:
  (a) the centre
  (b) the angle
  (c) the direction (e.g. clockwise).

$\triangle A'B'C'$ is the image of $\triangle ABC$ after a 90° clockwise rotation about centre O.

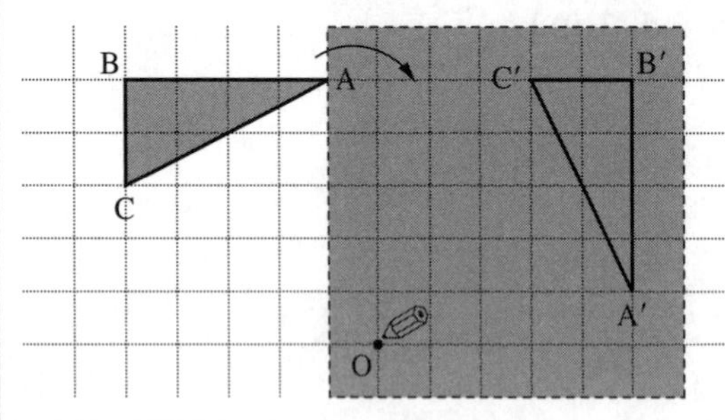

Draw $\triangle ABC$ on tracing paper and then put the tip of your pencil on O. Turn the tracing paper 90° clockwise about O. The tracing paper now shows the position of $\triangle A'B'C'$.

Exercise 3

Draw the object and its image under the rotation given. Take O as the centre of rotation in each case.

1.

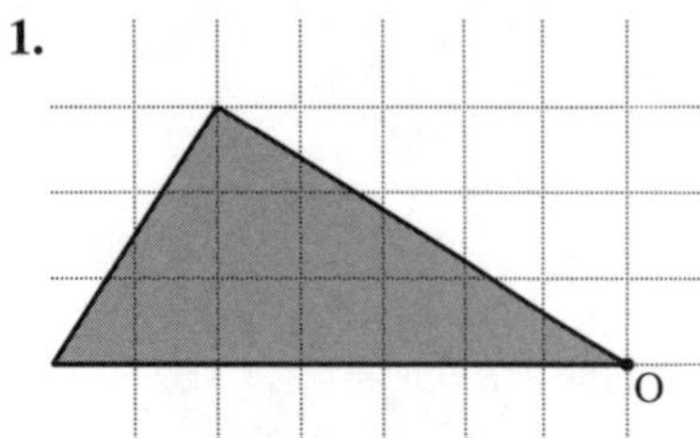

90° anticlockwise

2.

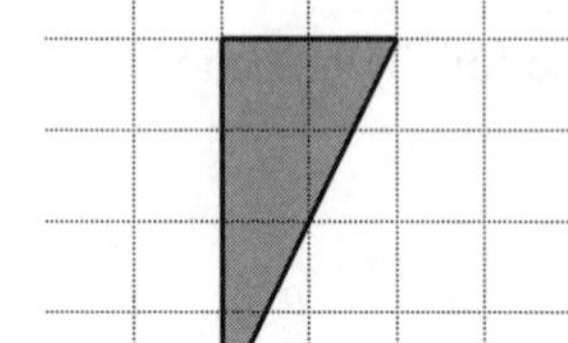

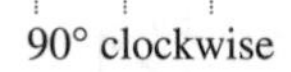

90° clockwise

3.

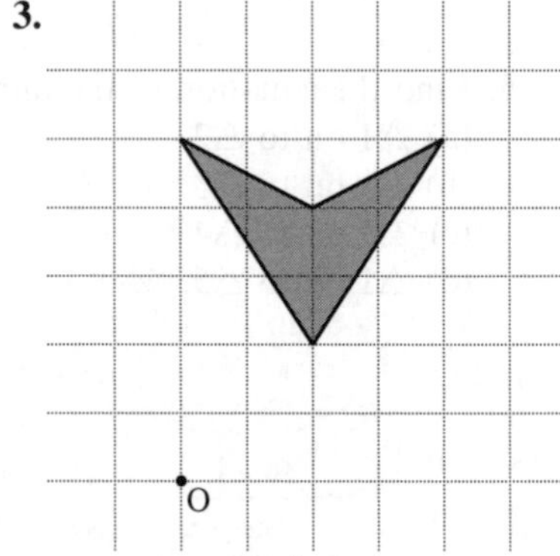

90° clockwise

4.

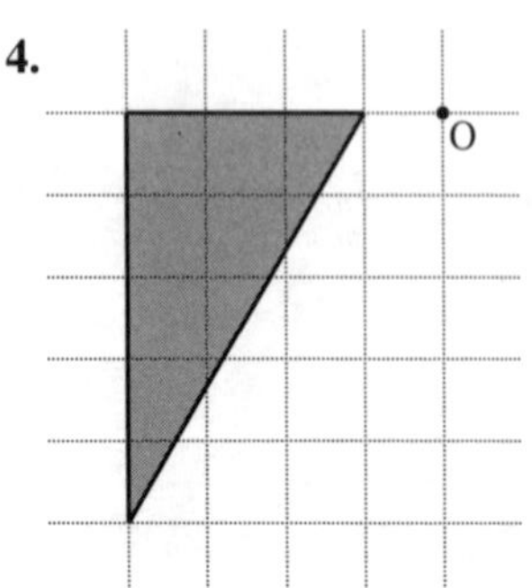

180°

5.

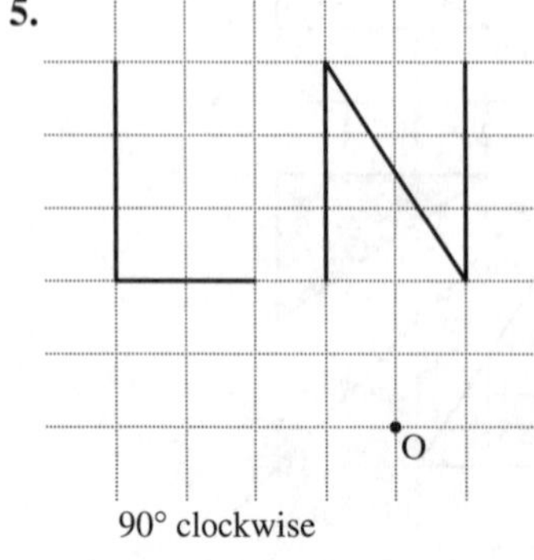

90° clockwise

6.

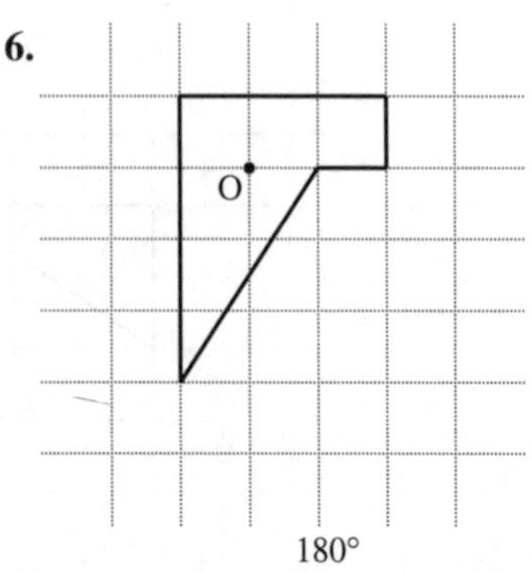

180°

7. The shape on the right has been rotated about several different centres to form the pattern below.

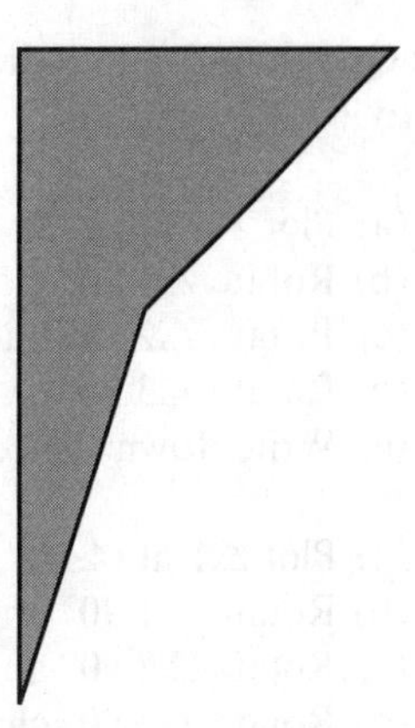

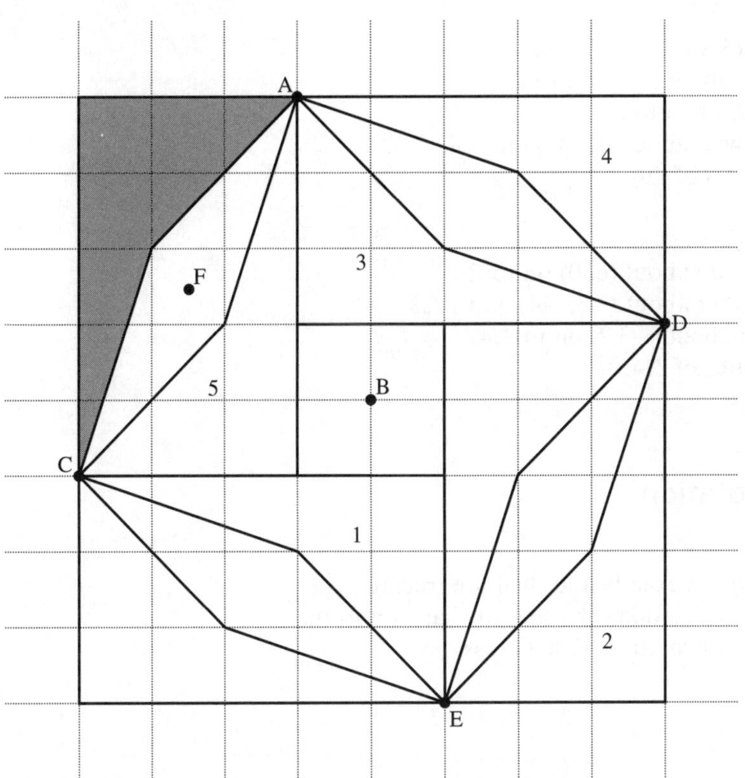

Describe the rotation which takes the shaded shape on to shape 1, shape 2, shape 3, shape 4 and shape 5.
For each one, give the centre (A, B, C, D, E or F), the angle and the direction of the rotation.
[e.g. 'centre C, 90°, clockwise']

Exercise 4

1. Copy the diagram on the right.

   (a) Rotate △ABC 90° clockwise about (0, 0). Label it △1.

   (b) Rotate △DEF 180° clockwise about (0, 0). Label it △2.

   (c) Rotate △GHI 90° clockwise about (0, 0). Label it △3.

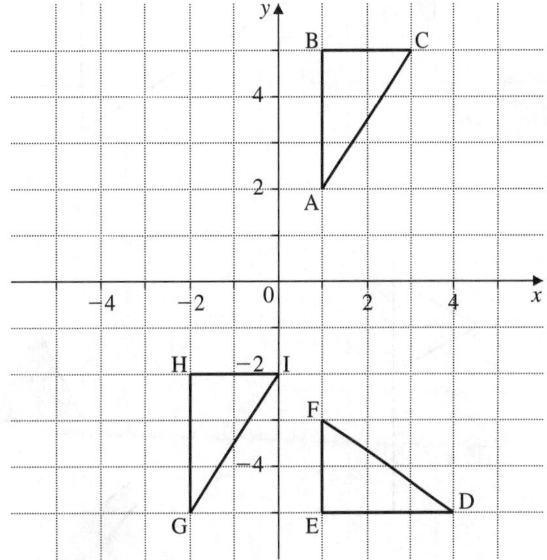

For Questions **2** and **3** draw a pair of axes with values of x and y from -7 to $+7$.

2. (a) Plot $\triangle 1$ at (2, 3), (6, 3), (3, 6).
(b) Rotate $\triangle 1$ 90° clockwise about (2, 1) on to $\triangle 2$.
(c) Rotate $\triangle 2$ 180° about (0, 0) on to $\triangle 3$.
(d) Rotate $\triangle 3$ 90° anticlockwise about (1, 1) on to $\triangle 4$.
(e) Write down the coordinates of $\triangle 4$.

3. (a) Plot $\triangle 1$ at (4, 4), (6, 6), (2, 6).
(b) Rotate $\triangle 1$ 90° anticlockwise about (6, 0) on to $\triangle 2$.
(c) Rotate $\triangle 2$ 90° anticlockwise about (−3, −4) on to $\triangle 3$.
(d) Rotate $\triangle 3$ 90° clockwise about (−3,2) on to $\triangle 4$.
(e) Write down the coordinates of $\triangle 4$.

Finding the centre of a rotation

Exercise 5

In Questions **1** to **3** copy the diagram exactly and then use tracing paper to find the centre of the rotation which takes the shaded shape on to the unshaded shape. Mark the centre of rotation with a cross.

1.

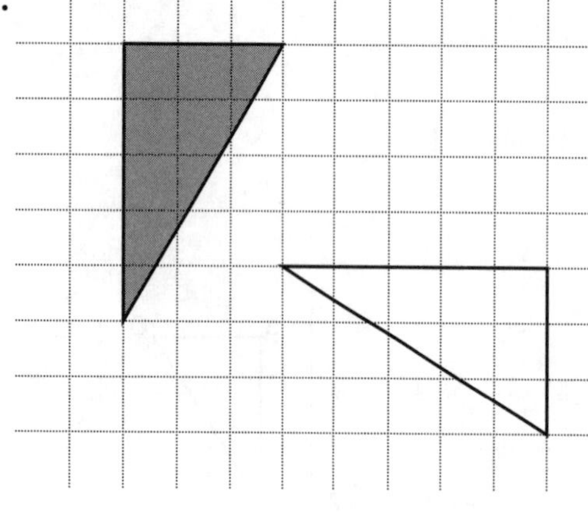

2.

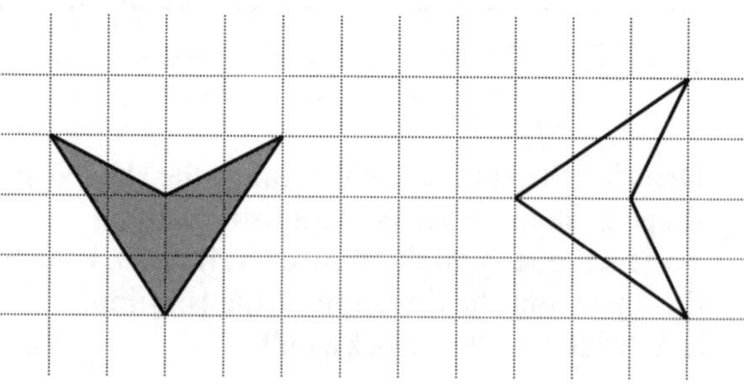

3.

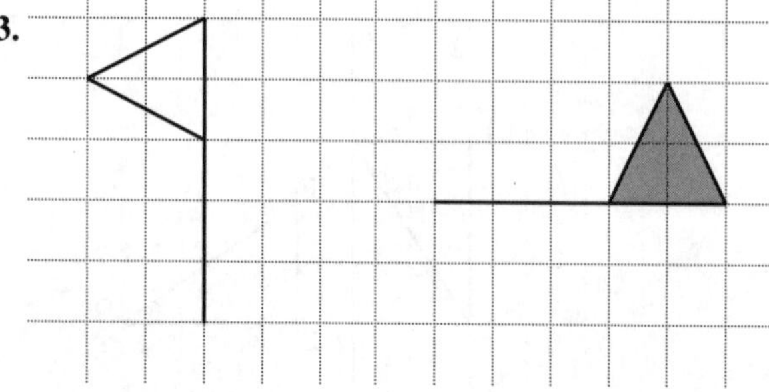

4. Copy the diagram below.

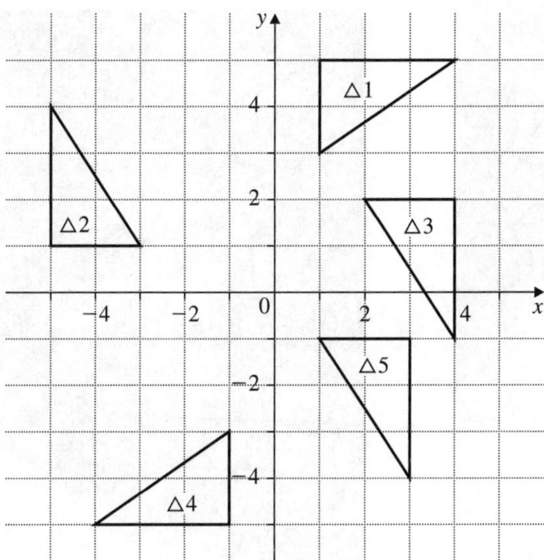

Find the coordinates of the centre of the following rotations:

(a) $\triangle 1 \to \triangle 2$ (b) $\triangle 1 \to \triangle 3$
(c) $\triangle 1 \to \triangle 4$ (d) $\triangle 1 \to \triangle 5$

For Questions **5**, **6** draw a pair of axes with values of x and y from -7 to $+7$.

5. (a) Plot and label the following triangles:
$\triangle 1$: (3, 4), (7, 4), (3, 7)
$\triangle 2$: (3, 2), (6, 2), (3, −2)
$\triangle 3$: (−7, −4), (−3, −4), (−3, −7)
$\triangle 4$: (−2, 1), (−5, 1), (−2, 5)
$\triangle 5$: (2, −3), (5, −3), (2, −7)

(b) Find the coordinates of the centre of the following rotations:
(i) $\triangle 1 \to \triangle 2$ (ii) $\triangle 1 \to \triangle 3$
(iii) $\triangle 1 \to \triangle 4$ (iv) $\triangle 1 \to \triangle 5$.

6. (a) Plot and label the following triangles:
$\triangle 1$: (−4, −3), (−4, −7), (−6, −7)
$\triangle 2$: (−3, 4), (−7, 4), (−7, 6)
$\triangle 3$: (−2, 1), (2, 1), (2, −1)
$\triangle 4$: (0, 7), (4, 7), (4, 5)
$\triangle 5$: (2, −3), (4, −3), (2, −7)

(b) Find the coordinates of the centre of the following rotations:
(i) $\triangle 1 \to \triangle 2$ (ii) $\triangle 1 \to \triangle 3$
(iii) $\triangle 1 \to \triangle 4$ (iv) $\triangle 1 \to \triangle 5$.

Enlargement

A

B

C

Photo A has been enlarged to give photos B and C. Notice that the shape of the face is exactly the same in all the pictures.

Photo A measures 22 mm by 27 mm
Photo B measures 44 mm by 54 mm
Photo C measures 66 mm by 81 mm

From A to B both the width and the height have been multiplied by 2.
We say B is an enlargement of A with a *scale factor* of 2.
Similarly C is an enlargement of A with a scale factor of 3.

Also C is an enlargement of B with a scale factor of $1\frac{1}{2}$.

The scale factor of an enlargement can be found by dividing corresponding lengths on two pictures.

In this enlargement the

scale factor is $\frac{21}{14}$ (= 1·5)

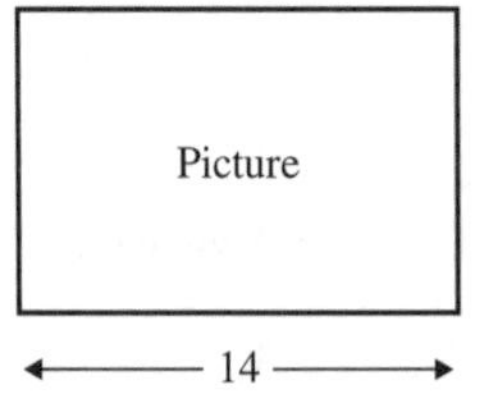

Enlargement

21

Exercise 6

1. This picture is to be enlarged and we want the enlargement to fit exactly in a frame.
   Which of the following frames will the picture fit?
   Write 'yes' or 'no'.
   (a) 100 mm by 76 mm
   (b) 110 mm by 76 mm
   (c) 150 mm by 114 mm
   (d) 75 mm by 57 mm.

2. This picture is to be enlarged so that it fits exactly into the frame. Find the length x.

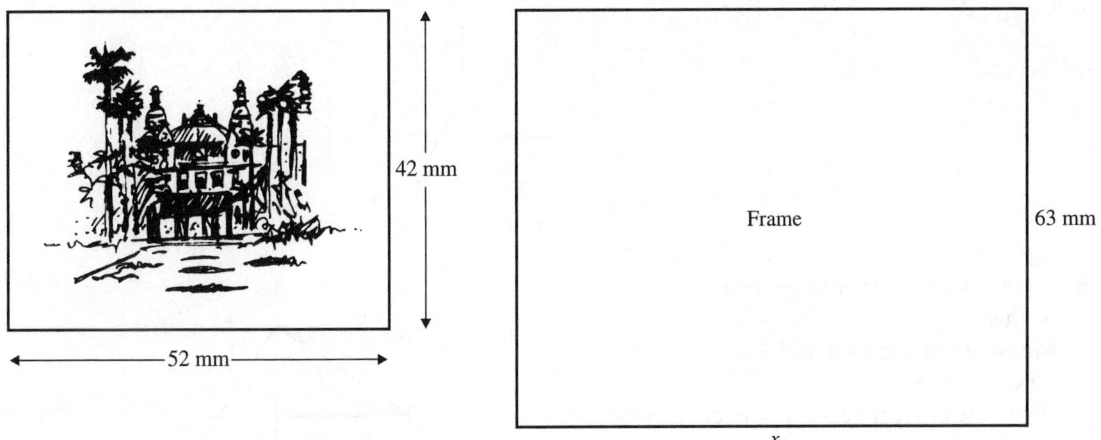

3. This picture is enlarged or reduced to fit into each of the frames shown. Calculate y and z.

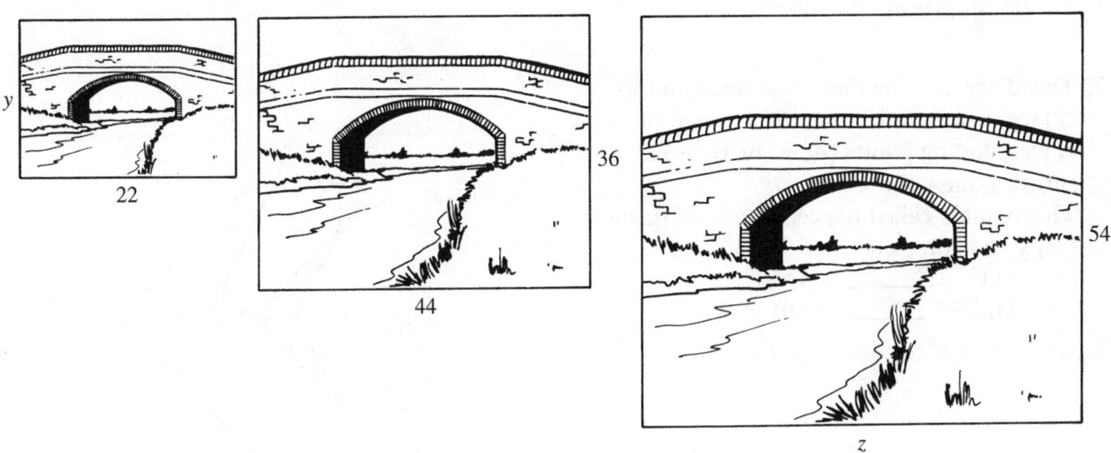

4. Here we have started to draw a two times enlargement of a house using the squares.

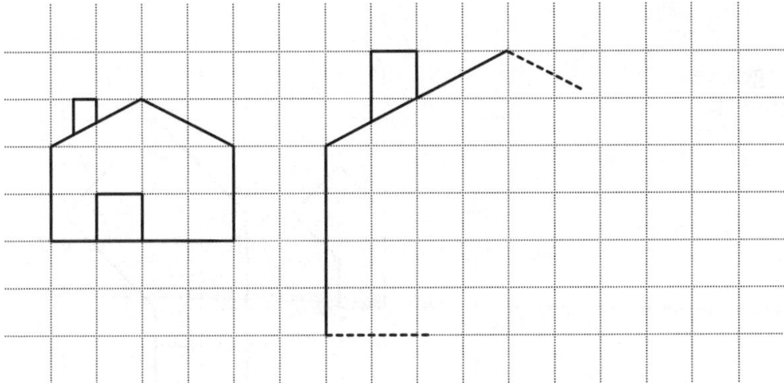

Draw the complete enlargement in your book (use squared paper).

5. Draw a three times enlargement of this figure.

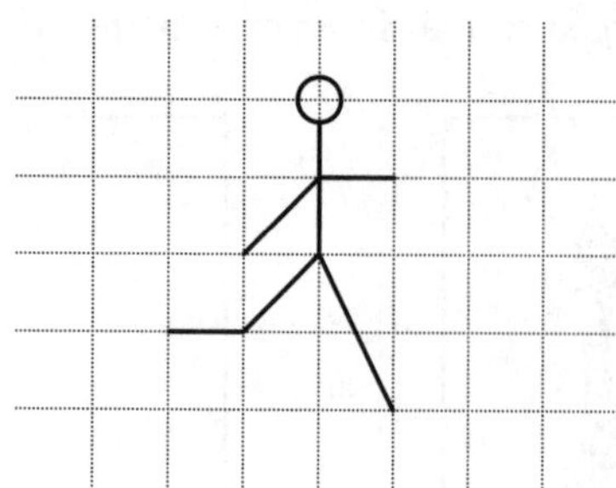

6. Draw a two times enlargement of this shape.
Measure the angles *a* and *b* on each shape.
Write the correct version of each sentence:
(a) 'In an enlargement, the angles in a shape are changed/unchanged.'
(b) 'In an enlargement, the object and the image are congruent/not congruent.'

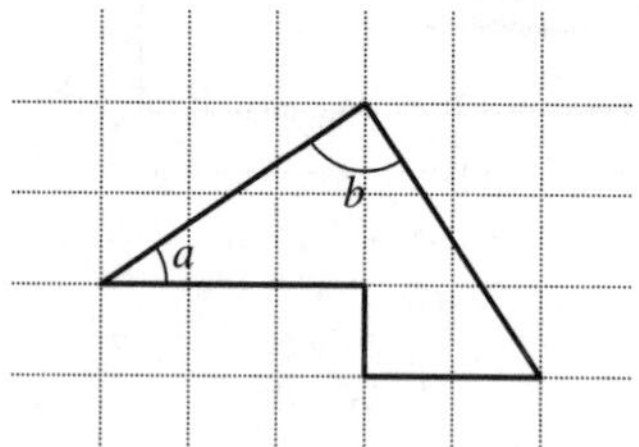

7. This diagram shows an arrowhead and its enlargement. Notice that lines drawn through corresponding points (A, A′ or B, B′) all go through one point O.
This point is called the centre of enlargement.
Copy and complete:

OA′ = ______ × OA
OB′ = ______ × OB.

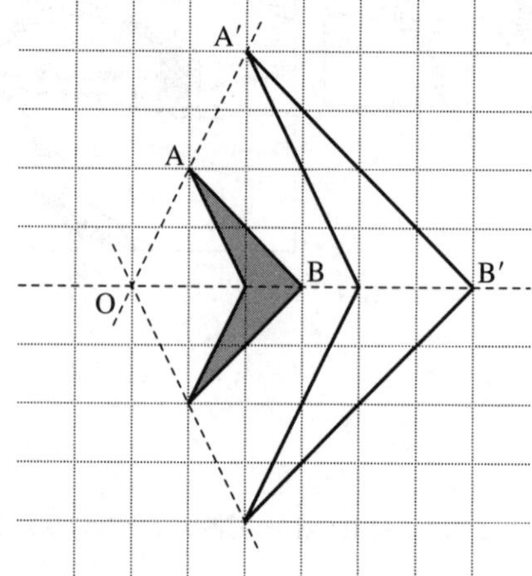

8. Copy this shape and its enlargement. Draw construction lines to find the centre of enlargement.

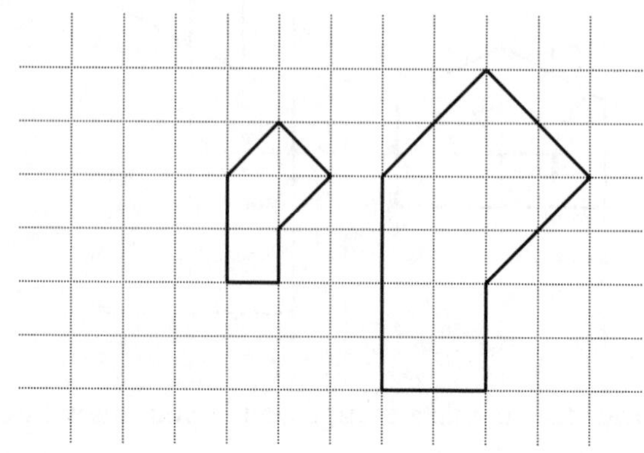

9. Copy the diagram shown, leaving space on the left for construction lines.

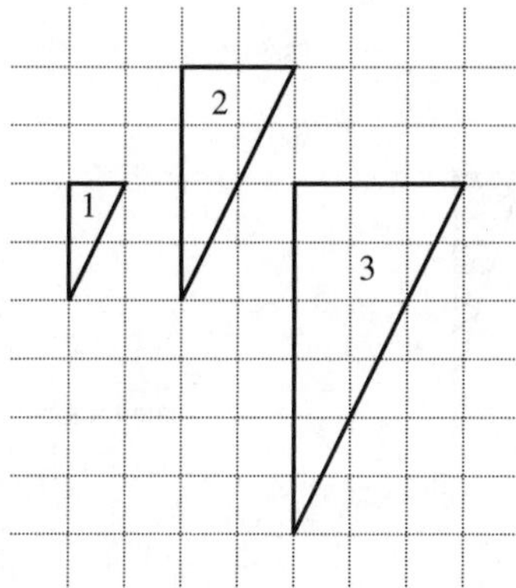

(a) Mark the centre of enlargement for the following:
(i) $\triangle 1 \longrightarrow \triangle 2$
(ii) $\triangle 1 \longrightarrow \triangle 3$
(iii) $\triangle 2 \longrightarrow \triangle 3$

(b) Write down the scale factor for the enlargement $\triangle 2 \longrightarrow \triangle 3$.

- For a mathematical description of an enlargement we need two things:

(a) the scale factor (b) the centre of enlargement.

The triangle ABC is enlarged on to triangle A′B′C′ with a scale factor of 3 and centre O.

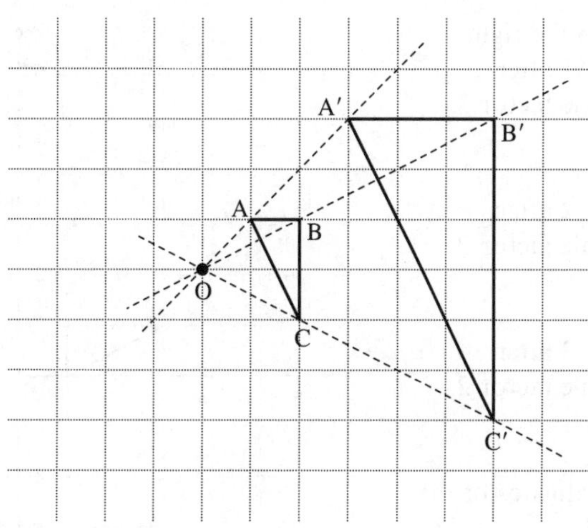

Note: $OA' = 3 \times OA$; $OB' = 3 \times OB$; $OC' = 3 \times OC$.

All lengths are measured from the *centre of enlargement*.

Exercise 7

Copy each diagram and draw an enlargement using the centre O and the scale factor given.

1.

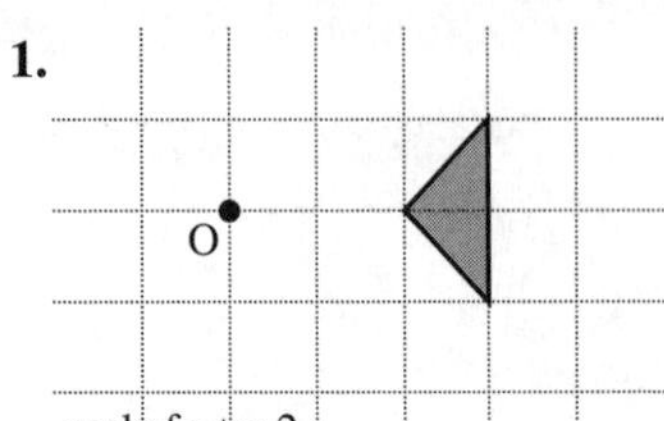

2.

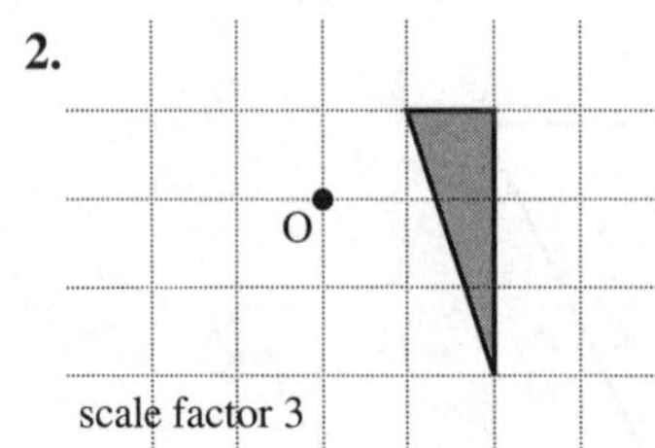

3.

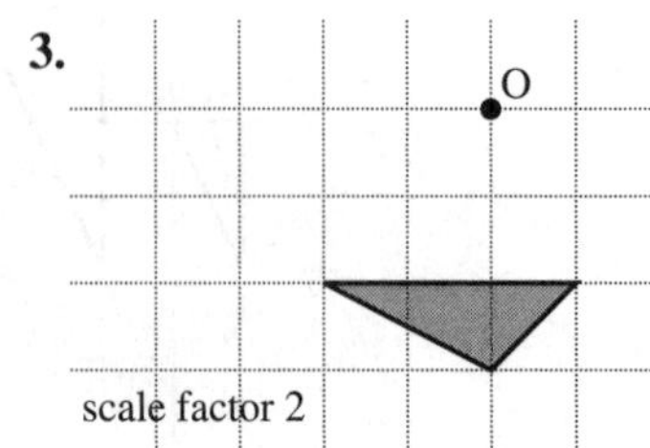

4.

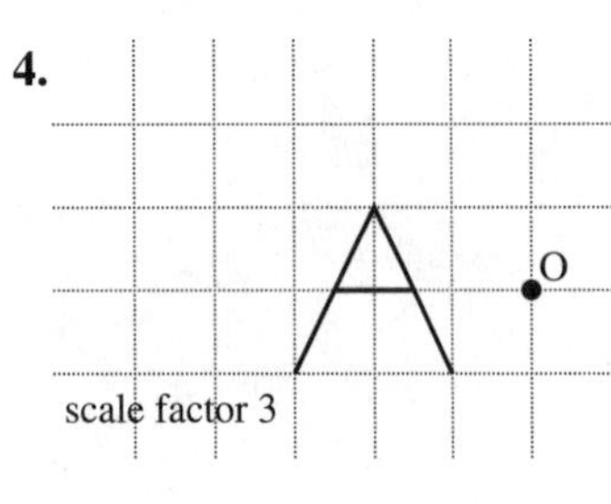

5.

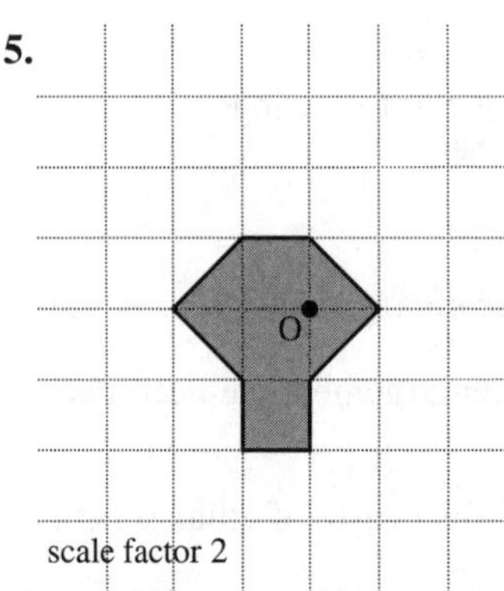

6.

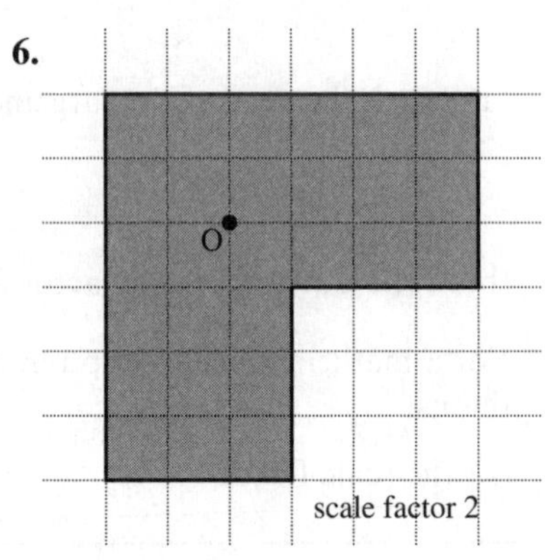

7. (a) Copy the diagram on the right.
(b) Draw the image of △1 after enlargement with scale factor 3, centre (0, 0).
Label the image △4.
(c) Draw the image of △2 after enlargement with scale factor 2, centre (−1, 3).
Label the image △5.
(d) Draw the image of △3 after enlargement with scale factor 2, centre (−1, −5).
Label the image △6.
(e) Write down the coordinates of the 'pointed ends' of △4, △5 and △6.
[The 'pointed end' is the vertex of the triangle with the smallest angle.]

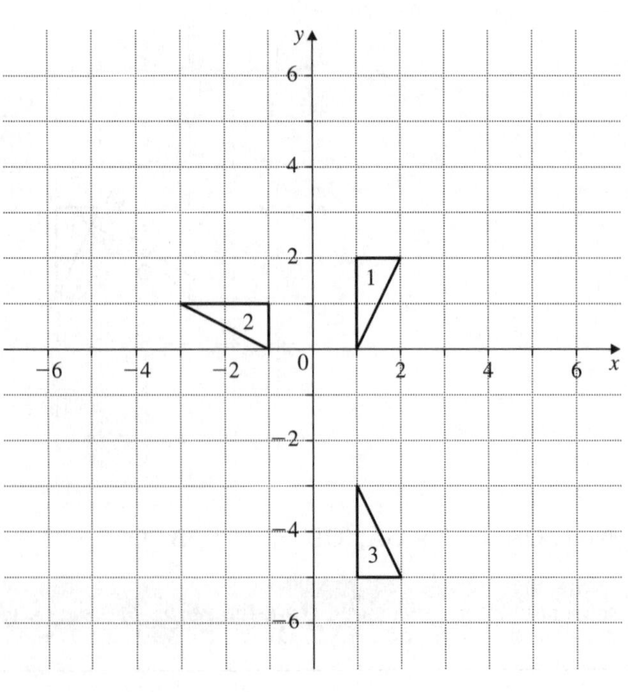

For Questions **8**, **9** draw a pair of axes with values from −7 to +7.

8. (a) Plot and label the triangles:
△1: (5, 5), (5, 7), (4, 7)
△2: (−6, −5), (−3, −5), (−3, −4)
△3: (1, −4), (1, −6), (2, −6).
(b) Draw the image of △1 after enlargement with scale factor 2, centre (7, 7). Label the image △4.
(c) Draw the image of △2 after enlargement with scale factor 3, centre (−6, −7). Label the image △5.
(d) Draw the image of △3 after enlargement with scale factor 2, centre (−1, −5). Label the image △6.
(e) Write down the coordinates of the 'pointed ends' of △4, △5 and △6.

9. (a) Plot and label the triangles:
△1: (5, 3), (5, 6), (4, 6)
△2: (4, −3), (1, −3), (1, −2)
△3: (−4, −7), (−7, −7), (−7, −6).
(b) Draw the image of △1 after enlargement with scale factor 2, centre (7, 7). Label the image △4.
(c) Draw the image of △2 after enlargement with scale factor 3, centre (5, −4). Label the image △5.
(d) Draw the image of △3 after enlargement with scale factor 4, centre (−7, −7). Label the image △6.
(e) Write down the coordinates of the 'pointed ends' of △4, △5 and △6.

Enlargements with fractional scale factors (reductions)

- Even though a shape has undergone a reduction, mathematicians prefer to call it an enlargement with a fractional scale factor.

The unshaded shape is the image of the shaded shape after an enlargement with scale factor $\frac{1}{2}$, centre O.

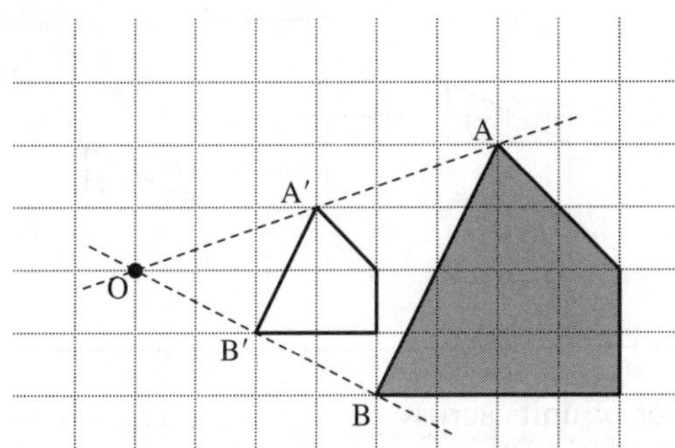

Note that $OA' = \frac{1}{2} \times OA$

$OB' = \frac{1}{2} \times OB$

Exercise 8

Copy each diagram and draw an enlargement using the centre O and the scale factor given.

1.

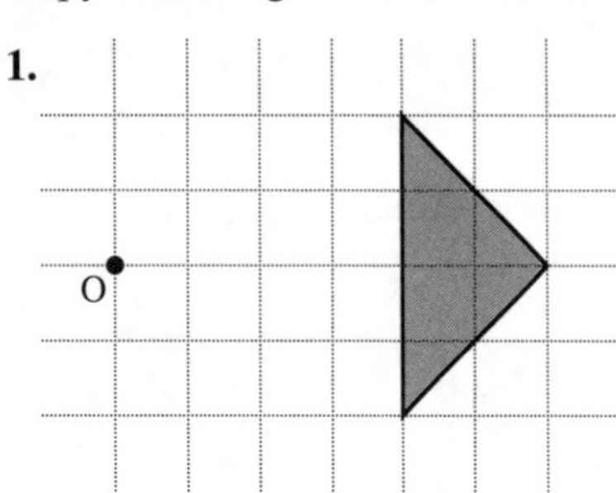

scale factor $\frac{1}{2}$

2.

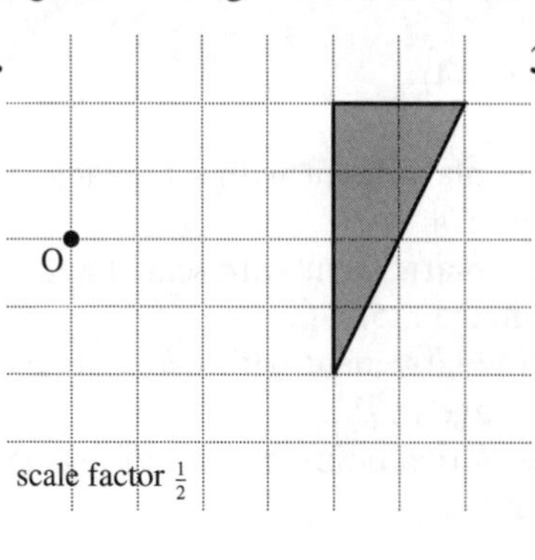

scale factor $\frac{1}{2}$

3.

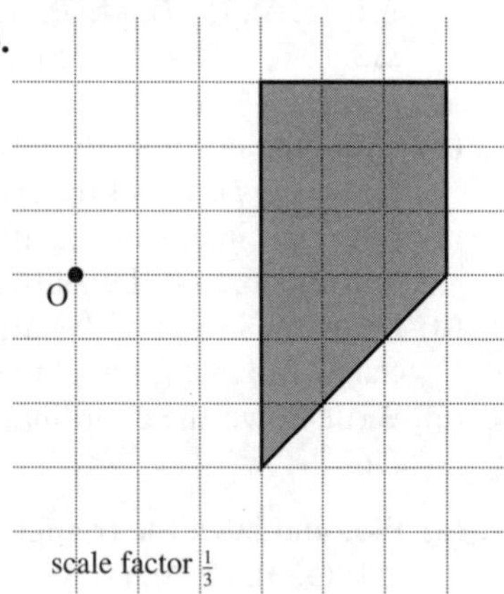

scale factor $\frac{1}{3}$

4. (a) Plot and label the triangles:
$\triangle 1$: (7, 6), (1, 6), (1, 3)
$\triangle 2$: (7, −1), (7, −7), (3, −7)
$\triangle 3$: (−5, 7), (−5, 1), (−7, 1).

(b) Draw $\triangle 4$, the image of $\triangle 1$ after an enlargement with scale factor $\frac{1}{3}$, centre (−2, 0).

(c) Draw $\triangle 5$, the image of $\triangle 2$ after an enlargement with scale factor $\frac{1}{2}$, centre (−5, −7).

(d) Draw $\triangle 6$, the image of $\triangle 3$ after an enlargement with scale factor $\frac{1}{2}$, centre (−7, −5).

Translation

- A translation is simply a 'shift'. There is no turning or reflection and the object stays the same size.

(a) $\triangle 1$ is mapped on to $\triangle 2$ by the

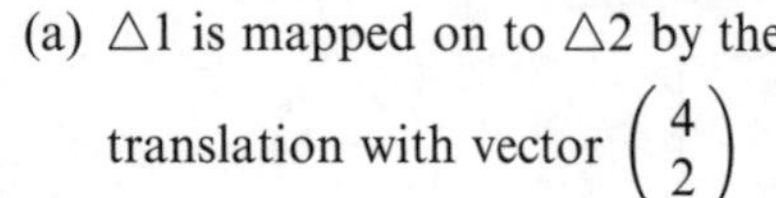
translation with vector $\begin{pmatrix} 4 \\ 2 \end{pmatrix}$

(b) $\triangle 2$ is mapped on to $\triangle 3$ by the translation with vector $\begin{pmatrix} 2 \\ -3 \end{pmatrix}$

(c) $\triangle 3$ is mapped on to $\triangle 2$ by the translation with vector $\begin{pmatrix} -2 \\ 3 \end{pmatrix}$

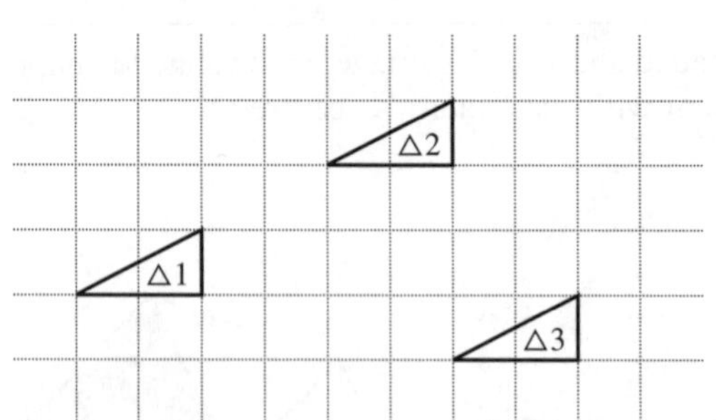

- In a vector the top number gives the number of units across (positive to the right) and the bottom number gives the number of units up/down (positive upwards).

So $\begin{pmatrix} 4 \\ 2 \end{pmatrix}$ is 4 across → 2 up ↑ $\qquad \begin{pmatrix} -2 \\ 3 \end{pmatrix}$ is 2 across ← 3 up ↑

Exercise 9

1. Look at the diagram shown.

Write down the vector for each of the following translations.

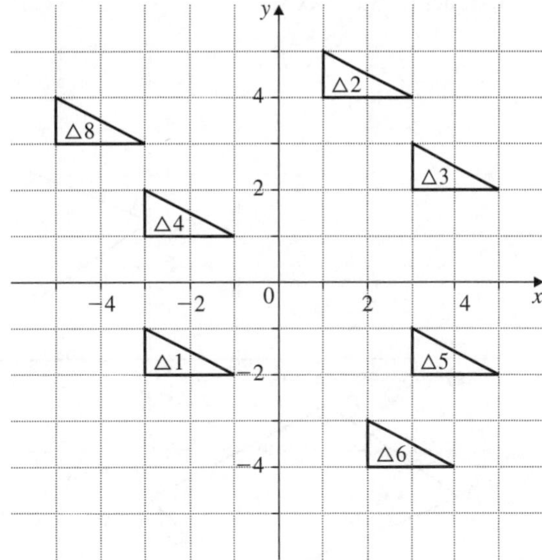

(a) △1 → △2 (b) △1 → △3

(c) △1 → △4 (d) △1 → △5

(e) △1 → △6 (f) △6 → △5

(g) △1 → △8 (h) △2 → △3

(i) △2 → △4 (j) △2 → △5

(k) △2 → △6 (l) △2 → △8

(m) △3 → △5 (n) △8 → △2

Successive transformations

Exercise 10

1. Copy the diagram shown.

(a) Rotate △1 180° about (4, 2). Label the image △2.
(b) Reflect △2 in the line $y = 2$. Label the image △3.
(c) Describe the *single* transformation which maps △1 on to △3.

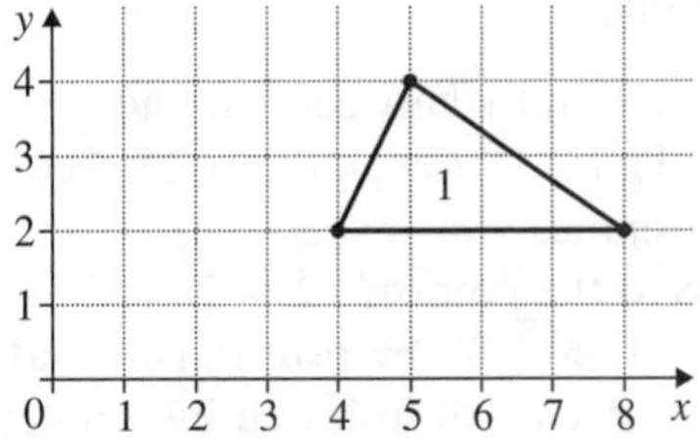

2. Copy the diagram shown.

(a) Reflect △A in the line $y = x$. Label the image △B.
(b) Reflect △B in the x-axis. Label the image △C.
(c) Describe fully the single transformation which maps △A on to △C.

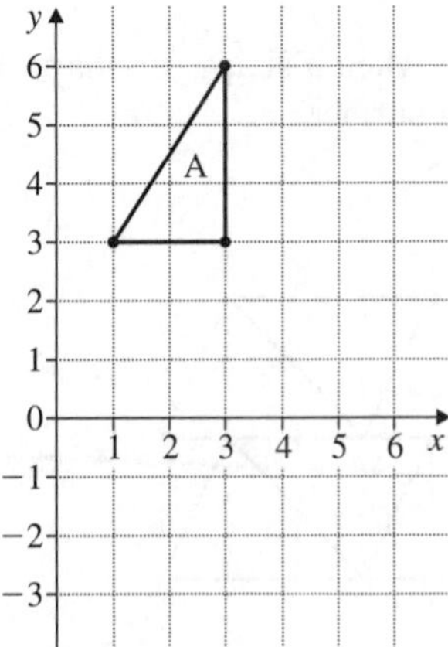

3. ABCD is mapped onto A′B′C′D′ by a reflection followed by a translation parallel to the x axis.

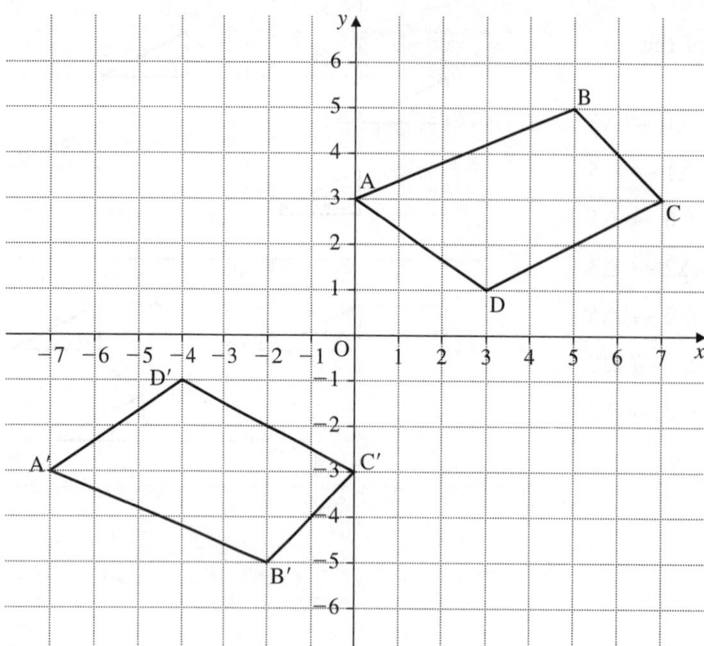

(a) Describe these two transformations as fully as possible.
(b) Would the image be the same if the translation was completed before the reflection?

4. Draw axes for both x and y between −8 and +8.
Plot the points (1, 1), (3, 1), (3, 2), (2, 2), (2, 4) and (1, 4) and join up to make an 'L' shape.
This is mapped on to the points (−2, −2), (−2, −6), (−4, −6), (−4, −4), (−8, −4), (−8, −2), by *two* transformations: an enlargement with centre (0, 0) followed by a reflection.
Describe these transformations as fully as possible.

Tessellations

- A tessellation is formed when a shape (or shapes) fit together without gaps to cover a surface.
Here are some examples.

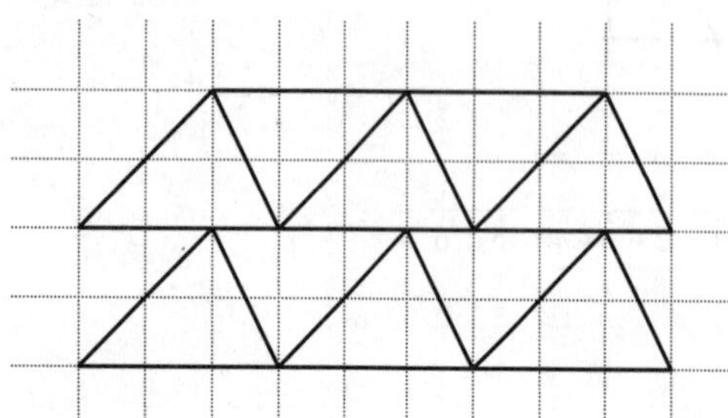

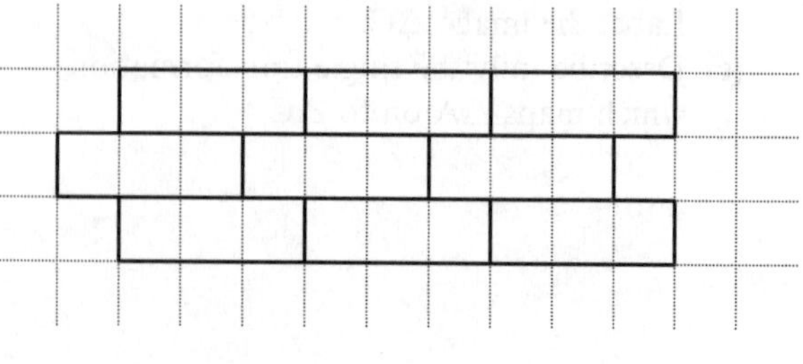

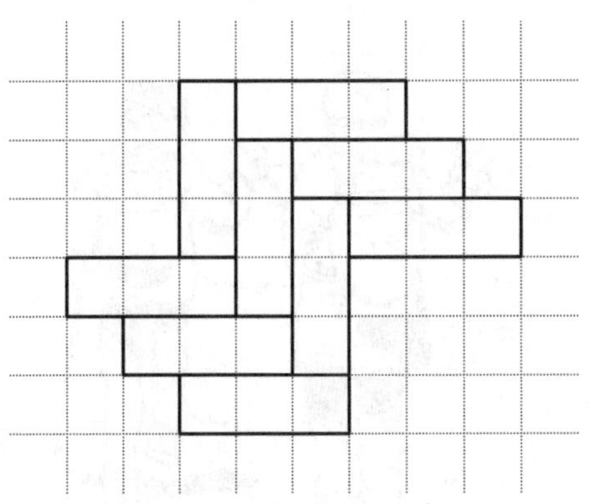

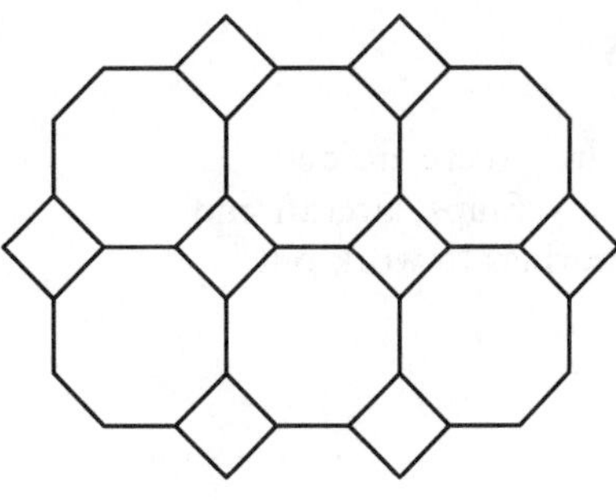

Exercise 11

1. Use squared paper to show that each of the shapes below tessellates.

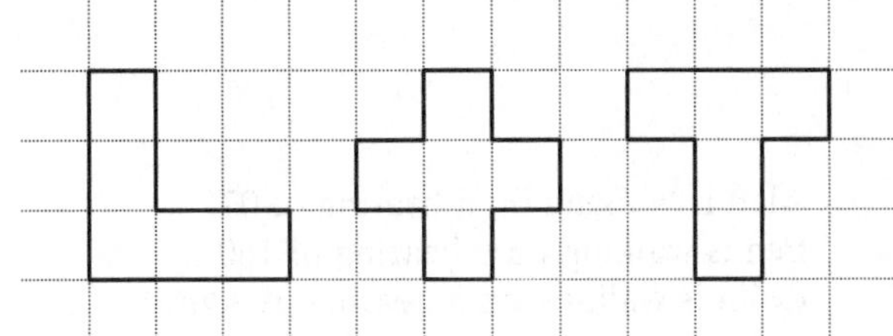

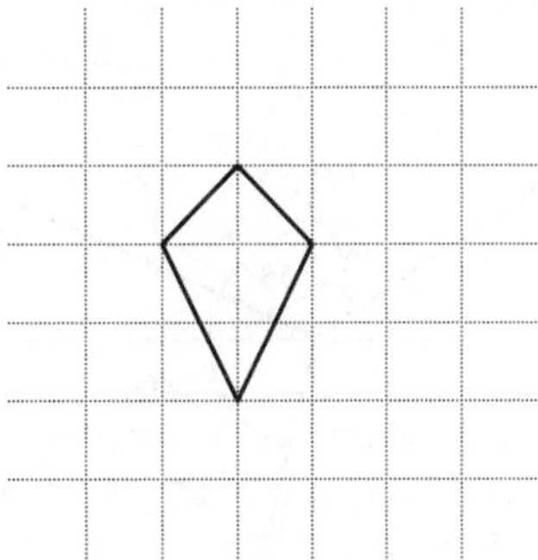

2. (a) Draw any irregular triangle or quadrilateral and cut twenty or so copies from cardboard. Fit them together, like a jigsaw puzzle, to cover a plane.
   (b) Say whether the statements below are true or false:
      (i) 'all triangles tessellate'
      (ii) 'all quadrilaterals tessellate'.

3. Is it true that 'all pentagons tessellate'?

4. Here is a tessellation made from isosceles right angled triangles.
   (a) What sort of transformation maps $\triangle 2$ on to $\triangle 8$?
   (b) Describe the rotation which maps $\triangle 5$ on to $\triangle 4$.
   (c) What is the mirror line for the reflection which maps $\triangle 7$ on to $\triangle 8$?
   (d) Describe, as fully as possible, the following transformations:
      (i) $\triangle 1 \longrightarrow \triangle 8$
      (ii) $\triangle 5 \longrightarrow \triangle 3$
      (iii) $\triangle 5 \longrightarrow \triangle 7$
      (iv) $\triangle 2 \longrightarrow \triangle 7$

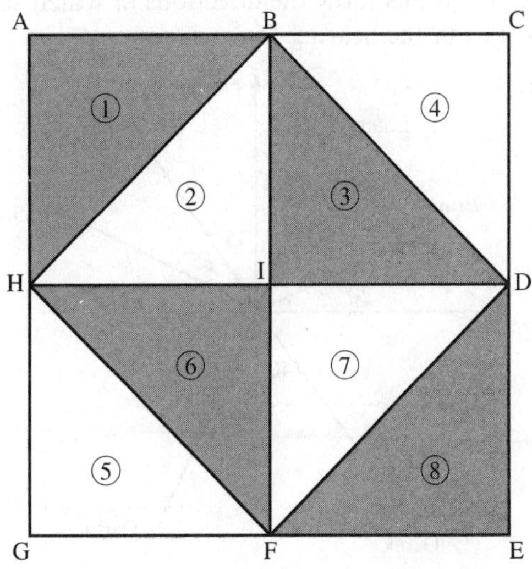

6.2 Bearings

Bearings are used where there are no roads to guide the way. Ships, aircraft and mountaineers use bearings to work out where they are.

- Bearings are measured *clockwise from North.*

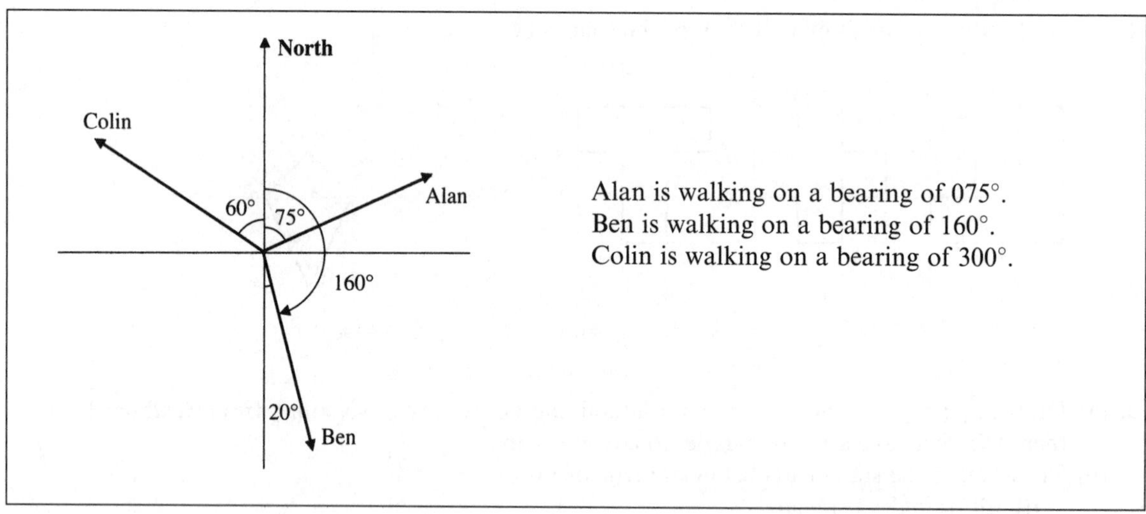

Alan is walking on a bearing of 075°.
Ben is walking on a bearing of 160°.
Colin is walking on a bearing of 300°.

Exercise 12

The diagrams show the directions in which several people are travelling.
Work out the bearing for each person.

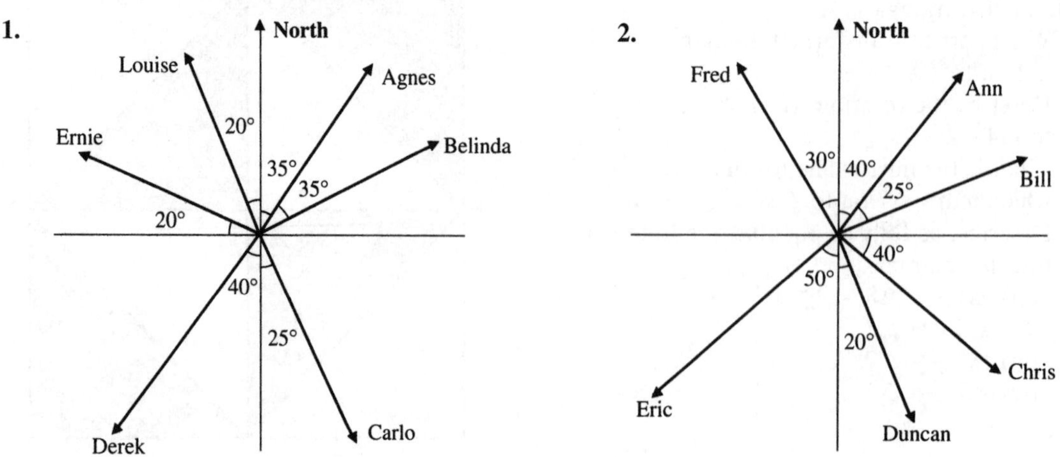

Relative bearings

- The bearing of A from B is the direction in which you travel to get to A from B.

It helps to show the journey with an arrow, as below.

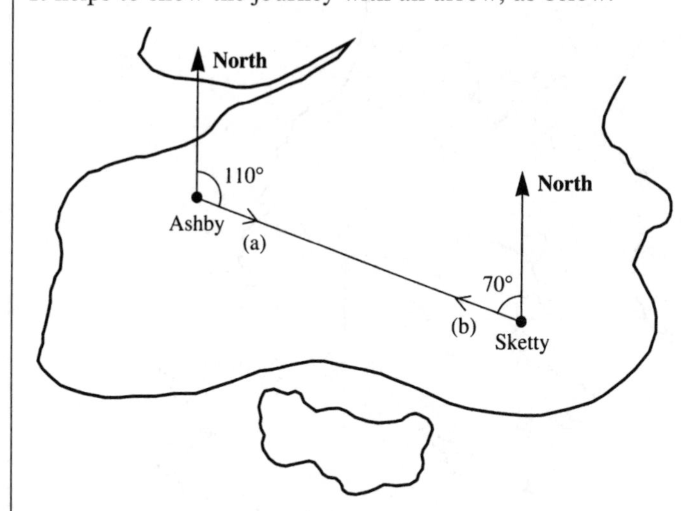

(a) The bearing of Sketty from Ashby is 110°.

(b) The bearing of Ashby from Sketty is 290°.

Exercise 13

The map of North America shows six radar tracking stations, A, B, C, D, E, F.

1. From A, measure the bearing of
(a) F (b) B (c) C.

2. From C, measure the bearing of
(a) E (b) B (c) D.

3. From F, measure the bearing of
(a) D (b) A.

4. From B, measure the bearing of
(a) A (b) E (c) C.

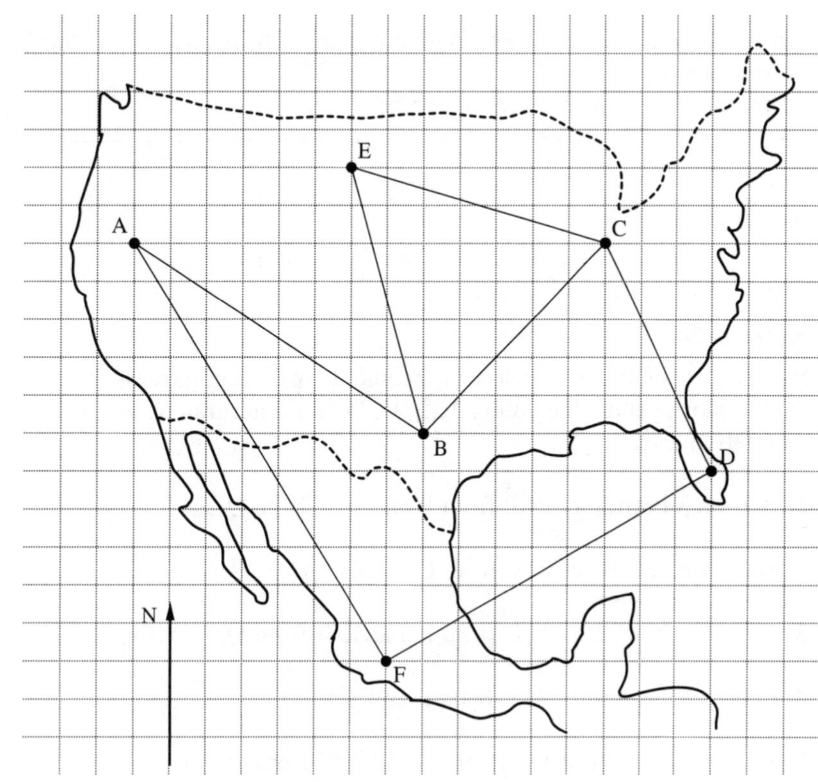

- Ships or aircraft can be located when their bearings from two places are known.

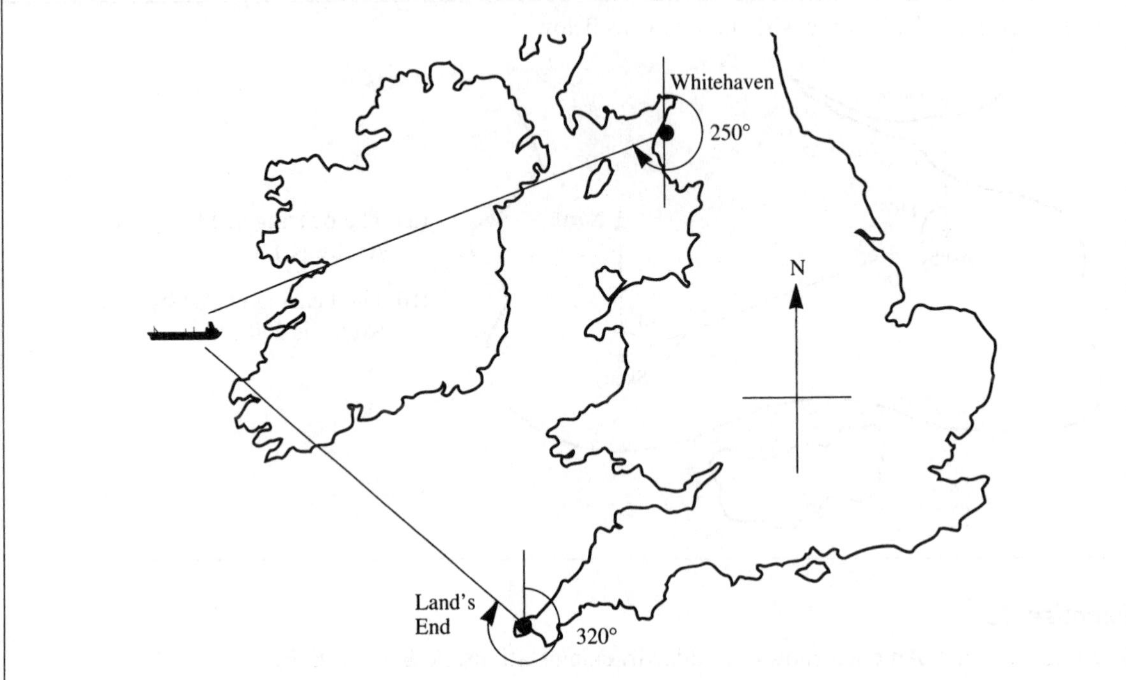

On the map the tanker 'Braer' is on a bearing 320° from Land's End. From Whitehaven, the Braer is on a bearing of 250°.
There is only one place where it can be.

Exercise 14

Draw the points P and Q below in the middle of a clean page of squared paper. Mark the points A, B, C, D and E accurately, using the information given.

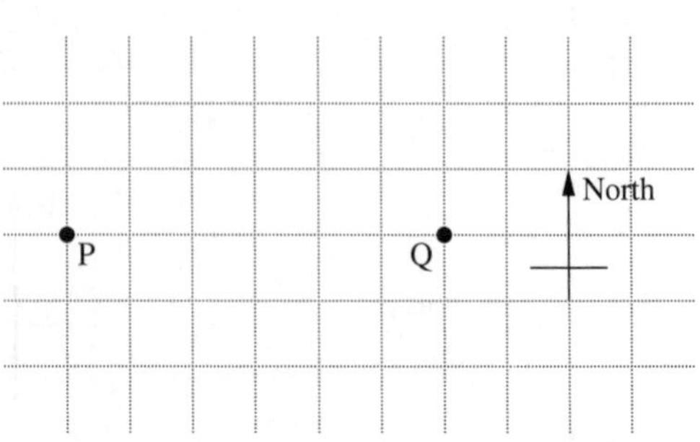

1. A is on a bearing of 040° from P and 015° from Q.
2. B is on a bearing of 076° from P and 067° from Q.
3. C is on a bearing of 114° from P and 127° from Q.
4. D is on a bearing of 325° from P and 308° from Q.
5. E is on a bearing of 180° from P and 208° from Q.

Exercise 15

Draw the points X and Y below in the middle of a clean page of squared paper. Mark the points K, L, M, N and O accurately, using the information given.

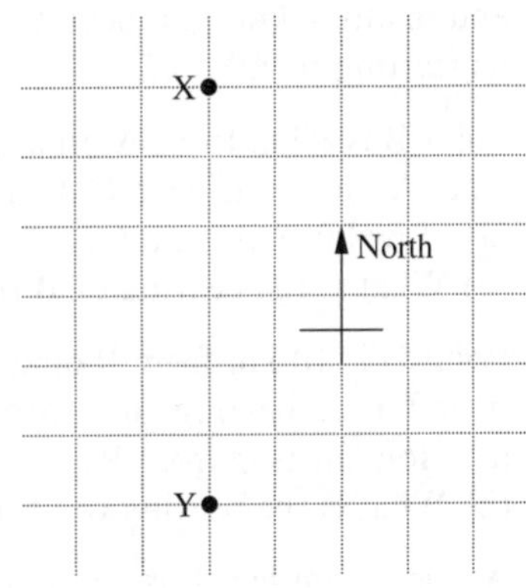

1. K is on a bearing of 041° from X and 025° from Y.
2. L is on a bearing of 090° from X and 058° from Y.
3. M is on a bearing of 123° from X and 090° from Y.
4. N is on a bearing of 203° from X and 215° from Y.
5. O is on a bearing of 288° from X and 319° from Y.

Exercise 16

Make accurate scale drawings with a scale of 1 cm to 1 km, unless told otherwise. Use squared paper and begin each question by drawing a small sketch of the journey.

1. A ship sails 8 km due North and then a further 7 km on a bearing 080°, as in the diagram (which is not drawn to scale). How far is the ship now from its starting point?

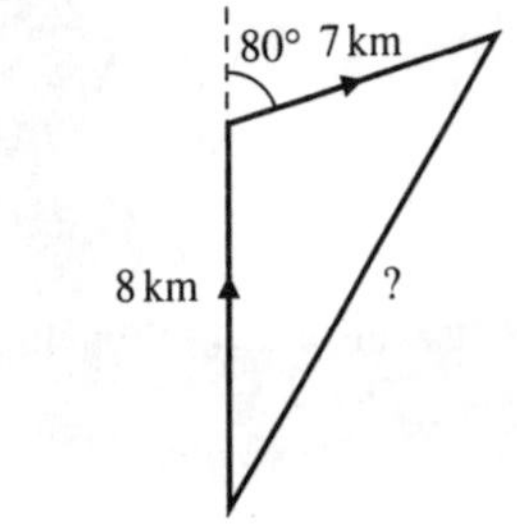

2. A ship sails 9 km on a bearing 090° and then a further 6 km on a bearing 050°, as shown in the diagram. How far is the ship now from its starting point?

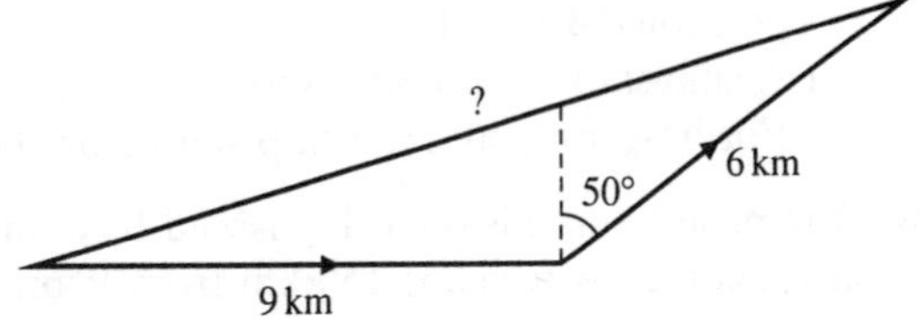

3. A ship sails 6 km on a bearing 160° and then a further 10 km on a bearing 240°, as shown.
   (a) How far is the ship from its starting point?
   (b) On what bearing must the ship sail so that it returns to its starting point?

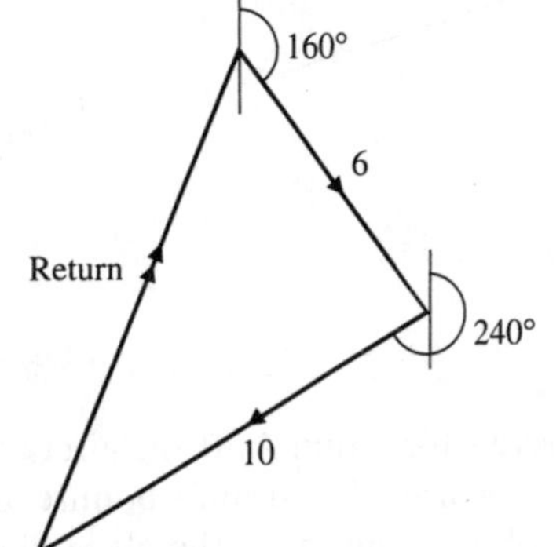

4. A ship sails 5 km on a bearing 030°, then 3 km on a bearing 090° and finally 4 km on a bearing 160°. How far is the ship now from its starting point?

5. Point B is 8 km from A on a bearing 140° from A. Point C is 9 km from A on a bearing 200° from A.
   (a) How far is B from C?
   (b) What is the bearing of B from C?

6. Point Q is 10 km from P on a bearing 052° from P. Point R is 4 km from P on a bearing 107° from P.
   (a) How far is Q from R?
   (b) What is the bearing of Q from R?

7. A laser beam gun L is 120 km from P on a bearing 068°. The laser beam destroys anything on a bearing 270° from L.

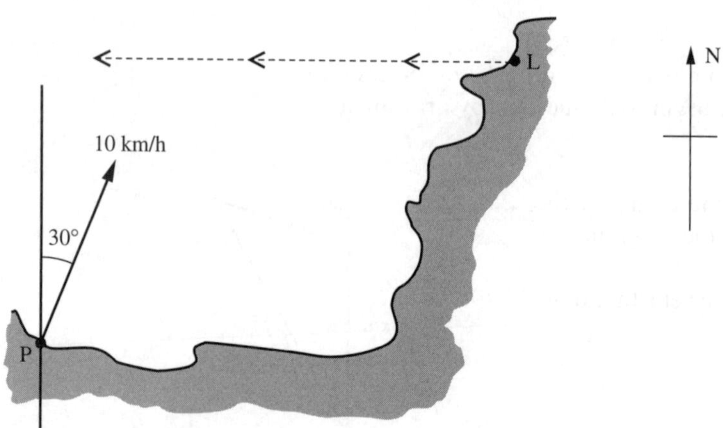

   (a) Draw a diagram, with a scale of 1 cm to 10 km, to show the positions of P and L.
   (b) A ship sails from P at a speed of 10 km/h on a bearing 030°. For how long does the ship sail before being destroyed?

8. Robinson Crusoe is on a tiny island R, dying of starvation. There is an airport at A which is 150 km from R on a bearing 295° from R.

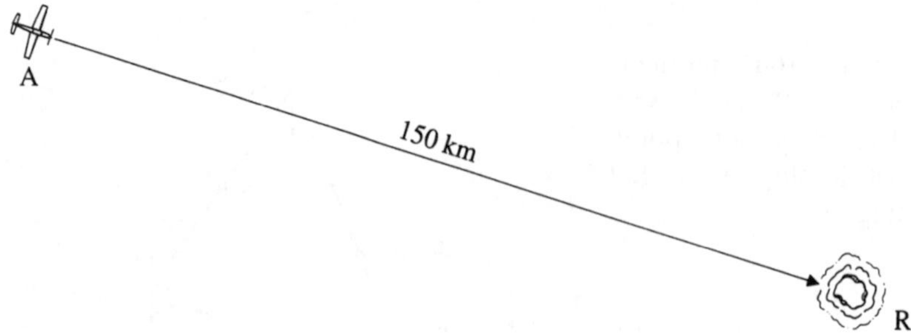

An aircraft flies from A. If the aircraft gets within 40 km of R, the pilot will see Robinson's bonfire and Mr Crusoe will be saved. Will Robinson survive if the plane flies on a bearing of 098°?

6.3 Locus

- In mathematics, the word *locus* describes the position of points which obey a certain rule. The locus can be the path traced out by a moving point.

Three important loci

(a) Circle

The locus of points which are equidistant from a fixed point O is shown. It is a circle with centre O.

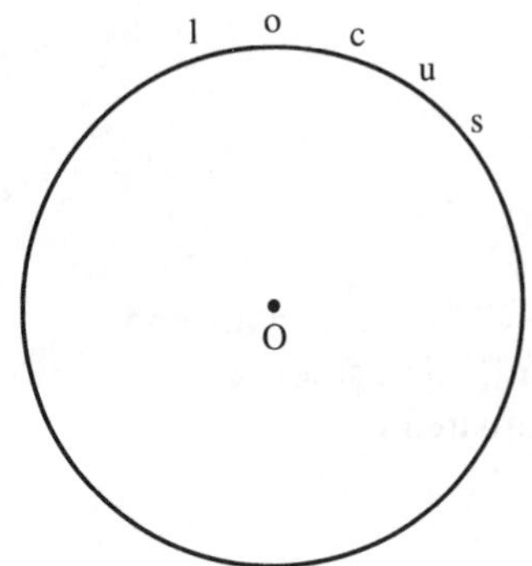

(b) Perpendicular bisector

The locus of points which are equidistant from two fixed points A and B is shown.

The locus is the perpendicular bisector of the line AB. Use compasses to draw arcs, as shown, or use a ruler and a protractor.

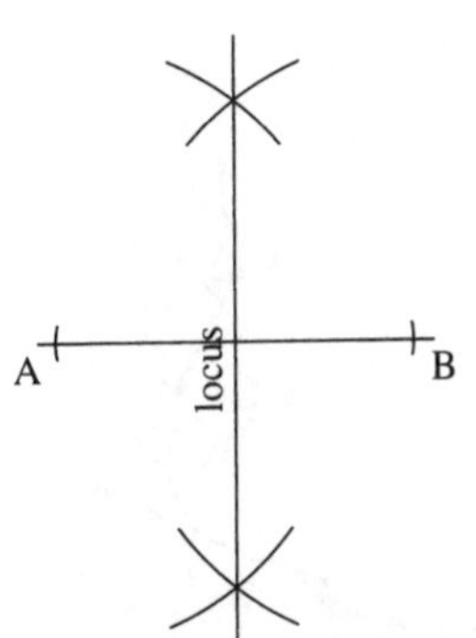

(c) Angle bisector

The locus of points which are equidistant from two fixed lines AB and AC is shown.

The locus is the line which bisects the angle BAC. Use compasses to draw arcs or use a protractor to construct the locus.

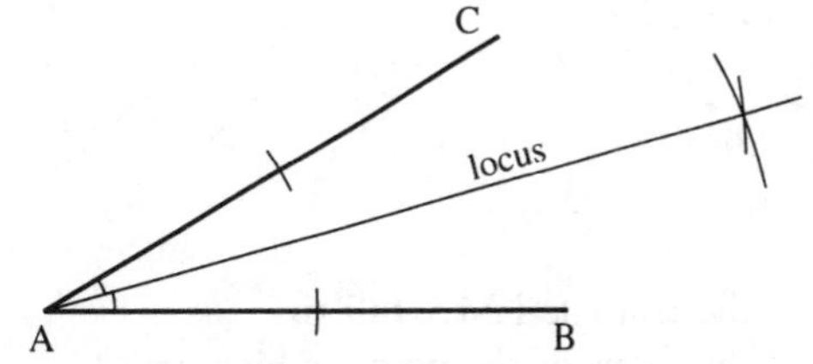

Exercise 17

1. Draw the locus of a point P which moves so that it is always 3 cm from a fixed point X.

•X

2. Mark two points P and Q which are 10 cm apart. Draw the locus of points which are equidistant from P and Q.
3. Draw two lines AB and AC of length 8 cm, where $B\hat{A}C = 40°$. Draw the locus of points which are equidistant from AB and AC.

4. A sphere rolls along a surface from A to B. Sketch the locus of the centre of the sphere in each case.

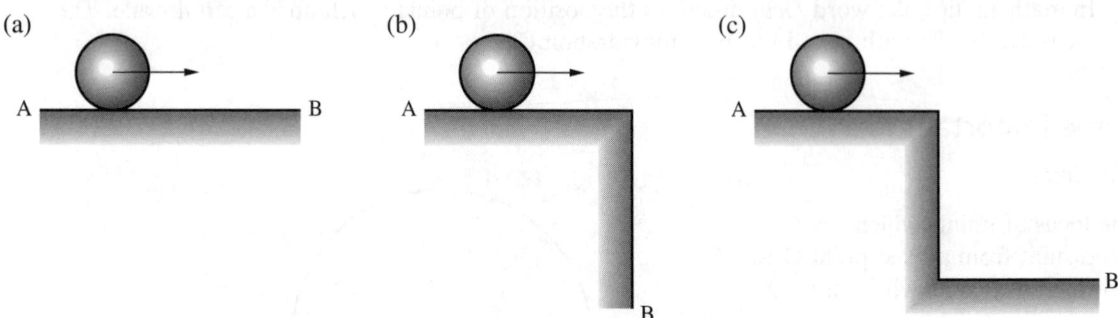

5. A rectangular slab ABCD is rotated around corner B from position 1 to position 2. Draw a diagram, on squared paper, to show:
(a) the locus of corner A
(b) the locus of corner C.

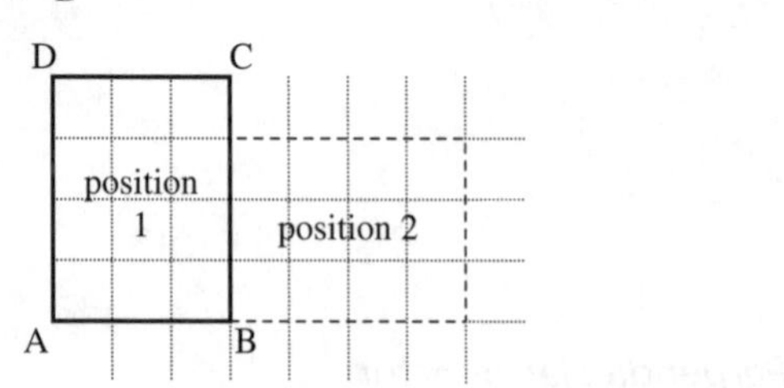

6.

C
sea
L
land
10 km

The diagram shows a section of coastline with a lighthouse L and coastguard C. A sinking ship sends a distress signal. The ship appears to be up to 40 km from L and up to 20 km from C. Copy the diagram and show the region in which the ship could be.

7. (a) Draw the triangle LMN full size.
(b) Draw the locus of the points which are:
(i) equidistant from L and N
(ii) equidistant from LN and LM
(iii) 4 cm from M.
[Draw the three loci in different colours.]

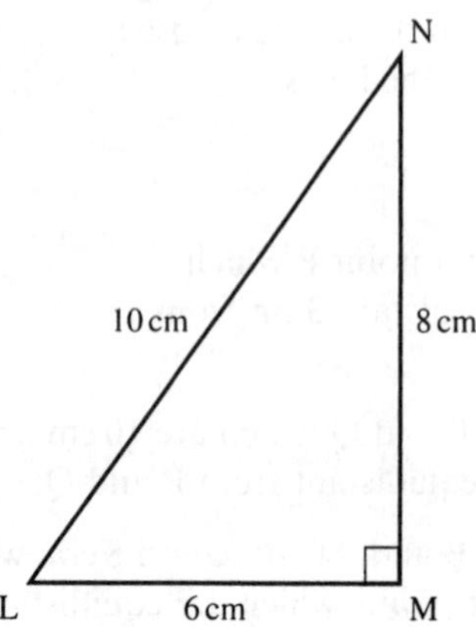

8. Draw a line AB of length 6 cm. Draw the locus of a point P so that angle ABP = 90°.

9. The diagram shows a garden with a fence on two sides and trees at two corners.

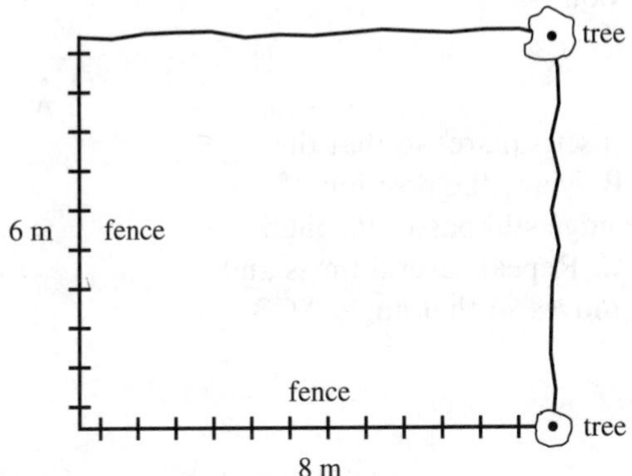

A sand pit is to be placed so that it is:
(a) equidistant from the 2 fences
(b) equidistant from the 2 trees.
Make a scale drawing (1 cm = 1 m) and mark where the sand pit goes.

10. Channel 9 in Australia is planning the position of a new TV satellite to send pictures all over the country. The new satellite is to be placed:
(a) an equal distance from Darwin and Adelaide
(b) not more than 2000 km from Perth
(c) not more than 1600 km from Brisbane.

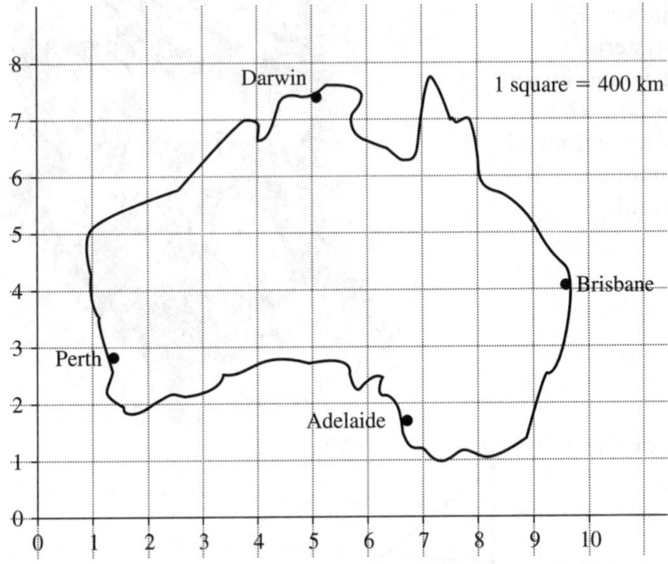

Make a copy of the map on squared paper using the grid lines as reference.
Show clearly where the satellite could be placed so that it satisfies the conditions (a), (b), (c) above.

11. Draw two points M and N 16 cm apart. Draw the locus of a point P which moves so that the area of triangle MNP is $80\,\text{cm}^2$.

12. Describe the locus of a point which moves in three dimensional space and is equidistant from two fixed points.

13. Draw two points A and B 10 cm apart.

Place the corner of a piece of paper (or a set square) so that the edges of the paper pass through A and B. Mark the position of corner C. Slide the paper around so the edge still passes through A and B and mark the new position of C. Repeat several times and describe the locus of the point C which moves so that angle ACB is always 90°.

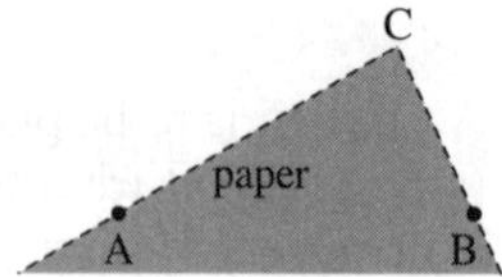

6.4 Pythagoras' theorem

Pythagoras (569–500 BC) was one of the first of the great mathematical names in Greek antiquity. He settled in southern Italy and formed a mysterious brotherhood with his students who were bound by an oath not to reveal the secrets of numbers and who exercised great influence. They laid the foundations of arithmetic through geometry and were among the first mathematicians to develop the idea of proof.

- In a right-angled triangle the square on the hypotenuse is equal to the sum of the squares on the other two sides.

  $a^2 + b^2 = c^2$

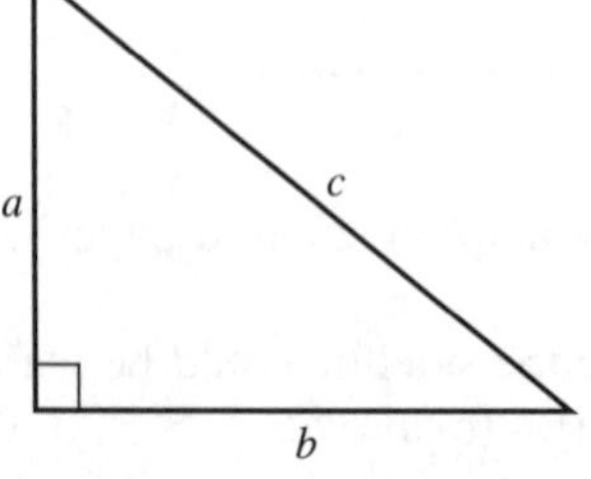

- The *converse* is also true.
  If the square on one side of a triangle is equal to the sum of the squares on the other two sides, then the triangle is right-angled.

Find the side marked d.

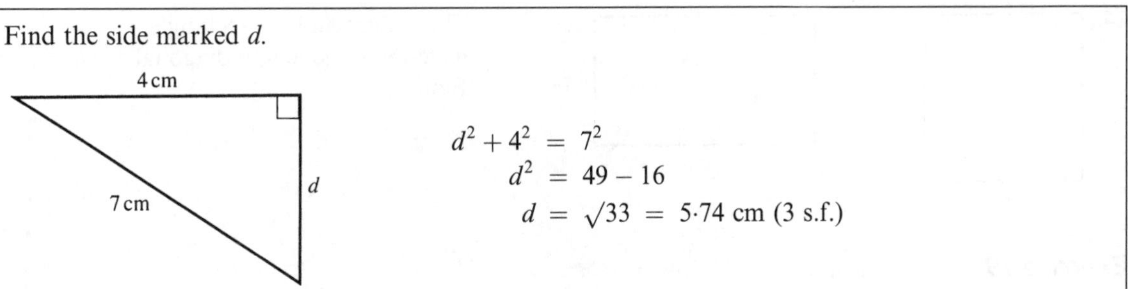

$$d^2 + 4^2 = 7^2$$
$$d^2 = 49 - 16$$
$$d = \sqrt{33} = 5{\cdot}74 \text{ cm (3 s.f.)}$$

Exercise 18

In Questions **1** to **4**, find x. All the lengths are in cm.

1.

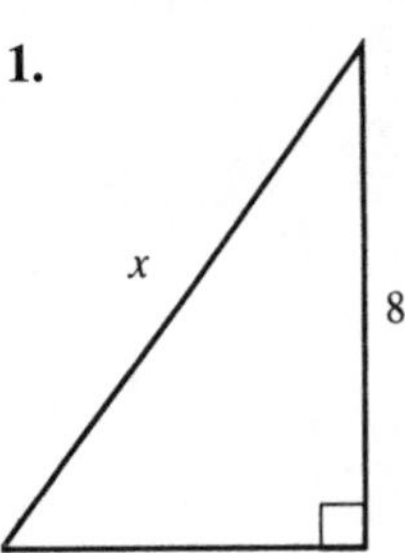

2.

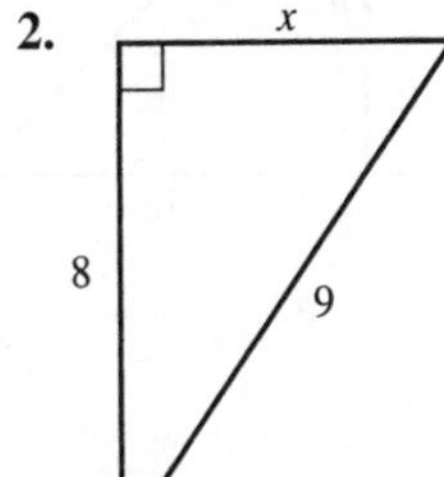

3.

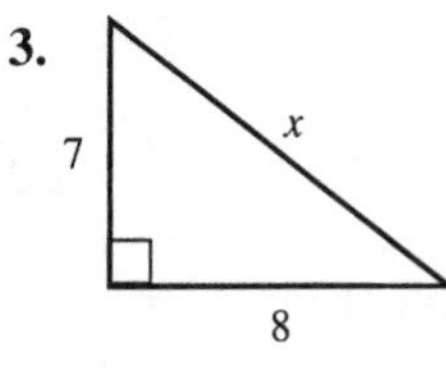

4.

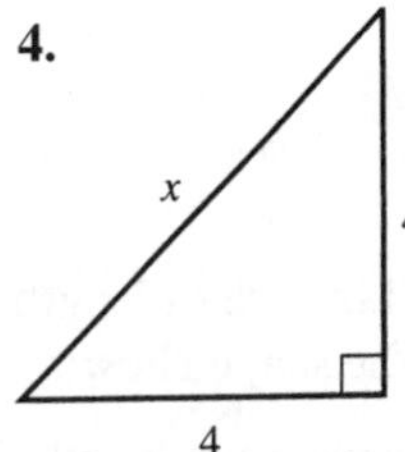

5.

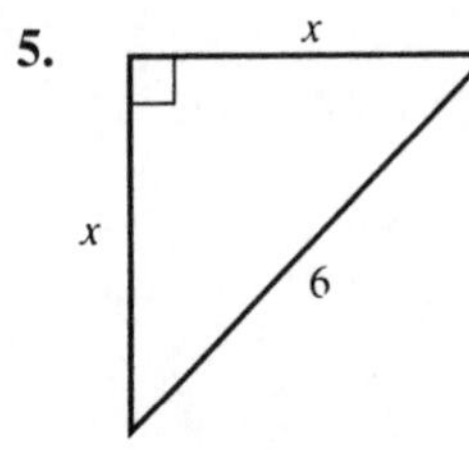

6.

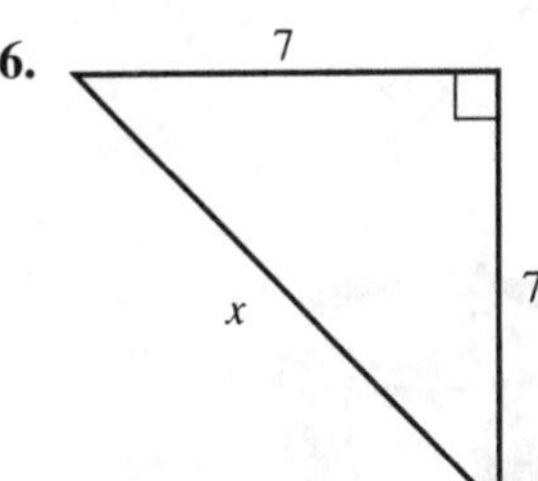

7.

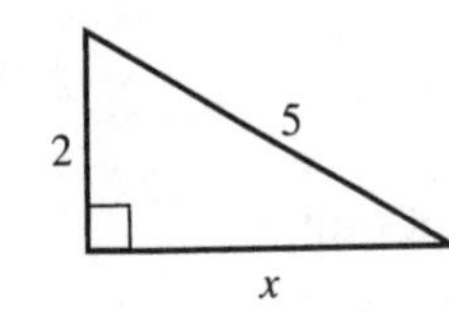

8.

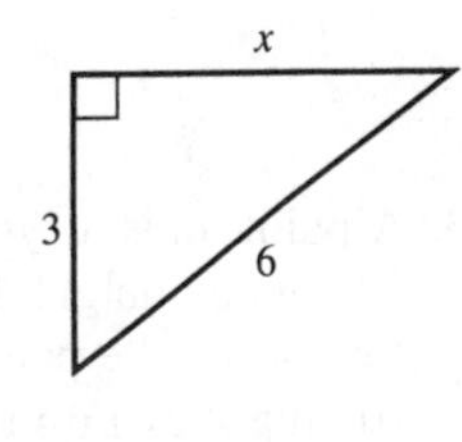

9. Find the length of a diagonal of a rectangle of length 9 cm and width 4 cm.

10. An isosceles triangle has sides 10 cm, 10 cm and 4 cm.
Find the height of the triangle.

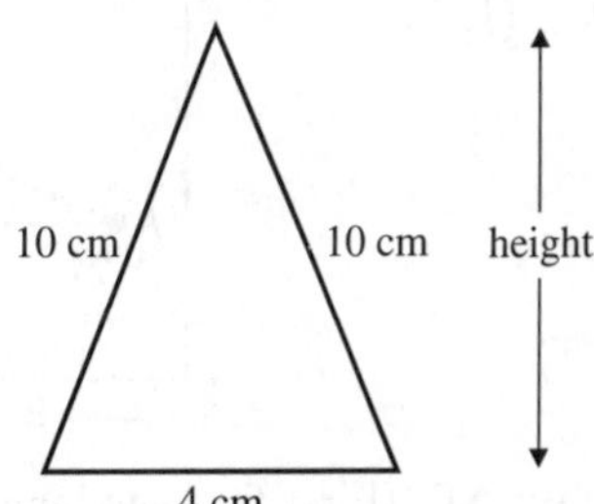

11. A 4 m ladder rests against a vertical wall with its foot 2 m from the wall. How far up the wall does the ladder reach?

12. A ship sails 20 km due North and then 35 km due East. How far is it from its starting point?

13. Find the length of a diagonal of a square of side 9 cm.

14.

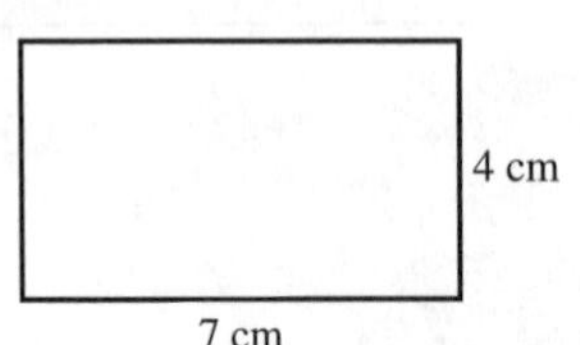

The square and the rectangle have the same length diagonal. Find x.

Exercise 19

1. (a) Find the height of the triangle, h.
(b) Find the area of the triangle ABC.

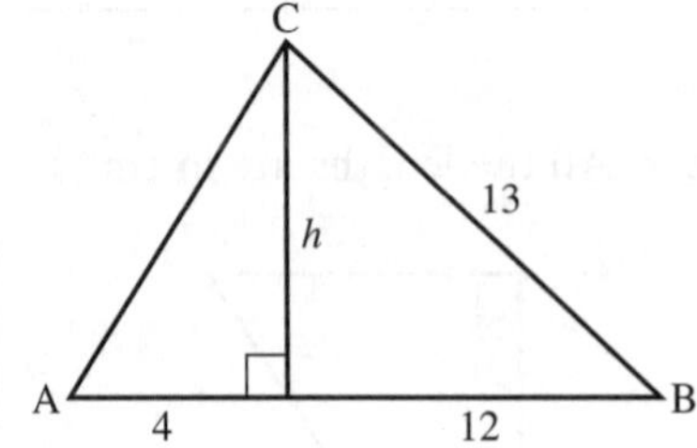

2. A thin wire of length 18 cm is bent in the shape shown.

Calculate the length from A to B.

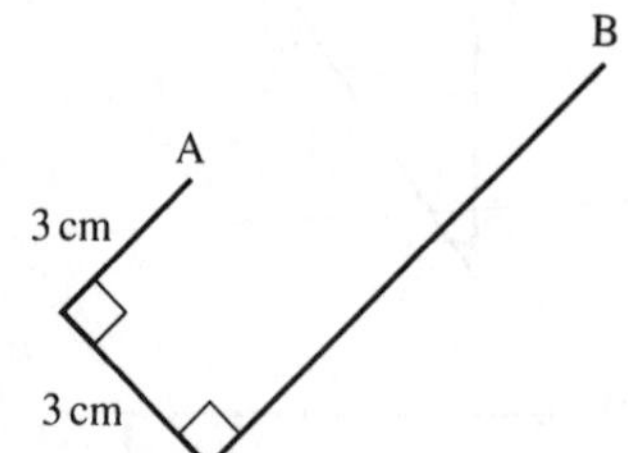

3. A paint tin is a cylinder of radius 12 cm and height 22 cm.
Leonardo, the painter, drops his stirring stick into the tin and it disappears.
Work out the maximum length of the stick.

4. In the diagram A is (1, 2) and B is (6, 4)

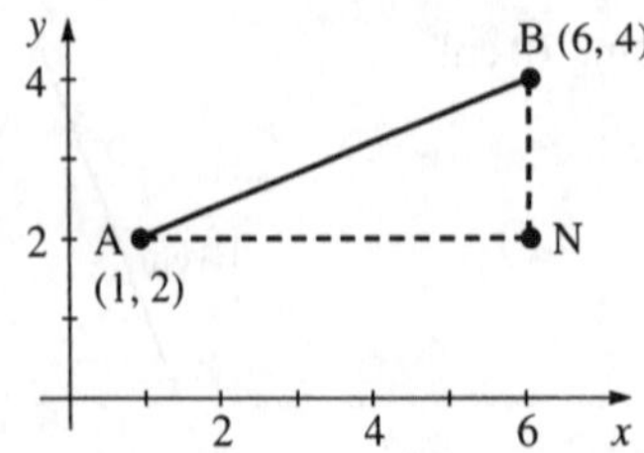

Work out the length AB. [First find the length of AN and BN.]

5. On squared paper plot P(1, 3), Q(6, 0), R(6, 6). Find the lengths of the sides of triangle PQR. Is the triangle isosceles?

In Questions **6** to **11** find x.

6.

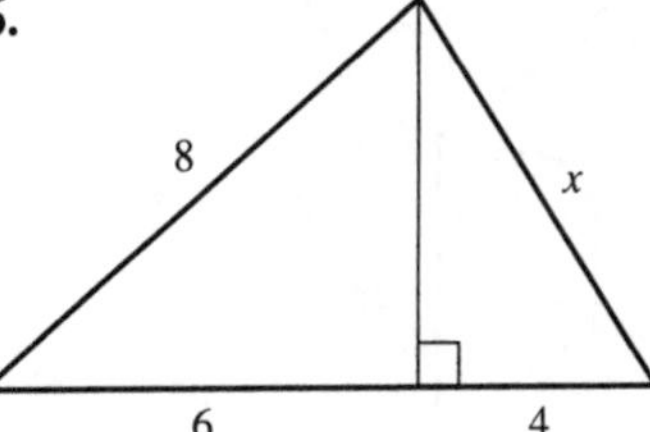

7.

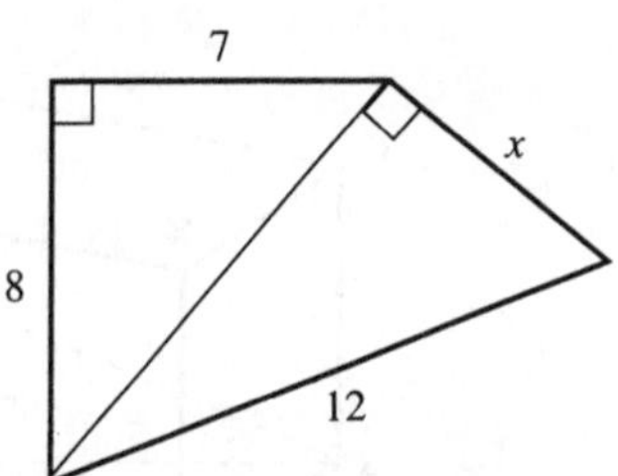

8.

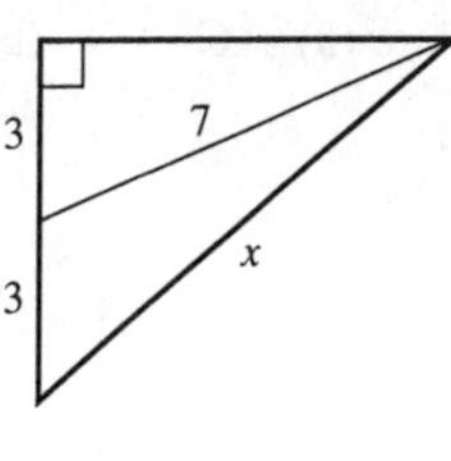

9.

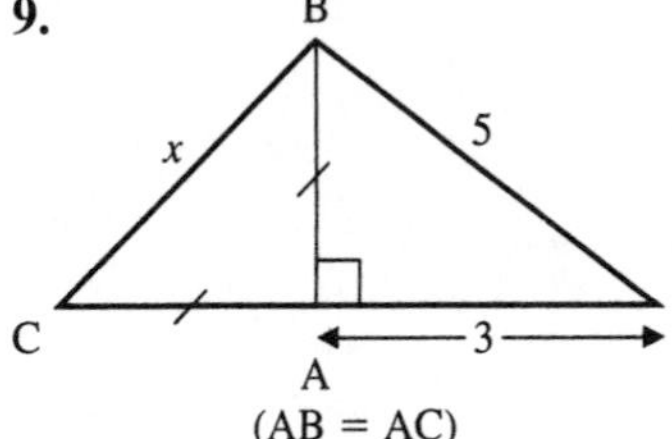

10.

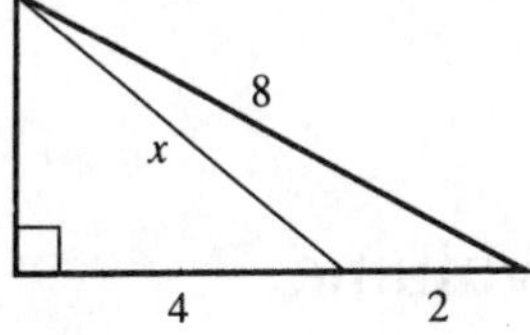

11.

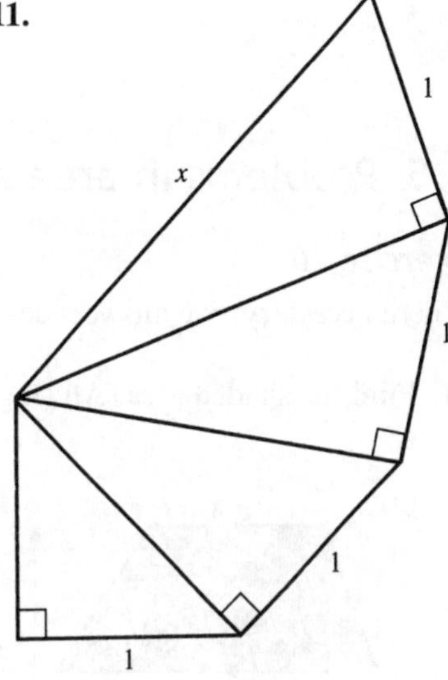

12. The most well known right-angled triangle is the 3, 4, 5 triangle $[3^2 + 4^2 = 5^2]$.
It is interesting to look at other right-angled triangles where all the sides are whole numbers.

(a) (i) Find c if $a = 5$, $b = 12$.
(ii) Find c if $a = 7$, $b = 24$.
(iii) Find a if $c = 41$, $b = 40$.

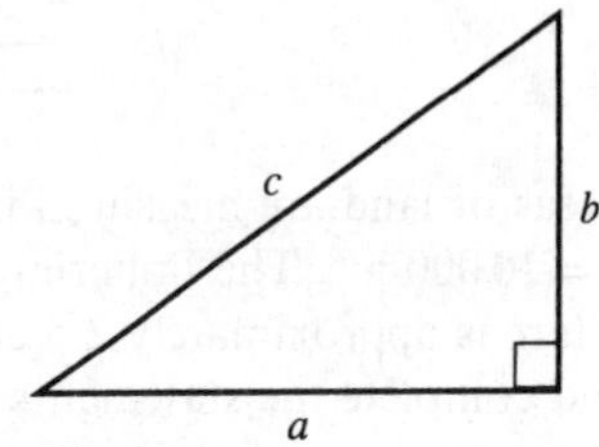

(b) Write the results in a table.

a	b	c
3	4	5
5	12	?
7	24	?
?	40	41

(c) Look at the sequences in the 'a' column and in the 'b' column. Also write down the connection between b and c for each triangle.

(d) Predict the next three sets of values of a, b, c. Check to see if they really do form right-angled triangles.

13. The diagram shows a rectangular block.

Calculate (a) AC (b) AY

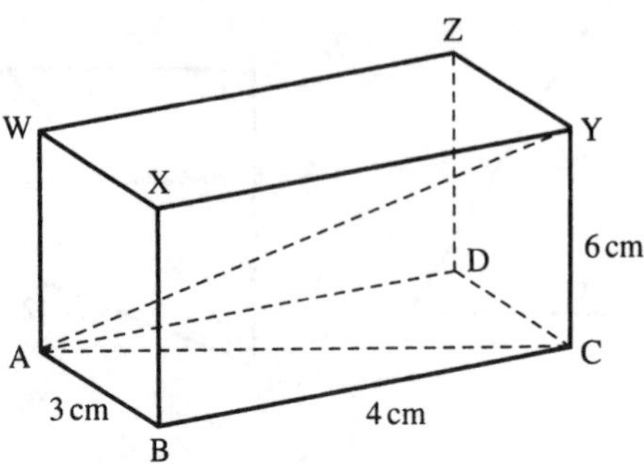

6.5 Problems in area and volume

Exercise 20

Where necessary give answers correct to 3 s.f.

1. Find the shaded area. All lengths are in cm.

(a)

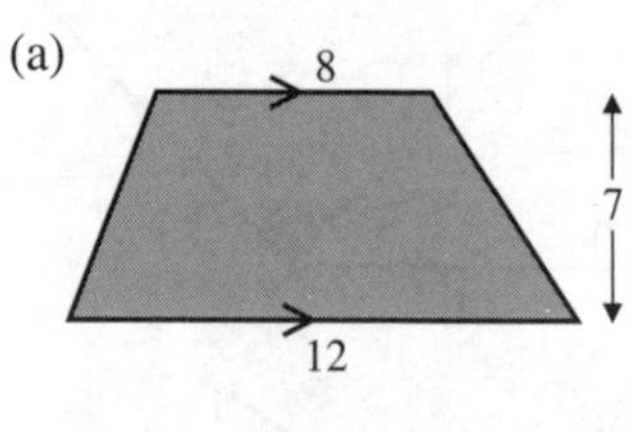

(b)

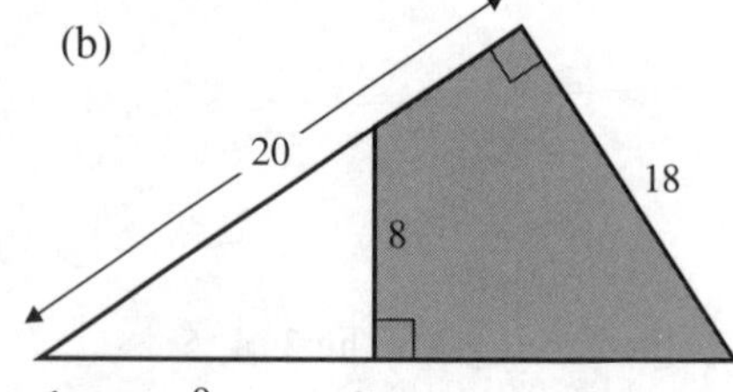

(c)

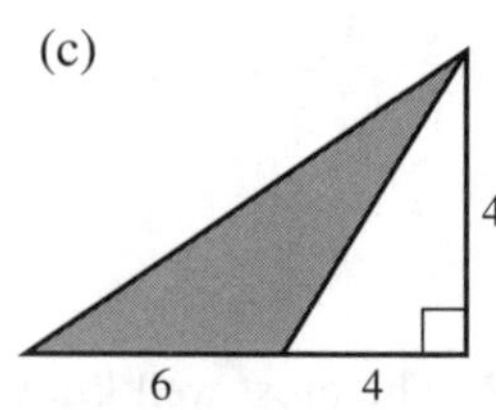

2. Large areas of land are measured in hectares. One hectare = 10 000 m^2. The Imperial unit, used in the past, is the acre. One hectare is approximately 2.5 acres.
Copy and complete the statements below.

(a)

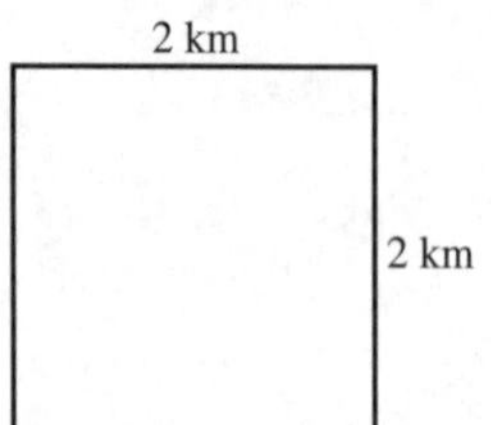

area of square = ________ m^2
area of square = ________ hectares.

(b)

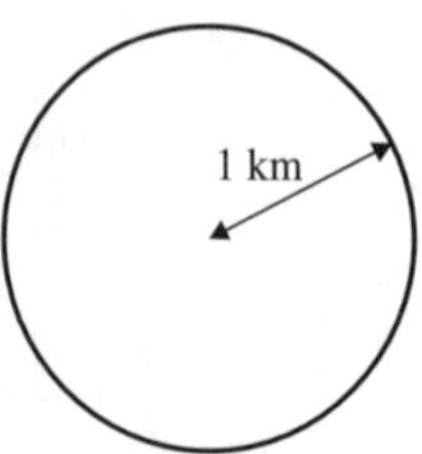

area of circle = ________ hectares.
area of circle is approximately ________ acres.

3. A decorator works out how many rolls of wallpaper he needs for a room from the table below.

Height from skirting	Measurement round walls (including doors and windows) in metres									
	8·6	9·8	11·0	12·2	13·4	14·6	15·8	17·0	18·2	19·4
2·20 m	4	4	0	5	6	6	7	7	8	8
2·35 m	4	4	5	5	6	6	7	8	8	9
2·50 m	4	5	5	6	6	7	7	8	8	9
2·65 m	4	5	5	6	6	7	8	8	9	9
2·80 m	4	5	6	6	7	7	8	9	9	10
2·95 m	5	5	6	7	7	8	9	9	10	10
3·10 m	5	5	6	7	8	8	9	10	10	11

A plan of one room is shown.
Work out:

(a) the total length round the walls (the perimeter)
(b) the number of rolls of wallpaper he needs
(c) the total cost of the wallpaper if one roll costs £3·20
(d) the area of the ceiling of the room.

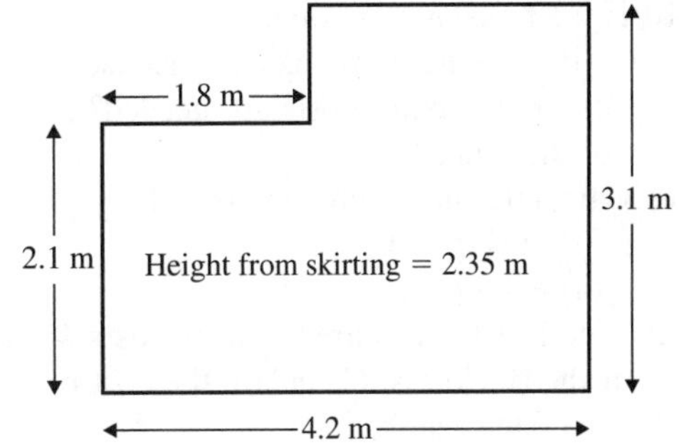

4. Here are two shapes both with a perimeter of 36 cm.
Calculate the *area* of each shape.

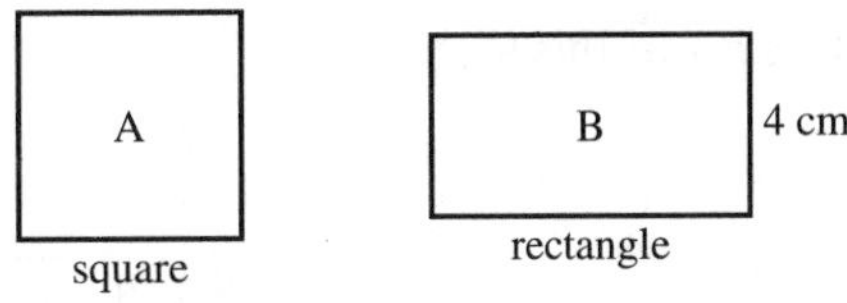

5. A square black tile of area 196 cm^2 is fitted next to a rectangular tile of area 112 cm^2.
Find the dimensions of each tile.

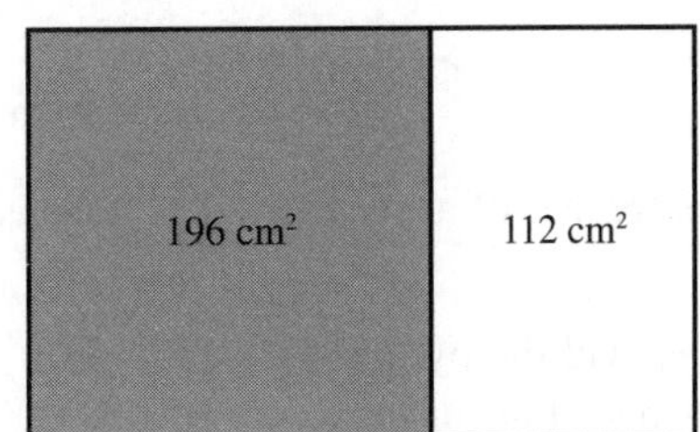

6. (a) What is the area of one page of this book?
(b) What area of paper (in m^2) is needed for the whole book?

7. Mr Hussein builds a fence at the end of his garden. The planks for the fence measure 1 m by 12 cm by 1 cm. The posts to which the planks are nailed are 10 cm square in cross section and 1·40 m long.

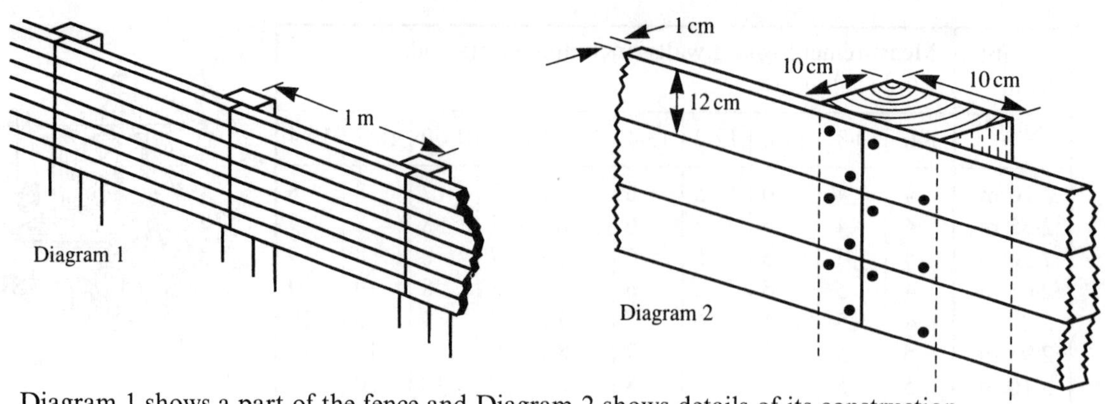

Diagram 1 shows a part of the fence and Diagram 2 shows details of its construction.

(a) How many planks are there between each pair of posts?

(b) If the fence is 5 m long:

(i) How many planks are needed?

(ii) How many posts are needed? (There is a post at each end of the fence.)

(c) Calculate the volume in cm^3 of

(i) each plank

(ii) each post.

(d) Wood of the required quality costs 4p per 100 cm^3, irrespective of the thickness. Calculate the cost of

(i) each plank

(ii) each post

(iii) all the wood for the whole fence.

8. Work out the area of this shape.

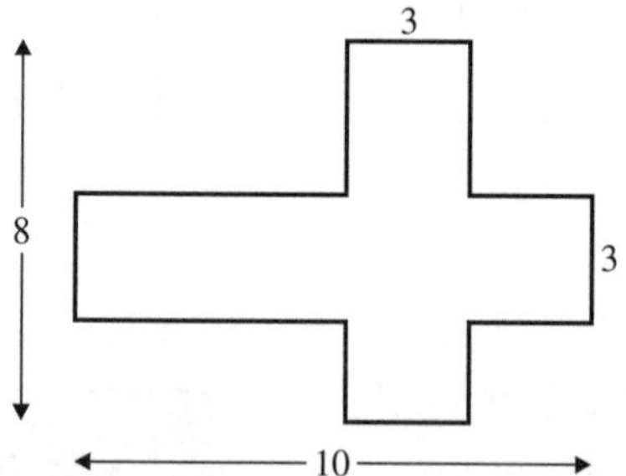

9. The diagram shows the net of a pyramid. The base is shaded. The lengths are in cm.

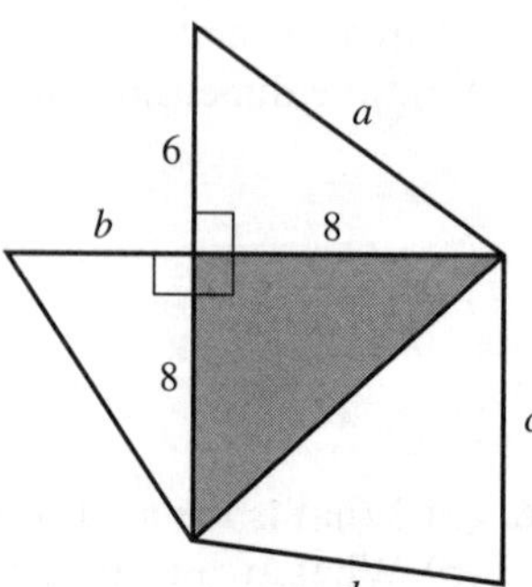

(a) How many edges will the pyramid have?

(b) How many vertices will it have?

(c) Find the lengths a, b, c, d.

(d) Use the formula $V = \frac{1}{3}$ base area$\times$height to calculate the volume of the pyramid.

10. Make a scale drawing and then use it to calculate the area of this field, correct to the nearest 100 m^2. Use a scale of 1 cm to 10 m.

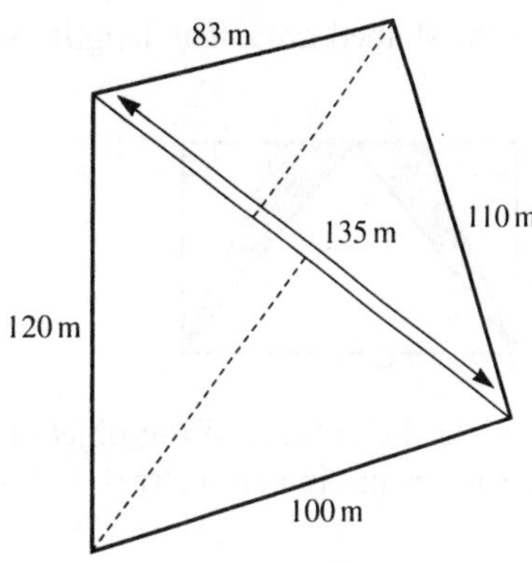

Exercise 21

1. Find the capacity in litres of the oil drum shown below. [1000 cm^3 = 1 litre]

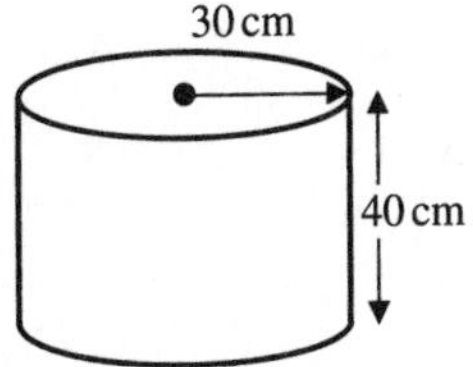

2. Find the volume in litres of a cylinder of height 55 cm and diameter 20 cm.

3. The diagram shows a square ABCD in which DX = XY = YC = AW. The area of the square is 45 cm^2.

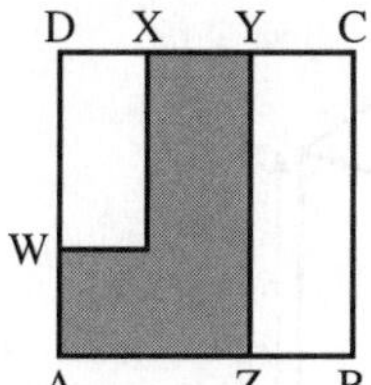

(a) What is the fraction $\frac{DX}{DC}$?

(b) What fraction of the square is shaded?

(c) Find the area of the unshaded part.

4. A floor 5 m by 20 m is covered by square tiles of side 20 cm. How many tiles are needed?

5. A rectangular field, 400 m long, has an area of 6 hectares. Calculate the perimeter of the field. [1 hectare = 10 000 m^2]

6. Find the shaded area. The lengths are in centimetres.

(a)

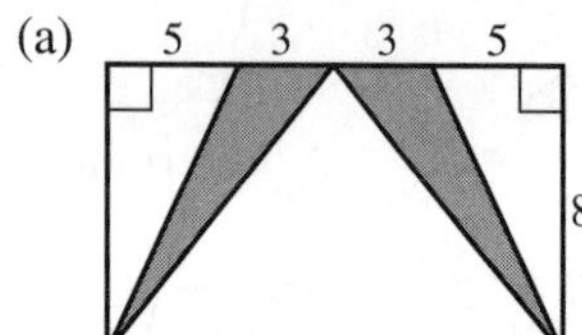

(b)

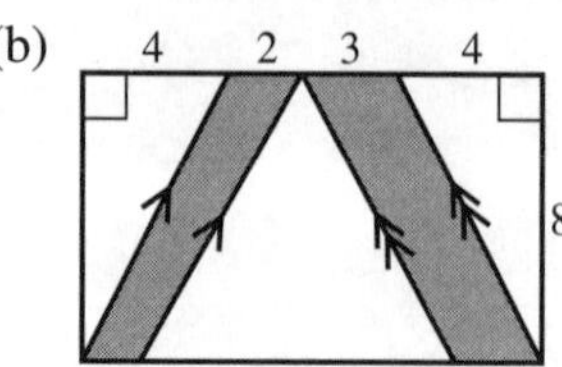

7. Calculate the volume of the object below.
The lengths are in centimetres.

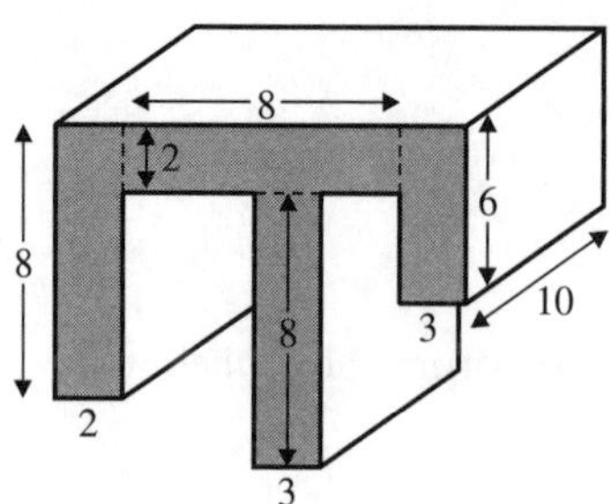

8. The arrowhead has an area of 3·6 cm^2. Find the length x.

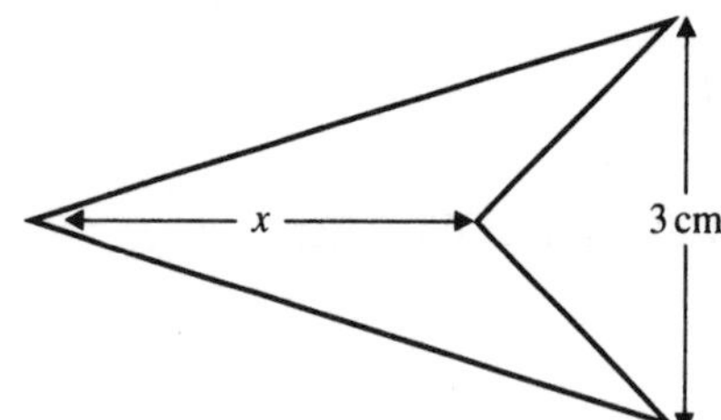

9. Find the length x.

(a)

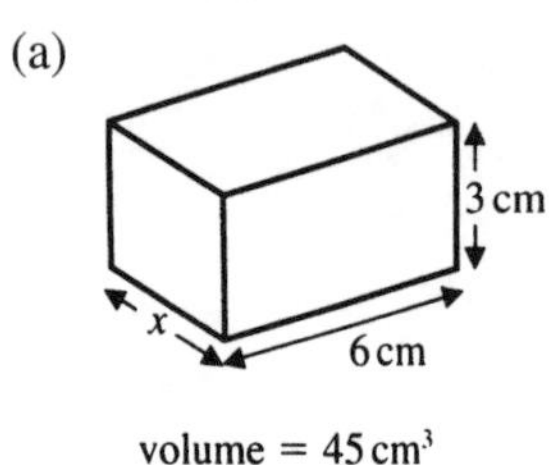

(b)

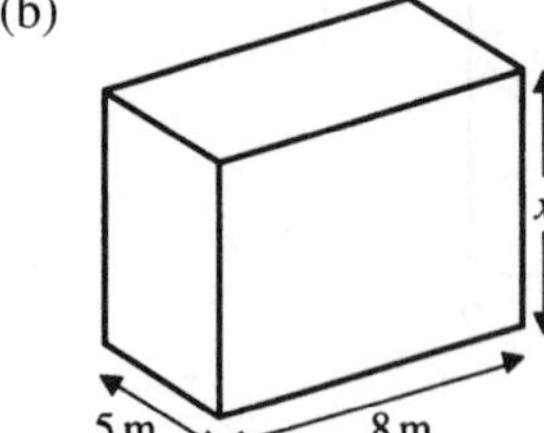

volume = 130 cm^3

10. A rectangular block of metal has dimensions 20 cm × 16 cm × 8 cm. It is melted down and recast into cubes of edge length 4 cm. How many cubes will be cast?

11. A freezer makes ice cubes which are rectangular blocks 5 cm × 3 cm × 2 cm. How many ice cubes can be made from 3 litres of water?

12. A wall, 12 m long, 150 cm high and 15 cm thick is constructed using bricks which measure 20 cm × 15 cm × 10 cm. How many bricks are needed (ignoring the cement)?

13. The diagonals of a rhombus measure 24 cm and 32 cm.
(a) Work out the area of the rhombus.
(b) Work out the perimeter of the rhombus.

14. The solid object shown is made from 27 small cubes each 1 cm by 1 cm by 1 cm. The small cubes are glued together and then the outside is painted red. Calculate
(a) the number of cubes with one face painted
(b) the number of cubes with two faces painted
(c) the number of cubes with three faces painted
(d) the number of cubes with no faces painted.
[Check that the answers to (a), (b), (c) and (d) add up to the correct number.]

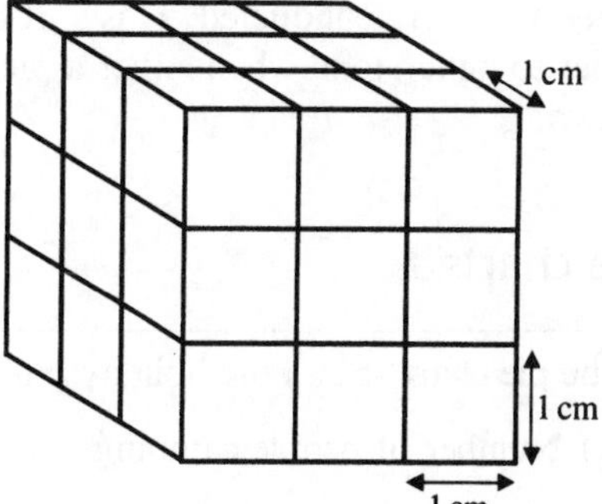

7 HANDLING DATA

7.1 Displaying data

Raw data in the form of numbers is collected when surveys or experiments are conducted. This sort of information is often much easier to understand when either a pie chart or a frequency diagram is drawn.

Pie charts

The pie chart shows the holiday intentions of 600 people.

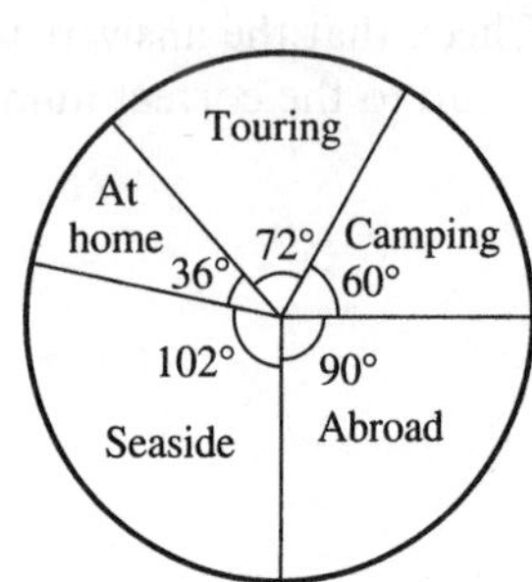

(a) Number of people camping $= \frac{60}{360} \times 600$

$= 100$

(b) Number of people touring $= \frac{72}{360} \times 600$

$= 120$

(c) Number of people at seaside $= \frac{102}{360} \times 600$

$= 170$

Exercise 1

1. The total cost of a holiday was £900.
   The pie chart shows how this cost was made up.

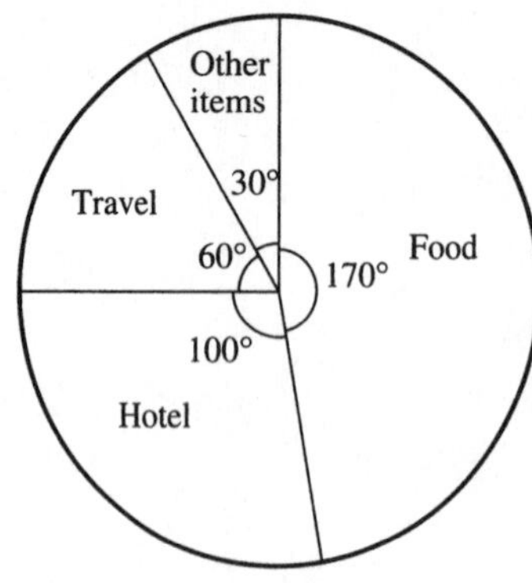

(a) How much was spent on food?
(b) How much was spent on travel?
(c) How much was spent on the hotel?
(d) How much was spent on other items?

2. Mr Billingsgate had an income of £60 000. The pie chart shows how he used the money.

   How much did he spend on
   (a) Food
   (b) Rent
   (c) Savings
   (d) Entertainment
   (e) Travel?

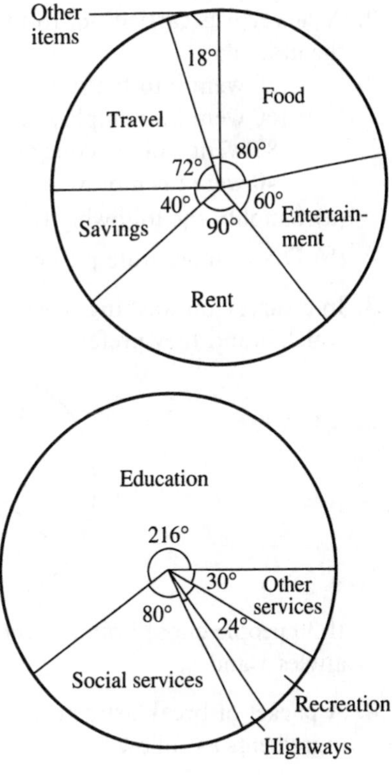

3. The total expenditure of a County Council is £36 000 000. The pie chart shows how the money was spent.

   (a) How much was spent on
       (i) Education (ii) Social services?
   (b) What is the angle representing expenditure on highways?
   (c) How much was spent on highways?

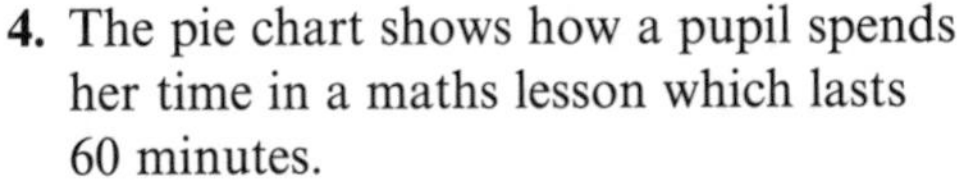

4. The pie chart shows how a pupil spends her time in a maths lesson which lasts 60 minutes.

   (a) How much time does she spend:
       (i) Getting ready to work
       (ii) Talking
       (iii) Sharpening a pencil?
   (b) She spends 3 minutes working. What is the angle on the pie chart for the time spent working?

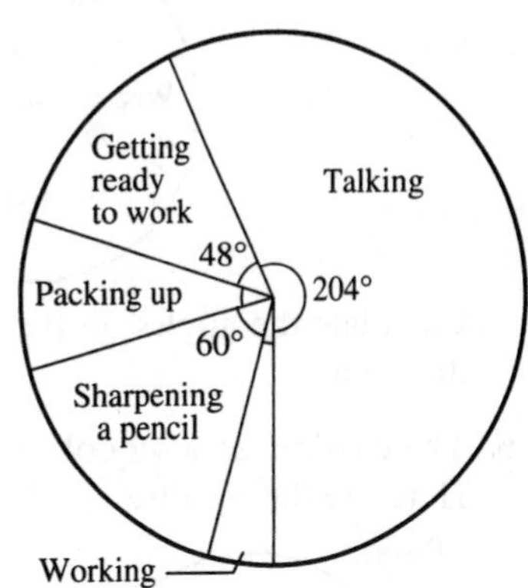

Exercise 2

1. At the semi-final stage of the F.A. Cup, 72 neutral referees were asked to predict who they thought would win. Their answers were:

Spurs	9	Everton	22
Manchester United	40	York City	1

   (a) Work out
       (i) $\frac{9}{72}$ of 360° (ii) $\frac{40}{72}$ of 360° (iii) $\frac{22}{72}$ of 360° (iv) $\frac{1}{72}$ of 360°
   (b) Draw an accurate pie chart to display the predictions of the 72 referees.

2. A survey was carried out to find what 400 pupils did at the end of the fifth year:

120 went into the sixth form
160 went into employment
80 went to F.E. colleges
40 were unemployed.

(a) Simplify the following fractions: $\frac{120}{400}$; $\frac{160}{400}$; $\frac{80}{400}$; $\frac{40}{400}$.

(b) Draw an accurate pie chart to show the information above.

3. In a survey on washing powder 180 people were asked to state which brand they preferred. 45 chose Brand A.

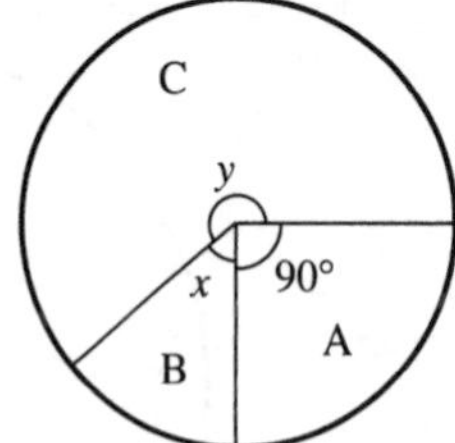

If 30 people chose brand B and 105 chose Brand C, calculate the angles x and y.

4. A packet of breakfast cereal weighing 600 g contains four ingredients as follows.

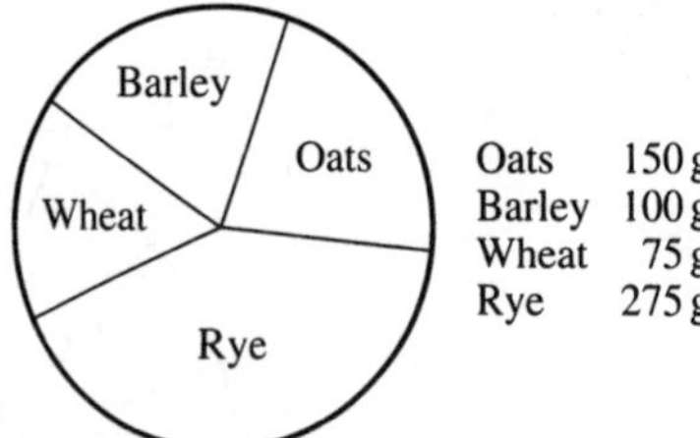

Calculate the angles on the pie chart shown and draw an accurate diagram.

5. The children at a school were asked to state their favourite colour. Here are the results.

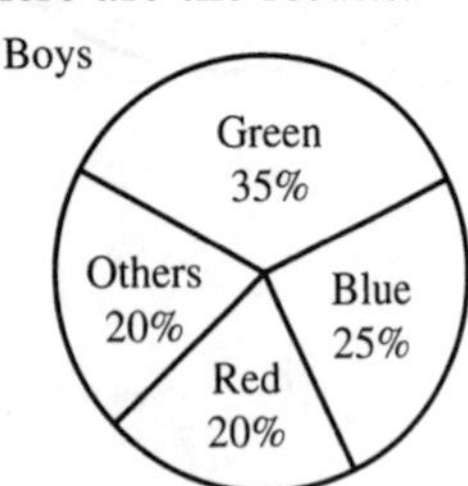

There were 100 boys

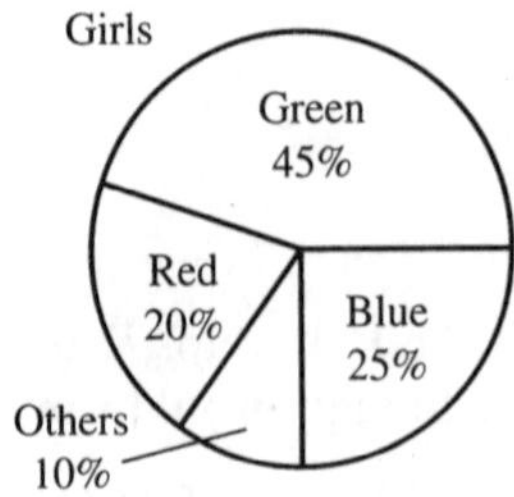

There were 60 girls

Tony says 'The same number of boys and girls chose red.'
Mel says 'More boys than girls chose blue.'

(a) Use both charts to explain whether or not Tony is right.

(b) Use both charts to explain whether or not Mel is right.

Frequency diagrams and bar charts

The marks obtained by 36 pupils in a test were as follows.

1	3	2	3	4	2	1	3	0
5	3	0	1	4	0	4	4	3
3	4	3	1	3	4	3	1	2
1	3	4	0	4	3	2	5	3

Here is the tally chart for this data.

Mark	Tally	Frequency
0	||||	4
1	~~||||~~ |	6
2	||||	4
3	~~||||~~ ~~||||~~ ||	12
4	~~||||~~ |||	8
5	||	2

The same information is shown on a frequency diagram.

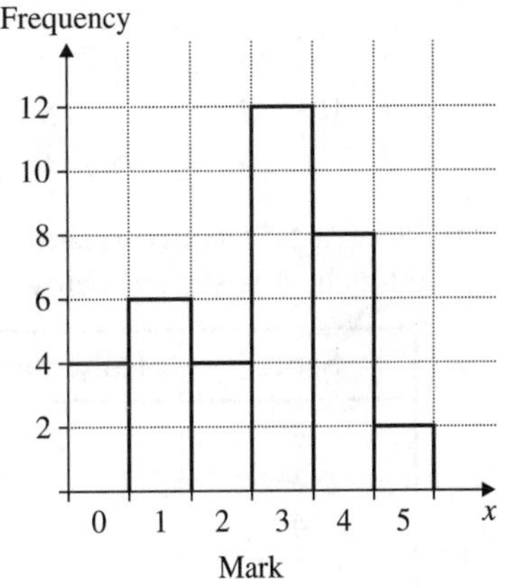

Exercise 3

1. In a survey, the number of occupants in the cars passing a school was recorded.

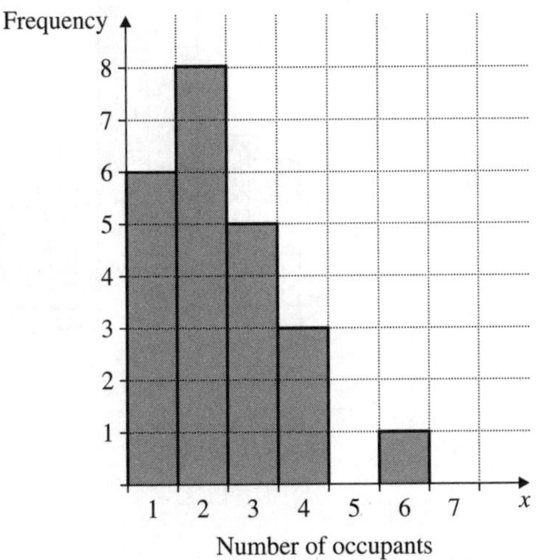

(a) How many cars had 3 occupants?

(b) How many cars had less than 4 occupants?

(c) How many cars were in the survey?

(d) What was the total number of occupants in all the cars in the survey?

(e) What fraction of the cars had only one occupant?

2. In an experiment, two dice were thrown sixty times and the total score showing was recorded.

2	3	5	4	8	6	4	7	5	10
7	8	7	6	12	11	8	11	7	6
6	5	7	7	8	6	7	3	6	7
12	3	10	4	3	7	2	11	8	5
7	10	7	5	7	5	10	11	7	10
4	8	6	4	6	11	6	12	11	5

(a) Draw a tally chart to show the results of the experiment. The tally chart is started below.

Score	Tally marks	Frequency
2	||	2
3	||||	4
4		
.		
.		

(b) Draw a frequency graph to illustrate the results. Plot the frequency on the vertical axis.

3. The bar chart shows the profit/loss made by a toy shop from September 1999 to April 2000.
(a) Estimate the total profit in this period.
(b) Describe what is happening to the shop's profits in this period. Try to think of an explanation for the shape of the bar chart.

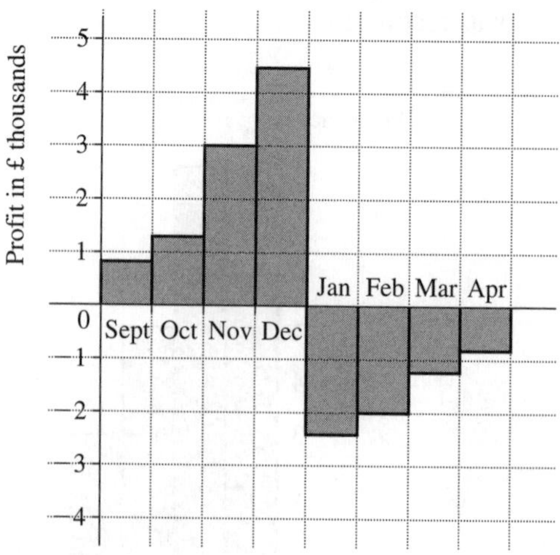

Discrete and continuous data

The data that we record can be either *discrete* or *continuous*.
Discrete data can take only certain values:

- the number of peas in a pod
- the number of children in a class
- shoe sizes.

Continuous data comes from measuring and can take any value:

- height of a child
- weight of an apple
- time taken to boil a kettle.

Grouped data

Sometimes the data to be displayed can take a wide range of values. In such cases, it is convenient to put the data into groups before drawing a tally chart and frequency diagram.

The hand spans  of children were measured as follows.

14·8	20·0	16·9	20·7	18·1	17·5	18·7
19·0	19·8	17·8	14·3	19·2	21·7	17·4
16·0	15·9	18·5	19·3	16·6	21·2	18·4

The data can be grouped as follows and the frequency diagram drawn.

Class intervals	Tally
$14 \leqslant s < 16$	|||
$16 \leqslant s < 18$	~~||||~~ |
$18 \leqslant s < 20$	~~||||~~ |||
$20 \leqslant s < 22$	||||

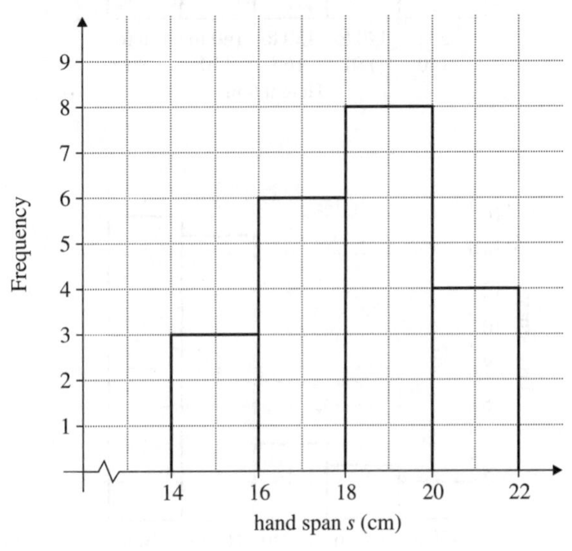

Notice that '20·0' goes into the last group $20 \leqslant s < 22$.

- This diagram is a *histogram*. The data is continuous so there are no gaps between the bars

  The data must be grouped into equal class intervals if the height of the bars is to represent frequency.

Exercise 4

1. The graph shows the heights of pupils in a class.
   (a) How many pupils were over 150 cm tall?
   (b) How many pupils had a height between 135 cm and 155 cm?
   (c) How many pupils were in the class?

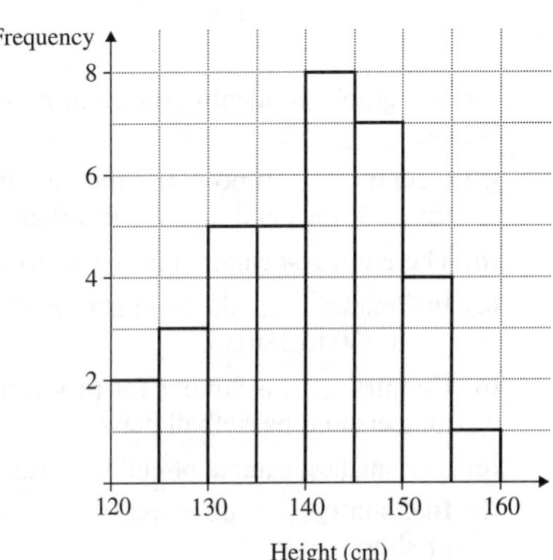

2. In a survey, the heights of children aged 15 were measured in four countries around the world. A random sample of children was chosen by computer, not necessarily the same number from each country.

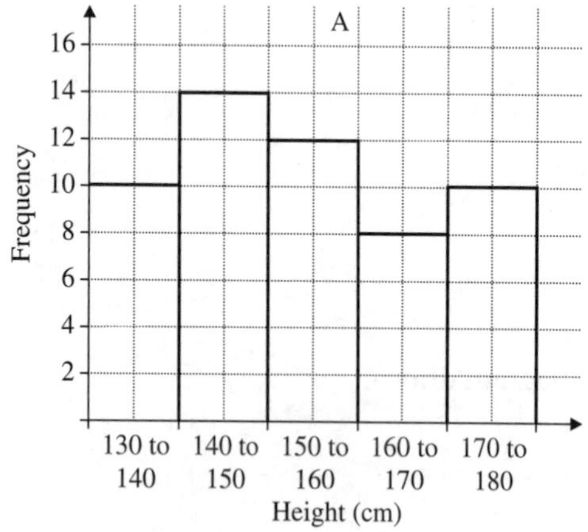

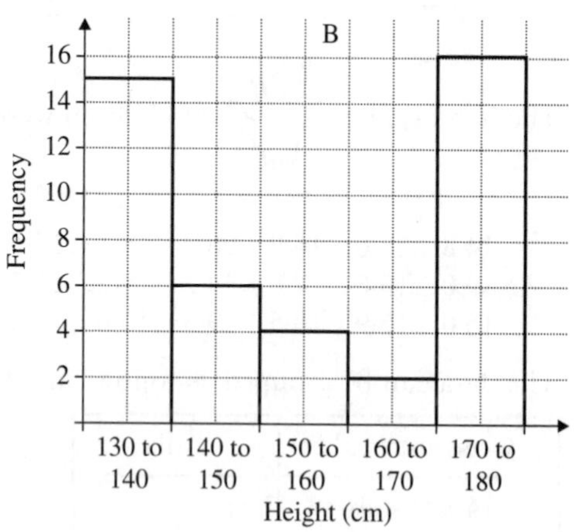

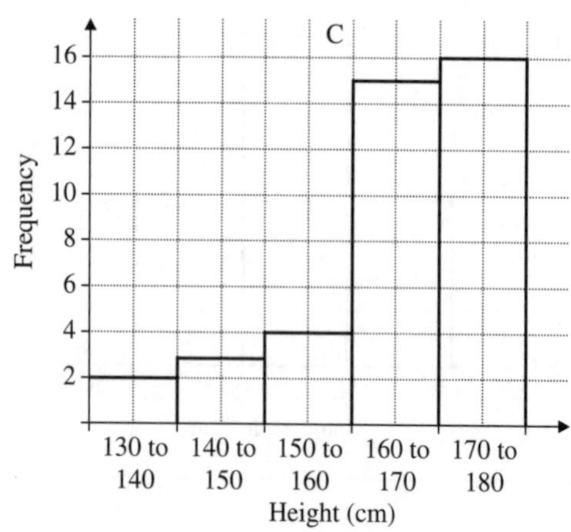

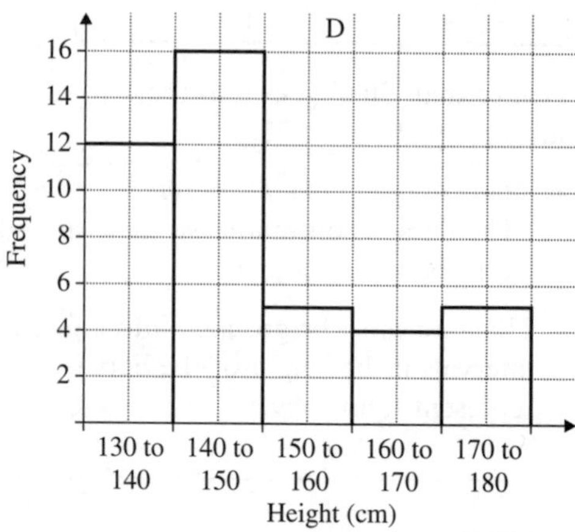

Use the graphs to identify the country in each of the statements below.

(a) Country ____ is poor and the diet of children is not good. Two-thirds of the children were less than 150 cm tall.

(b) There were 54 children in the sample from Country ____.

(c) In Country ____ the heights were spread fairly evenly across the range 130 to 180 cm.

(d) Country ____ is famous for producing lots of good high jumpers and basketball players.

(e) The smallest sample of children came from Country ____.

(f) In Country ____ three-quarters of the children were either tall or short.

3. Scientists have developed a new fertilizer which is supposed to increase the size of carrots. A farmer grew carrots in two adjacent fields A and B and treated one of the fields with the new fertilizer. A random sample of 50 carrots was taken from each field and weighed. Here are the results for Field A (all in grams).

118	91	82	105	72	92	103	95	73	109
63	111	102	116	101	104	107	119	111	108
112	97	100	75	85	94	76	67	93	112
70	116	118	103	65	107	87	98	105	117
114	106	82	90	77	88	66	99	95	103

Make a tally chart using the groups given.

Weight	Tally	Frequency
$60 \leqslant w < 70$		
$70 \leqslant w < 80$		
$80 \leqslant w < 90$		
$90 \leqslant w < 100$		
$100 \leqslant w < 110$		
$110 \leqslant w < 120$		

The frequency graph for Field B is shown below.

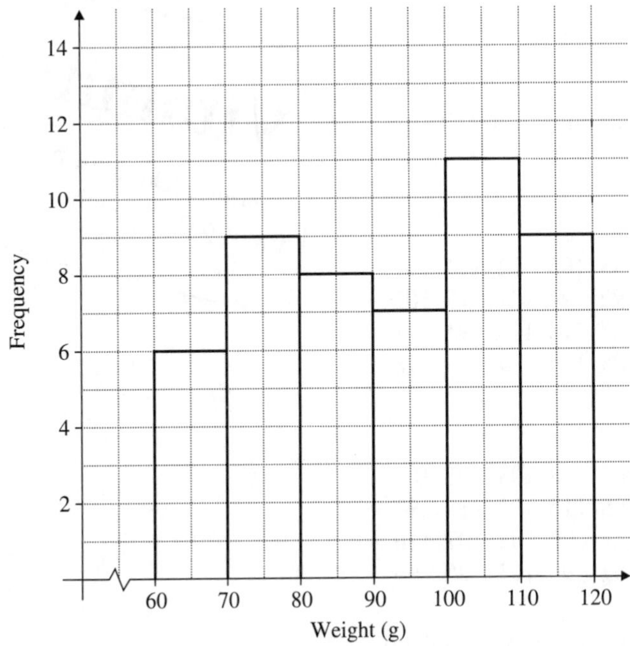

Copy the graph above and, in a different colour, draw the graph for Field A.
Which field do you think was treated with the new fertilizer?

4. Karine and Jackie intend to go skiing in February. They have information about the expected snowfall in February for two possible places.

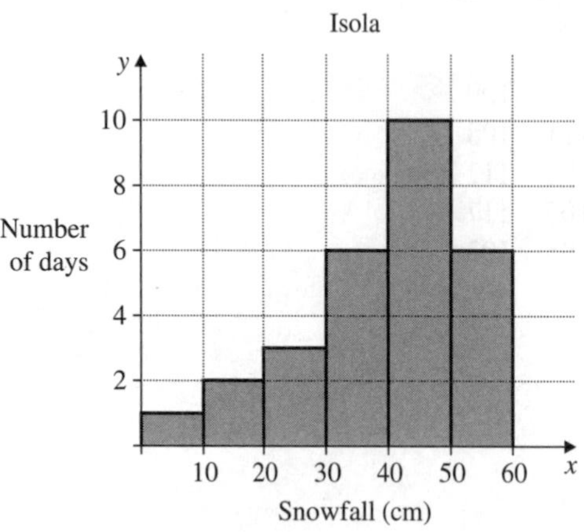

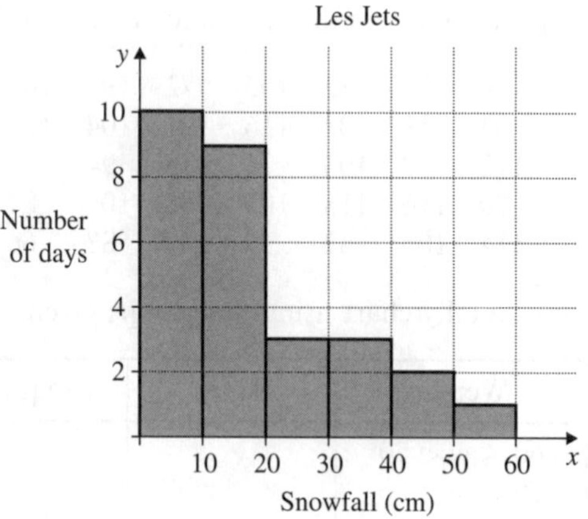

Decide where you think they should go. It doesn't matter where you decide, but you *must* say why, using the charts above to help you explain.

5. Some people think that children's IQs can be increased when they eat extra vitamins.
In an experiment, 52 children took an IQ test before and then after a course of vitamin pills.
Here are the results.

Before:

81	107	93	104	103	96	101	102	93	105	82	106	97
108	94	111	92	86	109	95	116	92	94	101	117	102
95	108	112	107	106	124	125	103	127	118	113	91	113
113	114	109	128	115	86	106	91	85	119	129	99	98

After:

93	110	92	125	99	127	114	98	107	128	103	91	104
103	83	125	91	104	99	102	116	98	115	92	117	97
126	100	112	113	85	108	97	101	125	93	102	107	116
94	117	95	108	117	96	102	87	107	94	103	95	96

(a) Put the scores into convenient groups between 80 and 130.

(b) Draw two frequency graphs to display the results.

(c) Write a conclusion. Did the vitamin pills make a significant difference?

Frequency polygons

We have seen earlier on page 266 how a frequency distribution can be shown in the form of a bar chart.

The number of peas in 40 pea pods is shown below. Note: Frequency goes on the vertical axis.

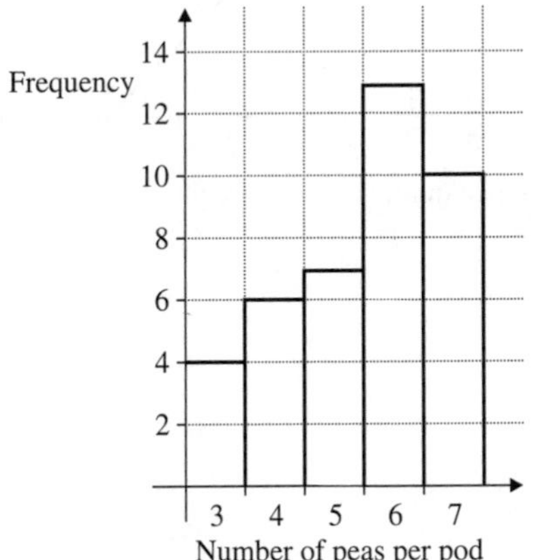

A *frequency polygon* is formed by joining the mid-points of the tops of the bars in a bar chart by straight lines.

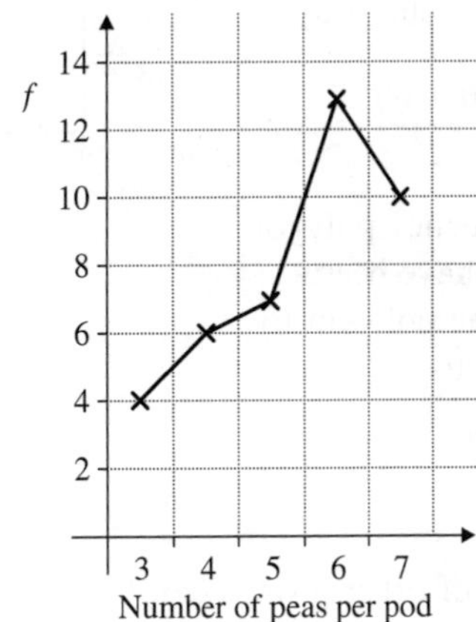

Class boundaries

The lengths of 36 pea pods were measured and rounded to the nearest mm. So a pea pod which is actually 59·2 mm long is rounded off to 59 mm.

52	80	65	82	77	60	72	83	63
78	84	75	53	73	70	86	55	88
85	59	76	86	73	89	91	76	92
66	93	84	62	79	90	73	68	71

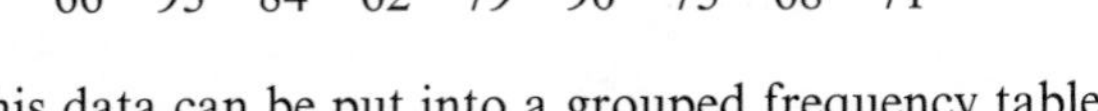

This data can be put into a grouped frequency table.

Length (mm)	Tally	Frequency
$50 \leqslant l < 60$	||||	4
$60 \leqslant l < 70$	~~||||~~ |	6
$70 \leqslant l < 80$	~~||||~~ ~~||||~~ ||	12
$80 \leqslant l < 90$	~~||||~~ ~~||||~~	10
$90 \leqslant l < 100$	||||	4

For the class $50 \leqslant l < 60$, the class boundaries are 50 and 60. The bar will go from 50 to 60 mm.

The frequency polygon for this data can be drawn in the same way as with discrete data. Note that you can draw the frequency polygon *without* drawing a bar chart first. You must calculate the mid-points of each group.

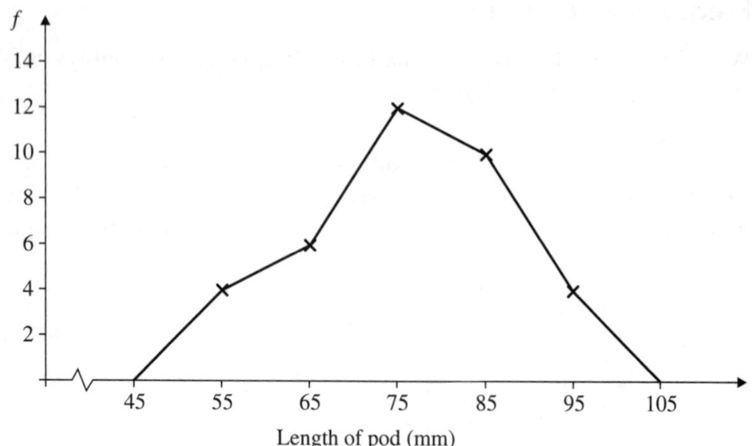

For the $50 \leqslant l < 60$ group:

$$\text{mid-point} = \frac{50 + 60}{2} = 55$$

Note: This frequency polygon is closed. Lines have been drawn to join the polygon to the horizontal axis.

Mid-points

The mid-points of other groups can be calculated as follows:

(a)

Mark	Mid-point
0–9	4·5 $\left(\frac{0+9}{2}\right)$
10–19	14·5 $\left(\frac{10+19}{2}\right)$

(b)

Height	Mid-point
$150 \leqslant h < 155$	152·5 $\left(\frac{150+155}{2}\right)$
$155 \leqslant h < 160$	157·5 $\left(\frac{155+160}{2}\right)$

Exercise 5

1. In a survey the number of people in 100 cars passing a set of traffic lights was counted. Here are the results:

Number of people in car	0	1	2	3	4	5	6
Frequency	0	10	35	25	20	10	0

(a) Draw a bar chart to illustrate this data.
(b) On the same graph draw the frequency polygon.

Here we have started the bar chart.
For frequency, use a scale of 1 cm for 5 units.

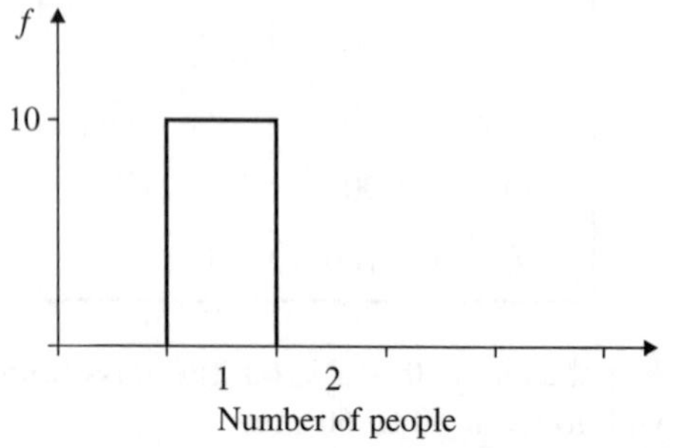

2. The frequency polygon shows the marks obtained by pupils in a maths test.

   (a) How many pupils got 7 marks?

   (b) How many pupils were there altogether?

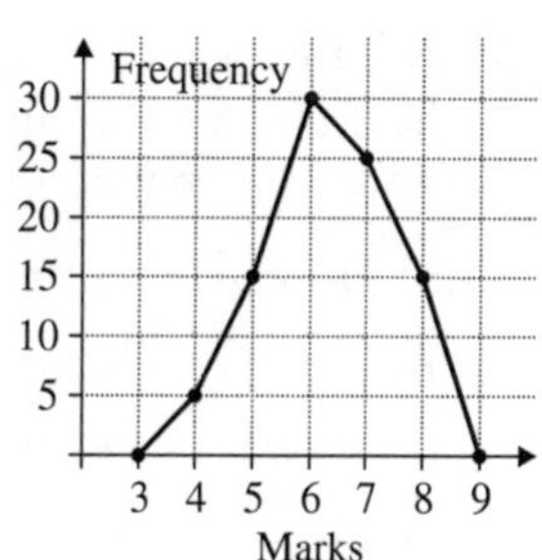

3. The members of several professional basketball teams were measured for their heights. The results were:

Height	Frequency
$180 \leqslant h < 185$	5
$185 \leqslant h < 190$	8
$190 \leqslant h < 195$	15
$195 \leqslant h < 200$	11
$200 \leqslant h < 205$	6
$205 \leqslant h < 210$	2

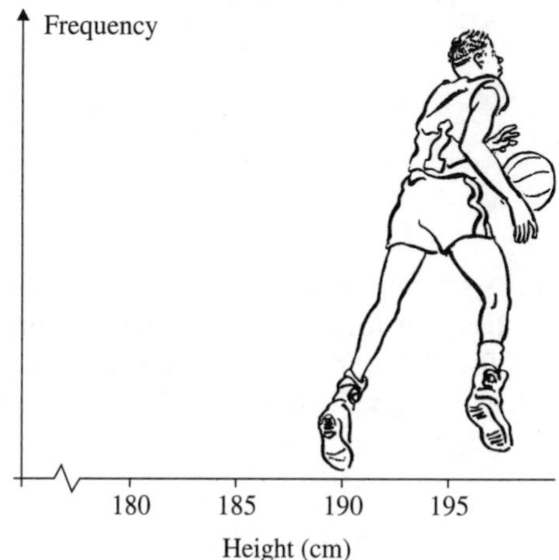

Draw a histogram and a frequency polygon to illustrate this data.

4. Using the same axes, with heights from 80 cm to 200 cm, draw frequency polygons for the heights of five year olds and sixteen year olds.

   Describe briefly the main differences between the two frequency polygons.

Five year olds	
Height (cm)	Frequency
80–90	0
90–100	6
100–110	15
110–120	3
120–130	1
130–140	0

Sixteen year olds	
Height (cm)	Frequency
120–130	0
130–140	2
140–150	3
150–160	4
160–170	7
170–180	6
180–190	3
190–200	0

5. Two frequency polygons are shown giving the distribution of the weights of players in two different sports A and B.

   (a) How many people played sport A?

   (b) Comment on two differences between the two frequency polygons.

   (c) Either for A or for B suggest a sport where you would expect the frequency polygon of weights to have this shape. Explain in one sentence why you have chosen that sport.

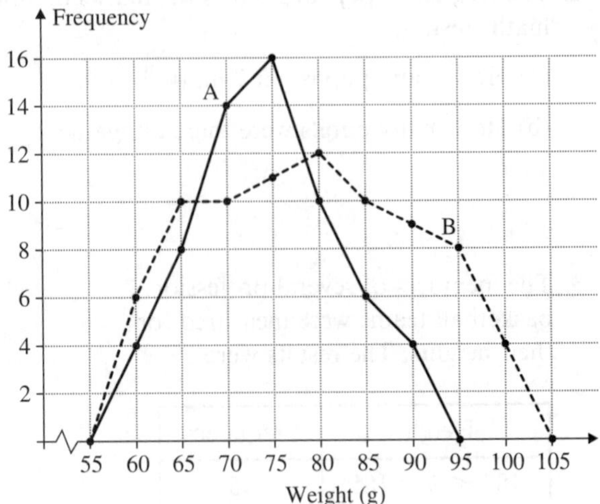

6. A scientist at an agricultural college is studying the effect of a new fertilizer for raspberries. She measures the heights of the plants and also the total weight of fruit collected. She does this for two sets of plants: one with the new fertilizer and one without it. Here are the frequency polygons.

--- with fertilizer
—— without fertilizer

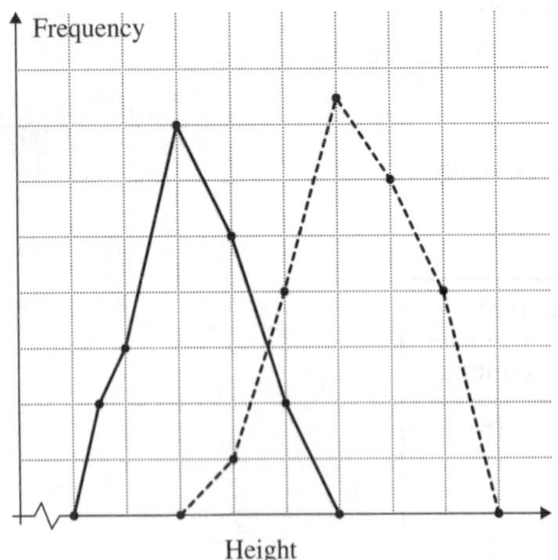

Frequency
Weight

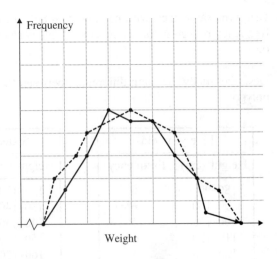

(a) What effect did the fertilizer have on the heights of the plants?

(b) What effect was there on the weights of fruit collected?

Stem and leaf diagrams

Data can be displayed in groups in a stem and leaf diagram.
Here are the marks of 20 girls in a science test.

54	42	61	47	24	43	55	62	30	27
28	43	54	46	25	32	49	73	50	45

We will put the marks into groups 20–29, 30–39,:... 70–79.
We will choose the tens digit as the 'stem' and the units as the 'leaf'.

The first four marks are shown [54, 42, 61, 47]

Stem (tens)	Leaf (units)
2	
3	
4	2 7
5	4
6	1
7	

The complete diagram is below ...... and then with the leaves in numerical order:

Stem	Leaf
2	4 7 8 5
3	0 2
4	2 7 3 3 6 9 5
5	4 5 4 0
6	1 2
7	3

Stem	Leaf
2	4 5 7 8
3	0 2
4	2 3 3 5 6 7 9
5	0 4 4 5
6	1 2
7	3

The diagram shows the shape of the distribution. It is also easy to find the mode, the median and the range.

Back-to-back stem plots

Two sets of data can be compared using a *back-to-back stem plot*.
Here are the marks of 20 boys who took the same science test as the girls above.

33	55	63	74	20	35	40	67	21	38
51	64	57	48	46	67	44	59	75	56

These marks are entered onto
the back-to-back stem plot shown.

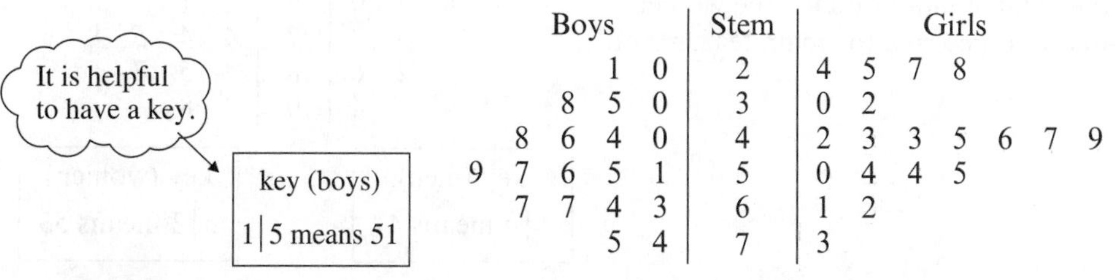

Boys	Stem	Girls
1 0	2	4 5 7 8
8 5 0	3	0 2
8 6 4 0	4	2 3 3 5 6 7 9
9 7 6 5 1	5	0 4 4 5
7 7 4 3	6	1 2
5 4	7	3

Exercise 6

1. The marks of 24 children in a test are shown

41	23	35	15	40	39	47	29
52	54	45	27	28	36	48	51
59	65	42	32	46	53	66	38

Draw a stem and leaf diagram. The first three entries are shown.

Stem	Leaf
1	
2	3
3	5
4	1
5	
6	

2. Draw a stem and leaf diagram for each set of data below

(a)

24	52	31	55	40	37	58	61	25	46
44	67	68	75	73	28	20	59	65	39

Stem	Leaf
2	
3	
4	
5	
6	
7	

(b)

30	41	53	22	72	54	35	47
44	67	46	38	59	29	47	28

3. Here is the stem and leaf diagram showing the masses, in kg, of some people in a lift.
(a) Write down the range of the masses
(b) How many people were in the lift?
(c) What is the median mass?

Stem (tens)	Leaf (units)
3	2 5
4	1 1 3 7 8
5	0 2 5 8
6	4 8
7	1
8	2

4. In this question the stem shows the units digit and the leaf shows the first digit after the decimal point.
Draw the stem and leaf diagram using the following data:

2·4	3·1	5·2	4·7	1·4	6·2	4·5	3·3
4·0	6·3	3·7	6·7	4·6	4·9	5·1	5·5
1·8	3·8	4·5	2·4	5·8	3·3	4·6	2·8

key
3 | 7 means 3·7

Stem	Leaf
1	
2	
3	
4	
5	
6	

5. Here is a back-to-back stem plot showing the pulse rates of several people.
(a) How many men were tested?
(b) What was the median pulse rate for the women?
(c) Write a sentence to describe the main features of the data.

Men		Women
5 1	4	
7 4 2	5	3
8 2 0	6	2 1
5 2	7	4 4 5 8 9
2 6	8	2 5 7
4	9	2 8

key (men)
1 | 4 means 41

key (women)
5 | 3 means 53

7.2 Questionnaires

Surveys are conducted by organisations for a variety of reasons.

- Newspapers publish opinion polls about the voting intentions of people or the popularity of the Prime Minister. They provide interesting stories for the newspaper.

- Car makers conduct surveys to find what features most people want to have in their cars such as radios, electric windows, sun roofs and so on. They then use the survey results to help with the design of future models.

- Supermarkets like Tesco or Sainsbury conduct surveys to discover what things are most important to their customers. They might want to find out how people felt about ease of car parking, price of food, quality of food, length of time queueing to pay, etc.

- Surveys are made to find the popularity of various TV programmes. Advertisers are prepared to pay a large sum for a 30 second advertisement in a programme with an audience of 10 million people.

- Most surveys are conducted using questionnaires. It is very important to design the questionnaire well so that:
  (a) people will cooperate and will answer the questions honestly
  (b) the questions are not biased
  (c) the answers to the questions can be analysed and presented for ease of understanding.

Checklist

A Provide an introduction to the sheet so that your subject knows the purpose of the questionnaire.

'Proposed new traffic lights'

B Make the questions easy to understand and specific to answer.
Do *not* ask vague questions like this. → ~~Did you see much of the Olympics on TV?~~
The answers could be:
'Yes, a lot'
'Not much'
'Only the best bits'
'Once or twice a day'
You will find it hard to analyse this sort of data.

A *better* question is:

'How much of the Olympic coverage did you watch?' Tick one box

Not at all ☐
Up to 1 hour per day ☐
1 to 2 hours per day ☐
More than 2 hours per day ☐

C Make sure that the questions are not *leading* questions. It is human nature not to contradict the questioner. Remember that the survey is to find out opinions of other people, not to support your own.
Do *not* ask:
'Do you agree that BBC has the best sports coverage?'
A better question is:

'Which of the following has the best sports coverage?'

BBC	ITV	Channel 4	Satellite TV
☐	☐	☐	☐

You might ask for one tick or possibly numbers 1, 2, 3, 4 to show an order of preference.

D If you are going to ask sensitive questions (about age or income, for example), design the question with care so as not to offend or embarrass.
Do *not* ask:
'How old are you?'
or 'Give your date of birth'
A better question is:

Tick one box for your age group.			
15–17	18–20	21–30	31–50
☐	☐	☐	☐

E Do not ask more questions than necessary and put the easy questions first.

Exercise 7

Criticise the following questions and suggest a better question which overcomes the problem involved.
Write some questions with 'yes/no' answers and some questions which involve multiple responses.
Remember to word your questions simply.

1. Do you think it is ridiculous to spend money on food 'mountains' in Europe while people in Africa are starving?
2. What do you think of the new head teacher?
3. How dangerous do you think it is to fly in a single-engined aeroplane?

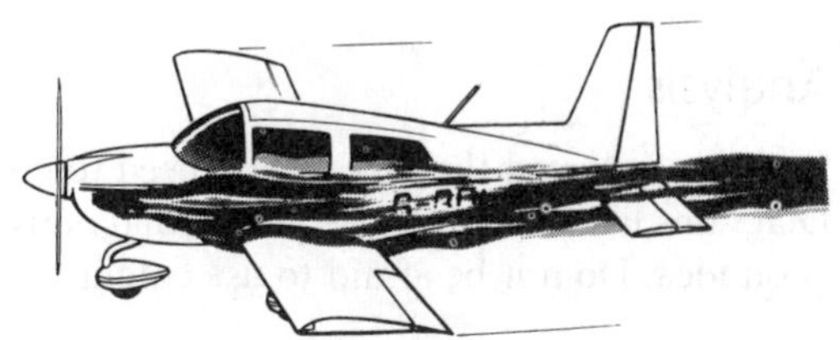

4. How much would you pay to use the new car park?

   ☐ less than £1 ☐ more than £2·50

5. Do you agree that English and Maths are the most important subjects at school?
6. Do you or your parents often hire videos from a shop?
7. Do you think that we get too much homework?
8. Do you think you would still eat meat if you had been to see the animals killed?

In Questions **9** to **12** decide whether the method of choosing people to answer questions is satisfactory or not. Consider whether or not the sample suggested might be *biased* in some way. Where necessary suggest a better way of obtaining a sample.

9. A teacher, with responsibility for school meals, wants to hear pupils' opinions on the meals currently provided. She waits next to the dinner queue and questions the first 50 pupils as they pass.

10. To find out how satisfied customers are with the service they receive from the telephone company, a person telephones 200 people chosen at random from the telephone directory.

11. A journalist wants to know the views of local people about a new one-way system in the town centre. She takes the electoral roll for the town and selects a random sample of 200 people.

12. A pollster working for the BBC wants to know how many people are watching a new series which is being shown. She questions 200 people as they are leaving Safeway between 10.00 and 12.00 one Thursday.

Analysis

Having conducted the survey, you need to display your results clearly. Diagrams like pie charts, frequency diagrams and scatter graphs are a good idea. Do not be afraid to use colours.

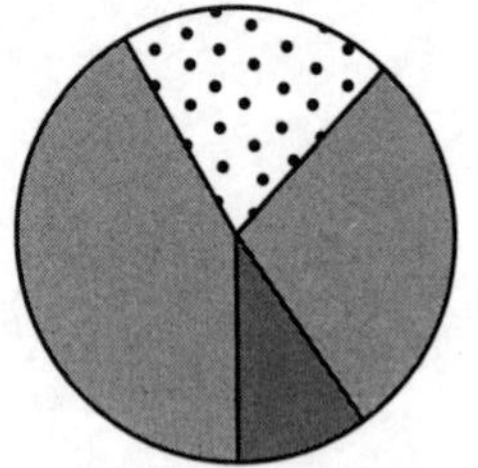

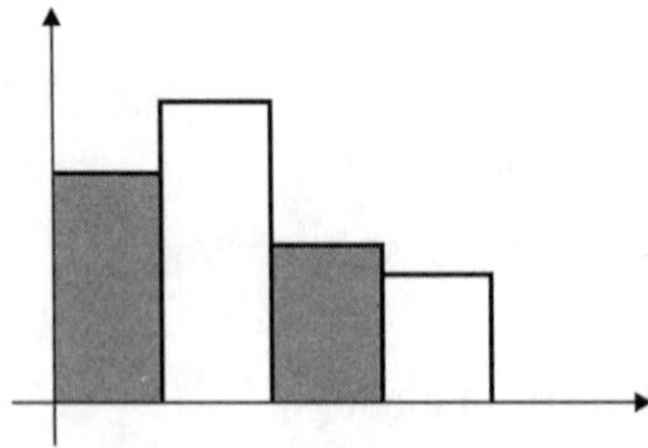

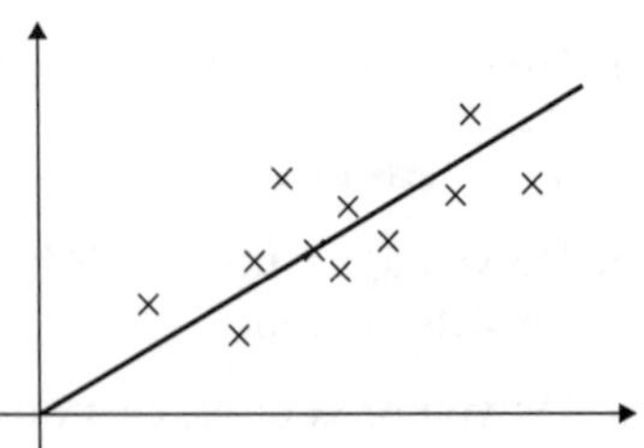

You might want to use a database or spreadsheet program on a computer if you think this would help your work.

Draw *conclusions* from your results but make sure they are justified by the evidence.

The best way to learn about questionnaires is to conduct your own survey on a topic which *you* find interesting.

Hypothesis testing

A hypothesis is defined as 'a statement which may be true, but for which a proof has not been found'. Statisticians are employed to collect and analyse information about a question with the aim of proving or disproving it. Questionnaires are often used for this purpose.
Here are some questions:

A 'Is there too much sport on television?'

B 'Are people who are good at spelling also good at arithmetic?'

castle ✓	$51 \times 17 = 867$ ✓
elefant ✗	$0.4 \times 0.2 = 0.08$ ✓
necessary ✓	$5.6 - 4 = 5.2$ ✗
tomorrow ✓	$\frac{1}{6} \times \frac{1}{2} = \frac{2}{8}$ ✗

C 'Does smoking damage your health?'

D 'Do pupils in Year 7 watch more TV than pupils in Year 11?'

Once you have the question, your first task is to make a hypothesis (make a statement) so that you have something concrete to test. Hypotheses for the above four questions could be:

A Most people would like TV schedules to contain less coverage of sport.

B People who are good at spelling are also good at arithmetic.

C Smokers have a shorter life span than non-smokers.

D Pupils in Year 7 watch more television than pupils in Year 11.

Your own work

Almost certainly the best idea for a hypothesis will be an idea which *you* think of because *you* want to know the answer. As a guide, here is a list of questions which some students have looked at. You can use one of these if you find it interesting or if you can't think of a better one yourself.

(a) Young people are more superstitious than older people.
(b) Given a free choice, most girls would hardly ever wear a dress in preference to something else.
(c) More babies are born in the Winter than the Summer.
(d) The age for part time jobs should be reduced from 16 to 14.
(e) The school day should start at 08.00 and end at 14.00.
(f) Most cars these days use unleaded petrol.

7.3 Scatter diagrams

Sometimes it is interesting to discover if there is a relationship (or *correlation*) between two sets of data.

Examples

- Do tall people weigh more than short people?
- If you spend longer revising for a test, will you get a higher mark?
- Do tall parents have tall children?
- If there is more rain, will there be less sunshine?
- Does the number of Olympic gold medals won by British athletes affect the rate of inflation?

If there is a relationship, it will be easy to spot if your data is plotted on a scatter diagram.

- A scatter diagram is a graph in which one set of data is plotted on the horizontal axis and the other on the vertical axis.

Each month the average outdoors temperature was recorded together with the number of therms of gas used to heat the house. The results are plotted on the scatter diagram as shown.

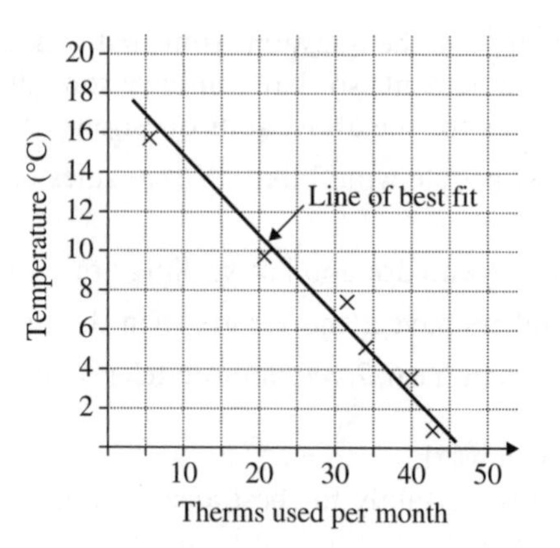

Clearly there is a high degree of *correlation* between these two figures. British Gas do in fact use weather forecasts as their main short-term predictor of future gas consumption over the whole country.

A *line of best fit* has been drawn 'by eye'.
We can estimate that if the outdoor temperature was 12 °C then about 17 therms of gas would be used.

Note: You can only predict within the range of values given.
If we extended the line for temperatures below zero the line of best fit predicts that about 60 therms would be used when the temperature is −4 °C. But −4 °C is well outside the range of the values plotted so the prediction is not valid.

[Perhaps at −4 °C a lot of people might stay in bed and the gas consumption would not increase by much. The point is you don't know!]

(a) The line in our example has a negative gradient and we say there is *negative correlation.*

(b) If the line of best fit has a positive gradient we say there is *positive correlation.*

(c) Some data when plotted on a scatter diagram does not appear to fit any line at all. In this case there is no correlation.

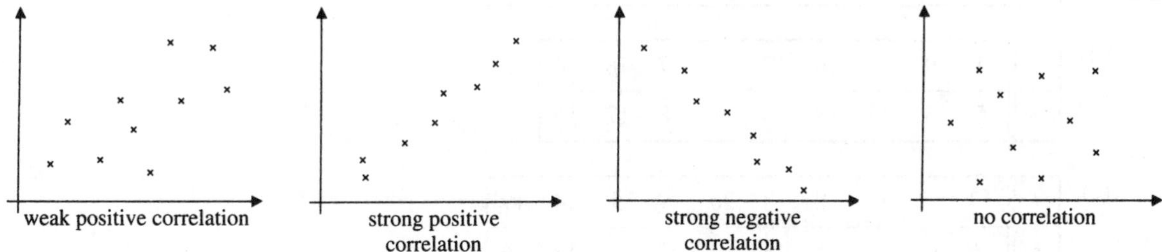

Exercise 8

1. For this question you need to make some measurements of people in your class.

(a) Measure everyone's height and 'armspan' to the nearest cm.

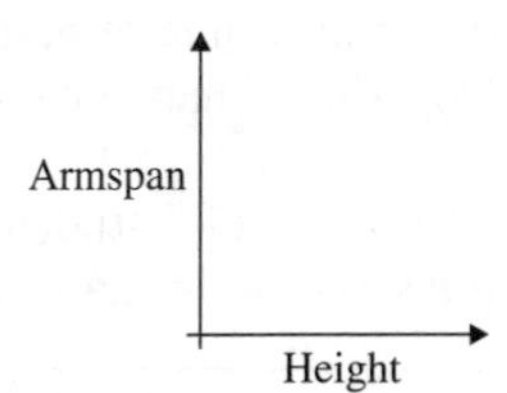

Plot the measurements on a scatter graph. Is there any correlation?

(b) Now measure everyone's 'head circumference' just above the eyes.
Plot head circumference and height on a scatter graph. Is there any correlation?

(c) Decide as a class which other measurements [e.g. pulse rate] you can (fairly easily) take and plot these to see if any correlation exists.

(d) Which pair of measurements gave the best correlation?

2. Plot the points given below on a scatter graph, with t across the page and z up the page. Draw axes with values from 0 to 20. Describe the correlation, if any, between the values of t and z. [i.e. 'strong positive', 'weak negative' etc.]

(a)

t	8	17	5	13	19	7	20	5	11	14
z	9	16	7	13	18	10	19	8	11	15

(b)

t	4	9	13	16	17	6	7	18	10
z	5	3	11	18	6	11	18	12	16

(c)

t	12	2	17	8	3	20	9	5	14	19
z	6	13	8	15	18	2	12	9	12	6

3. Describe the correlation, if any, in these scatter graphs.

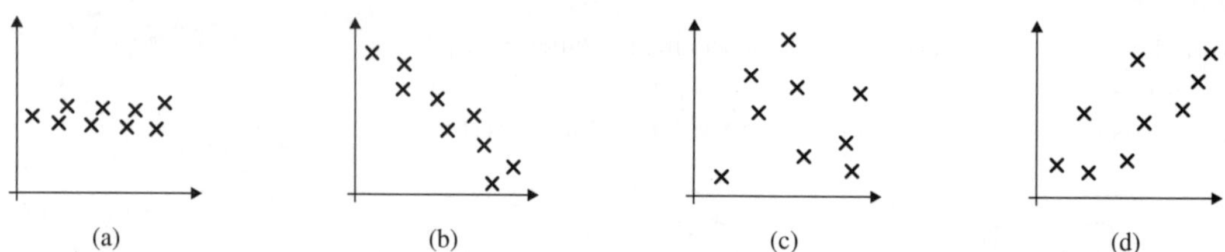

4. Plot the points given below on a scatter graph, with s across the page and h up the page. Draw axes with values from 0 to 20.

s	3	13	20	1	9	15	10	17
h	6	13	20	6	12	16	12	17

(a) Draw a line of best fit.
(b) What value would you expect for h when s is 6?

5. The marks of 7 students in the two papers of a physics examination were as follows.

Paper 1	20	32	40	60	71	80	91
Paper 2	15	25	40	50	64	75	84

(a) Plot the marks on a scatter diagram, using a scale of 1 cm to 10 marks, and draw a line of best fit.
(b) A student scored a mark of 50 on Paper 1. What would you expect her to get on Paper 2?

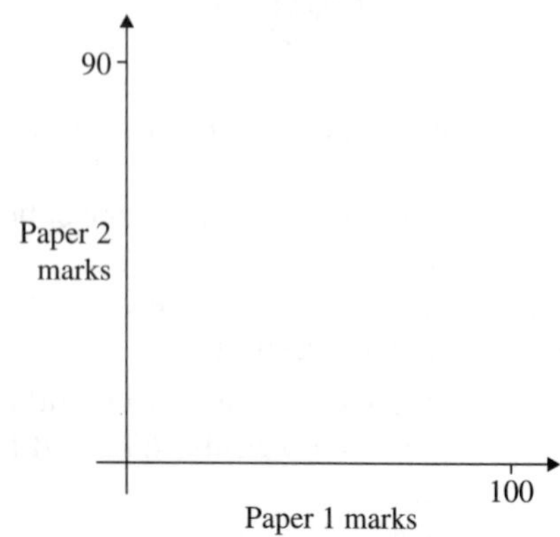

6. The table shows (i) the engine size in litres of various cars and (ii) the distance travelled in km on one litre of petrol.

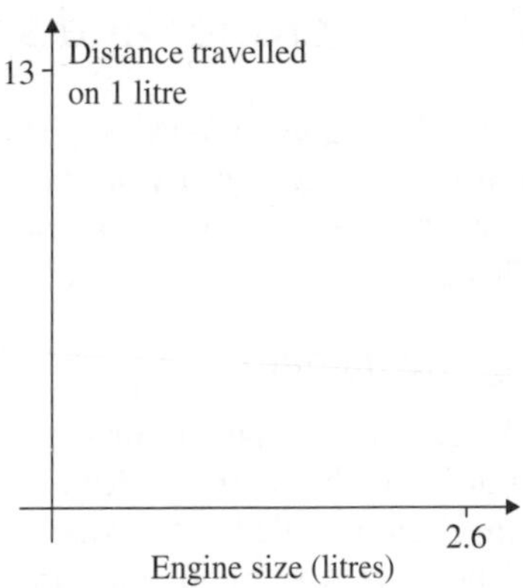

Engine	0·8	1·6	2·6	1·0	2·1	1·3	1·8
Distance	13	10·2	5·4	12	7·8	11·2	8·5

(a) Plot the figures on a scatter graph using a scale of 5 cm to 1 litre across the page and 1 cm to 1 km up the page. Draw a line of best fit.

(b) A car has a 2·3 litre engine. How far would you expect it to go on one litre of petrol?

7. The data shows the latitude of 10 cities in the northern hemisphere and the average high temperatures.

City	Latitude (degrees)	Mean high temperature (°F)
Bogota	5	66
Bombay	19	87
Casablanca	34	72
Dublin	53	56
Hong Kong	22	77
Istanbul	41	64
St Petersburg	60	46
Manila	15	89
Oslo	60	50
Paris	49	59

(a) Draw a scatter diagram and draw a line of best fit. Plot latitude across the page with a scale of 2 cm to 10°. Plot temperature up the page from 40 °F to 90 °F with a scale of 2 cm to 10 °F.

(b) Which city lies well off the line?
Do you know what factor might cause this apparent discrepancy?

(c) The latitude of Shanghai is 31° N. What do you think its mean high temperature is?

8. What sort of pattern would you expect if you took readings of the following and drew a scatter diagram?

(a) cars on roads; accident rate.

(b) sales of perfume; advertising costs.

(c) birth rate; rate of inflation.

(d) petrol consumption of car; price of petrol.

(e) outside temperature; sales of ice cream.

7.4 Averages and spread

If you have a set of data, say exam marks or heights, and are told to find the 'average', just what are you trying to find? The answer is: a single number which can be used to represent the entire set of data. This could be done in three different ways.

(a) The median

The data is arranged in order from the smallest to the largest; the middle number is then selected. This is really the central number of the range and is called the median.
If there are two 'middle' numbers, the median is in the middle of these two numbers.

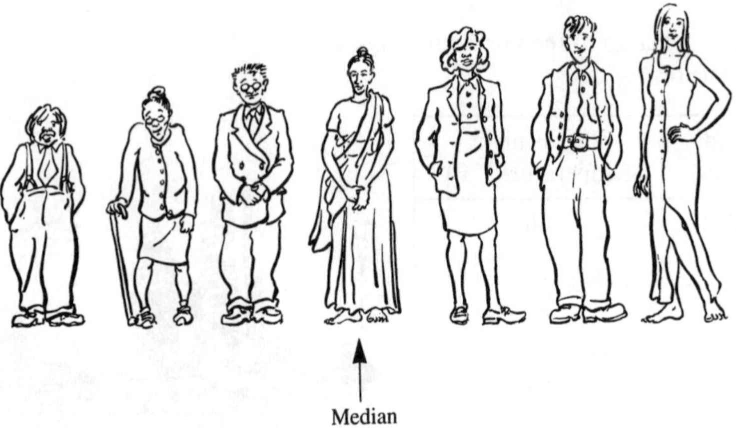

Median

(b) The mean

All the data is added up and the total divided by the number of items. This is called the mean and is equivalent to sharing out all the data evenly.

(c) The mode

The number of items which occurs most frequently in a frequency table is selected. This is the most popular value and is called the mode (from the French 'à la mode' meaning 'fashionable').

Each 'average' has its purpose and sometimes one is preferable to the others.

The median is fairly easy to find and has an advantage in being hardly affected by untypical values such as very large or very small values that occur at the ends of the distribution.
Consider these exam marks:

20, 21, 21, 22, 23, 23, 25, 27, 27, 27, 29, 98, 98
↑

The median (25) gives a truer picture of the centre of the distribution than the mean (35·5).

The mean takes account of all of the data and is the 'average' which most people readily think of. It does, of course, take a little longer to calculate than either the mode or the median.

The mode of this data is 27. It is easy to calculate and it eliminates some of the effects of extreme values. However it does have disadvantages, particularly in data which has two 'most popular' values, and it is not widely used.

Range

In addition to knowing the centre of a distribution, it is useful to know the range or spread of the data.

range = (largest value) – (smallest value)

For the examination marks, range = 98 – 20 = 78.

Find the median, the mean, the mode and the range of this set of 10 numbers:
5, 4, 10, 3, 3, 4, 7, 4, 6, 5.

(a) Arrange the numbers in order of size to find the median.

3, 3, 4, 4, 4, 5, 5, 6, 7, 10

↑

the median is the 'average' of 4 and 5

$\therefore$ median = 4·5

(b) $\text{mean} = \dfrac{(5+4+10+3+3+4+7+4+6+5)}{10} = \dfrac{51}{10} = 5{\cdot}1$

(c) mode = 4 because there are more 4's than any other number

(d) range = 10 – 3 = 7

Exercise 9

1. Find the mean, median and mode of the following sets of numbers.
(a) 3, 12, 4, 6, 8, 5, 4
(b) 7, 21, 2, 17, 3, 13, 7, 4, 9, 7, 9
(c) 12, 1, 10, 1, 9, 3, 4, 9, 7, 9
(d) 8, 0, 3, 3, 1, 7, 4, 1, 4, 4

2. The temperature in °C on 17 days was:
1, 0, 2, 2, 0, 4, 1, 3, 2, 1, 2, 3, 4, 5, 4, 5, 5.
(a) What was the modal temperature?
(b) What was the range?

3. A dice was thrown 14 times as follows.

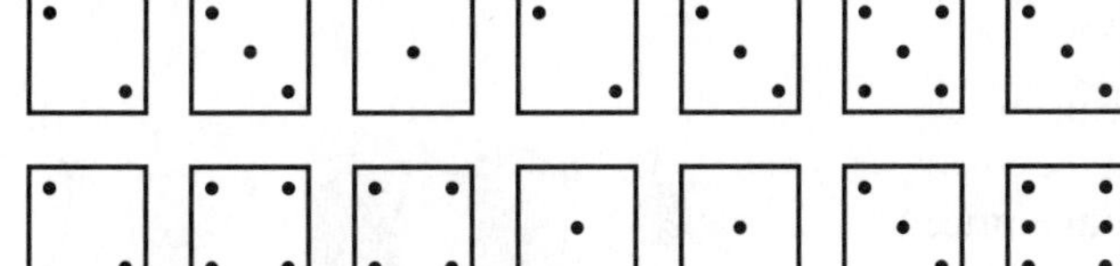

(a) What was the modal score?
(b) What was the median score?

4. Find (a) the range and (b) the mode of this data.

4	2	5	4	5	12	4	1	3	3
3	5	5	3	4	5	2	7	4	2
4	12	1	7	12	1	3	8	10	4

5. The range for the eight numbers shown is 40.
Find the *two* possible values of the missing number.

6. The mean weight of ten people in a lift is 70 kg. The weight limit for the lift is 1000 kg. Roughly how many more people can get into the lift?

7. The bar chart shows the marks scored in a test. What was the modal mark?

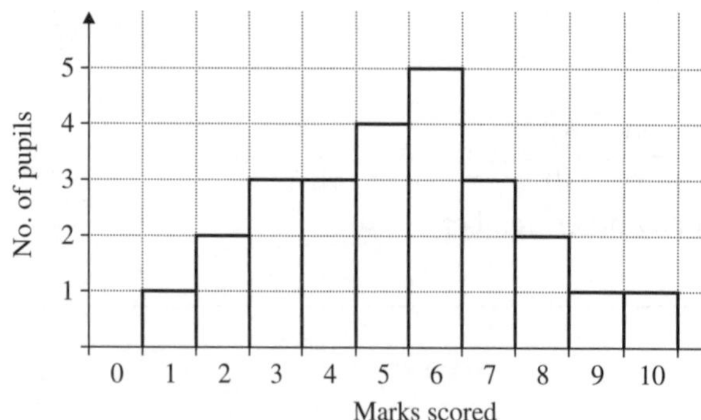

8. Six boys have heights of 1·53 m, 1·49 m, 1·60 m, 1·65 m, 1·90 m and 1·43 m.
(a) Find the mean height of the six boys.
(b) Find the mean height of the remaining five boys when the shortest boy leaves.

9. In a maths test the marks for the boys were 9, 7, 8, 7, 5 and the marks for the girls were 6, 3, 9, 8, 2, 2.
(a) Find the mean mark for the boys.
(b) Find the mean mark for the girls.
(c) Find the mean mark for the whole class.

10. Five different drinks have an average (mean) price of £1·50.
When a sixth drink is added the new average price is £1·60.
How much did the sixth drink cost?

11. Write down five numbers so that:
the mean is 6
the median is 5
the mode is 4.

12. There were ten cowboys in a saloon. The mean age of the men was 25 and the range of their ages was 6. Write each statement below and then write next to it whether it is *True*, *Possible* or *False*.
(a) The youngest man was 18 years old.
(b) All the men were at least 20 years old.
(c) The oldest person was 4 years older than the youngest.
(d) Every man was between 20 and 26 years old.

13. The following are the salaries of 5 employees in a small business.

Mr A : £22,500	Mr B : £17,900	Mr C : £21,400
Mr D : £22,500	Mr E : £155,300	

(a) Find the mean and the median of their salaries.
(b) Which does *not* give a fair 'average'? Explain why in one sentence.

14. A farmer has 32 cattle to sell.
The weights of the cattle in kg are:

81	81	82	82	83	84	84	85
85	86	86	87	87	88	89	91
91	92	93	94	96	150	152	153
154	320	370	375	376	380	381	390

[Total weight = 5028 kg.]

On the telephone to a potential buyer, the farmer describes the cattle and says the 'average' weight is 'over 157 kg'.
(a) Find the mean weight and the median weight.
(b) Which 'average' has the farmer used to describe his animals?
Does this average describe the cattle fairly?

15. A gardening magazine sells seedlings of a plant through the post and claims that the average height of the plants after one year's growth will be 85 cm. A sample of 24 of the plants were measured after one year with the following results (in cm).

6	7	7	9	34	56	85	89
89	90	90	91	91	92	93	93
93	94	95	95	96	97	97	99

[The sum of the heights is 1788 cm.]

(a) Find the mean and the median height of the sample.
(b) Is the magazine's claim about average height justified?

Calculating the mean from a frequency table

The frequency table shows the weights of the eggs bought in a supermarket.
Find the mean, median and modal weight.

Weight	58 g	59 g	60 g	61 g	62 g	63 g
Frequency	3	7	11	9	8	2

(a) Mean weight of eggs

$$= \frac{(58 \times 3) + (59 \times 7) + (60 \times 11) + (61 \times 9) + (62 \times 8) + (63 \times 2)}{(3 + 7 + 11 + 9 + 8 + 2)}$$

$$= \frac{2418}{40} = 60{\cdot}45 \text{ g}$$

(b) There are 40 eggs so the median weight is the number between the 20th and 21st numbers. By inspection, both the 20th and 21st numbers are 60 g.

$\therefore$ Median weight = 60 g

(c) The modal weight = 60 g.

Exercise 10

1. The frequency table shows the weights of the 40 apples sold in a shop.

Weight	70 g	80 g	90 g	100 g	110 g	120 g
Frequency	2	7	9	11	8	3

Calculate the mean weight of the apples.

2. The frequency table shows the price of a packet of butter in 30 different shops.

Price	49p	50p	51p	52p	53p	54p
Frequency	2	3	5	10	6	4

Calculate the mean price of a packet of butter.

3. A box contains 50 nails of different lengths as shown in the frequency table.

Length of nail	2 cm	3 cm	4 cm	5 cm	6 cm	7 cm
Frequency	4	7	9	12	10	8

Calculate the mean length of the nails.

4. The following tables give the distribution of marks obtained by different classes in various tests. For each table, find the mean, median and mode.

(a)

Mark	0	1	2	3	4	5	6
Frequency	3	5	8	9	5	7	3

(b)

Mark	15	16	17	18	19	20
Frequency	1	3	7	1	5	3

5. A teacher conducted a mental arithmetic test for 26 pupils and the marks out of 10 were as follows.

Mark	3	4	5	6	7	8	9	10
Frequency	6	3	1	2	0	5	5	4

(a) Find the mean, median and mode.
(b) The teacher congratulated the class saying that "over three-quarters were above 'average' ". Which 'average' justifies this statement?

6. The number of goals scored in a series of football matches was as follows.

Number of goals	1	2	3
Number of matches	8	8	x

(a) If the mean number of goals is 2·04, find x.
(b) If the modal number of goals is 3, find the smallest possible value of x.
(c) If the median number of goals is 2, find the largest possible value of x.

7. In a survey of the number of occupants in a number of cars, the following data resulted.

Number of occupants	1	2	3	4
Number of cars	7	11	7	x

(a) If the mean number of occupants is $2\frac{1}{3}$, find x.
(b) If the mode is 2, find the largest possible value of x.
(c) If the median is 2, find the largest possible value of x.

Data in groups

The results of 51 students in a test are given in the frequency table.
Find the (a) mean, (b) median, (c) mode.

Mark	30–39	40–49	50–59	60–69
Frequency	7	14	21	9

In order to find the mean we approximate by saying each interval is represented by its mid-point. For the 30–39 interval we say there are 7 marks of 34·5 [ie $(30 + 39) \div 2 = 34{\cdot}5$].

(a) Mean $= \dfrac{(34{\cdot}5 \times 7) + (44{\cdot}5 \times 14) + (54{\cdot}5 \times 21) + (64{\cdot}5 \times 9)}{(7 + 14 + 21 + 9)}$

$= 50{\cdot}7745098$

$= 51$ (2 s.f.)

Don't forget this is only an *estimate* because we do not have the raw data and we have made an assumption with the mid-point of each interval.

(b) The median is the 26th mark, which is in the interval 50–59. We cannot find the exact median. [Later we will get an estimate by drawing a cumulative frequency curve.]

(c) The *modal group* is 50–59. You cannot find an exact mode.

Exercise 11

1. The table gives the number of words in each sentence of a page of writing.
(a) Copy and complete the table.
(b) Work out an estimate for the mean number of words in a sentence.

Number of words	Frequency f	Mid-point x	fx
1–5	6	3	18
6–10	5	8	40
11–15	4		
16–20	2		
21–25	3		
Totals	20	—	

2. The results of 24 students in a test are given below.

Mark	40–54	55–69	70–84	85–99
Frequency	5	8	7	4

Find the mid-point of each group of marks and calculate an estimate of the mean mark.

3. The number of letters delivered to the 26 houses in a street was as follows.

Number of letters delivered	Number of houses (i.e. frequency)
0–2	10
3–4	8
5–7	5
8–12	3

Calculate an estimate of the mean number of letters delivered per house.

7.5 Cumulative frequency

Quartiles, interquartile range

- The range is a simple measure of spread but one extreme (very high or very low) value can have a big effect.
  The *interquartile range* is a better measure of spread.

Find the quartiles and the interquartile range for these numbers:

12 6 4 9 8 4 9 8 5 9 8 10

In order: 4 4 5 ¦ 6 8 8 ¦ 8 9 9 ¦ 9 10 12

lower quartile is 5·5 — median is 8 — upper quartile is 9

Interquartile range = upper quartile − lower quartile
= 9 − 5·5
= 3·5

Box plot

A *box plot* or *box and whisker diagram* shows the spread of a set of data.
It shows the quartiles (Q_1 and Q_3) and the median.
The 'whiskers' extend from the lowest to the highest value and show the range.

Here is a box plot.

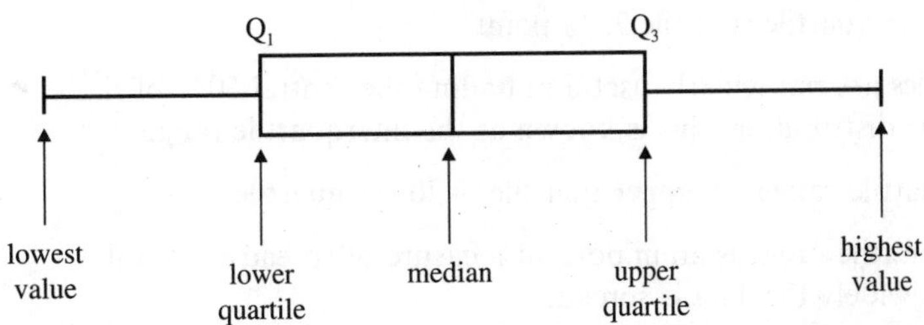

Exercise 12

For each set of data, work out: (a) the lower and upper quartile and (b) the inter-quartile range.

1. 1 1 4 4 5 8 8 8 9 10 11 11

2. 5 2 6 4 1 9 3 2 8 4 1 0

3. 7 9 11 15 18 19 23 27

4. 0 0 1 1 2 3 3 4 4 4 4 6 6 6 7 7

5. Here are three box plots. Estimate (a) the median
(b) the interquartile range
(c) the range

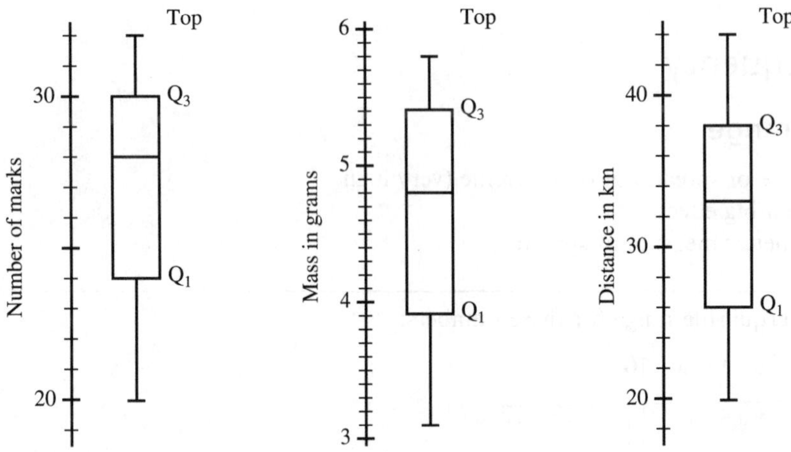

Cumulative frequency

- The total of the frequencies up to a particular value is called the *cumulative frequency.*

Data given in a frequency table can be used to calculate cumulative frequencies. These new values, when plotted and joined, form a cumulative frequency curve, sometimes called an S-shaped curve.

It is a simple matter to find the median from the halfway point of a cumulative frequency curve.
Other points of location can also be found from this curve. The cumulative frequency axis can be divided into 100 parts.

- The upper quartile is at the 75% point.
- The lower quartile is at the 25% point.

The quartiles are particularly useful in finding the central 50% of the range of the distribution; this is known as the interquartile range.

- Interquartile range = upper quartile − lower quartile.

The interquartile range is an important measure of spread in that it shows how widely the data is spread.

Half the distribution is in the interquartile range. If the interquartile range is small, then the middle half of the distribution is bunched together.

In a survey, 200 people were asked to state their weekly earnings. The results were plotted on the cumulative frequency curve.

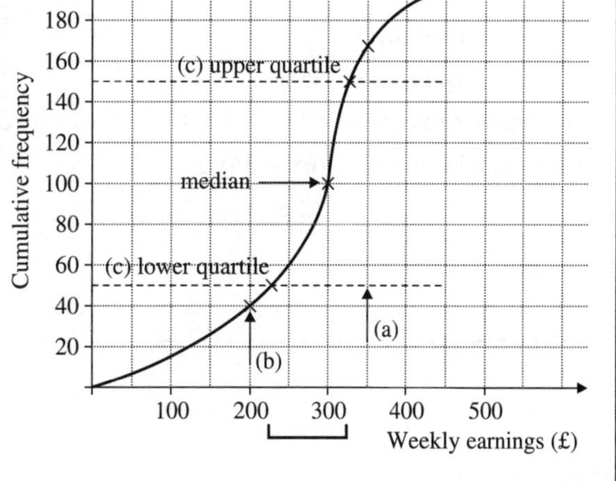

(a) How many people earned up to £350 a week?

From the curve about 170 people earned up to £350 a week.

(b) How many people earned more than £200 a week?

About 40 people earned up to £200 per week. There are 200 people in the survey. So 160 people earned more than £200 a week.

(c) Find the interquartile range.

$$\begin{aligned} \text{Lower quartile (50 people)} &= £225 \\ \text{Upper quartile (150 people)} &= £325 \\ \therefore \quad \text{Interquartile range} &= 325 - 225 \\ &= £100 \end{aligned}$$

A pet shop owner likes to weigh all his mice every week as a check on their state of health. The weights of the 80 mice are shown below.

Weight (g)	Frequency	Cumulative frequency	Weight represented by cumulative frequency
0–10	3	3	$\leqslant$ 10 g
10–20	5	8	$\leqslant$ 20 g
20–30	5	13	$\leqslant$ 30 g
30–40	9	22	$\leqslant$ 40 g
40–50	11	33	$\leqslant$ 50 g
50–60	15	48	$\leqslant$ 60 g
60–70	14	62	$\leqslant$ 70 g
70–80	8	70	$\leqslant$ 80 g
80–90	6	76	$\leqslant$ 90 g
90–100	4	80	$\leqslant$ 100 g

The table also shows the cumulative frequency.

Plot a cumulative frequency curve and hence estimate

(a) the median
(b) the interquartile range.

- Note: The points on the graph are plotted at the *upper limit* of each group of weights.

From the cumulative frequency curve:

median = 55 g
lower quartile = 36 g
upper quartile = 68 g
interquartile range = (68 – 36) g
= 32 g

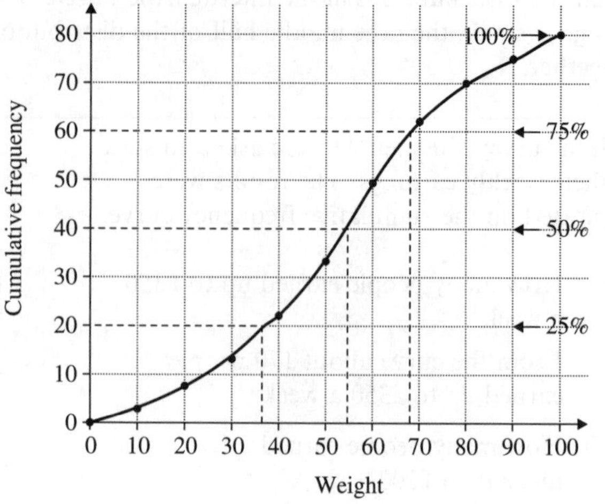

Exercise 13

1. The graph shows the cumulative frequency curve for the marks of 40 students in an examination.
From the graph, estimate:
(a) the median mark
(b) the mark at the lower quartile and at the upper quartile
(c) the interquartile range
(d) the pass mark if three-quarters of the students passed.

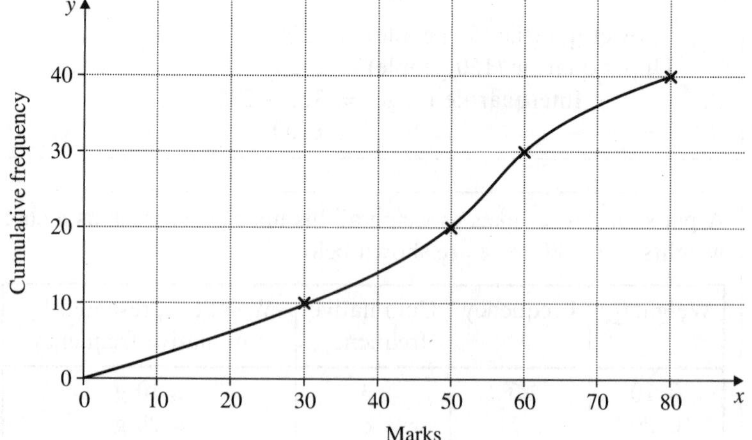

2. The graph shows the cumulative frequency curve for the marks of 60 students in an examination.
From the graph, estimate:
(a) the median mark
(b) the mark at the lower quartile and at the upper quartile
(c) the interquartile range
(d) the pass mark if two-thirds of the students passed.

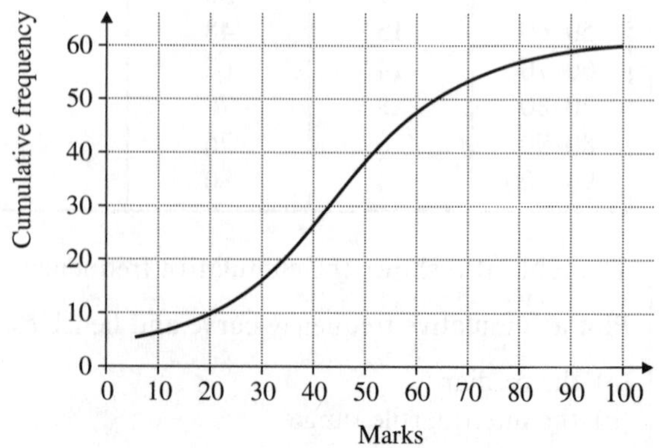

3. The lifetime of 500 electric light bulbs was measured in a laboratory. The results are shown in the cumulative frequency diagram.
   (a) How many bulbs had a lifetime of 1500 hours or less?
   (b) How many bulbs had a lifetime of between 2000 and 3000 hours?
   (c) After how many hours were 70% of the bulbs dead?
   (d) What was the shortest lifetime of a bulb?

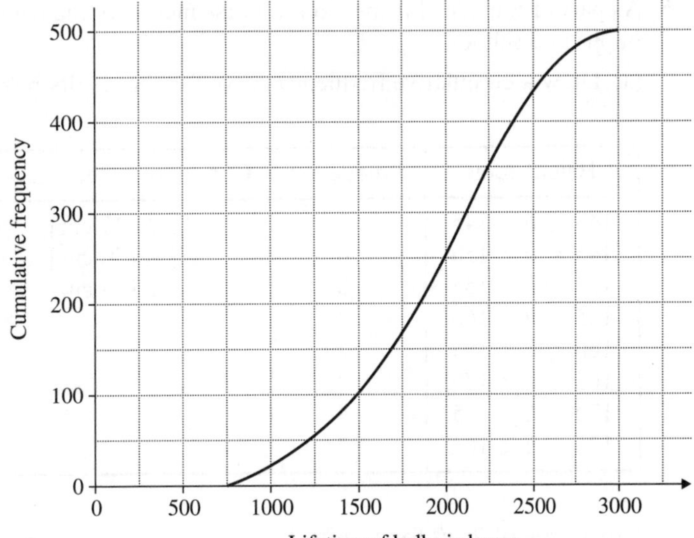

4. A photographer measures all the snakes required for a scene in a film involving a snake pit.

(a) Draw a cumulative frequency curve for the results below.

Length (cm)	Frequency	Cumulative frequency	Upper limit
0–10	0	0	⩽10
10–20	2	2	⩽20
20–30	4	6	⩽30
30–40	10	16	⩽40
40–50	17		⋮
50–60	11		
60–70	3		
70–80	3		

Use a scale of 2 cm for 10 units across the page for the lengths and 2 cm for 10 units up the page for the cumulative frequency. Remember to plot points at the *upper* end of the classes (10, 20, 30 etc.).

(b) Find (i) the median (ii) the interquartile range.

5. As part of a medical inspection, a nurse measures the heights of 48 pupils in a school.

(a) Draw a cumulative frequency curve for the results below.

Height (cm)	Frequency	Cumulative frequency
$140 \leqslant h < 145$	2	2 [$\leqslant$145 cm]
$145 \leqslant h < 150$	4	6 [$\leqslant$150 cm]
$150 \leqslant h < 155$	8	14 [$\leqslant$155 cm]
$155 \leqslant h < 160$	9	
$160 \leqslant h < 165$	12	
$165 \leqslant h < 170$	7	
$170 \leqslant h < 175$	4	
$175 \leqslant h < 180$	2	

Use a scale of 2 cm for 5 units across the page and 2 cm for 10 units up the page.

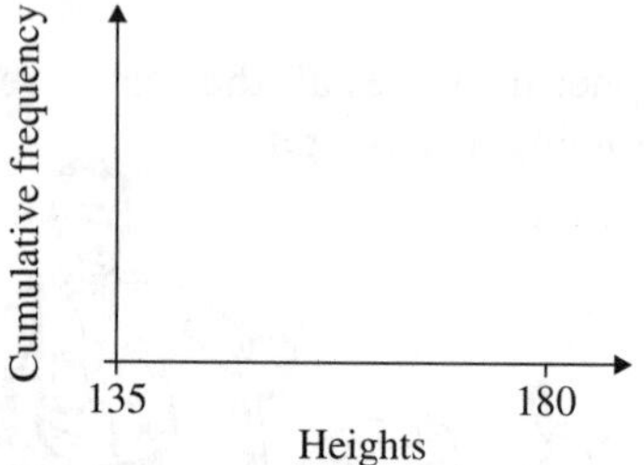

(b) Find (i) the median
(ii) the interquartile range.

6. Hugo and Boris are brilliant darts players. They recorded their scores over 60 throws.
Here are Hugo's scores:

Score (x)	$30 < x \leqslant 60$	$60 < x \leqslant 90$	$90 < x \leqslant 120$	$120 < x \leqslant 150$	$150 < x \leqslant 180$
Frequency	10	4	13	23	10

Draw a cumulative frequency curve.

Use a scale of 2 cm for 20 points across the page and 2 cm for 10 throws up the page.

For Hugo, find (a) his median score
(b) the interquartile range of his scores.

For his 60 throws, Boris had a median score of 105 and an interquartile range of 20.

(c) Which of the players is more consistent? Give a reason for your answer.

7. The 'life' of a Mickey Mouse photocopying machine is tested by timing how long it works before breaking down. The results for 50 machines are.

Time, t (hours)	$2 < t \leqslant 4$	$4 < t \leqslant 6$	$6 < t \leqslant 8$	$8 < t \leqslant 10$	$10 < t \leqslant 12$
Frequency	9	6	15	15	5

(a) Draw a cumulative frequency graph.
[t across the page, 1 cm = 1 hour; C.F. up the page.]
(b) Find (i) the median life of a machine
(ii) the interquartile range.
(c) The makers claim that their machines will work for at least 10 hours. What percentage of the machines do not match this description?

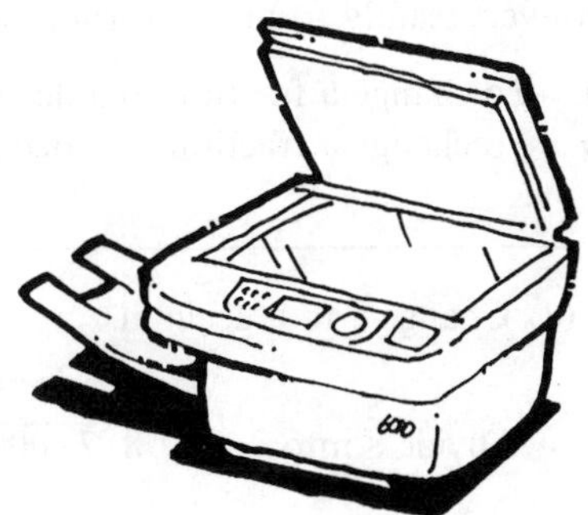

8. In an international competition 60 children from Britain and France did the same science test.

Marks	Britain frequency	France frequency	Britain cum. freq.	France cum. freq.
1–5	1	2	1 [$\leqslant$5·5]	2 [$\leqslant$5·5]
6–10	2	5	3 [$\leqslant$10·5]	7 [$\leqslant$10·5]
11–15	4	11	7 [$\leqslant$15·5]	
16–20	8	16		
21–25	16	10		
26–30	19	8		
31–35	10	8		

Note: The upper class boundaries for the marks are 5·5, 10·5, 15·5, etc.
The cumulative frequency graph should be plotted for values $\leqslant$ 5·5, $\leqslant$ 10·5, $\leqslant$ 15·5, and so on.
(a) Using the same axes, draw the cumulative frequency curves for the British and French results.
Use a scale of 2 cm for 5 marks across the page
and 2 cm for 10 people up the page.
(b) Find the median mark for each country.
(c) Find the interquartile range for the British results.
(d) Describe in one sentence the main difference between the two sets of results.

8 NUMBER 3

8.1 Fractions, ratio, decimals and percentage

Percentages are simply a convenient way of expressing fractions or decimals. '50% of £60' is the same as '$\frac{1}{2}$ of £60'. You should be able to convert readily from one form to another.

- To change a fraction to a decimal divide out the fraction.
- To change a fraction or a decimal to a percentage, multiply by 100.

(a) Change $\frac{7}{8}$ to a decimal.

Divide 8 into 7 $\quad 8\overline{)7\cdot000}$ gives $0\cdot875$

(b) Change 0·35 to a fraction.

$0{\cdot}35 = \frac{35}{100} = \frac{7}{20}$

(c) Change $\frac{3}{8}$ to a percentage.

$\frac{3}{8} = \frac{3}{8} \times 100\% = 37\frac{1}{2}\%$

(d) Change 0.85 to a percentage.

$0.85 = 0.85 \times 100\% = 85\%$

(e) Change $\frac{5}{6}$ to a decimal.

$6\overline{)5\cdot0000}$ gives $0\cdot8333\ldots$

This is a *recurring* decimal.

we write $\frac{5}{6} = 0.8\dot{3}$

Similarly, $0.525252\ldots = 0.\dot{5}\dot{2}$

(f) Work out $\frac{1}{6} + 0.72$, correct to 2 d.p.

$\frac{1}{6} = 0{\cdot}1666\ldots$ [divide 6 into 1]

$\therefore \frac{1}{6} + 0{\cdot}72 = 0{\cdot}1666 + 0{\cdot}7200 = 0{\cdot}8866$

Answer $= 0{\cdot}89$ (2 d.p.)

Exercise 1

1. Two shops had sale offers on an article which previously cost £69. One shop had '$\frac{1}{3}$ off' and the other had '70% of old price'. Which shop had the lower price?
2. Shareholders in a company can opt for either '$\frac{1}{6}$ of £5000' or '15% of £5000'. Which is the greater amount?
3. A photocopier increases the sides of a square in the ratio 4 : 5. By what percentage are the sides increased?

4. In an alloy the ratio of copper to iron to lead is 5 : 7 : 3. What percentage of the alloy is lead?

5. Change the fractions to decimals.

(a) $\frac{1}{4}$ (b) $\frac{2}{5}$ (c) $\frac{3}{8}$

(d) $\frac{5}{12}$ (e) $\frac{1}{6}$ (f) $\frac{2}{7}$

6. Change the decimals to fractions and simplify.

(a) 0·2 (b) 0·45 (c) 0·36

(d) 0·125 (e) 1·05 (f) 0·007

7. Change to percentages.

(a) $\frac{1}{4}$ (b) $\frac{1}{10}$ (c) 0·72

(d) 0·075 (e) 0·02 (f) $\frac{1}{3}$

8. In July 2000, 360 000 people visited Bali for their holiday.

(a) One-eighth of the people were American. Find the number of American visitors.

(b) 11% of the people were French. How many people was that?

(c) There were 12 000 people from Japan. What fraction of the total were from Japan?

9. Copy and complete the table:

	Fraction	Decimal	Percentage
(a)	$\frac{1}{4}$		
(b)		0·2	
(c)			80%
(d)	$\frac{1}{100}$		
(e)			30%
(f)	$\frac{1}{3}$		

10. Here are some fractions:

$\frac{4}{10}$ $\frac{11}{33}$ $\frac{1}{5}$ $\frac{7}{12}$

Select one that is:

(a) equal to 0.2 (b) equal to 40%

(c) equal to $\frac{1}{3}$ (d) greater than $\frac{1}{2}$.

11. Max wants 3 bottles of Coke, which normally costs 90p per bottle. Which of the three offers shown is the cheapest for 3 bottles?

A

B

30% off
marked price

C

BUY ONE get
the 2nd HALF PRICE !

12. Work out (a) $\frac{3}{4}$ of 65% of 0·3
(b) 11% of $\frac{3}{5}$ of £240

13. Arrange in order of size (smallest first).
(a) $\frac{1}{2}$; 45%; 0·6 (b) 0·38; $\frac{6}{16}$; 4% (c) 0·111; 11%; $\frac{1}{9}$

Evaluate, giving the answer to 2 decimal places.

14. $\frac{1}{4}+\frac{1}{3}$
15. $\frac{2}{3}+0{\cdot}75$
16. $\frac{8}{9}-0{\cdot}24$
17. $\frac{7}{8}+\frac{5}{9}+\frac{2}{11}$
18. $\frac{1}{3}\times 0{\cdot}2$
19. $\frac{5}{8}\times\frac{1}{4}$
20. $\frac{8}{11}\div 0{\cdot}2$
21. $(\frac{4}{7}-\frac{1}{3})\div 0{\cdot}4$

22. Pure gold is 24 carat gold.
What percentage of pure gold is 15 carat gold?

8.2 Standard form

When dealing with either very large or very small numbers, it is not convenient to write them out in full in the normal way. It is better to use standard form. Most calculators represent large and small numbers in this way.

This calculator shows $2{\cdot}3 \times 10^8$.

2.3 08

- The number $a \times 10^n$ is in standard form when $1 \leq a < 10$ and n is a positive or negative integer.

Write the following numbers in standard form.

(a) $2000 = 2 \times 1000 = 2 \times 10^3$

(b) $150 = 1{\cdot}5 \times 100 = 1{\cdot}5 \times 10^2$

(c) $0{\cdot}0004 = 4 \times \frac{1}{10\,000} = 4 \times 10^{-4}$

Exercise 2

Write the following numbers in standard form.

1. 4000
2. 500
3. 70 000
4. 60
5. 2400
6. 380
7. 46 000
8. 46
9. 900 000
10. 2560
11. 0·007
12. 0·0004
13. 0·0035
14. 0·421
15. 0·000 055
16. 0·01
17. 564 000
18. 19 million
19. The population of China is estimated at 1 100 000 000. Write this in standard form.

20. A hydrogen atom weighs 0·000 000 000 000 000 000 000 001 67 grams.
Write this weight in standard form.

21. The area of the surface of the Earth is about 510 000 000 km^2.
Express this in standard form.

22. A certain virus is 0·000 000 000 25 cm in diameter.
Write this in standard form.

23. Avogadro's number is 602 300 000 000 000 000 000 000.
Express this in standard form.

24. The speed of light is 300 000 km/s. Express this speed in cm/s in standard form.

25. A very rich oil sheikh leaves his fortune of £$3{\cdot}6 \times 10^8$ to be divided between his 100 children.

How much does each child receive? Give the answer in standard form.

Work out $1500 \times 8\,000\,000$

$$1500 \times 8\,000\,000 = (1{\cdot}5 \times 10^3) \times (8 \times 10^6)$$
$$= 12 \times 10^9 \qquad [1{\cdot}5 \times 8 = 12, \quad 10^3 \times 10^6 = 10^9]$$
$$= 1{\cdot}2 \times 10^{10}$$

Notice that we multiply the numbers and the powers of 10 separately.

Many calculators have an [EXP] button which is used for standard form.

(a) To enter $1{\cdot}6 \times 10^7$ into the calculator:

press [1·6] [EXP] [7]

(b) To enter $3{\cdot}8 \times 10^{-3}$:

press [3·8] [EXP] [3] [+/−]

(c) To calculate $(4{\cdot}9 \times 10^{11}) \div (3{\cdot}5 \times 10^{-4})$:

[3·8] [EXP] [11] [÷] [3·5] [EXP] [3·8] [+/−] [=]

The answer is $1{\cdot}4 \times 10^{15}$.

Common error:

DO NOT press the

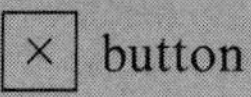 button!

Exercise 3

In Questions **1** to **22**, give the answer in standard form.

1. 5000×3000

2. $60\,000 \times 5000$

3. $0{\cdot}000\,07 \times 400$

4. $0{\cdot}0007 \times 0{\cdot}000\,01$

5. $8000 \div 0{\cdot}004$

6. $(0{\cdot}002)^2$

7. $150 \times 0{\cdot}0006$

8. $0{\cdot}000\,033 \div 500$

9. $0{\cdot}007 \div 20\,000$

10. $(0{\cdot}0001)^4$

11. $(2000)^3$

12. $0{\cdot}005\,92 \div 8000$

13. $(1{\cdot}4 \times 10^7) \times (3{\cdot}5 \times 10^4)$

14. $(8{\cdot}8 \times 10^{10}) \div (2 \times 10^{-2})$

15. $(1{\cdot}2 \times 10^{11}) \div (8 \times 10^7)$

16. $(4 \times 10^5) \times (5 \times 10^{11})$

17. $(2{\cdot}1 \times 10^{-3}) \times (8 \times 10^{15})$

18. $(8{\cdot}5 \times 10^{14}) \div 2000$

19. $(3{\cdot}3 \times 10^{12}) \times (3 \times 10^{-5})$

20. $(2{\cdot}5 \times 10^{-8})^2$

21. $(1{\cdot}2 \times 10^5)^2 \div (5 \times 10^{-3})$

22. $(6{\cdot}2 \times 10^{-4}) \times (1{\cdot}1 \times 10^{-3})$

23. A certain dinosaur laid its eggs 30 million years ago. How many days ago was that? Round off your answer to 2 significant figures.

24. A pile of ten thousand sheets of paper is 1·3 m high. How thick is each sheet of paper in metres?

25. If $a = 512 \times 10^2$
$b = 0{\cdot}478 \times 10^6$
$c = 0{\cdot}0049 \times 10^7$
arrange a, b and c in order of size (smallest first).

26. If the number $2{\cdot}74 \times 10^{15}$ is written out in full, how many zeros follow the 4?

27. If the number $7{\cdot}31 \times 10^{-17}$ is written out in full, how many zeros would there be between the decimal point and the first significant figure?

28. If $x = 2 \times 10^5$ and $y = 3 \times 10^{-3}$, find the values of

(i) xy (ii) $\dfrac{x}{y}$

29. Oil flows through a pipe at a rate of $40\,m^3/s$. How long will it take to fill a tank of volume $1{\cdot}2 \times 10^5\,m^3$?

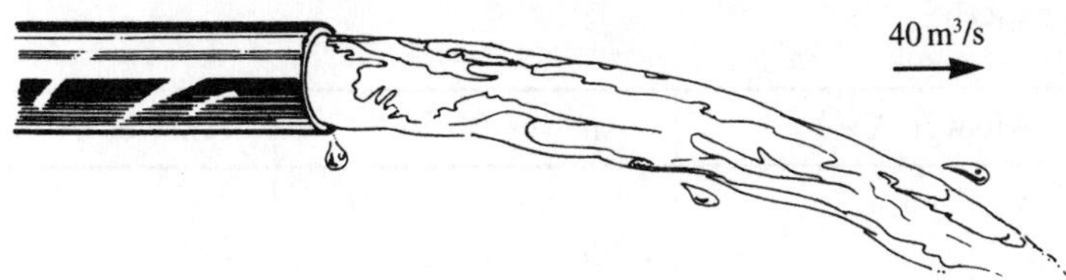

30. Given that $L = 2\sqrt{\frac{a}{k}}$, find the value of L in standard form when $a = 4{\cdot}5 \times 10^{12}$ and $k = 5 \times 10^7$.

31. A light year is the distance travelled by a beam of light in a year. Light travels at a speed of approximately 3×10^5 km/s.
(a) Work out the length of a light year in km.
(b) Light takes about 8 minutes to reach the Earth from the Sun. How far is the Earth from the Sun in km?

8.3 Estimating

In some circumstances it is unrealistic to work out the exact answer to a problem. It might be quite satisfactory to give an estimate for the answer. For example a builder does not know *exactly* how many bricks a new garage will require. He may estimate that he needs 2500 bricks and place an order for that number. In practice he may need only 2237.

Estimate the answers to the following questions.

(a) $9{\cdot}7 \times 3{\cdot}1 \approx 10 \times 3$. About 30.
(b) $81{\cdot}4 \times 98{\cdot}2 \approx 80 \times 100$. About 8000.
(c) $19{\cdot}2 \times 49{\cdot}1 \approx 20 \times 50$. About 1000.
(d) $102{\cdot}7 \div 19{\cdot}6 \approx 100 \div 20$. About 5.

Exercise 4

Write down each question and decide (by estimating) which answer is correct. Do not do the calculations exactly.

	Question	Answer A	Answer B	Answer C
1.	$7{\cdot}79 \div 1{\cdot}9$	8·2	4·1	1·9
2.	$27{\cdot}03 \div 5{\cdot}1$	5·3	0·5	8·7
3.	$59{\cdot}78 \div 9{\cdot}8$	12·2	2·8	6·1
4.	$58{\cdot}4 \times 102$	600·4	5956·8	2450·4
5.	$6{\cdot}8 \times 11{\cdot}4$	19·32	280·14	77·52
6.	$97 \times 1{\cdot}08$	104·76	55·66	1062·3
7.	$972 \times 20{\cdot}2$	2112·4	19 634·4	8862·4
8.	$7{\cdot}1 \times 103$	74·3	731·3	7210·3
9.	$18{\cdot}9 \times 21$	396·9	58·7	201·9
10.	$1{\cdot}078 \div 0{\cdot}98$	6·4	10·4	1·1
11.	$1250{\cdot}5 \div 6{\cdot}1$	21·4	205	66·2
12.	$20{\cdot}48 \div 3{\cdot}2$	6·4	12·2	2·8
13.	$25{\cdot}11 \div 3{\cdot}1$	8·1	15·1	19·3
14.	$216 \div 0{\cdot}9$	56·3	24·3	240
15.	$19{\cdot}2 + 0{\cdot}41$	23·3	8·41	19·61
16.	$207 + 18{\cdot}34$	25·34	225·34	1248
17.	$68{\cdot}2 - 1{\cdot}38$	97·82	48·82	66·82
18.	$7 - 0{\cdot}64$	6·36	1·48	0·48
19.	$974 \times 0{\cdot}11$	9·14	107·14	563·14
20.	$551{\cdot}1 \div 11$	6·92	50·1	5623
21.	$207{\cdot}1 + 11{\cdot}65$	310·75	23·75	218·75
22.	$664 \times 0{\cdot}51$	256·2	338·64	828·62
23.	$(5{\cdot}6 - 0{\cdot}21) \times 39$	389·21	210·21	20·51
24.	$\dfrac{17{\cdot}5 \times 42}{2{\cdot}5}$	294	504	86
25.	$(906 + 4{\cdot}1) \times 0{\cdot}31$	473·21	282·131	29·561
26.	$\dfrac{543 + 472}{18{\cdot}1 + 10{\cdot}9}$	65	35	85
27.	$\dfrac{112{\cdot}2 \times 75{\cdot}9}{6{\cdot}9 \times 5{\cdot}1}$	242	20·4	25·2
28.	$51{\cdot}2\%$ of 987	49·3	493	4937
29.	$\sqrt{99{\cdot}14} \times 10{\cdot}2$	101·4	57·3	573
30.	$\dfrac{203{\cdot}4 \times 2{\cdot}956}{\sqrt{26{\cdot}17}}$	87·4	8·72	41·1

Exercise 5

Do not use a calculator.

1. For a wedding the caterers provided food at £39·75 per head. There were 207 guests at the wedding. Estimate the total cost of the food.
2. 985 people share the cost of hiring an ice rink. About how much does each person pay if the total cost was £6017?
3. On a charity walk, Susie walked 31 miles in 11 hours 7 minutes. Estimate the number of minutes it took to walk one mile.

In Questions **4** to **11** estimate which answer is closest to the actual answer.

4. The height of a double-decker bus:

A	B	C
3 m	6 m	10 m

5. The height of the tallest player in the Olympic basketball competition:

A	B	C
1·8 m	3·0 m	2·2 m

6. The mass of a £1 coin:

A	B	C
1 g	10 g	100 g

7. The volume of your classroom:

A	B	C
700 cu.ft.	7000 cu.ft.	70 000 cu.ft.

8. The top speed of a Grand Prix racing car:

A	B	C
600 km/h	80 km/h	300 km/h

9. The number of times your heart beats in one day (24 h):

A	B	C
10 000	100 000	1 000 000

[There are about 200 pages, not 400!]

10. The thickness of one page in this book:

A	B	C
0·01 cm	0·001 cm	0·0001 cm

11. The number of cars in a traffic jam 10 km long on a 3-lane motorway:

A	B	C
3000	30 000	300 000

[Assume each car takes up 10 m of road.]

12. The newspaper article contains several numbers in bold type.
(a) For each number decide whether or not to replace the number with an approximate value to an *appropriate* degree of accuracy.
['appropriate' means 'sensible']
(b) Some of the numbers should *not* be replaced. State which these are.

> The Olympic swimming pool in Sydney contained **1493.2** m^3 of water at a temperature of **23.41**°C. The crowd of **2108** cheered as Marisa won the **100** m butterfly in a new World Record time of **58.23** seconds. Altogether there were about **5173** swimmers taking part in the swimming events. The next Games take place in **2004** in the . . .

Exercise 6

In Questions **1** and **2** there are six calculations and six answers. Write down each calculation and insert the correct answer from the list given. Use estimation.

1. (a) 8·9 × 10·1 (b) 7·98 ÷ 1·9 (c) 112 × 3·2
(d) 11·6 + 47·2 (e) 2·82 ÷ 9·4 (f) 262 ÷ 100
Answers: 2·62, 58·8, 0·3, 89·89, 358·4, 4·2

2. (a) 49·5 ÷ 11 (b) 21 × 22 (c) 9·1 × 104
(d) 86 − 8·2 (e) 2·4 ÷ 12 (f) 651 ÷ 31
Answers: 21, 946·4, 0·2, 4·5, 462, 77·8

3. There are about 7000 cinemas in the U.K. and every day about 300 people visit each one. The population of the U.K. is about 60 million.

Here is a film magazine report.

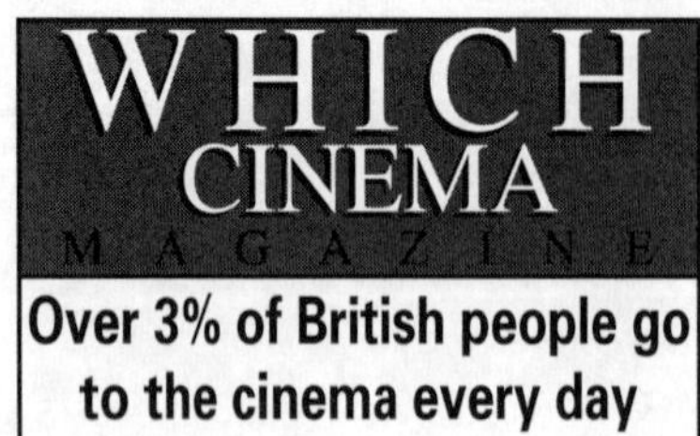

WHICH
CINEMA
MAGAZINE
Over 3% of British people go to the cinema every day

Is the magazine report fair?
Show the working you did to decide.

4. The petrol consumption of a car is 22 miles per gallon and petrol costs £2·45 per gallon.
Jasper estimates that the petrol costs of a round trip of about 1200 miles will be £130. Is this a reasonable estimate?

5. Mr Gibson, the famous maths teacher, has won the pools. He decides to give a rather unusual prize for the person who comes top in his next maths test. The prize winner receives his or her own weight in coins and they can choose to have either 1p, 2p, 5p, 10p, 20p, 50p or £1 coins. All the coins must be the same.

Approximate masses	
1 p	3·6 g
2 p	7·2 g
5 p	3·2 g
10 p	6·5 g
20 p	5·0 g
50 p	7·5 g
£1	9·0 g

Shabeza is the winner and she weighs 47 kg. *Estimate* the highest value of her prize.

6. The largest tree in the world has a diameter of 11 m.
Estimate the number of 'average' 15 year olds required to circle the tree so that they form an unbroken chain.

7. • When you multiply by a number greater than 1 you make it bigger.

so $\mathbf{5{\cdot}3} \times 1{\cdot}03 > \mathbf{5{\cdot}3}$ and $\mathbf{6{\cdot}75} \times 0{\cdot}89 < \mathbf{6{\cdot}75}$

• When you divide by a number greater than 1 you make it smaller.

so $\mathbf{8{\cdot}92} \div 1{\cdot}13 < \mathbf{8{\cdot}92}$ and $\mathbf{11{\cdot}2} \div 0{\cdot}73 > \mathbf{11{\cdot}2}$

State whether 'true' or 'false':

(a) $3{\cdot}72 \times 1{\cdot}3 > 3{\cdot}72$
(b) $253 \times 0{\cdot}91 < 253$
(c) $0{\cdot}92 \times 1{\cdot}04 > 0{\cdot}92$
(d) $8{\cdot}5 \div 1{\cdot}4 > 8{\cdot}5$
(e) $113 \div 0{\cdot}73 < 113$
(f) $17{\cdot}4 \div 2{\cdot}2 < 17{\cdot}4$
(g) $0{\cdot}73 \times 0{\cdot}73 < 0{\cdot}73$
(h) $2511 \div 0{\cdot}042 < 2511$
(i) $614 \times 0{\cdot}993 < 614$

8. The 44 teachers in a rather difficult school decide to buy 190 canes at £2·42 each. They share the cost equally between them.
The headmaster used a calculator to work out the cost per teacher and got an answer of £1·05 to the nearest penny.
Without using a calculator, work out an estimate for the answer to check whether or not he got it right. Show your working.

9. [This question involves weighing newspapers.]
Each year in Britain about 150 million trees are cut down to make paper. One tree is enough to make about 650 kg of paper.

(a) Weigh several newspapers (large and small) and estimate the number of newspapers which can be made from one tree.
(b) Estimate the number of newspapers which could be made from all the trees cut down each year.
(c) Weigh some of the exercise books you use at school. Estimate the number of books your class will use in a whole year and hence estimate the number of trees required to supply the paper for your class for one year.

8.4 Measurement is approximate

(a) If you measure the length of some cloth for a dress you might say the length is 145 cm to the nearest cm. The actual length could be anything from 144·5 cm to 145·49999... cm if we use the normal convention which is to round up a figure of 5 or more. Clearly 145·4999... is effectively 145·5 and we could use this figure.

(b) If you measure the length of a page in a book you might say the length is 437 mm to the nearest mm. In this case the actual length could be anywhere from 436·5 mm to 437·5 mm. We write 'length is between 436·5 mm and 437·5 mm'.

In both cases (a) and (b) the measurement expressed to a given unit is in *possible error* of *half a unit.*

(c) (i) Similarly if you say you weigh 57 kg to the nearest kg you could actually weigh anything from 56·5 kg to 57·5 kg.

The 'unit' is 1 so half a 'unit' is 0·5.

(ii) If your brother was weighed on more sensitive scales and the result was 57·2 kg, his actual weight could be from 57·15 kg to 57·25 kg.

The 'unit' is 0·1 so half a 'unit' is 0·05.

(iii) The weight of a butterfly might be given as 0·032 g. The actual weight could be from 0·0315 g to 0·0325 g.

The 'unit' is 0·001 so half a 'unit' is 0·0005.

(d) Here are some futher examples:

	lower limit	upper limit
(i) The diameter of a CD is 12 cm to the nearest cm.	11·5 cm	12·5 cm
(ii) The mass of a coin is 6·2 g to the nearest 0·1 g.	6·15 g	6·25 g
(iii) The length of a fence is 330 m to the nearest 10 m.	325 m	335 m

Exercise 7

1. In a DIY store the height of a door is given as 195 cm to the nearest cm. Write down the greatest possible height of the door.

2. A vet weighs a sick goat at 37 kg to the nearest kg. What is the least possible weight of the goat?

3. A surveyor using a laser beam device can measure distances to the nearest 0·1 m. What is the least possible length of a warehouse which he measures at 95·6 m?

4. A cook's weighing scales weigh to the nearest 0·1 kg.
What is the greatest possible weight of a chicken which she weighs at 3·2 kg?

5. In the county sports Jill was timed at 28·6 s for the 200 m. What is the greatest time she could have taken?

6. Copy and complete the table.

	lower limit	upper limit
(a) temperature in a fridge = 2°C, to nearest degree.		
(b) mass of an acorn = 2·3 g, to 1 d.p.		
(c) length of telephone cable = 64 m, to nearest m.		
(d) time taken to run 100 m = 13·6 s, to nearest 0·1 s.		

7. The length of a telephone is measured as 193 mm, to the nearest mm. The length lies between:

A	B	C
192 and 194 mm	192·5 and 193·5 mm	188 and 198 mm

8. The weight of a labrador is 35 kg, to the nearest kg.
The weight lies between:

A	B	C
30 and 40 kg	34 and 36 kg	34·5 and 35·5 kg

9. Liz and Julie each measure a different worm and they both say that their worm is 11 cm long to the nearest cm.
(a) Does this mean that both worms are the same length?
(b) If not, what is the maximum possible difference in the length of the two worms?

10. A card measuring 11·2 cm (to the nearest 0·1 cm) is to be posted in an envelope which is 12 cm (to the nearest cm).
Can you guarantee that the card will fit inside the envelope? Explain your answer.

11.2 cm

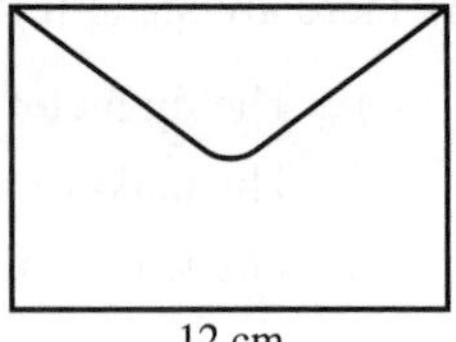
12 cm

In Questions **11** to **24** you are given a measurement. Write down the upper and lower bounds of the number. For example if you are given a length as 13 cm you can write 'length is between 12·5 cm and 13·5 cm'.

11. mass = 17 kg
12. d = 256 km
13. length = 2·4 m
14. m = 0·34 grams
15. v = 2·04 m/s
16. x = 12·0 cm [N.B. not 12 cm!]
17. T = 81·4 °C
18. M = 0·3 kg
19. d = 4·80 cm
20. y = 0·07 m
21. mass = 0·7 tonne
22. t = 615 seconds
23. d = 7·13 m
24. n = 52 million (nearest million)

8.5 Mental arithmetic

Ideally these questions should be read out by a teacher or friends and you should not be looking at them. Each question should be repeated once and then the answer, and only the answer, should be written down.
Each test, including the recording of results, should take about 30 minutes.
If you do not have anyone to read out the questions for you, try to do the test without writing down any detailed working.

Test 1

1. Find the cost in pounds of ten books at 35 pence each.
2. Add together £4·20 and 75 pence.
3. What number divided by six gives an answer of eight?
4. I spend £1·60 and pay with £2. My change consists of three coins. What are they?
5. Find the difference between $13\frac{1}{2}$ and 20.
6. Write one centimetre as a fraction of one metre.
7. How many ten pence coins are there in a pile worth £5.60?
8. Ten per cent of the pupils in a school play hockey, 15% play basketball and the rest play football. What percentage play football?
9. In a room of 20 people, three-quarters were women. What was the number of women?
10. Four lemons costing eleven pence each are bought with a one pound coin. What is the change?
11. I arrive at the railway station at 5.20 p.m. and my train is due at 6.10 p.m. How long do I have to wait?
12. What number is ten times as big as 0·65?
13. A hockey pitch measures 25 metres by 40 metres. Find the distance around the pitch.
14. Write the number 768 correct to the nearest ten.

15. By how many does a half of 62 exceed 20?
16. How many 2p coins are worth the same as ten 5p coins?
17. What number must be added to $1\frac{1}{4}$ to make $2\frac{1}{2}$?
18. Three books cost six pounds. How much will five books cost?
19. A rubber costs 20 pence. How many can be bought for £2?
20. What number is a hundred times as big as 0·605?
21. How many millimetres are there in $5\frac{1}{2}$ cm?
22. Find the average of 12 and 20.
23. A car travelling at 80 kilometres per hour takes 30 minutes for a journey. How long will the car take at 40 kilometres per hour?
24. A certain number multiplied by itself gives 81 as the answer. What is half of that number?
25. The difference between two numbers is 15. One of the numbers is 90. What is the other?
26. How many half-litre glasses can be filled from a vessel containing ten litres?
27. How much will a dozen oranges cost at 20 pence each?
28. On a coach forty-one out of fifty people are men. What percentage is this?
29. A prize of £400 000 is shared equally between one hundred people. How much does each person receive?
30. If electric cable is 6 pence for 50 cm, how much will 4 metres cost?

Test 2

1. What are 48 twos?
2. How many fives are there in ninety-five?
3. What is 6.30 a.m. on the 24-hour clock?
4. Add together £2·25 and 50 pence.
5. I go shopping with £2·80 and buy a magazine for ninety pence. How much money have I left?
6. Two angles of a triangle are 65° and 20°. What is the third angle?
7. Write in figures the number 'five million, eighteen thousand and one.'
8. How many 20 pence biros can be bought for £3?
9. Work out 1% of £600.
10. A packet of 10 small cakes costs 35 pence. How much does each cake cost?
11. Add eight to 9 fives.
12. A packet of flour weighing 2400 grams is divided into three equal parts. How heavy is each part?
13. Add together 7, 23 and 44.
14. A car does 40 miles per gallon of petrol. How far does the car travel on seven gallons of petrol?
15. How many twenty pence coins are needed to make eight pounds?
16. A certain butterfly lives for just 96 hours. How many days is this?
17. What number is 25 more than 37?
18. Find the average of 2, 5 and 8.
19. Pears cost eleven pence each. How many can I buy for sixty pence?
20. How many minutes are there in eight hours?
21. What number is twice as big as seventy-nine?
22. How many minutes are there between 6.25 p.m. and 8.00 p.m.?
23. Write one-fifth as a decimal.
24. Which is the larger: 0·7 or 0·071?
25. If a woman earns £8·40 per hour, how much does she earn in ten hours?

26. A car costing £2500 is reduced by £45. What is the new price?
27. How many half kilogram packets of sugar can be filled from a large bowl containing 32 kilograms?
28. My daily paper costs 15 pence and I buy the paper six days a week. What is my weekly bill?
29. A car journey of 110 miles took two hours. What was the average speed of the car?
30. How many days will there be in February 2003?

Test 3

1. What number is fifteen more than fifty-five?
2. What is a tenth of 2400?
3. What is twenty times forty-five?
4. Write in figures the number ten thousand, seven hundred and five.
5. A play lasting $2\frac{1}{4}$ hours starts at half-past eight. When does it finish?
6. What number is fifty-five less than 300?
7. How many twelves are there in 240?
8. A book costs £1·95. How much change do I receive from a five pound note?
9. Find the cost of eight biros at 22 pence each.
10. What four coins make 61 pence?
11. Work out $\frac{1}{2}$ plus $\frac{1}{4}$ and give the answer as a decimal.
12. A box holds 16 cans. How many boxes are needed for 80 cans?
13. If the 25th of December is a Tuesday, what day of the week is the first of January?
14. By how much is two kilos more than 500 g?
15. Write down fifteen thousand and fifty pence in pounds and pence.
16. The sides of a square field measure 160 metres. Find the total distance around the field.
17. A three-piece suite costing £970 is reduced by £248. What is the new price?
18. A bingo prize of £150 000 is shared equally between six people. How much does each person receive?
19. Ice creams cost twenty-four pence each. How many can I buy with one pound?
20. A bag contains 22 five pence coins. How much is in the bag?
21. How many pounds are there in two stones?
22. A wine merchant puts 100 bottles in crates of 12. How many crates does he need?
23. Add together 73 and 18.
24. What is 5% of £120?
25. Peaches cost fourteen pence each. How much do I pay for seven peaches?
26. A toy costs 54 pence. Find the change from a five pound note.
27. A boy goes to and from school by bus and a ticket costs 33 pence each way. How much does he spend in a five-day week?
28. In your purse, you have two ten pound notes, three five pound notes and seven one pound coins. How much have you got altogether?
29. What are eighty twelves?
30. Sweets cost 72 pence a pound. How much do I pay if I buy four ounces of sweets?

Test 4

1. What is the change from a £10 note for goods costing £1·95?
2. Add 12 to 7 nines.
3. How many 20 pence coins are needed to make £5?
4. A pile of 100 sheets of paper is 10 cm thick. How thick is each sheet?
5. Lemons cost 7 pence each or 60 pence a dozen. How much is saved by buying a dozen instead of 12 separate lemons?

6. How many weeks are there in two years?

7. What is 1% of £40?

8. How much more than £92 is £180?

9. My watch reads five past 6. It is 15 minutes fast. What is the correct time?

10. If a pint of beer costs 82p, how much does a man pay for a round of 10 pints?

11. A cycle track is 800 metres long. How far do I go in kilometres if I complete 5 laps of the track?

12. A train travels at an average speed of 30 mph for $1\frac{1}{2}$ hours. How far does it travel?

13. I go shopping with £5 and buy 3 items at 25 pence each. How much money have I left?

14. From one thousand and seven take away nine.

15. If I can cycle a mile in 3 minutes, how many miles can I cycle in one hour?

16. How many millimetres are there in 20 cm?

17. A metal rod 90 cm long is cut into four equal parts. How long is one part?

18. Find the cost of fifteen items at 5 pence each.

19. A 2 pence coin is about 2 mm thick. How many coins are in a pile which is 2 cm high?

20. Add up the first four odd numbers.

21. Add up the first four even numbers.

22. My daily paper costs 18 pence. I pay for it with a £10 note. What change do I receive?

23. A film starts at 8.53 p.m. and finishes at 9.15 p.m. How long is the film?

24. We finish school at twenty to four. What is that on the 24-hour clock?

25. Add together £2·34 and £5·60.

26. What is 10% of £7?

27. How many 2 pence coins are needed to make £4?

28. 35% of a class prefer BBC1 and 30% prefer ITV. What percentage prefer the other channels?

29. How many minutes is it between 6.20 p.m. and 8.00 p.m.?

30. What is the cost of 1000 books at £2·50 each?

The questions in the next three tests are a little harder.

Test 5

1. I bought an article costing 63p and paid with a one pound coin. My change consisted of four coins. What were they?

2. I bought two books costing £2·50 and £1·90. How much did I spend altogether?

3. What is the cost of six items at thirty-five pence each?

4. Tickets for a concert cost £6·50 each. What is the cost of four tickets?

5. It takes me 24 minutes to walk to school. I cycle three times as fast as I walk. How long do I take to cycle to school?

6. Work out as a single number, four squared plus three squared.

7. Write down an approximate value for forty-nine times eleven.

8. Write one metre as a fraction of one kilometre.

9. What number is exactly half-way between 2·5 and 2·8?

10. The First World War started in 1914. How long ago was that?

11. Lottery tickets cost £2·50 each. How much is raised from the sale of six thousand tickets?

12. Train fares are increased by ten per cent. If the old fare was £3·50, what is the new fare?

13. If a man earns £5·50 per hour, how much does he earn in five hours?

14. A beer crate holds twelve bottles. How many crates are needed for 90 bottles?

15. When playing darts you score double ten, double twenty and treble eight. What is your total score?
16. How many inches are there in three yards?
17. A petrol pump delivered $2\frac{1}{2}$ litres in 5 seconds. How many litres will it deliver in one minute?
18. A square has sides of length 5 cm. How long is a diagonal to the nearest centimetre?
19. How much more than 119 is 272?
20. What is the cube root of 64?
21. Find the average of 4, 8 and 9.
22. A rectangular lawn is 7 yards wide and 15 yards long. What area does it cover?
23. How many centimetres are there in 20 km?
24. A ship was due at noon on Tuesday, but arrived at 15 00 on Thursday. How many hours late was it?
25. A litre of wine fills 9 glasses. How many litre bottles are needed to fill 50 glasses?
26. Work out 15% of £40.
27. A cake weighs two pounds. How many ounces is that?
28. How many seconds are there in $2\frac{1}{2}$ minutes?
29. How many days are there altogether in 19 weeks?
30. If the eighth of May is a Monday, what day of the week is the seventeenth?

Test 6

1. What is the angle between the hands of a clock at two o'clock?
2. What is a half of a half of 0·2?
3. In a test Paul got 16 out of 20. What percentage is that?
4. Work out $2 \times 20 \times 200$.
5. Two friends share a bill for £33·80. How much does each person pay?
6. Work out $\frac{1}{2}$ plus $\frac{1}{5}$ and give the answer as a decimal.
7. How long will it take a car to travel 320 miles at an average speed of 60 m.p.h.?
8. What is $\frac{1}{8}$ as a percentage?
9. What is the height of a triangle with base 12 cm and area 36 cm^2?
10. Work out 0·1 cubed.
11. Between which two consecutive whole numbers does the square root of 58 lie?
12. What is eight per cent of £25?
13. A car has a 1795 c.c. engine. What is that approximately in litres?
14. The mean of four numbers is 12·3. What is their sum?
15. Find the cost of smoking 40 cigarettes a day for five days if a packet of 20 costs £3·85.
16. How many minutes are there in $2\frac{3}{4}$ hours?
17. A pie chart has a red sector representing 20% of the whole chart. What is the angle of the sector?
18. How many five pence coins are needed to make £12?
19. I buy three pounds of oranges for £1·02. How much do they cost per pound?
20. A rectangular pane of glass is 3 feet long and 2 feet wide. Glass costs £1·50 per square foot. How much will the pane cost?
21. A car journey of 150 miles took $2\frac{1}{2}$ hours. What was the average speed?
22. Add 218 to 84.
23. Pencils cost 5 pence each. How many can I buy with £2·50?
24. Write down the next prime number after 31.
25. A ruler costs 37 pence. What is the total cost of three rulers?

26. A salesman receives commission of $1\frac{1}{2}$% on sales. How much commission does he receive when he sells a computer for £1000?
27. How many edges does a cube have?
28. Between which two consecutive whole numbers does the square root of 80 lie?
29. A coat is marked at a sale price of £60 after a reduction of 25%. What was the original price?
30. Theatre tickets cost £3·45 each. How much will four tickets cost?

Test 7

1. Two angles of a triangle are 42° and 56°. What is the third angle?
2. Telephone charges are increased by 20%. What is the new charge for a call which previously cost 60p?
3. What number is exactly half-way between 0·1 and 0·4?
4. A boat sails at a speed of 18 knots for five hours. How far does it go?
5. How many 23p stamps can be bought for £2?
6. The mean age of three girls is 12 years. If two of the girls are aged 9 and 16 years, how old is the third girl?
7. Multiply $3\frac{1}{4}$ by 100.
8. What is a quarter of a third?
9. A prize of five million pounds is shared between 200 people. How much does each person receive?
10. The attendance at an athletics meeting was forty-eight thousand, seven hundred and eleven. Write this number correct to two significant figures.
11. Work out 0·1 multiplied by 63.
12. Find the cost of 6 litres of wine at £1·45 per litre.
13. Three people agree to share a bill equally. The cost comes to £7·20. How much does each person pay?
14. A pump removes water at a rate of 6 gallons per minute. How many hours will it take to remove 1800 gallons?
15. Work out three-eighths of £100.
16. A metal rod of length 27·1 cm is cut exactly in half. How long is each piece?
17. A square has sides of length 7 cm. How long is a diagonal to the nearest centimetre?
18. The cost of five tins of salmon is £7·50. How much will six tins cost?
19. What number is a thousand times as big as 0·2?
20. Pencils cost five pence each. How much will two dozen pencils cost?
21. How many fours are there in a thousand?
22. Work out the area, in square metres, of a rectangular field of width twenty metres and length twenty-five metres.
23. A packet of peanuts costs 65 pence. I buy two packets and pay with a ten pound note. Find the change.
24. What is a half of a half of 0·1?
25. I bought three kilograms of flour and I use four hundred and fifty grams of it. How many grams of flour do I have left?
26. A bingo prize of two hundred thousand pounds is shared equally between five people. How much does each person receive?
27. What is the angle between the hands of a clock at 5 o'clock?
28. Five boys and three girls share £240. How much do the boys get altogether?
29. How many 17p stamps can I buy for £2?
30. A milk crate has space for 24 bottles. How many crates are needed for 200 bottles?

Mathematical magic

Here is a trick which you can perform to demonstrate that you can add even quicker than a calculator!

(a) Ask someone to give a five-digit number with the figures all jumbled up to make it more 'difficult'.

(b) Ask for two more five-digit numbers. You may now have:

47563 ...A
25608 ...B
87265 ...C

(c) Pretend to add two more five-digit numbers at random. In fact choose the fourth number so that when added to number B it makes 99999. Similarly the fifth number is chosen so that when added to number C it also makes 99999. We now have:

47563
25608
87265
74391
12734

(d) You now add them together 'in your head' and write down the answer. (Check this on a calculator.)

Answer = 247561

How does it work?

The first digit is always a '2'.
The next five digits are simply 2 less than number A.
i.e. 47563 − 2 = 47561.

Here is another example.

58627
43817
38065
56182
\+ 61934
258625

Can you work out why it works?

Now challenge your friends or relatives to an addition race: your brain versus their calculator.

8.6 Using a calculator

Order of operations

Calculators cannot think for themselves. *You* have to decide in which order the buttons have to be pressed.

- Always perform operations in the following order:
  (a) Brackets
  (b) Divide and multiply
  (c) Add and subtract.

'BoDMAS'

B rackets
D ivide
M ultiply
A dd
S ubtract

(a) $7 + 6 \div 3 = 7 + 2$
$= 9$

(b) $6 \times 4 - 8 \div 2 = 24 - 4$
$= 20$

(c) $5 + (28 + 5) \div 3 = 5 + 33 \div 3$
$= 5 + 11$
$= 16$

(d) $\dfrac{4{\cdot}2}{1{\cdot}2 - 0{\cdot}7} = \dfrac{4{\cdot}2}{0{\cdot}5}$
$= 8{\cdot}4$

In (d) notice that the division line acts like a pair of brackets so that we work out 1·2 – 0·7 first.

Exercise 8

Work out, without a calculator.

1. $11 + 8 \div 1$
2. $60 - 7 \times 8$
3. $15 - 2 \times 6$
4. $15 \div 5 - 3$
5. $30 + 15 \div 3$
6. $9 \times 5 + 15$
7. $40 - 3 \times 8$
8. $12 - 36 \div 6$
9. $3 + 20 \div 2$
10. $13 + 8 \div 8$
11. $2 \times 4 + 3 \times 5$
12. $6 \times 6 + 7 \times 5$
13. $1 \times 6 + 7 \times 2$
14. $2 \times 8 + 2 \times 10$
15. $3 \times 5 - 12 \div 2$
16. $3 \times 5 - 28 \div 4$
17. $7 \times 4 + 2 \times 2$
18. $30 \div 3 + 5 \times 4$
19. $20 \div 2 - 3 \times 2$
20. $8 \div 8 - 1 \times 1$
21. $\dfrac{27 + 3 \times 3}{(3 \times 2)}$
22. $\dfrac{6 + 8 \times 3}{(8 \times 2 - 10)}$
23. $\dfrac{13 - 12 \div 4}{4 + 3 \times 2}$
24. $\dfrac{11 + 6 \times 6}{5 - 8 \div 2}$
25. $\dfrac{12 + 3 \times 6}{4 + 3 \div 3}$
26. $\dfrac{24 - 18 \div 3}{1{\cdot}5 + 4{\cdot}5}$

27. $(42 - 5 \times 6) \times (8 - 4 \times 2) + (7 + 3 \times 3)$
28. $(10 - 24 \div 3) + (8 + 3 \times 4) \div (8 - 6 \times 1)$
29. $7 + 9 \times (8 - 6 \div 2)$
30. $[(7 - 2) \times 5] - (6 \times 3 - 2 \times 4)$
31. $[(60 - 7 \times 5) \div 5] + (12 + 7 \times 10)$
32. $(15 - 3 \times 4) \times 4 + [60 \div (24 \div 2)]$
33. $[(9 - 7) \times 12] - (7 \times 3 - 5 \times 4)$
34. $(50 - 8 \times 6) \times 2 + [40 \div (5 \times 2)]$
35. $[(12 - 8) \times 4] \div (11 - 3 \times 1)$
36. $(7 \times 2 - 6) + (7 + 16 \div 8) \times (10 - 4 \times 2)$

Exercise 9

This exercise is more difficult. Write down each question and find the missing signs (+, –, ×, ÷). There are no brackets.

1. 7 5 4 = 27
2. 3 5 10 = 25
3. 4 2 3 = 5
4. 11 3 3 = 20
5. 31 10 2 = 11
6. 10 6 5 = 40
7. 4 8 7 = 25
8. 12 9 2 = 30
9. 18 4 4 = 2
10. 28 10 2 = 8
11. 21 3 5 = 2
12. 7 3 3 = 16
13. 10 2 3 = 8
14. 10 3 12 = 42
15. 18 3 7 = 13
16. 31 40 5 = 39
17. 15 16 4 = 11
18. 15 8 9 = 87
19. 37 35 5 = 44
20. 11 5 9 = 64
21. 8 3 2 4 = 10
22. 12 3 3 1 = 4
23. 11 4 1 6 = 9
24. 15 5 2 4 = 11
25. 7 2 3 3 = 5
26. 12 2 3 4 = 22
27. 8 9 6 11 = 6
28. 20 20 9 0 = 1
29. 20 30 10 8 = 25
30. 30 6 11 11 = 85

Calculator

(a) Work out $8{\cdot}43 + \frac{9{\cdot}72}{3{\cdot}3}$ correct to four significant figures.

Perform the division first and *don't forget* to press the [=] button.

[9·72] [÷] [3·3] [=] [+] [8·43] [=]

Answer = 11·38 (to 4 s.f.)

(b) Work out $(5{\cdot}2 - 4{\cdot}737)^2$.

[5·2] [−] [4·737] [=] [x^2]

Answer = 0·2144 (to 4 s.f.)

Exercise 10

Work out, correct to four significant figures.

1. $85{\cdot}3 \times 21{\cdot}7$

2. $18{\cdot}6 \div 2{\cdot}7$

3. $10{\cdot}074 \div 8{\cdot}3$

4. $0{\cdot}112 \times 3{\cdot}74$

5. $8 - 0{\cdot}111\,11$

6. $19 + 0{\cdot}3456$

7. $0{\cdot}841 \div 17$

8. $11{\cdot}02 \times 20{\cdot}1$

9. $18{\cdot}3 \div 0{\cdot}751$

10. $0{\cdot}982 \times 6{\cdot}74$

11. $\frac{8{\cdot}3 + 2{\cdot}94}{3{\cdot}4}$

12. $\frac{6{\cdot}1 - 4{\cdot}35}{0{\cdot}76}$

13. $\frac{19{\cdot}7 + 21{\cdot}4}{0{\cdot}985}$

14. $7{\cdot}3 + \left(\frac{8{\cdot}2}{9{\cdot}5}\right)$

15. $\left(\frac{6{\cdot}04}{18{\cdot}7}\right) - 0{\cdot}214$

16. $\frac{2{\cdot}4 \times 0{\cdot}871}{4{\cdot}18}$

17. $19{\cdot}3 + \left(\frac{2{\cdot}6}{1{\cdot}95}\right)$

18. $6{\cdot}41 + \frac{9{\cdot}58}{2{\cdot}6}$

19. $\frac{19{\cdot}3 \times 0{\cdot}221}{0{\cdot}689}$

20. $8{\cdot}3 + \frac{0{\cdot}64}{0{\cdot}325}$

21. $2{\cdot}4 + (9{\cdot}7 \times 0{\cdot}642)$

22. $11{\cdot}2 + (9{\cdot}75 \times 1{\cdot}11)$

23. $0{\cdot}325 + \frac{8{\cdot}6}{11{\cdot}2}$

24. $8{\cdot}35^2 - 25$

25. $6{\cdot}71^2 + 0{\cdot}64$

26. $3{\cdot}45^3 + 11{\cdot}8$

27. $2{\cdot}93^3 - 2{\cdot}641$

28. $\frac{7{\cdot}2^2 - 4{\cdot}5}{8{\cdot}64}$

29. $\frac{13{\cdot}9 + 2{\cdot}97^2}{4{\cdot}31}$

30. $(3{\cdot}3 - 2{\cdot}84)^2$

Using the memory

(a) Work out $\dfrac{4{\cdot}2 + 1{\cdot}75}{3{\cdot}63 - 2{\cdot}14}$, correct to 4 s.f., using the memory buttons.

Find the bottom line first:

[3·63] [−] [2·14] [=] [Min] [C] [4·2] [+] [1·75] [=] [÷] [MR] [=]

The calculator reads 3·9932886

∴ Answer = 3·993 (to 4 s.f.)

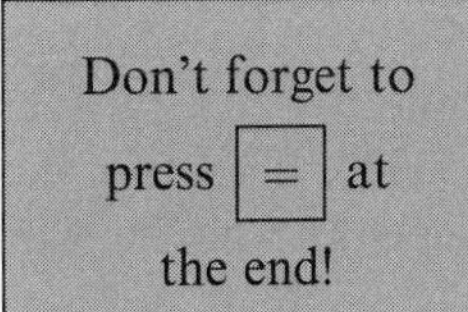
Don't forget to
press [=] at
the end!

(b) Work out $18{\cdot}75 - 2{\cdot}11^3$.

[2·11] [x^y] [3] [=] [Min] [18·75] [−] [MR] [=]

Answer = 9·356 (to 4 s.f.)

Exercise 11

Work out the following, correct to four significant figures. Use the memory buttons where necessary.

1. $\dfrac{7{\cdot}3 + 2{\cdot}14}{3{\cdot}6 - 2{\cdot}95}$
2. $\dfrac{2{\cdot}3 + 0{\cdot}924}{1{\cdot}3 + 0{\cdot}635}$
3. $\dfrac{5{\cdot}89}{7 - 3{\cdot}83}$
4. $\dfrac{102}{58{\cdot}1 + 65{\cdot}32}$
5. $\dfrac{18{\cdot}8}{3{\cdot}72 \times 1{\cdot}86}$
6. $\dfrac{904}{65{\cdot}3 \times 2{\cdot}86}$
7. $12{\cdot}2 - \left(\dfrac{2{\cdot}6}{1{\cdot}95}\right)$
8. $8{\cdot}047 - \left(\dfrac{6{\cdot}34}{10{\cdot}2}\right)$
9. $14{\cdot}2 - \left(\dfrac{1{\cdot}7}{2{\cdot}4}\right)$
10. $\dfrac{9{\cdot}75 - 8{\cdot}792}{4{\cdot}31 - 3{\cdot}014}$
11. $\dfrac{19{\cdot}6 \times 3{\cdot}01}{2{\cdot}01 - 1{\cdot}958}$
12. $3{\cdot}7^2 - \left(\dfrac{8{\cdot}59}{24}\right)$
13. $8{\cdot}27 - 1{\cdot}56^2$
14. $111{\cdot}79 - 5{\cdot}04^2$
15. $18{\cdot}3 - 2{\cdot}841^2$
16. $(2{\cdot}93 + 71{\cdot}5)^2$
17. $(8{\cdot}3 - 6{\cdot}34)^4$
18. $54{\cdot}2 - 2{\cdot}6^4$
19. $(8{\cdot}7 - 5{\cdot}95)^4$
20. $\sqrt{68{\cdot}4} + 11{\cdot}63$
21. $9{\cdot}45 - \sqrt{8{\cdot}248}$
22. $3{\cdot}24^2 - \sqrt{1{\cdot}962}$
23. $\dfrac{3{\cdot}54 + 2{\cdot}4}{8{\cdot}47^2}$
24. $2065 - \sqrt{44\,000}$
25. $\sqrt{(5{\cdot}69 - 0{\cdot}0852)}$
26. $\sqrt{(0{\cdot}976 + 1{\cdot}03)}$
27. $\sqrt{\left(\dfrac{17{\cdot}4}{2{\cdot}16 - 1{\cdot}83}\right)}$
28. $\sqrt{\left(\dfrac{28{\cdot}9}{\sqrt{8{\cdot}47}}\right)}$
29. $257 - \dfrac{6{\cdot}32}{0{\cdot}059}$
30. $75\,000 - 5{\cdot}6^4$
31. $\dfrac{11{\cdot}29 \times 2{\cdot}09}{2{\cdot}7 + 0{\cdot}082}$
32. $85{\cdot}5 - \sqrt{105{\cdot}8}$
33. $\dfrac{4{\cdot}45^2}{8{\cdot}2^2 - 51{\cdot}09}$
34. $\left(\dfrac{8{\cdot}53 + 7{\cdot}07}{6{\cdot}04 - 4{\cdot}32}\right)^4$
35. $2{\cdot}75 + \dfrac{5}{8{\cdot}2} + \dfrac{11{\cdot}2}{4{\cdot}3}$
36. $8{\cdot}2 + \dfrac{6{\cdot}3}{0{\cdot}91} + \dfrac{2{\cdot}74}{8{\cdot}4}$

37. $\dfrac{18{\cdot}5}{1{\cdot}6}+\dfrac{7{\cdot}1}{0{\cdot}53}+\dfrac{11{\cdot}9}{25{\cdot}6}$

38. $\dfrac{83{\cdot}6}{105}+\dfrac{2{\cdot}95}{2{\cdot}7}+\dfrac{81}{97}$

39. $\left(\dfrac{98{\cdot}76}{103}+\dfrac{4{\cdot}07}{3{\cdot}6}\right)^2$

40. $\dfrac{(5{\cdot}843-\sqrt{2{\cdot}07})^2}{88{\cdot}4}$

41. $\left(\dfrac{1}{7{\cdot}6}-\dfrac{1}{18{\cdot}5}\right)^3$

42. $\dfrac{\sqrt{(4{\cdot}79)}+1{\cdot}6}{9{\cdot}63}$

43. $\dfrac{(0{\cdot}761)^2-\sqrt{(4{\cdot}22)}}{1{\cdot}96}$

44. $\sqrt[3]{\left(\dfrac{1{\cdot}74\times 0{\cdot}761}{0{\cdot}0896}\right)}$

45. $\left(\dfrac{8{\cdot}6\times 1{\cdot}71}{0{\cdot}43}\right)^3$

46. $\dfrac{\sqrt[3]{(86{\cdot}6)}}{\sqrt[4]{(4{\cdot}71)}}$

47. $\dfrac{1}{8{\cdot}2^2}-\dfrac{3}{19^2}$

48. $\dfrac{100}{11^3}+\dfrac{100}{12^3}$

Exercise 12

If we work out $25 \times 503 \times 4 + 37$ on a calculator we should obtain the number 50337. If we turn the calculator upside down (and use a little imagination) we see the word 'LEEDS'.

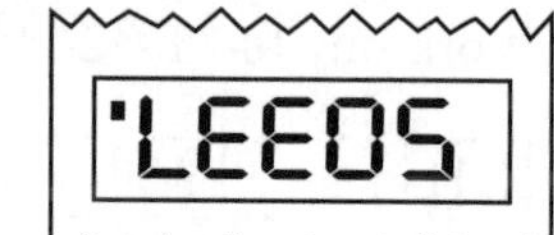

Find the words given by the clues below.

1. $83 \times 85 + 50$ (Lots of this in the garden)
2. $211 \times 251 + 790$ (Tropical or Scilly)
3. $19 \times 20 \times 14 - 2{\cdot}66$ (Not an upstanding man)
4. $(84 + 17) \times 5$ (Dotty message)
5. $0{\cdot}01443 \times 7 \times 4$ (Three times as funny)
6. $79 \times 9 - 0{\cdot}9447$ (Greasy letters)
7. $50{\cdot}19 - (5 \times 0{\cdot}0039)$ (Not much space inside)
8. $2 \div 0{\cdot}5 - 3{\cdot}295$ (Rather lonely)
9. $6{\cdot}2 \times 0{\cdot}987 \times 1\,000\,000 - 860^2 + 118$ (Flying ace)
10. $7420 \times 7422 + 118^2 - 30$ (Big Chief)

11. $(13 \times 3 \times 25 \times 8 \times 5) + 7$ (Dwelling for masons)
12. $71^2 - 11^2 - 5$ (Sad gasp)
13. $904^2 + 89621818$ (Prickly customer)
14. $(559 \times 6) + (21 \times 55)$ (What a surprise!)
15. $566 \times 711 - 23617$ (Bolt it down)

16. $\dfrac{9999 + 319}{8{\cdot}47 + 2{\cdot}53}$ (Sit up and plead)

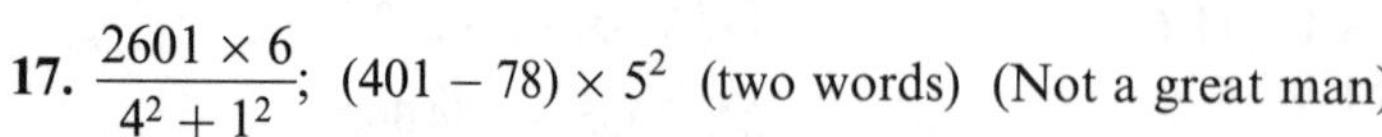

17. $\dfrac{2601 \times 6}{4^2 + 1^2}$; $(401 - 78) \times 5^2$ (two words) (Not a great man)

18. $0{\cdot}4^2 - 0{\cdot}1^2$ (Little Sidney)

19. $\dfrac{(27 \times 2000 - 2)}{(0{\cdot}63 \div 0{\cdot}09)}$ (Not quite a mountain)

20. $(5^2 - 1^2)^4 - 14239$ (Just a name)

21. $48^4 + 102^2 - 4^2$ (Pursuits)
22. $615^2 + (7 \times 242)$ (Almost a goggle)
23. $14^4 - 627 + 29$ (Good book, by God!)
24. $0{\cdot}034 \times 11 - 0{\cdot}00292$; $9^4 - (8 \times 71)$ (two words) (Nice for breakfast)

25. $(426 \times 474) + (318 \times 487) + 22018$ (Close to a bubble)
26. $\frac{36^3}{4} - 1530$ (Foreign-sounding girl's name)
27. $(594 \times 571) - (154 \times 132) - 38$ (Female Bobby)
28. $(7^2 \times 100) + (7 \times 2)$ (Lofty)
29. $240^2 + 134$; $241^2 - 7^3$ (two words) (Devil of a chime)
30. $1384{\cdot}5 \times 40 - 1{\cdot}991$ (Say this after sneezing)
31. $(2 \times 2 \times 2 \times 2 \times 3)^4 + 1929$ (Unhappy ending)
32. $141918 + 83^3$ (Hot stuff in France)

8.7 Mixed problems 3

Making a profit

A shopkeeper buys potatoes at a wholesale price of £180 per tonne and sells them at a retail price of 22p per kg.
How much profit does he make on one kilogram of potatoes?

He pays £180 for 1000 kg of potatoes. $\therefore$ he pays £[180 ÷ 1000] for 1 kg of potatoes.
i.e. he pays 18p for 1 kg

He sells at 22p per kg.
$\therefore$ profit = 4p per kg.

Exercise 13

Find the profit in each case.

Commodity	Retail price	Wholesale price	Profit
1. cans of drink	15p each	£11 per 100	profit per can?
2. rulers	24p each	£130 per 1000	profit per ruler?
3. birthday cards	22p each	£13 per 100	profit per card?
4. soup	27p per can	£8·50 for 50 cans	profit per can?
5. newspapers	22p each	£36 for 200	profit per paper?
6. box of matches	37p each	£15·20 for 80	profit per box?
7. potatoes	22p per kg	£160 per tonne	profit per kg?
8. carrots	38p per kg	£250 per tonne	profit per kg?
9. T-shirts	£4·95 each	£38·40 per dozen	profit per T-shirt?
10. eggs	96p per dozen	£50 per 1000	profit per dozen?
11. oranges	5 for 30p	£14 for 400	profit per orange?
12. car tyres	£19·50 each	£2450 for 200	profit per tyre?
13. wine	55p for 100 ml	£40 for 10 litres	profit per 100 ml?
14. sand	16p per kg	£110 per tonne	profit per kg?
15. wire	23p per m	£700 for 10 km	profit per m?

Commodity	Retail price	Wholesale price	Profit
16. cheese	£2·64 per kg	£87·50 for 50 kg	profit per kg?
17. copper tube	46p per m	£160 for 500 m	profit per m?
18. apples	9p each	£10·08 per gross	profit per apple?
19. carpet	£6·80 per m^2	£1600 for 500 m^2	profit per m^2?
20. tin of soup	33p per tin	£72 for 400 tins	profit per tin?

Exercise 14

Each empty square contains either a number or a mathematical symbol (+, −, ×, ÷). Copy each square and fill in the details.

1.

5			→	60
×		÷		
		24	→	44
↓		↓		
	×	$\frac{1}{2}$	→	50

2.

	×	6	→	42
÷		÷		
14	−		→	
↓		↓		
		2	→	1

3.

	×	2	→	38
−		÷		
			→	48
↓		↓		
7	−		→	$6\frac{1}{2}$

4.

17	×		→	170
−		÷		
	÷		→	
↓		↓		
8	−	0.1	→	

5.

0.3	×	20	→	
		−		
11	÷		→	
↓		↓		
11.3	−		→	2.3

6.

	×	50	→	25
−		÷		
		$\frac{1}{2}$	→	0.6
↓		↓		
0.4	×		→	

7.

7	×		→	0.7
÷		×		
	÷		→	
↓		↓		
1.75	+	0.02	→	

8.

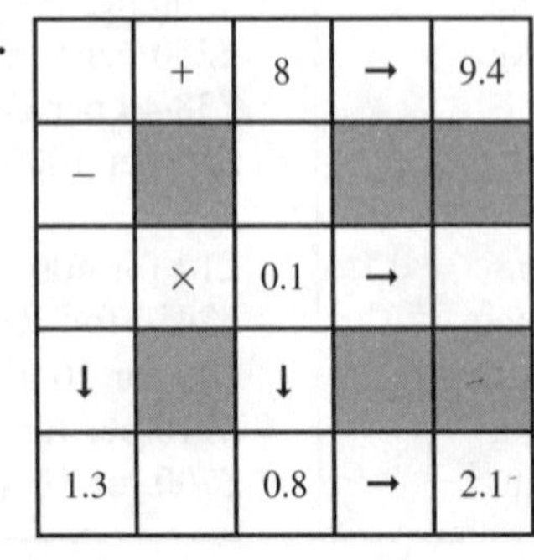

	+	8	→	9.4
−				
	×	0.1	→	
↓		↓		
1.3		0.8	→	2.1

9.

	×		→	30
−				
	÷	10	→	0.25
↓		↓		
97.5	+	3	→	

10.

3	÷	2	→	
÷		÷		
8	÷		→	
↓		↓		
	+	$\frac{1}{8}$	→	

11.

	−	$\frac{1}{16}$	→	$\frac{3}{16}$
×				
	÷	4	→	
↓		↓		
$\frac{1}{8}$		$\frac{1}{4}$	→	$\frac{3}{8}$

12.

0.5	−	0.01	→	
		×		
	×		→	35
↓		↓		
4	÷	0.1	→	

13.

	−	1.8	→	3.4
−		÷		
	×		→	
↓		↓		
	+	0.36	→	1

14.

	×	30	→	21
×		−		
	−		→	35
↓		↓		
	−	49	→	

15.

	×	−6	→	72
÷		+		
4	+		→	
↓		↓		
	+	1	→	−2

Exercise 15

1. Write down each calculation and find the missing digits.

(a)
```
   5 7 □ 2
 + □ 6 9 □
 ---------
   8 □ 2 8
```

(b)
```
   8 □ 5
 − 2 6 □
 -------
   □ 7 3
```

(c) □□□ ÷ 7 = 35

2. A hotel manager was able to buy loaves of bread at £4·44 per dozen, whereas the shop price was 43p per loaf. How much did he save on each loaf?

3. A high performance car uses one litre of petrol every 2·5 miles. How much petrol does it use on a journey of 37·5 miles?

4. John Lowe made darts history in 1984 with the first ever perfect game played in a tournament, 501 scored in just nine darts. He won a special prize of £100 000 from the sponsors of the tournament. His first eight darts were six treble 20s, treble 17 and treble 18.

(a) What did he score with the ninth dart?

(b) How much did he win per dart thrown, to the nearest pound?

5. An engineering firm offers all of its workers a choice of two pay rises. Workers can choose either an 8% increase on their salaries or they can accept a rise of £800.
   (a) A fitter earns £5200 a year. Which pay rise should he choose?
   (b) The personnel manager earns £11 500 a year. Which pay rise should he choose?

6. A map is 280 mm wide and 440 mm long. When reduced on a photocopier, the copy is 110 mm long. What is the width of the copy?

7. I have 213 mugs and one tray takes 9 mugs. How many trays do I need?

8. How many prime numbers are there between 120 and 130?

9. Write down these answers, without a calculator.
   (a) $0{\cdot}03 \times 10$ (b) $0{\cdot}03 \div 10$ (c) $115 \div 1000$ (d) $0{\cdot}07 \times 1$ million

10. Work out $\frac{2}{5} + 0{\cdot}14 + \frac{3}{4}$, and write the answer as a decimal.

Exercise 16

1. A maths teacher bought 40 calculators at £8.20 each and a number of other calculators costing £2.95 each. In all she spent £387. How many of the cheaper calculators did she buy?

2. The total mass of a jar one-quarter full of jam is 250 g. The total mass of the same jar three-quarters full of jam is 350 g.

$\frac{1}{4}$ 250g

$\frac{3}{4}$ 350g

   What is the mass of the empty jar?

3. I have lots of 1p, 2p, 3p and 4p stamps. How many different combinations of stamps can I make which total 5p?

4. 8% of 2500 + 37% of P = 348. Find the value of P.

5. Eggs are packed twelve to a box. A farmer has enough eggs to fill 316 boxes with unbroken eggs and he has 62 cracked eggs left over. How many eggs had he to start with?

6. A car travels 30 miles on a gallon of petrol and petrol costs £3·20 per gallon. Over a period of one year the car travels a distance of 9600 miles.
   How much does the petrol cost for the whole year?

7. You are given that $41 \times 271 = 11\,111$. Work out the following *in your head.*
   (a) 82×271
   (b) $33\,333 \div 271$

8. Booklets have a mass of 19 g each, and they are posted in an envelope of mass 38 g. Postage charges are shown in the table below.

Mass (in grams) not more than	60	100	150	200	250	300	350	600
Postage (in pence)	24	30	37	44	51	59	67	110

   (a) A package consists of 15 booklets in an envelope. What is the total mass of the package?
   (b) The mass of a second package is 475 g. How many booklets does it contain?
   (c) What is the postage charge on a package of mass 320 g?
   (d) The postage on a third package was £1.10. What is the largest number of booklets it could contain?

Exercise 17

1. A wicked witch stole a new-born baby from its parents.
   On the baby's first birthday the witch sent the grief-stricken parents 1 penny.
   On the second birthday she sent 2 pence.
   On the third birthday she sent 4 pence and so on, doubling the amount each time.
   How much did the witch send the parents on the twenty-first birthday?

2. The diagrams show magic squares in which the sum of the numbers in any row, column or diagonal is the same. Find the value of x in each square.

(a)

	x	6
3		7
		2

(b)

4		5	16
x		10	
	7	11	2
1			13

3. Find a pair of positive integers a and b for which
$18a + 65b = 1865$.

4. Work out $100 - 99 + 98 - 97 + 96 - \ldots + 4 - 3 + 2 - 1$.

5. Use a calculator to work out, correct to 3 significant figures.

(a) $19{\cdot}6 - (6{\cdot}2 \times 2{\cdot}13)$ (b) $\dfrac{18{\cdot}7}{5{\cdot}6 - 2{\cdot}91}$ (c) $\left(\dfrac{8{\cdot}2 + 1{\cdot}173}{7{\cdot}59}\right)^2$

6. Apart from 1, 3 and 5 all odd numbers less than 100 can be written in the form $p + 2^n$ where p is a prime number and n is greater than or equal to 2.

e.g. $43 = 11 + 2^5$
$27 = 23 + 2^2$

For the odd numbers 7, 9, 11, ... 27 write as many as you can in the form $p + 2^n$.

7. Evaluate

(a) $\frac{1}{3} \times \frac{2}{4} \times \frac{3}{5} \times \frac{4}{6} \times \frac{5}{7} \times \frac{6}{8} \times \frac{7}{9}$.

(b) $[(-2)^{-2}]^{-2}$

8. What is the smallest number greater than 1000 that is exactly divisible by 13 and 17?

9. Find the smallest value of n for which
$1^2 + 2^2 + 3^2 + 4^2 + 5^2 + \ldots + n^2 > 800$

10. The reciprocal of 2 is $\frac{1}{2}$. The reciprocal of 7 is $\frac{1}{7}$. The reciprocal of x is $\frac{1}{x}$.
Find the square root of the reciprocal of the square root of the reciprocal of ten thousand.

Income tax

The tax which employees pay on their income depends on
(a) how much they are paid (b) their allowances (c) the rate of taxation.

Tax is paid only on the 'taxable income'.

- Taxable income = Total income − allowances.

Allowances depend on whether a person is married or single and on various expenses involved in doing the job.
Employees can check their allowances by looking at the 'Tax Code Number' on their payslips.

- Allowances = (Tax Code Number) × 10

A man earns £6500 per year. If his Tax Code Number is 238, calculate his taxable income.

Allowances = 238 × 10 = £2380. Taxable income = £6500 − £2380
= £4120.

Exercise 18

Calculate the taxable income from the details given.

	Earnings	Tax Code Number		Earnings	Tax Code Number
1.	£3500 per year	213	**2.**	£5000 per year	274
3.	£8000 per year	315	**4.**	£4200 per year	289
5.	£3650 per year	265	**6.**	£9800 per year	341
7.	£8655 per year	286	**8.**	£600 per month	412
9.	£450 per month	263	**10.**	£825 per month	311
11.	£710 per month	278	**12.**	£985 per month	415
13.	£160 per week	342	**14.**	£144 per week	214
15.	£180 per week	289			

A woman earns £95 per week and her Tax Code Number is 215. Find the total amount of tax paid in a year when the tax rate is 30%.

Amount earned in year = £95 × 52
= £4940

Allowances = 215 × 10 = £2150

∴ Taxable income = £4940 − £2150
= £2790

Tax paid = 30% of £2790

$= \frac{30}{100} \times \frac{2790}{1} = £837$

Exercise 19

In all questions the tax rate is 30%.

1. A man earns £110 per week and his Tax Code Number is 304. Find the total amount of tax paid in a year.
2. A man earns £204 per week and his Tax Code Number is 361. Find the total amount of tax paid in a year.
3. Ann earns £165 per week. How much tax does she pay in a year if her Tax Code Number is 247?
4. John earns £148·50 per week. How much tax does he pay in a year if his Tax Code Number is 302?
5. Louise earns a salary of £620 per month. How much tax does she pay in a year if her Tax Code Number is 342?
6. David earns £950 per month and his Tax Code Number is 357. Find the total amount of tax paid in a year.
7. Mr Tebbit's salary is £9650 per year and his Tax Code Number is 465. Find the total amount of tax paid in a year.

9 PROBABILITY

9.1 Relative frequency

To work out the probability of a drawing pin landing point up we can conduct an experiment in which a drawing pin is dropped many times. If the pin lands 'point up' on x occasions out of a total number of N trials, the *relative frequency* of landing 'point up' is $\frac{x}{N}$.

When an experiment is repeated many times we can use the relative frequency as an estimate of the probability of the event occurring.

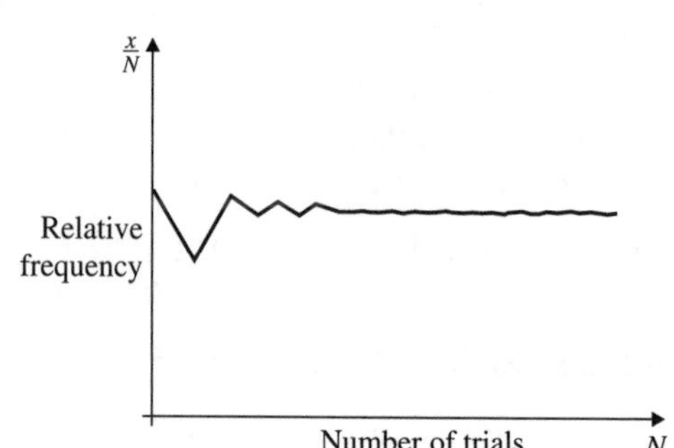

The graph shows how the ratio $\frac{x}{N}$ settles down to a consistent value as N becomes larger (say 1000 or 10 000 trials).

- The *probability* of an event is a measure of how likely it is to occur. This probability can be any number between 0 and 1 (inclusive).

There are four different ways of estimating probabilities.

Method A Use symmetry (the theoretical probability)

- The probability of rolling a 3 on a fair dice is $\frac{1}{6}$. This is because all the scores 1, 2, 3, 4, 5, 6 are equally likely.
- Similarly the probability of getting a head when tossing a fair coin is $\frac{1}{2}$.

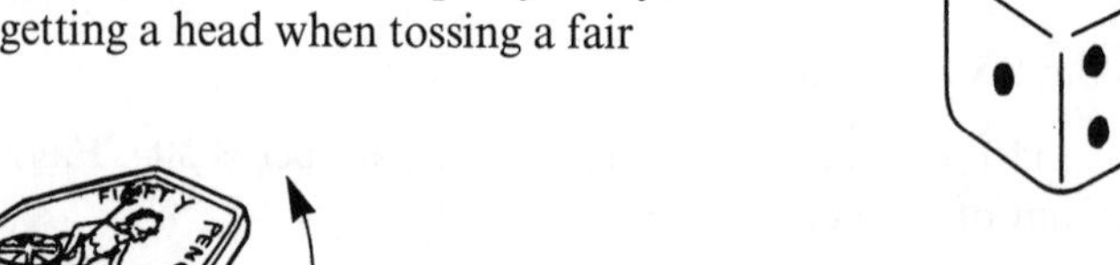

Method B Conduct an experiment or survey to collect data

- The dice shown has 5 faces, not all the same shape. To estimate the probability of the dice landing with a '1' showing, I could conduct an experiment to see what happened in, say, 500 trials.

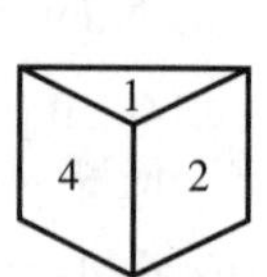

- I might want to know the probability that the next car going past the school gates is driven by a woman.
  I could conduct a survey in which the drivers of cars are recorded over a period of time.

Method C Look at past data

- If I wanted to estimate the probability of my plane crashing as it lands at Heathrow airport I could look at accident records at Heathrow over the last five years or so.

Method D Make a subjective estimate

We have to use this method when the event is not repeatable. It is not really a 'method' in the same sense as are methods A, B, C.

- We might want to estimate the probability of England beating France in a soccer match next week. We could look at past results but these could be of little value for all sorts of reasons. We might consult 'experts' but even they are notoriously inaccurate in their predictions.

Exercise 1

In Questions **1** to **10** state which method A, B, C or D you would use to estimate the probability of the event given.

1. The probability that a person chosen at random from a class will be left handed.

2. The probability that there will be snow in the ski resort to which a school party is going in February next year.

3. The probability of drawing an 'ace' from a pack of playing cards.

4. The probability that you hole a six foot putt when playing golf.

5. The probability that the world record for running 1500 m will be under 3 min 20 seconds by the year 2020.

6. The probability of winning the National Lottery.

7. The probability of rolling a 3 using a dice which is suspected of being biased.

8. The probability that a person selected at random would vote 'Labour' in a general election tomorrow.

9. The probability that a train will arrive within ten minutes of its scheduled arrival time.

10. The probability that the current Wimbledon Ladies Champion will successfully defend her title next year.

11. Conduct an experiment where you cannot predict the result.
You could roll a dice with a piece of 'Blu-tack' stuck to it.
Or make a spinner where the axis is not quite in the centre.
Or drop a drawing pin.
Conduct the experiment many times and work out the relative frequency of a 'success' after every 10 or 20 trials.
Plot a relative frequency graph to see if the results 'settle down' to a consistent value.

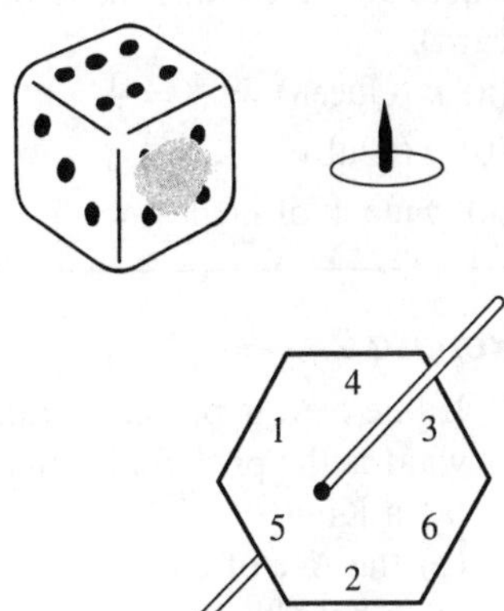

12. The spinner has an equal chance of giving any digit from 0 to 9.
Four friends did an experiment when they spun the pointer a different number of times and recorded the number of zeroes they got.
Here are their results.

	Number of spins	Number of zeroes	Relative frequency
Steve	10	2	0·2
Nick	150	14	0·093
Mike	200	41	0·205
Jason	1000	104	0·104

One of the four recorded his results incorrectly. Say who you think this was and explain why.

9.2 Working out probabilities

The probability of an event occurring can be calculated using symmetry. We argue, for example, that when we toss a coin we have an equal chance of getting a 'head' or a 'tail'. So the probability of spinning a 'head' is a half.
We write 'p (spinning a head) $= \frac{1}{2}$'.

A single card is drawn from a pack of 52 playing cards. Find the probability of the following results:
(a) the card is a Queen
(b) the card is a club
(c) the card is the Jack of hearts.

There are 52 equally likely outcomes of the 'trial' (drawing a card).
(a) p (Queen) $= \frac{4}{52} = \frac{1}{13}$
(b) p (Club) $= \frac{13}{52} = \frac{1}{4}$
(c) p (Jack of hearts) $= \frac{1}{52}$

13 Spades
13 Hearts
13 Diamonds
13 Clubs

Total = 52

Exercise 2

1. If one card is picked at random from a pack of 52 playing cards, what is the probability that it is:
(a) a King
(b) the Ace of clubs
(c) a heart?

2. Nine counters numbered 1, 2, 3, 4, 5, 6, 7, 8, 9 are placed in a bag. One is taken out at random. What is the probability that it is:
(a) a '5'
(b) divisible by 3
(c) less than 5
(d) divisible by 4?

3. A bag contains 5 green balls, 2 red balls and 4 yellow balls. One ball is taken out at random. What is the probability that it is:
(a) green
(b) red
(c) yellow?

4. A cash bag contains two 20p coins, four 10p coins, five 5p coins, three 2p coins and three 1p coins. Find the probability that one coin selected at random is:
(a) a 10p coin
(b) a 2p coin
(c) a silver coin.

5. A bag contains 8 orange balls, 5 green balls and 4 silver balls. Find the probability that a ball picked out at random is:
(a) silver
(b) orange
(c) green.

6. One card is selected at random from those below.

Find the probability of selecting:
(a) a heart
(b) an Ace
(c) the 10 of clubs
(d) a spade
(e) a heart or a diamond.

7. A pack of playing cards is well shuffled and a card is drawn. Find the probability that the card is:
(a) a Jack
(b) a Queen or a Jack
(c) the ten of hearts
(d) a club higher than the 9 (count the Ace as high).

8. The numbers of matches in ten boxes is as follows.
48, 46, 45, 49, 44, 46, 47, 48, 45, 46
One box is selected at random. Find the probability of the box containing:
(a) 49 matches
(b) 46 matches
(c) more than 47 matches.

9. One ball is selected at random from those below.

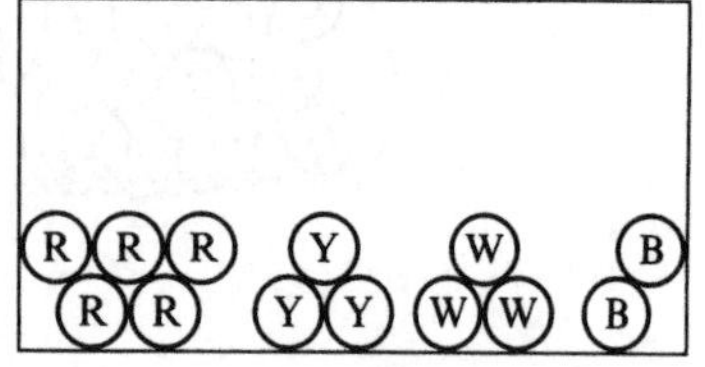

R = red
Y = yellow
W = white
B = black

Find the probability of selecting:
(a) a white ball
(b) a yellow or a black ball
(c) a ball which is not red.

10. (a) A bag contains 5 red balls, 6 green balls and 2 black balls. Find the probability of selecting:
(i) a red ball (ii) a green ball.
(b) One black ball is removed from the bag. Find the new probability of selecting:
(i) a red ball (ii) a black ball.

11. A pack of playing cards is split so that all the picture cards (Kings, Queens, Jacks) are in Pile A and all the other cards are in Pile B.
Find the probability of selecting:
(a) the Queen of clubs from pile A
(b) the seven of spades from pile B
(c) any heart from pile B.

pile A

pile B

12. A bag contains 12 white balls, 12 green balls and 12 purple balls. After 3 white balls, 4 green balls and 9 purple balls have been removed, what is the probability that the next ball to be selected will be white?

13. A large firm employs 3750 people.
One person is chosen at random.
What is the probability that
that person's birthday is on a Monday in the year 2000?

14. The numbering on a set of 28 dominoes is as follows:

6	6	6	6	6	6	6	5	5	5
6	5	4	3	2	1	0	5	4	3

5	5	5	4	4	4	4	4	3	3
2	1	0	4	3	2	1	0	3	2

3	3	2	2	2	1	1	0
1	0	2	1	0	1	0	0

(a) What is the probability of drawing a domino from a full set with:
  (i) at least one six on it?
  (ii) at least one four on it?
  (iii) at least one two on it?

(b) What is the probability of drawing a 'double' from a full set?

(c) If I draw a double five which I do not return to the set, what is the probability of drawing another domino with a five on it?

Expectation

- Expected number of successes = (probability of a success) × (number of trials)

> A fair dice is rolled 240 times. How many times would you expect to roll a number greater than 4?
>
> We can roll a 5 or a 6 out of the six equally likely outcomes.
>
> $\therefore\ p(\text{number greater than 4}) = \frac{2}{6} = \frac{1}{3}$.
>
> Expected number of scores greater than 4 $= \frac{1}{3} \times 240$
>
> $= 80$

Exercise 3

1. A fair dice is rolled 300 times. How many times would you expect to roll:
(a) an even number
(b) a 'six'?

2. The spinner shown has four equal sectors. How many 3's would you expect in 100 spins?

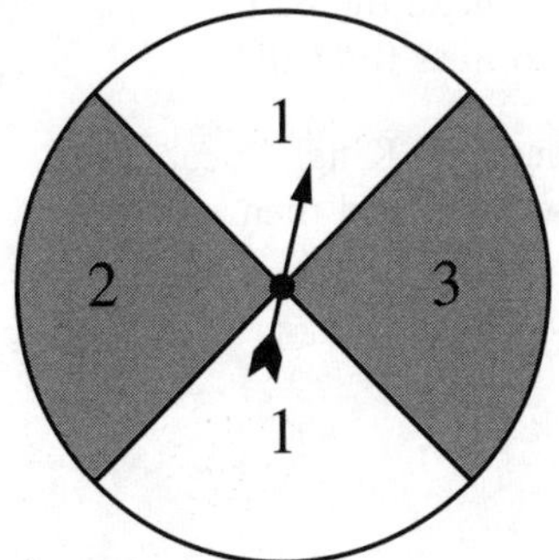

3. About one in eight of the population is left-handed. How many left-handed people would you expect to find in a firm employing 400 people?

4. A bag contains a large number of marbles of which one in five is red. If I randomly select one marble on 200 occasions how many times would I expect to select a red marble?

5. The spinner shown is used for a simple game. A player pays 10p and then spins the pointer, winning the amount indicated.
   (a) What is the probability of winning nothing?
   (b) If the game is played by 200 people how many times would you expect the 50p to be won?

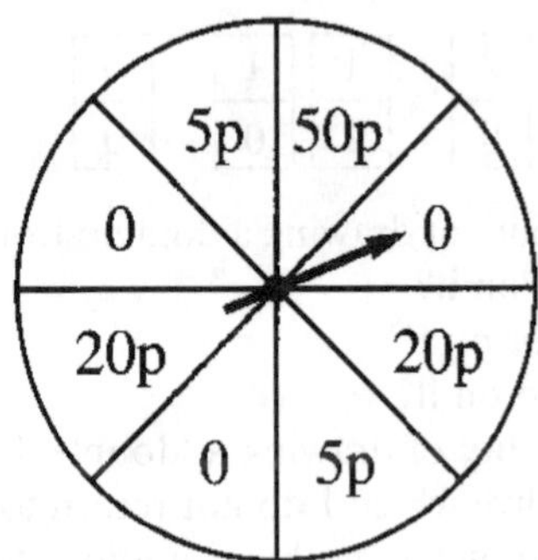

6. The numbered cards are shuffled and put into a pile.

One card is selected at random and not replaced. A second card is then selected.
   (a) If the first card was the '11', find the probability of selecting an even number with the second draw.
   (b) If the first card was an odd number, find the probability of selecting another odd number.

7. When the ball is passed to Vinnie, the probability that he kicks it is 0·2 and the probability that he heads it is 0·1. Otherwise he will miss the ball completely, fall over and claim a foul.
In one game his ever-optimistic team mates pass the ball to Vinnie 150 times.
   (a) How often would you expect him to head the ball?
   (b) How often would you expect him to miss the ball?

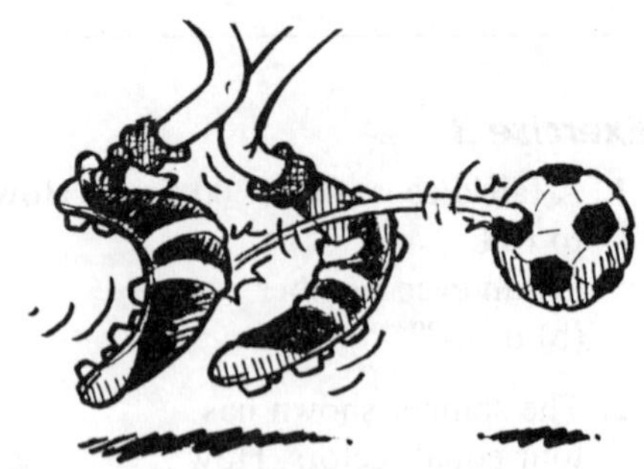

8. A small pack of 20 cards consists of the Ace, King, Queen, Jack and ten of all four suits. One card is selected and then replaced. This procedure is repeated 100 times.
How many times would you expect to select:
   (a) an Ace
   (b) the Queen of spades
   (c) a red card
   (d) any King or Queen?

Listing possible outcomes

When a 10p coin and a 50p coin are tossed together we have two events occurring:

- tossing the 10p coin
- tossing the 50p coin.

The result of tossing the 10p coin does not affect the result of the 50p coin.
We say the two events are *independent*.
We can list all the possible outcomes as shown:

(10p first)	head,	head
	head,	tail
	tail,	head
	tail,	tail.

A red dice and a black dice are thrown together. Show all the possible outcomes.

We could list them in pairs with the red dice first:

(1, 1), (1,2), (1, 3), ... (1, 6)
(2, 1), (2, 2), ...
and so on.

In this example it is easier to see all the possible outcomes when they are shown on a grid.

The X shows 6 on the red dice and 2 on the black.

The O shows 3 on the red dice and 5 on the black.

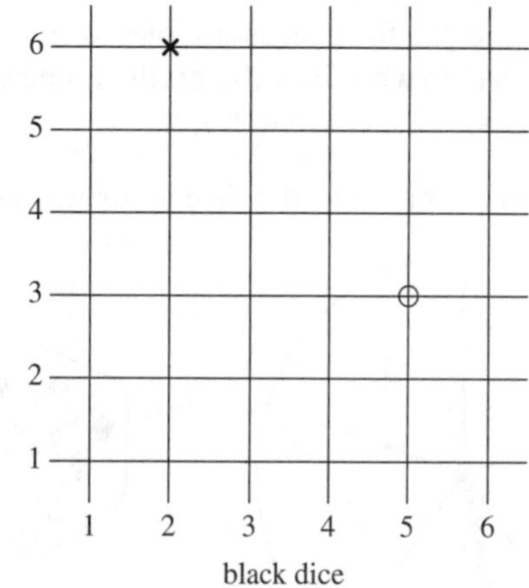

Exercise 4

1. Three coins (10p, 20p, 50p) are tossed together.
   (a) List all the possible ways in which they could land.
   (b) What is the probability of getting three heads?

2. List all the possible outcomes when four coins are tossed together. How many are there altogether?

3. A black dice and a white dice are thrown together.
   (a) Draw a grid to show all the possible outcomes. [See the box above.]
   (b) How many ways can you get a total of nine on the two dice?
   (c) What is the probability that you get a total of nine?

4. A red spinner and a white spinner are spun together.

Red

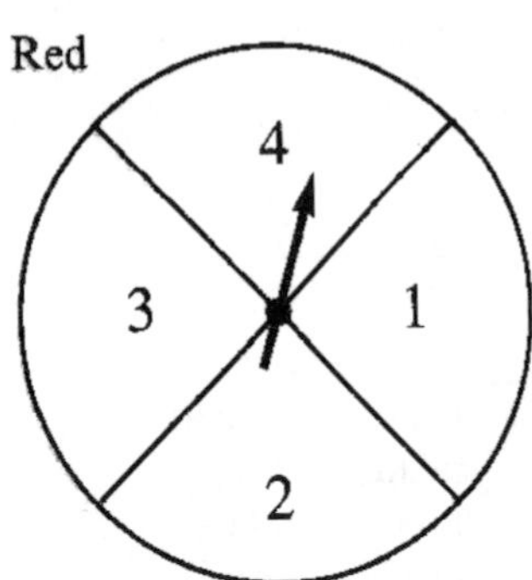

White

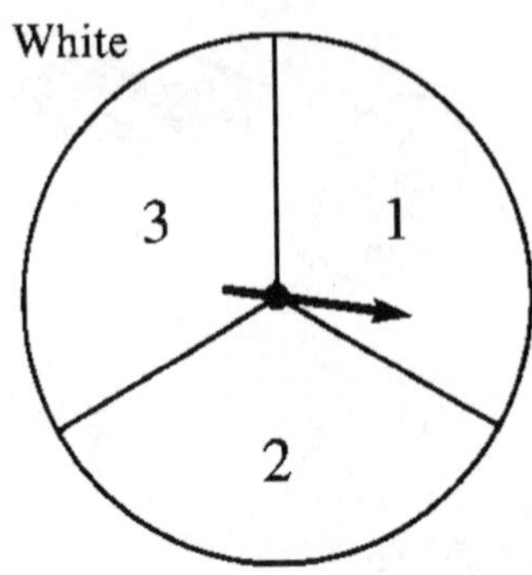

(a) List all the possible outcomes.
(b) In how many ways can you get a total of 4?
(c) What is the probability that you get a total of 4?

5. Four friends, Wayne, Xavier, Yves and Zara, each write their name on a card and the four cards are placed in a hat. Two cards are chosen to decide who does the maths homework that night.
List all the possible combinations.

6. The spinner is spun and the dice is thrown at the same time.

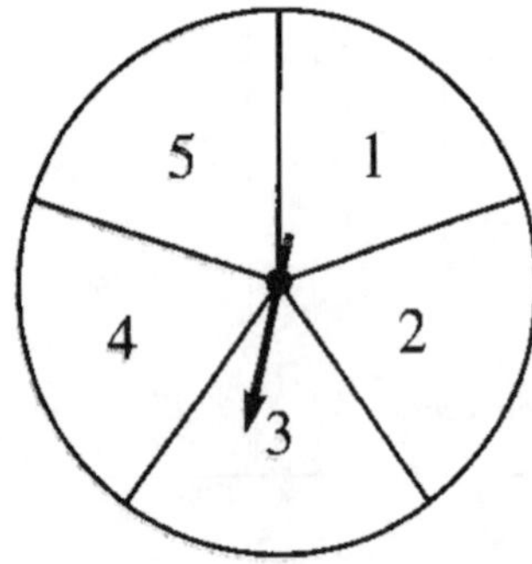

(a) Draw a grid to show all the possible outcomes.
(b) A 'win' occurs when the number on the spinner is greater than or equal to the number on the dice. Find the probability of a 'win'.

7. The menu in a restaurant has two choices of starter, three choices of main course and two choices of dessert.
List all the different combinations I could choose from this menu.
Gourmet Greg always chooses his three courses at random.
What is the probability that he chooses Melon, Chicken pie and Gateau?

Starters	
Melon	*(A)*
or Pineapple	*(B)*
Main course	
Steak	*(C)*
or Cod fillet	*(D)*
or Chicken pie	*(E)*
Dessert	
Ice cream	*(F)*
or Gateau	*(G)*

8. A motorway service station offers a meal consisting of four courses: soup, salad, meat, dessert.

There are:	two kinds of soup	A and B
	three kinds of salad	C, D and E
	four kinds of meat	F, G, H and I
	two kinds of dessert	J and K.

How many different choices of meal are there altogether?

9. By a strange coincidence the Branson family, the Green family and the Webb family all have the same first names for the five members of their families: James, Don, Samantha, Laura and Kate. One year Father Christmas decides to give each person a monogrammed handkerchief with two initials.

(a) How many different handkerchiefs does he need for these three families?

(b) How many different monograms are there if *any* first name and *any* surname is possible [e.g. 'Zak Quilfeldt']?

10. Keith, Len, Mike and Neil enter a cycling race.

(a) List all the possible orders in which they could finish. State the number of different finishing orders.

(b) In how many of the above does Mike finish in front of Len?

11. Shirin and Dipika are playing a game in which three coins are tossed. Shirin wins if there are no heads or one head. Dipika wins if there are either two or three heads. Is the game fair to both players?

12. Pupils X, Y and Z play a game in which four coins are tossed.

X wins if there is 0 or 1 head.
Y wins if there are 2 heads.
Z wins if there are 3 or 4 heads.

Is the game fair to all three players?

13. Four cards numbered 2, 4, 5 and 7 are mixed up and placed face down.

In a game you pay 10p to select two cards. You win 25p if the total of the two cards is nine.
How much would you expect to win or lose if you played the game 12 times?

Exercise 5 A practical exercise

1. The RAN # button on a calculator generates random numbers between 0·000 and 0·999. It can be used to simulate tossing three coins.
We could say any *odd* digit is a *tail* and any *even* digit is a *head.*
So the number 0·568 represents THH
and 0·605 represents HHT.

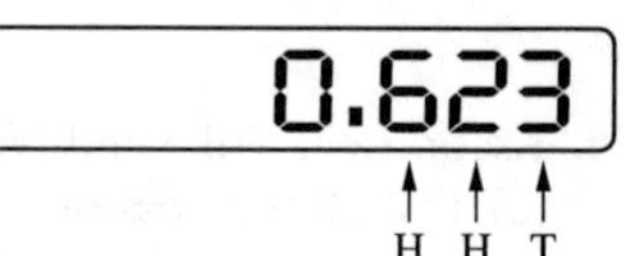

Use the RAN # button to simulate the tossing of three coins.
'Toss' the three coins 32 times and work out the relative frequencies of (a) three heads and (b) two heads and a tail.
Compare your results with the values that you would expect to get theoretically.

2. A calculator can be used to simulate throwing imaginary dice with 10 faces numbered 0, 1, 2, 3, 4, 5, 6, 7, 8, 9.
The RAN # button gives a random 3 digit number between 0·000 and 0·999. We can use the first 2 digits after the point to represent the numbers on two ten-sided dice.
So 0·763 means 7 on one dice and 6 on the second. [Ignore the '3'.]
and 0·031 means 0 on one dice and 3 on the second. [Ignore the '1'.]
We add the numbers on the two 'dice' to give the total.
So for 0·763 the total is 13 and for 0·031 the total is 3.
Press the RAN # button lots of times and record the totals in a tally chart.

Total	0	1	2	...	18
Tally				...	

This grid can be used to predict the result.
There are 100 equally likely outcomes like (3, 7) or (4, 1). The ten results shown each give a total of 9 which is the most likely score.
So in 100 throws you could expect to get a total of 9 on ten occasions.
Plot your results on a frequency graph.
Compare your results with the values you would expect.

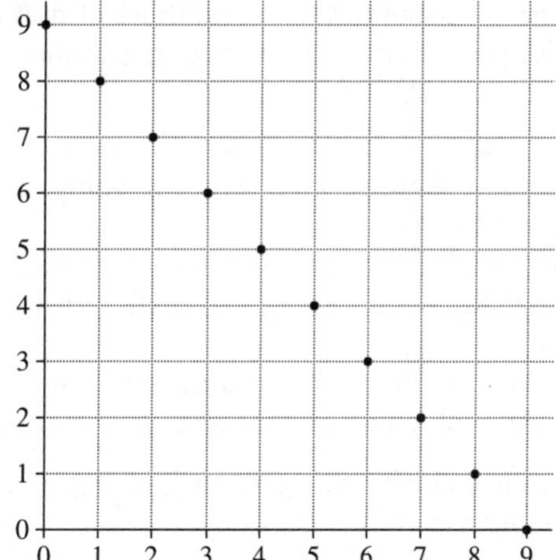

3. In Gibson Academy there are six forms (A, B, C, D, E, F) in Year 10 and the Mathematics Department has been asked to work out a schedule so that, over 5 weeks, each team can play each of the others in a basketball competition.
The games are all played at lunch time on Wednesdays and three games have to be played at the same time.
For example in Week 1 we could have:

Form A *v* Form B
Form C *v* Form D
Form E *v* Form F

Work out a schedule for the remaining four weeks so that each team plays each of the others. Check carefully that each team plays every other team just once.

9.3 Exclusive events

- Events are *mutually exclusive* if they cannot occur at the same time.

Example 1 Selecting an Ace and selecting a ten } from a pack of cards

Example 2 Tossing a 'head' and tossing a 'tail'

Example 3 Getting a total of 5 on two dice and getting a total of 7 on two dice

- The total sum of the probabilities of mutually exclusive events is 1.
- The probability of something happening is 1 minus the probability of it not happening.

Every day Anna has the choice of going to work by bus, by train or by taxi.
The probability of choosing to go by bus is 0·5 and the probability of choosing to go by train is 0·3.
Find:
(a) the probability of choosing not to go by train
(b) the probability of choosing to go by taxi.

The three events 'going by bus', 'going by train' and 'going by taxi' are mutually exclusive.

(a) $p(\text{not going by train}) = 1 - p(\text{going by train})$
$= 1 - 0{\cdot}3$
$= 0{\cdot}7$

(b) The sum of the probabilities is 1.
$\therefore\ p(\text{going by taxi}) = 1 - (0{\cdot}5 + 0{\cdot}3)$
$= 0{\cdot}2$

Exercise 6

1. A bag contains a large number of balls including some red balls. The probability of selecting a red ball is $\frac{1}{5}$. What is the probability of selecting a ball which is not red?

2. A card is selected from a pack of 52. Find the probability of selecting:
(a) a 'King'
(b) a card which is not a 'King'
(c) any picture card (King, Queen or Jack)
(d) a card which is not a picture card.

3. On a roulette wheel the probability of getting '21' is $\frac{1}{36}$. What is the probability of not getting '21'?

4. A motorist does a survey at some traffic lights on his way to work every day. He finds that the probability that the lights are 'red' when he arrives is 0·24. What is the probability that the lights are not 'red'?

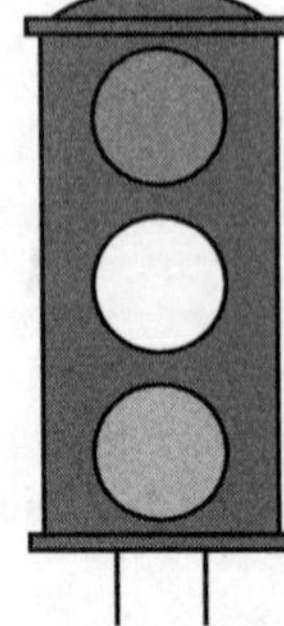

5. Government birth statistics show that the probability of a woman giving birth to a boy is 0·506.
What is the probability of having a girl?

6. The spinner has 8 equal sectors.
Find the probability of:
(a) spinning a 5
(b) not spinning a 5
(c) spinning a 2
(d) not spinning a 2
(e) spinning a 7
(f) not spinning a 7.

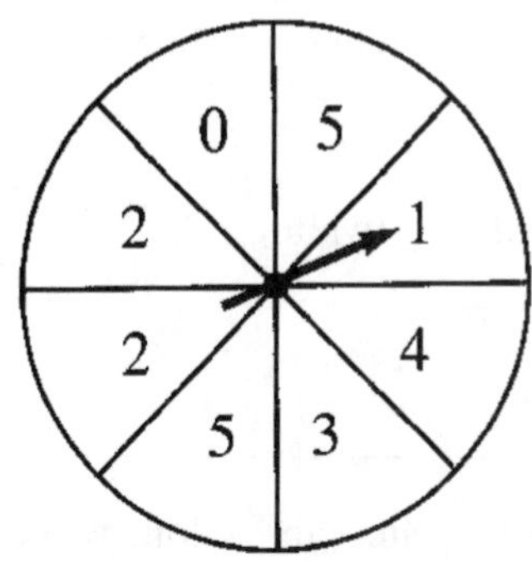

7. The King of clubs is removed from a normal pack of cards. One card is selected from the remaining cards. Find the probability of:
(a) selecting a King
(b) not selecting a King
(c) selecting a club.

8. A bag contains a large number of balls coloured red, white, black or green. The probabilities of selecting each colour are as follows.

Colour	red	white	black	green
Probability	0·3	0·1		0·3

Find the probability of selecting a ball:
(a) which is black
(b) which is not white.

9. In a survey the number of people in cars is recorded. When a car passes the school gates the probability of having 1, 2, 3,... occupants is as follows.

Number of people	1	2	3	4	>4
Probability	0·42	0·23		0·09	0·02

(a) Find the probability that the next car past the school gates contains
(i) three people (ii) less than 4 people.
(b) One day 2500 cars passed the gates. How many of the cars would you expect to have 2 people inside?

The 'OR' rule:

- For mutually exclusive events A and B: $p(\text{A } or \text{ B}) = p(\text{A}) + p(\text{B})$

One ball is selected at random from a bag containing 5 red balls, 2 yellow balls and 4 white balls. Find the probability of selecting a red ball or a white ball.

The two events are exclusive.

$$\begin{aligned} p(\text{red ball } or \text{ white ball}) &= p(\text{red}) + p(\text{white}) \\ &= \tfrac{5}{11} + \tfrac{4}{11} \\ &= \tfrac{9}{11} \end{aligned}$$

Many questions involving exclusive events can be done without using the addition rule.

A card is selected at random from a pack of 52 playing cards. What is the probability of selecting any King or Queen?

(a) This question can be done by counting the number of ways in which we can get a King or a Queen. That is 8 ways.

$$p(\text{selecting a King or a Queen}) = \tfrac{8}{52} = \tfrac{2}{13}.$$

(b) Since 'selecting a King' and 'selecting a Queen' are exclusive events we could use the addition law.

$$p(\text{selecting a King}) = \tfrac{4}{52}$$

$$p(\text{selecting a Queen}) = \tfrac{4}{52}$$

$$\therefore\ p(\text{selecting a King or a Queen}) = \tfrac{4}{52} + \tfrac{4}{52} = \tfrac{8}{52} \text{ as before.}$$

You can decide for yourself which method is easier in any given question.

- Important! If the events are not exclusive we cannot use the addition rule.

Here is a spinner with numbers and colours.

The events 'spinning a red' and 'spinning a 1' are *not* exclusive because we can get a red and a 1 at the same time.

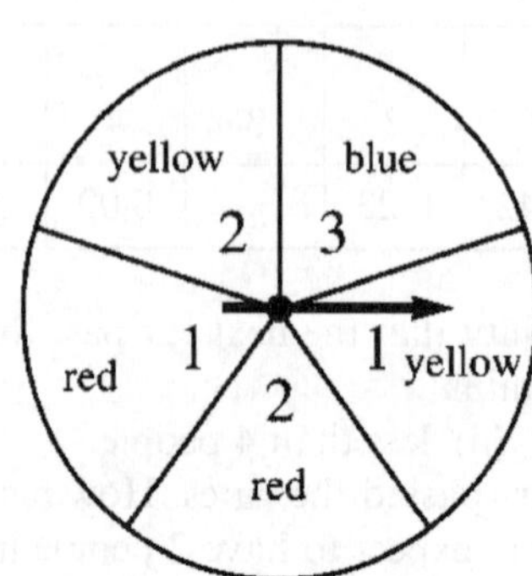

Exercise 7

1. A bag contains 10 red balls, 5 blue balls and 7 green balls. Find the probability of selecting at random:
   (a) a red ball
   (b) a green ball
   (c) a blue *or* a red ball
   (d) a red *or* a green ball.

2. A roulette wheel has the numbers 1 to 36. What is the probability of spinning either a 10 or a 20?

3. A fair dice is rolled. What is the probability of rolling either a 1 or a 6?

4. From a pack of cards I have already selected the King, Queen, Jack and ten of diamonds.
   What is the probability that on my next draw I will select either the Ace or the nine of diamonds?

5. The grid shows the 36 equally likely outcomes when two dice are rolled.
   (a) How many outcomes give a total of 9?
   (b) Find the probability of getting a total of:
      (i) 9
      (ii) 7
      (iii) 4.

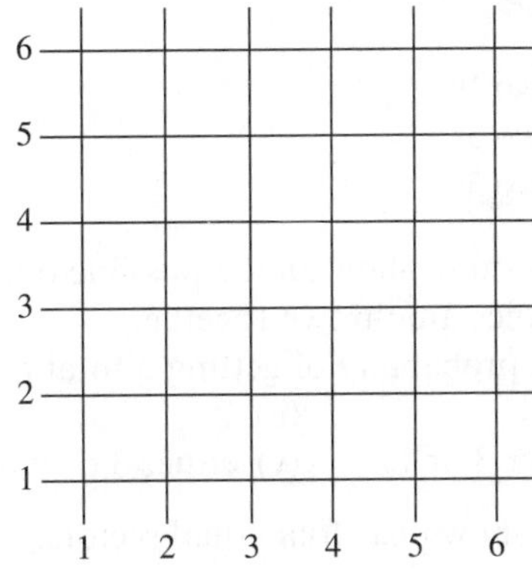

6. Two dice are thrown together. Find the probability of getting:
   (a) a total of 10 or 11
   (b) a total less than 6
   (c) the same number on both dice or a total of 5.

7. Three coins are tossed at the same time. List all the possible outcomes. Find the probability of getting:
   (a) three heads
   (b) three heads or three tails
   (c) two heads and one tail (in any order).

8. (a) How many possible outcomes are there when four coins are tossed together?
   (b) What is the probability of tossing either four heads or four tails?

9. Two dice are thrown together and the 'score' is the *difference* between the two numbers showing. So if I throw a '4' and a '6' the score is 2.
Copy and complete the table showing the scores for two dice.
Find the probability of obtaining a score of:
(a) 2 (b) 0
(c) 5 (d) 6.

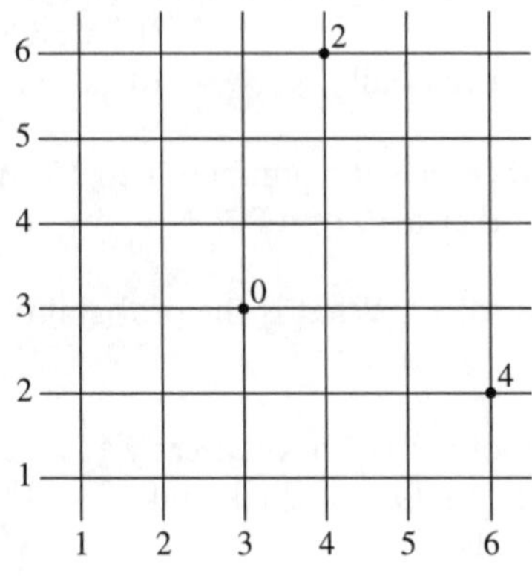

10. Two special dice are made.

Dice A has two 1s
two 3s
two 5s

Dice B has two 2s
two 4s
two 6s

(a) Draw a grid to show all the possible outcomes when the two dice are thrown together.
(b) Find the probability of getting a total of:
(i) 11 (ii) 7 (iii) 8
(iv) either 3 or 11 (v) either 3 or 9 or 11.

11. The spinner shown has four equal sectors.

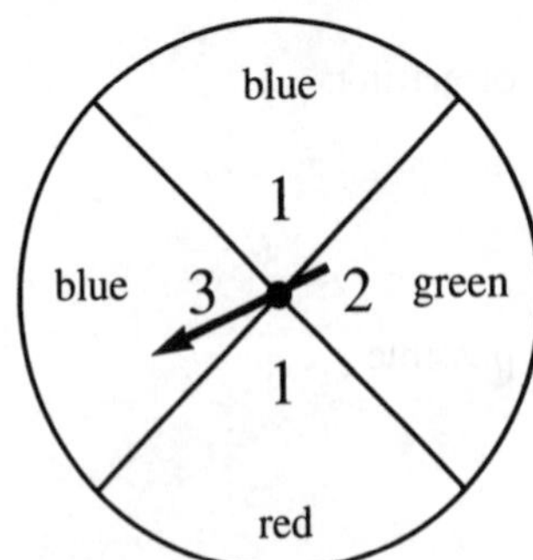

(a) Which of the following pairs of events are exclusive?
(i) 'spinning 1', 'spinning green'.
(ii) 'spinning 3', 'spinning 2'.
(iii) 'spinning blue', 'spinning 1'.
(b) What is the probability of spinning either a 1 or a green?

12. Here is a spinner with unequal sectors. When the pointer is spun, the probability of getting each colour and number is given in the tables.

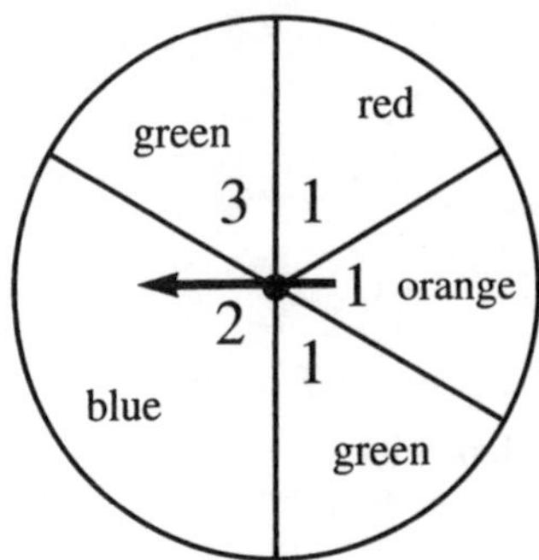

Colour	Probability
red	0·1
blue	0·3
orange	0·2
green	0·4

Number	Probability
1	0·5
2	0·3
3	0·2

(a) What is the probability of spinning either 1 or 2?
(b) What is the probability of spinning either blue or green?
(c) Why is the probability of spinning either 1 or green *not* $0{\cdot}5 + 0{\cdot}4$?

9.4 Independent events

- Two events are *independent* if the occurrence of one event is unaffected by the occurrence of the other.

  Example Obtaining a 'head' on one coin, and a tail on another coin when the coins are tossed at the same time.

The 'AND' rule

- For independent events A and B: $p(\text{A } \textit{and} \text{ B}) = p(\text{A}) \,.\, p(\text{B})$

This is the multiplication law. It only works for independent events.

When two coins are tossed we have seen previously by listing the outcomes [HH, HT, TH, TT] that the probability of tossing two heads is $\frac{1}{4}$.
By the multiplication rule for independent events:

$$p\,(\text{two heads}) = p\,(\text{head on first coin}) \times p\,(\text{head on second coin})$$
$$\therefore\ p\,(\text{two heads}) = \tfrac{1}{2} \times \tfrac{1}{2}$$
$$= \tfrac{1}{4} \quad \text{as before.}$$

A fair coin is tossed and a fair dice is rolled. Find the probability of obtaining a 'head' and a 'six'.

The two events are independent.

$$p\,(\text{head } \textit{and} \text{ six}) = p\,(\text{head}) \times p\,(\text{six})$$
$$= \tfrac{1}{2} \times \tfrac{1}{6}$$
$$= \tfrac{1}{12}$$

When the two spinners are spun, what is the probability of getting a B on the first and a 3 on the second?

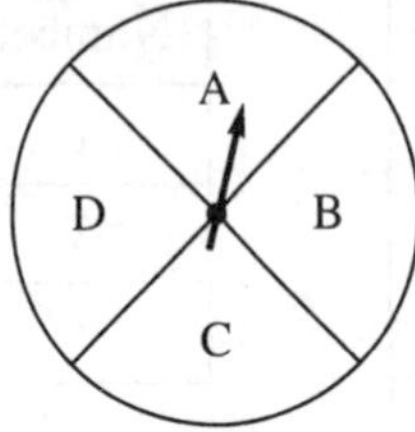

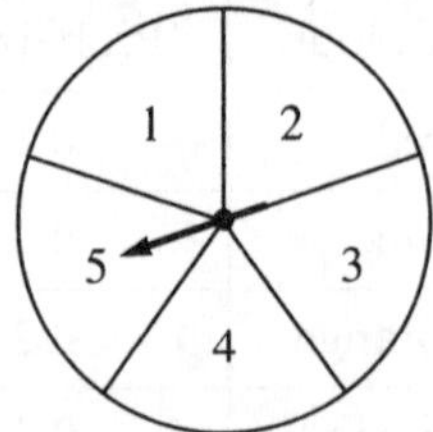

The events 'B on the first spinner' and '3 on the second spinner' are independent.

$$\therefore \quad p(\text{spinning B and 3}) = p(\text{B}) \times p(3)$$
$$= \tfrac{1}{4} \times \tfrac{1}{5}$$
$$= \tfrac{1}{20}$$

Exercise 8

1. A card is drawn from a pack of playing cards and a dice is thrown. Events A and B are as follows.
   A: 'a Jack is drawn from the pack'
   B: 'a three is thrown on the dice'.
   (a) Write down the values of p(A), p(B).
   (b) Write down the value of p(A and B).

2. A coin is tossed and a dice is thrown. Write down the probability of obtaining:
   (a) a 'head' on the coin
   (b) an odd number on the dice
   (c) a 'head' on the coin and an odd number on the dice.

3. Box A contains 3 red balls and 3 white balls. Box B contains 1 red and 4 white balls.

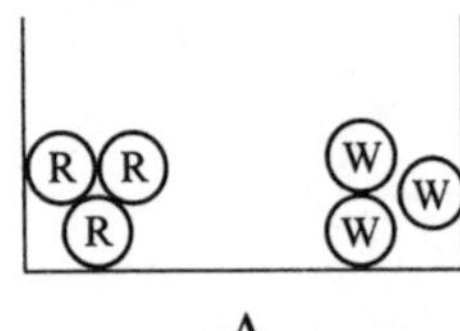

A

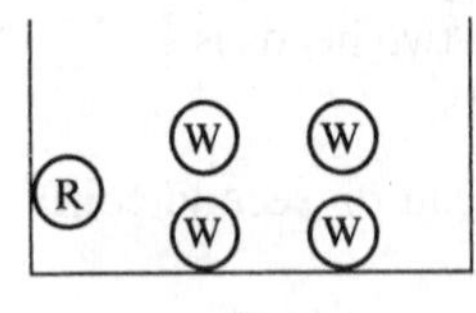

B

   One ball is randomly selected from box A and from box B.
   What is the probability that both balls selected are red?
   [i.e. a red from A *and* a red from B]

4. In an experiment, a card is drawn from a pack of playing cards and a dice is thrown.
   Find the possibility of obtaining:
   (a) a card which is an Ace and a six on the dice
   (b) the King of clubs and an even number on the dice
   (c) a heart and a 'one' on the dice.

5. A card is taken at random from a pack of playing cards and replaced. After shuffling, a second card is selected.
Find the probability of obtaining:
(a) two cards which are clubs
(b) two Kings
(c) two picture cards.

6. A ball is selected at random from a bag containing 3 red balls, 4 black balls and 5 green balls. The first ball is replaced and a second is selected. Find the probability of obtaining:
(a) two red balls
(b) two green balls.

7. The letters of the word 'INDEPENDENT' are written on individual cards and the cards are put into a box. A card is selected and then replaced and then a second card is selected. Find the probability of obtaining:
(a) the letter 'P' twice
(b) the letter 'E' twice.

8. A fruit machine has three reels and pays out a Jackpot of £1000 when three apples are obtained.

Each reel has 15 pictures. The first reel has 3 apples, the second has 4 apples and the third has 2 apples.
Find the probability of winning the Jackpot.

9. Three coins are tossed and two dice are thrown at the same time.
Find the probability of obtaining:
(a) three heads and a total of 12 on the dice
(b) three tails and a total of 9 on the dice.

10. A coin is biased so that it shows 'heads' with a probability of $\frac{2}{3}$. The same coin is tossed three times. Find the probability of obtaining:
(a) two tails on the first two tosses
(b) a head, a tail and a head (in that order).

11. A fair dice and a biased dice are thrown together. The probabilities of throwing the numbers 1 to 6 are shown for the biased dice.

Fair   Biased

$p(6) = \frac{1}{4}$; $p(1) = \frac{1}{12}$

$p(2) = p(3) = p(4) = p(5) = \frac{1}{6}$

Find the probability of obtaining a total of 12 on the two dice.

12. Philip and his sister toss a coin to decide who does the washing up. If it's heads Philip does it. If it's tails his sister does it. What is the probability that Philip does the washing up every day for a week (7 days)?

13. Here is the answer sheet for five questions in a multiple choice test. What is the probability of getting all five correct by guessing?

Answer sheet

1.	(A)	(B)	(C)	
2.	(A)	(B)		
3.	(A)	(B)	(C)	
4.	(A)	(B)	(C)	(D)
5.	(A)	(B)		

Tree diagrams

A bag contains 5 red balls and 3 green balls. A ball is drawn at random and then replaced. Another ball is drawn.

What is the probability that both balls are green?

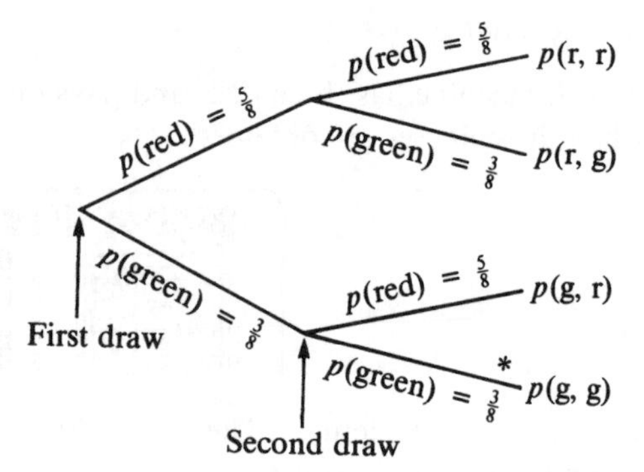

The branch marked * involves the selection of a green ball twice. The probability of this event is obtained by simply multiplying the fractions on the two branches.

$\therefore \quad p(\text{two green balls}) = \frac{3}{8} \times \frac{3}{8} = \frac{9}{64}$

A bag contains 5 red balls and 3 green balls. A ball is selected at random and *not* replaced. A second ball is then selected. Find the probability of selecting:
(a) two green balls
(b) one red ball and one green ball.

p(red) = 5/8, p(green) = 3/8 (First draw)
p(red) = 4/7 → $p(\text{r, r}) = \frac{5}{8} \times \frac{4}{7}$
p(green) = 3/7 → $p(\text{r, g}) = \frac{5}{8} \times \frac{3}{7}$
p(red) = 5/7 → $p(\text{g, r}) = \frac{3}{8} \times \frac{5}{7}$
p(green) = 2/7 → $p(\text{g, g}) = \frac{3}{8} \times \frac{2}{7}$
First draw
Second draw

(a) $p(\text{two green balls}) = \frac{3}{8} \times \frac{2}{7} = \frac{3}{28}$

(b) $p(\text{one red, one green}) = \left(\frac{5}{8} \times \frac{3}{7}\right) + \left(\frac{3}{8} \times \frac{5}{7}\right) = \frac{15}{28}$

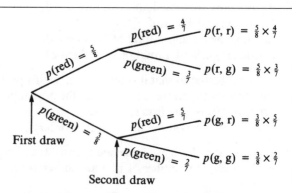

Notice that we can add here because the events 'red then green' and 'green then red' are exclusive.

As a check all the fractions at the ends of the branches should add up to one.

So $\left(\frac{5}{8} \times \frac{4}{7}\right) + \left(\frac{5}{8} \times \frac{3}{7}\right) + \left(\frac{3}{8} \times \frac{5}{7}\right) + \left(\frac{3}{8} \times \frac{2}{7}\right) = \frac{20}{56} + \frac{15}{56} + \frac{15}{56} + \frac{6}{56} = 1$

Exercise 9

1. A bag contains 10 discs; 7 are black and 3 white. A disc is selected, and then replaced. A second disc is selected. Copy and complete the tree diagram showing all the probabilities and outcomes.

   Find the probability that:
   (a) both discs are black
   (b) both discs are white.

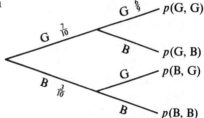

B $\frac{7}{10}$ — B $\frac{7}{10}$ $p(\text{B, B})$; W $p(\text{B, W})$
W $\frac{3}{10}$ — B $p(\text{W, B})$; W $p(\text{W, W})$
first draw
second draw

2. A bag contains 5 red balls and 3 green balls.
   A ball is drawn and then replaced before a ball is drawn again. Draw a tree diagram to show all the possible outcomes. Find the probability that:
   (a) two green balls are drawn
   (b) the first ball is red and the second is green.

3. A bag contains 7 green discs and 3 blue discs. A disc is drawn and *not* replaced.
   A second disc is drawn. Copy and complete the tree diagram.
   Find the probability that:
   (a) both discs are green
   (b) both discs are blue.

G $\frac{7}{10}$ — G $\frac{6}{9}$ $p(\text{G, G})$; B $p(\text{G, B})$
B $\frac{3}{10}$ — G $p(\text{B, G})$; B $p(\text{B, B})$

4. A bag contains 5 red balls, 3 blue balls and 2 yellow balls. A ball is drawn and not replaced. A second ball is drawn.
   Find the probability of drawing:
   (a) two red balls
   (b) one blue ball and one yellow ball (in any order)
   (c) two yellow balls.

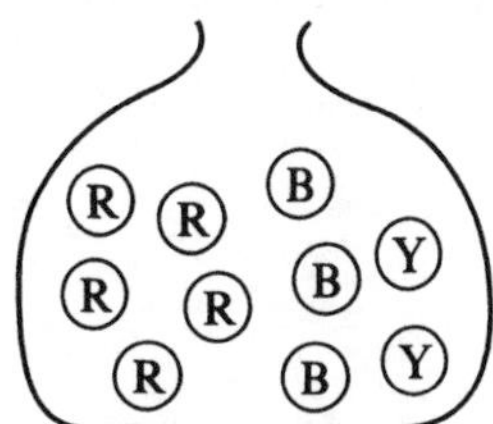

5. A bag contains 4 red balls, 2 green balls and 3 blue balls. A ball is drawn and not replaced. A second ball is drawn.
   Find the probability of drawing:
   (a) two blue balls
   (b) two red balls
   (c) one red ball and one blue ball (in any order)
   (d) one green ball and one red ball (in any order).

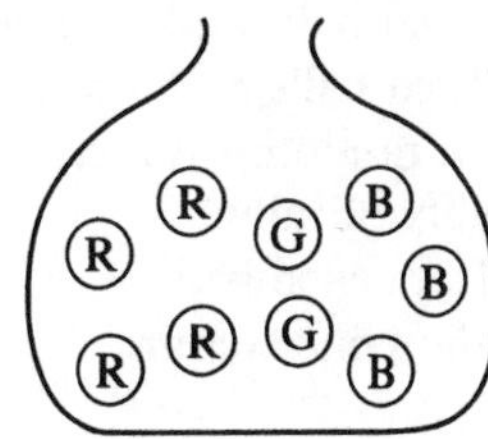

6. A six-sided dice is thrown three times. Complete the tree diagram, showing at each branch the two events: 'three' and 'not three' (written $\bar{3}$).
   What is the probability of throwing a total of:
   (a) three threes
   (b) no threes
   (c) one three
   (d) at least one three? [Hint: Use part (b).]

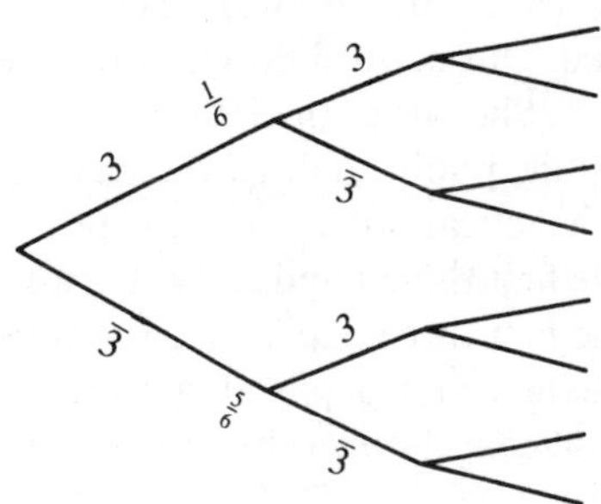

7. A card is drawn at random from a pack of 52 playing cards. The card is replaced and a second card is drawn. This card is replaced and a third card is drawn. What is the probability of drawing:
(a) three hearts
(b) at least two hearts
(c) exactly one heart?

8. A bag contains 6 red marbles and 4 yellow marbles. A marble is drawn at random and *not* replaced. Two further draws are made, again without replacement. Find the probability of drawing:
(a) three red marbles
(b) three yellow marbles
(c) no red marbles
(d) at least one red marble. [Hint: Use part (c).]

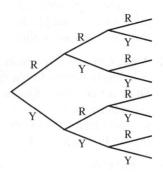

9. When a cutting is taken from a geranium the probability that it grows is $\frac{3}{4}$. Two cuttings are taken. What is the probability that:
(a) both cuttings grow
(b) neither of them grow?

10. A dice has its six faces marked 0, 1, 1, 1, 6, 6. Two of these dice are thrown together and the total score is recorded.
Draw a tree diagram.
(a) How many different totals are possible?
(b) What is the probability of obtaining a total of 7?

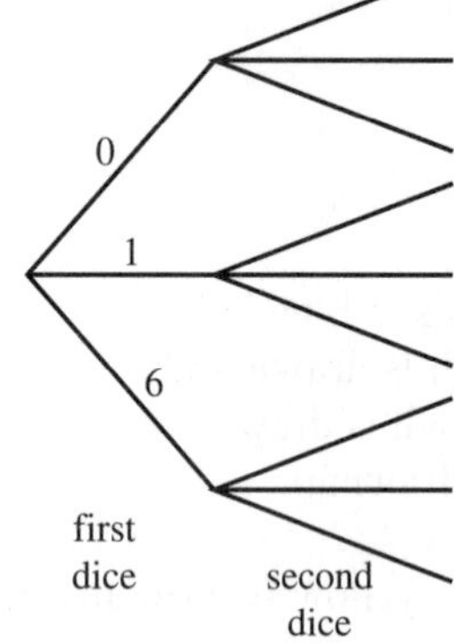

11. Bag A contains 3 red balls and 1 white ball.
Bag B contains 2 red balls and 3 white balls.
A ball is chosen at random from each bag in turn.
Find the probability of taking:
(a) a white ball from each bag
(b) two balls of the same colour.

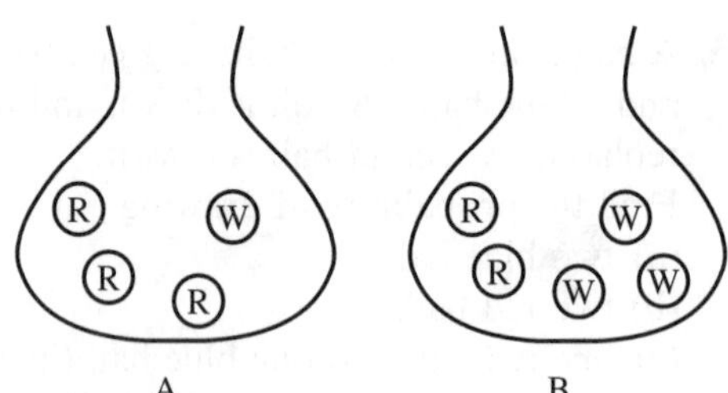

12. A teacher decides to award exam grades A, B or C by a new fairer method. Out of 20 children, three are to receive A's, five B's and the rest C's. She writes the letters A, B and C on 20 pieces of paper and invites the pupils to draw their exam result, going through the class in alphabetical order. Find the probability that:
(a) the first three pupils all get grade 'A'
(b) the first three pupils all get grade 'B'
(c) the first four pupils all get grade 'B'.
(Do not cancel down the fractions.)

10 ALGEBRA 3

10.1 Brackets and factors

Two brackets

Suppose we need to work out $(x + 3)(x + 2)$. We can use the area of a rectangle to help.

$$\begin{aligned}\text{Total area} &= (x+3)(x+2)\\ &= x^2 + 2x + 3x + 6\\ &= x^2 + 5x + 6\end{aligned}$$

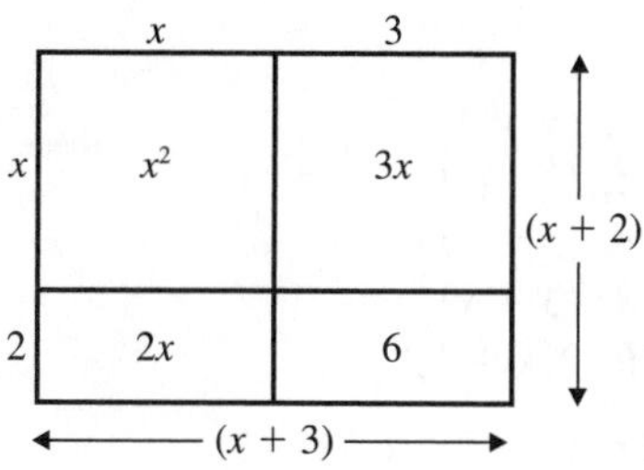

After a little practice, it is possible to do without the diagram.

(a) $$\begin{aligned}(3x-2)(2x-1) &= 3x(2x-1) - 2(2x-1)\\ &= 6x^2 - 3x - 4x + 2\\ &= 6x^2 - 7x + 2\end{aligned}$$

(b) $$\begin{aligned}3(x+1)(x-2) &= 3[x(x-2) + 1(x-2)]\\ &= 3[x^2 - 2x + x - 2]\\ &= 3x^2 - 3x - 6\end{aligned}$$

Exercise 1

Remove the brackets and simplify.

1. $(x + 1)(x + 3)$

2. $(x + 3)(x + 2)$

3. $(y + 4)(y + 5)$

4. $(x - 3)(x + 4)$

5. $(x + 5)(x - 2)$

6. $(x - 3)(x - 2)$

7. $(a - 7)(a + 5)$

8. $(z + 9)(z - 2)$

9. $(x - 3)(x + 3)$

10. $(k - 11)(k + 11)$

11. $(2x + 1)(x - 3)$

12. $(3x + 4)(x - 2)$

13. $(2y - 3)(y + 1)$

14. $(7y - 1)(7y + 1)$

15. $(3x - 2)(3x + 2)$

16. $(5 - x)(4 + x)$

17. $2(x - 1)(x + 2)$

18. $3(x - 1)(2x + 3)$

19. $4(2y - 1)(3y + 2)$

20. $2(3x + 1)(x - 2)$

Be careful with an expression like $(x-3)^2$. It is not x^2-9, or even x^2+9.

$$\begin{aligned}(x-3)^2 &= (x-3)(x-3)\\ &= x(x-3)-3(x-3)\\ &= x^2-6x+9\end{aligned}$$

Exercise 2

Remove the brackets and simplify.

1. $(x+4)^2$
2. $(x+2)^2$
3. $(x-2)^2$
4. $(2x+1)^2$
5. $(y-5)^2$
6. $(3y+1)^2$
7. $3(x+2)^2$
8. $(3-x)^2$
9. $(3x+2)^2$
10. $2(x+1)^2$
11. $(x+1)^2+(x+2)^2$
12. $(x-2)^2+(x+3)^2$
13. $(x+2)^2+(2x+1)^2$
14. $(y-3)^2+(y-4)^2$
15. $(x+2)^2-(x-3)^2$
16. $(x-3)^2-(x+1)^2$

Solve the equation.

$$\begin{aligned}(x+3)^2 &= (x+2)^2+3^2\\ (x+3)(x+3) &= (x+2)(x+2)+9\\ x^2+6x+9 &= x^2+4x+4+9\\ 6x+9 &= 4x+13\\ 2x &= 4\\ x &= 2\end{aligned}$$

Exercise 3

Solve the following equations.

1. $x^2+4 = (x+1)(x+3)$
2. $x^2+3x = (x+3)(x+1)$
3. $(x+3)(x-1) = x^2+5$
4. $(x+1)(x+4) = (x-7)(x+6)$
5. $(x-2)(x+3) = (x-7)(x+7)$
6. $(x-5)(x+4) = (x+7)(x-6)$
7. $2x^2+3x = (2x-1)(x+1)$
8. $(2x-1)(x-3) = (2x-3)(x-1)$
9. $x^2+(x+1)^2 = (2x-1)(x+4)$
10. $x(2x+6) = 2(x^2-5)$

In Questions **11** and **12**, form an equation in x by means of Pythagoras' Theorem, and hence find the length of each side of the triangle. (All the lengths are in cm.)

11.

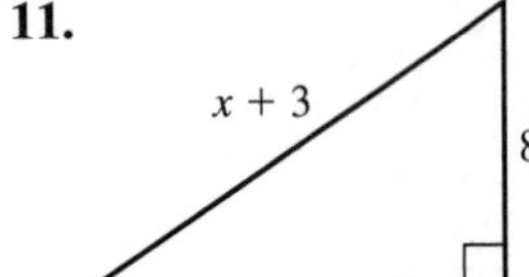

12.

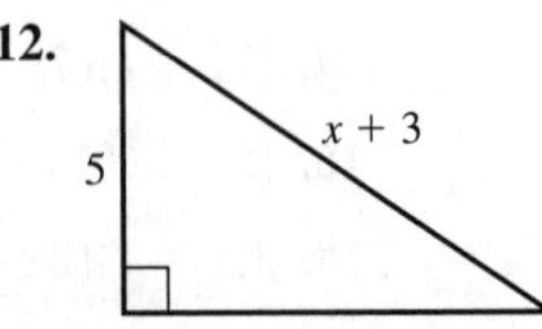

13. The area of the rectangle shown exceeds the area of the square by $2\,\text{cm}^2$. Find x.

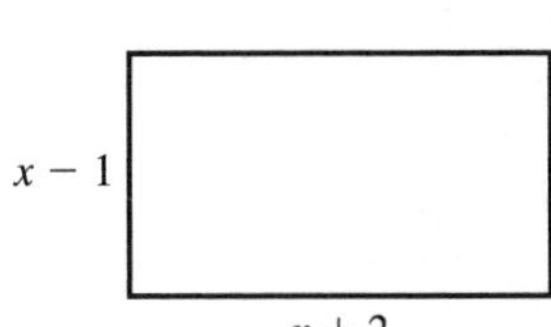

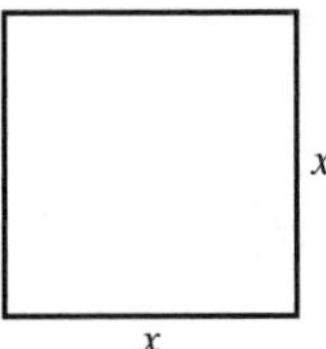

14. The area of the square exceeds the area of the rectangle by $13\,\text{m}^2$. Find y.

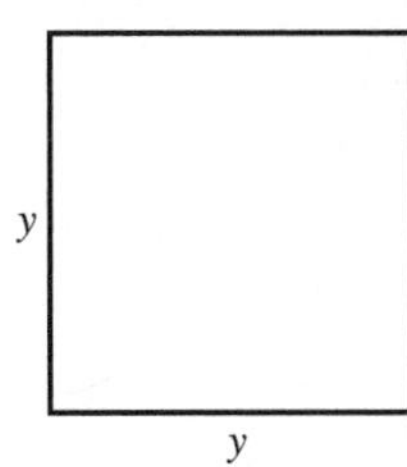

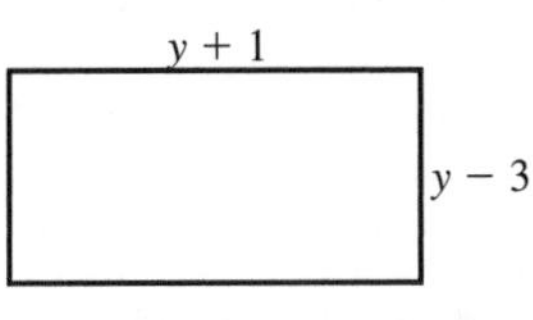

Factors

Factorise the following: (a) $12a - 15b$
(b) $3x^2 - 2x$
(c) $2xy + 6y^2$

(a) $12a - 15b = 3(4a - 5b)$
(b) $3x^2 - 2x = x(3x - 2)$
(c) $2xy + 6y^2 = 2y(x + 3y)$

Exercise 4

In Questions **1** to **10** copy and complete the statement.

1. $6x + 4y = 2(3x + \square)$

2. $9x + 12y = 3(\square + 4y)$

3. $10a + 4b = 2(5a + \square)$

4. $4x + 12y = 4(\square + \square)$

5. $10a + 15b = 5(\square + \square)$

6. $18x - 24y = 6(3x - \square)$

7. $8u - 28v = \square(\square - 7v)$

8. $15s + 25t = \square(3s + \square)$

9. $24m + 40n = \square(3m + \square)$

10. $27c - 72d = \square(\square - 8d)$

In Questions **11** to **31** factorise the expression.

11. $20a + 8b$

12. $30x - 24y$

13. $27c - 33d$

14. $35u + 49v$

15. $12s - 32t$

16. $40x - 16t$

17. $24x + 84y$

18. $12x + 8y + 16z$

19. $12a - 6b + 9c$

20. $10x - 20y + 25z$

21. $20a - 12b - 28c$

22. $48m + 8n - 24x$

23. $42x + 49y - 21z$

24. $6x^2 + 15y^2$

25. $20x^2 - 15y^2$

26. $7a^2 + 28b^2$

27. $27a + 63b - 36c$

28. $12x^2 + 24xy + 18y^2$

29. $64p - 72q - 40r$

30. $36x - 60y + 96z$

31. $9x + 6xy - 3x^2$

Factorise the following.

32. $x^2 - 5x$ **33.** $2x^2 - 3x$ **34.** $7x^2 + x$
35. $y^2 + 4y$ **36.** $2x^2 + 8x$ **37.** $4y^2 - 4y$
38. $p^2 - 2p$ **39.** $6a^2 + 2a$ **40.** $2ab - a$
41. $3xy + 2x$ **42.** $3t + 9t^2$ **43.** $4 - 8x^2$
44. $5x - 10x^3$ **45.** $4\pi r^2 + \pi rh$ **46.** $\pi r^2 + 2\pi r$

Factorising quadratic expressions

The pair of brackets $(x + 3)(x + 2)$ are multiplied to give $x^2 + 5x + 6$.
The reverse of this process is called factorising.

Factorise $x^2 + 6x + 8$

(a) Find two numbers which multiply to give 8 and add up to 6.

(b) Put these numbers into brackets.
So $x^2 + 6x + 8 = (x + 4)(x + 2)$.

Factorise (a) $x^2 + 2x - 15$ (b) $x^2 - 6x + 8$

(a) Two numbers which multiply to give -15 and add up to $+2$ are -3 and 5.
$\therefore \quad x^2 + 2x - 15 = (x - 3)(x + 5)$.

(b) Two numbers which multiply to give $+8$ and add up to -6 are -2 and -4.
$\therefore \quad x^2 - 6x + 8 = (x - 2)(x - 4)$.

Exercise 5

Factorise the following.

1. $x^2 + 7x + 10$ **2.** $x^2 + 7x + 12$ **3.** $x^2 + 8x + 15$
4. $x^2 + 10x + 21$ **5.** $x^2 + 8x + 12$ **6.** $x^2 + 12x + 35$
7. $x^2 + 11x + 24$ **8.** $x^2 + 10x + 25$ **9.** $x^2 + 13x + 36$
10. $x^2 + 5x + 6$ **11.** $x^2 + 6x + 8$ **12.** $x^2 + 9x + 18$

13. $x^2 + 3x - 10$ **14.** $x^2 + 2x - 15$ **15.** $x^2 + 2x - 8$
16. $x^2 + 4x - 5$ **17.** $x^2 + x - 6$ **18.** $x^2 + 5x - 14$
19. $x^2 - 3x - 10$ **20.** $x^2 - x - 12$ **21.** $x^2 + x - 6$
22. $x^2 - 2x - 35$ **23.** $x^2 - 5x - 24$ **24.** $x^2 - 6x + 8$

25. $y^2 - 5y + 6$ **26.** $x^2 - 8x + 15$ **27.** $a^2 - a - 6$
28. $a^2 + 14a + 45$ **29.** $b^2 - 4b - 21$ **30.** $x^2 - 8x + 16$
31. $y^2 + 2y + 1$ **32.** $y^2 - 3y - 28$ **33.** $x^2 - x - 20$
34. $x^2 - 8x - 240$ **35.** $x^2 + 13x - 30$ **36.** $x^2 - 8x - 33$

Methods of solving quadratic equations

The last exercise was about factorising expressions. These contain no 'equals' sign, but equations do.
Quadratic equations always have an x^2 term, and often an x term as well as a number term. They generally have two different solutions.

Solution by factors

Consider the equation $a \times b = 0$, where a and b are numbers. The product $a \times b$ can only be zero if either a or b (or both) is equal to zero. Can you think of other possible pairs of numbers which multiply together to give zero?

Solve the equation $x^2 + x - 12 = 0$

Factorising, $(x - 3)(x + 4) = 0$

either $x - 3 = 0$ or $x + 4 = 0$

$x = 3$ $x = -4$

Exercise 6

Solve the following equations.

1. $x^2 + 7x + 12 = 0$
2. $x^2 + 7x + 10 = 0$
3. $x^2 + 2x - 15 = 0$
4. $x^2 + x - 6 = 0$
5. $x^2 - 8x + 12 = 0$
6. $x^2 + 10x + 21 = 0$
7. $x^2 - 5x + 6 = 0$
8. $x^2 - 4x - 5 = 0$
9. $x^2 + 5x - 14 = 0$
10. $x^2 + 6x + 8 = 0$
11. $x^2 + 5x + 6 = 0$
12. $x^2 + 9x + 18 = 0$
13. $x^2 - 2x - 35 = 0$
14. $x^2 - x - 12 = 0$
15. $y^2 - 15y + 56 = 0$
16. $y^2 + 2y - 63 = 0$
17. $y^2 + 2y + 1 = 0$
18. $y^2 - 6y + 9 = 0$
19. $x^2 - 9x - 36 = 0$
20. $x^2 - 14x + 49 = 0$

The solution to a problem can involve an equation which does not at first appear to be quadratic. The terms in the equation may need to be rearranged as shown below.

Solve:

$$x(x - 5) + 7 = 3$$
$$x^2 - 5x + 7 = 3$$
$$x^2 - 5x + 4 = 0$$
$$(x - 4)(x - 1) = 0$$
$$x = 4 \quad \text{or} \quad x = 1$$

Exercise 7

Solve the following equations.

1. $x^2 = 6 - x$
2. $x(x + 10) = -21$
3. $10 = 7x - x^2$
4. $x^2 + 3 = 2x$
5. $x^2 + 4 = 5x$
6. $2x(x - 1) = x(x + 1) - 2$
7. $x(3x - 1) = 2x(x + 1) + 4$
8. $x(2x - 5) + 20 = x(x - 3) + 55$

In Questions **9** to **11** form a quadratic equation and then solve it.

9. The length of a rectangle is 7 cm more than the width. If the area of the rectangle is 60 cm^2, find the width.

10. Two numbers, which differ by 3, have a product of 88. Find the two numbers. [Let the numbers be x and $(x + 3)$.]

11. The area of the rectangle exceeds the area of the square by 24 m^2. Find x.

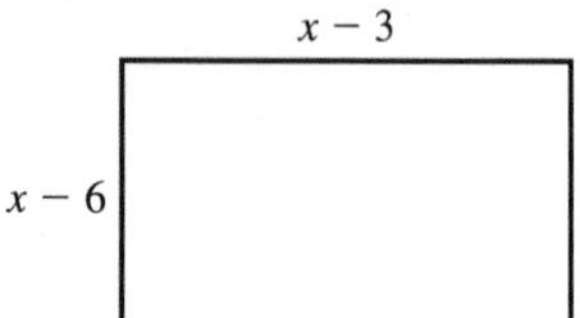

$x - 7$

$x - 7$

10.2 Changing the subject of a formula

Make x the subject in the formulae below.

(a)
$$ax - p = t$$
$$ax = t + p$$
$$x = \frac{t + p}{a}$$

(b)
$$y(x + y) = v^2$$
$$yx + y^2 = v^2$$
$$yx = v^2 - y^2$$
$$x = \frac{v^2 - y^2}{y}$$

Exercise 8

Make x the subject.

1. $x + b = e$
2. $x - t = m$
3. $x - f = a + b$
4. $x + h = A + B$
5. $x + t = y + t$
6. $a + x = b$
7. $k + x = m$
8. $v + x = w + y$
9. $ax = b$
10. $hx = m$
11. $mx = a + b$
12. $kx = c - d$
13. $vx = e + n$
14. $3x = y + z$
15. $xp = r$
16. $xm = h - m$
17. $ax + t = a$
18. $mx - e = k$
19. $ux - h = m$
20. $ex + q = t$
21. $kx - u^2 = v^2$

22. $gx + t^2 = s^2$ **23.** $xa + k = m^2$ **24.** $xm - v = m$

25. $a + bx = c$ **26.** $t + sx = y$ **27.** $y + cx = z$

28. $a + hx = 2a$ **29.** $mx - b = b$ **30.** $kx + ab = cd$

31. $a(x - b) = c$ **32.** $c(x - d) = e$ **33.** $m(x + m) = n^2$

34. $k(x - a) = t$ **35.** $h(x - h) = k$ **36.** $m(x + b) = n$

37. $a(x - a) = a^2$ **38.** $c(a + x) = d$ **39.** $m(b + x) = e$

Formulae involving fractions

Make x the subject in the formulae below.

(a) $\frac{x}{a} = p$

$x = ap$

(b) $\frac{m}{x} = t$

$m = xt$

$\frac{m}{t} = x$

(c) $\frac{a^2}{m} = \frac{d}{x}$

$xa^2 = dm$

$x = \frac{dm}{d^2}$

Exercise 9

Make x the subject.

1. $\frac{x}{t} = m$ **2.** $\frac{x}{e} = n$ **3.** $\frac{x}{p} = a$

4. $am = \frac{x}{t}$ **5.** $bc = \frac{x}{a}$ **6.** $e = \frac{x}{y^2}$

7. $\frac{x}{a} = (b + c)$ **8.** $\frac{x}{t} = (c - d)$ **9.** $\frac{x}{m} = s + t$

10. $\frac{x}{k} = h + i$ **11.** $\frac{x}{b} = \frac{a}{c}$ **12.** $\frac{x}{m} = \frac{z}{y}$

13. $\frac{x}{h} = \frac{c}{d}$ **14.** $\frac{m}{n} = \frac{x}{e}$ **15.** $\frac{b}{e} = \frac{x}{h}$

16. $\frac{x}{(a + b)} = c$ **17.** $\frac{x}{(h + k)} = m$ **18.** $\frac{x}{u} = \frac{m}{y}$

19. $\frac{x}{(h - k)} = t$ **20.** $\frac{x}{(a + b)} = (z + t)$ **21.** $t = \frac{e}{x}$

22. $a = \frac{e}{x}$ **23.** $m = \frac{h}{x}$ **24.** $\frac{a}{b} = \frac{c}{x}$

25. $\frac{u}{x} = \frac{c}{d}$ **26.** $\frac{m}{x} = t^2$ **27.** $\frac{h}{x} = \sin 20^\circ$

28. $\frac{e}{x} = \cos 40^\circ$ **29.** $\frac{m}{x} = \tan 46^\circ$ **30.** $\frac{a^2}{b^2} = \frac{c^2}{x}$

Formulae with x^2 and negative x terms

Make x the subject of the formulae.

(a)
$$ax^2 = e$$
$$x^2 = \frac{e}{a}$$
$$x = \pm\sqrt{\left(\frac{e}{a}\right)}$$

(b)
$$h - bx = m$$
$$h = m + bx \quad \text{[Make the } x \text{ term positive.]}$$
$$h - m = bx$$
$$\frac{h - m}{b} = x$$

Exercise 10

Make x the subject.

1. $cx^2 = h$	**2.** $bx^2 = f$	**3.** $x^2t = m$	**4.** $x^2y = (a + b)$
5. $mx^2 = (t + a)$	**6.** $x^2 - a = b$	**7.** $x^2 + c = t$	**8.** $x^2 + y = z$
9. $x^2 - a^2 = b^2$	**10.** $x^2 + t^2 = m^2$	**11.** $x^2 + n^2 = a^2$	**12.** $ax^2 = c$
13. $hx^2 = n$	**14.** $cx^2 = z + k$	**15.** $ax^2 + b = c$	**16.** $dx^2 - e = h$
17. $gx^2 - n = m$	**18.** $x^2m + y = z$	**19.** $a + mx^2 = f$	**20.** $a^2 + x^2 = b^2$
21. $a - x = y$	**22.** $h - x = m$	**23.** $z - x = q$	**24.** $v = b - x$
25. $m = k - x$	**26.** $h - cx = d$	**27.** $y - mx = c$	**28.** $k - ex = h$
29. $a^2 - bx = d$	**30.** $m^2 - tx = n^2$	**31.** $v^2 - ax = w$	**32.** $y - x = y^2$
33. $k - t^2x = m$	**34.** $e = b - cx$	**35.** $z = h - gx$	**36.** $a + b = c - dx$
37. $y^2 = v^2 - kx$	**38.** $h = d - fx$	**39.** $a(b - x) = c$	**40.** $h(m - x) = n$

Exercise 11

1. A formula for calculating velocity is $v = u + at$.
(a) Rearrange the formula to express a in terms of v, u and t.
(b) Calculate a when $v = 20$, $u = 4$, $t = 8$.

2. The area of a sector of a circle is given by the formula $A = \frac{x\pi r^2}{360}$

Express x in terms of A, π and r.

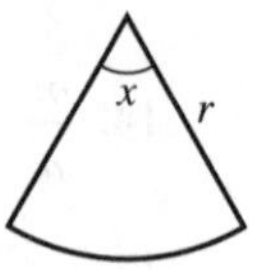

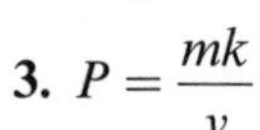

3. $P = \frac{mk}{y}$ (a) Express k in terms of P, m and y.
(b) Express y in terms of P, m and k.

4. A formula for calculating repair bills, R, is $R = \frac{n - d}{p}$.
(a) Express n in terms of R, p and d.
(b) Calculate n when $R = 400$, $p = 3$ and $d = 55$.

Exercise 12

Make the letter in brackets the subject.

1. $ax - d = h$ [x]
2. $zy + k = m$ [y]
3. $d(y + e) = f$ [y]
4. $m(a + k) = d$ [k]
5. $a + bm = c$ [m]
6. $ae^2 = b$ [e]
7. $yt^2 = z$ [t]
8. $x^2 - c = e$ [x]
9. $my - n = b$ [y]
10. $a(z + a) = b$ [z]
11. $\frac{a}{x} = d$ [x]
12. $\frac{k}{m} = t$ [k]
13. $\frac{u}{m} = n$ [u]
14. $\frac{y}{x} = d$ [x]
15. $\frac{a}{m} = t$ [m]
16. $\frac{d}{g} = n$ [g]
17. $\frac{t}{k} = (a + b)$ [t]
18. $y = \frac{v}{e}$ [e]
19. $c = \frac{m}{y}$ [y]
20. $\frac{a^2}{m} = b$ [a]
21. $g(m + a) = b$ [m]
22. $h(h + g) = x^2$ [g]
23. $y - t = z$ [t]
24. $me^2 = c$ [e]
25. $a(y + x) = t$ [x]
26. $uv - t^2 = y^2$ [v]
27. $k^2 + t = c$ [k]
28. $k - w = m$ [w]
29. $b - an = c$ [n]
30. $m(a + y) = c$ [y]
31. $pq - x = ab$ [x]
32. $a^2 - bk = t$ [k]
33. $v^2z = w$ [z]
34. $c = t - u$ [u]
35. $xc + t = 2t$ [c]
36. $m(n + w) = k$ [w]
37. $v - mx = t$ [m]
38. $c = a(y + b)$ [y]
39. $m(a - c) = e$ [c]
40. $ba^2 = c$ [a]
41. $\frac{a}{p} = q$ [p]
42. $\frac{a}{n^2} = e$ [n]
43. $\frac{h}{f^2} = m$ [f]
44. $\frac{v}{x^2} = n$ [x]
45. $v - ac = t^3$ [c]
46. $a(a^2 + y) = b^3$ [y]
47. $ah^2 - d = b$ [h]
48. $h(h + k) = bc$ [k]
49. $u^2 - n^2 = v^2$ [n]
50. $m(b - z) = b^3$ [z]

10.3 Sketching graphs

Gradient

The gradient of a straight line is a measure of how steep it is.

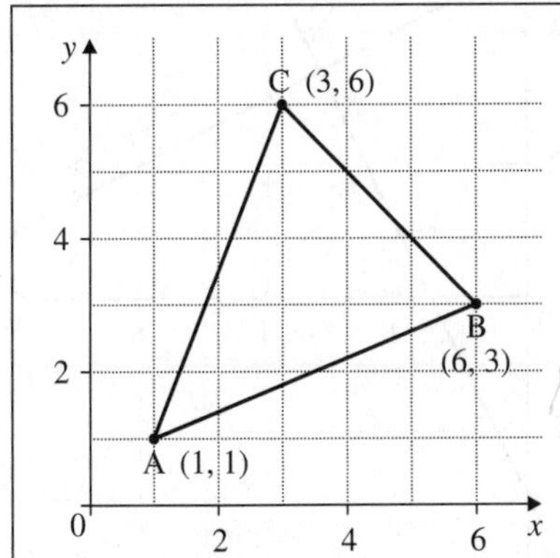

$$\text{Gradient of line AB} = \frac{3-1}{6-1} = \frac{2}{5}.$$

$$\text{Gradient of line AC} = \frac{6-1}{3-1} = \frac{5}{2}.$$

$$\text{Gradient of line BC} = \frac{6-3}{3-6} = -1.$$

- A line which slopes upwards to the right has a *positive* gradient.
- A line which slopes upwards to the left has a *negative* gradient.
- Gradient $= \dfrac{\text{difference in } y\text{-coordinates}}{\text{difference in } x\text{-coordinates}}$

Exercise 13

1. Find the gradients of AB, BC, AC.

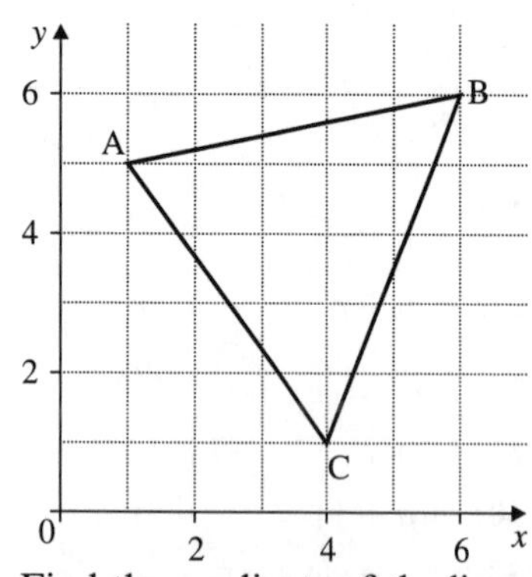

2. Find the gradients of PQ, PR, QR.

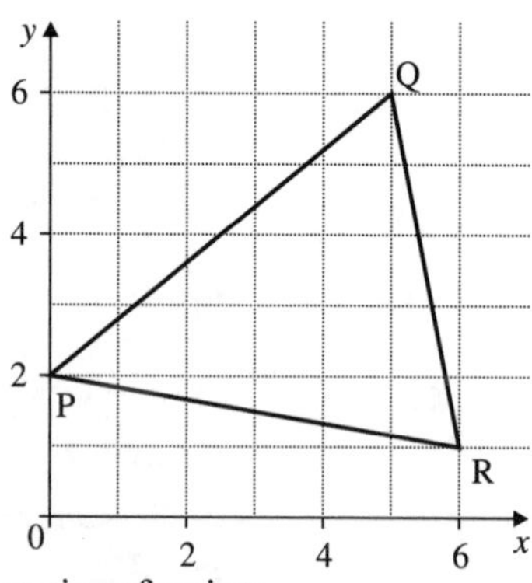

3. Find the gradients of the lines joining the following pairs of points.
(a) $(5, 2) \to (7, 8)$ (b) $(-1, 3) \to (1, 6)$
(c) $(\frac{1}{2}, 1) \to (\frac{3}{4}, 2)$ (d) $(3{\cdot}1, 2) \to (3{\cdot}2, 2{\cdot}5)$

4. Find the value of a if the line joining the points $(3a, 4)$ and $(a, -3)$ has a gradient of 1.

5. (a) Write down the gradient of the line joining the points $(2m, n)$ and $(3, -4)$.
(b) Find the value of n if the line is parallel to the x-axis.
(c) Find the value of m if the line is parallel to the y-axis.

The form $y = mx + c$

Here are two straight lines.

For $y = 2x - 3$, the gradient is 2 and the y-intercept is -3.

For $y = -\frac{1}{2}x + 5$, the gradient is $-\frac{1}{2}$ and the y-intercept is 5.

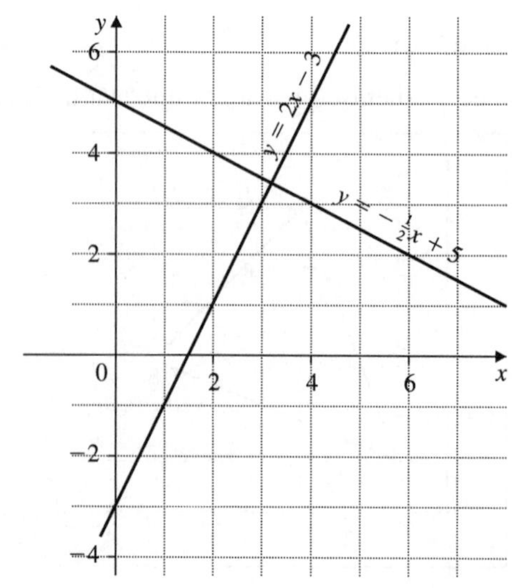

These two lines illustrate a general rule.

- When the equation of a straight line is written in the form $y = mx + c$, the gradient of the line is m and the intercept on the y-axis is c.

Draw the line $y = 2x + 3$ on a sketch graph.

The word 'sketch' implies that we do not plot a series of points but simply show the position and slope of the line.

The line $y = 2x + 3$ has a gradient of 2 and cuts the y-axis at (0, 3).

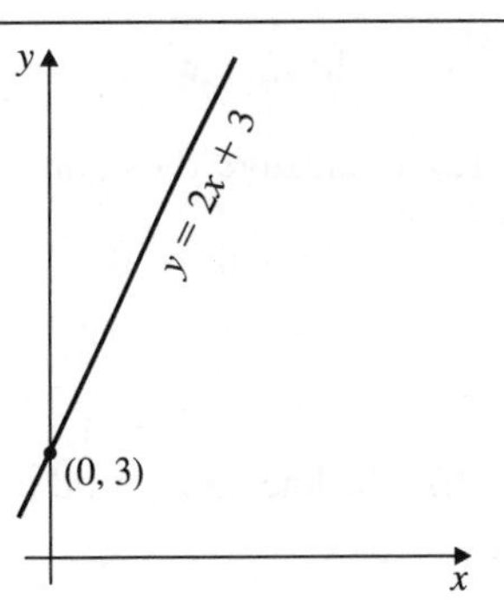

Exercise 14

1. Write down the equations of these lines.

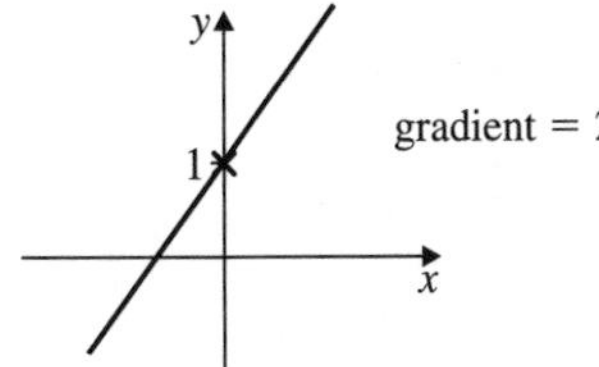

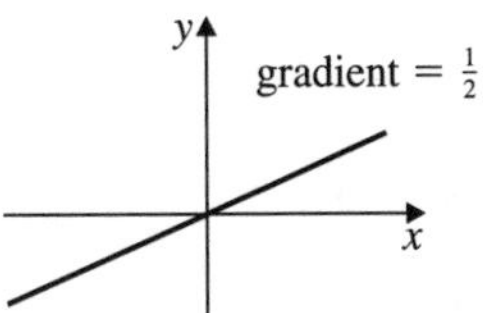

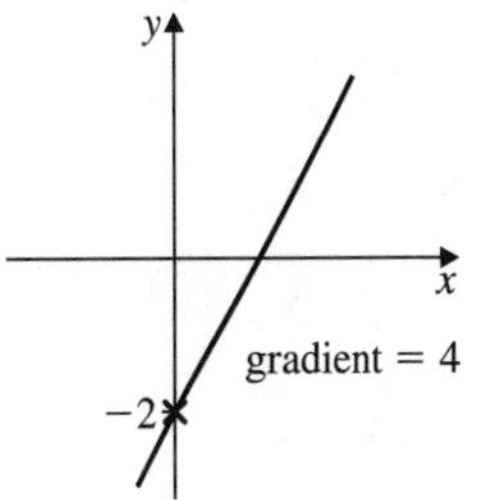

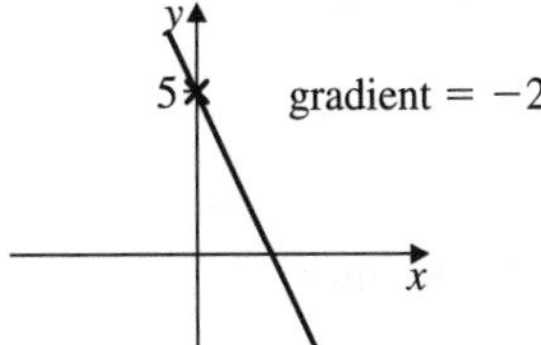

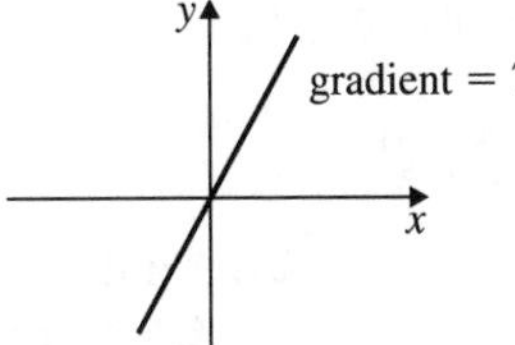

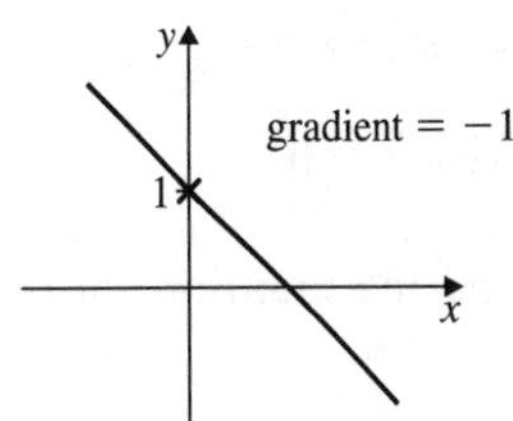

2. Here are the equations of four lines:

$y = 3x - 7$	$y = 2x - 7$	$y = -2x$	$y = 3x$

Which two lines are parallel?

3. Write down the equation of the line with
   (a) gradient 4 and y-intercept -3
   (b) gradient -3 and y-intercept 5
   (c) gradient $\frac{1}{3}$ and y-intercept -2

4. Write down the equation of any line which is parallel to the line $y = 5x - 11$.

Draw the line $x + 2y - 6 = 0$ on a sketch graph.

(a) Rearrange the equation to make y the subject.

$$x + 2y - 6 = 0$$
$$2y = -x + 6$$
$$y = -\frac{1}{2}x + 3$$

(b) The line has a gradient of $-\frac{1}{2}$ and cuts the y-axis at (0, 3).

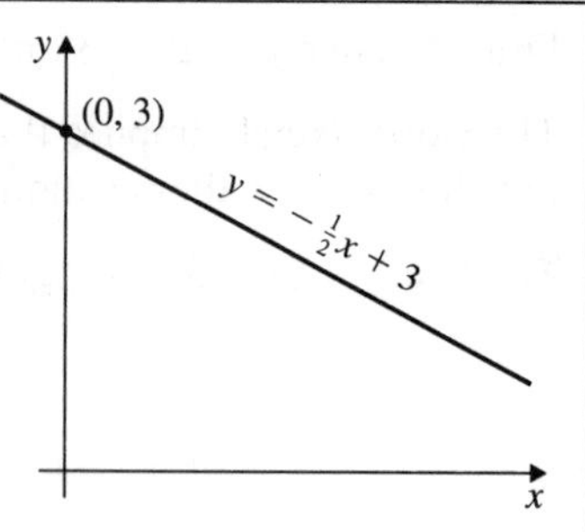

Exercise 15

In Questions **1** to **20**, write down (a) the gradient of the line and (b) the intercept on the y-axis. Hence draw a small sketch graph of each line.

1. $y = x + 3$

2. $y = x - 2$

3. $y = 2x + 1$

4. $y = 2x - 5$

5. $y = 3x + 4$

6. $y = \frac{1}{2}x + 6$

7. $y = 3x - 2$

8. $y = 2x$

9. $y = \frac{1}{4}x - 4$

10. $y = -x + 3$

11. $y = 6 - 2x$

12. $y = 2 - x$

13. $y + 2x = 3$

14. $3x + y + 4 = 0$

15. $2y - x = 6$

16. $3y + x - 9 = 0$

17. $4x - y = 5$

18. $3x - 2y = 8$

19. $10x - y = 0$

20. $y - 4 = 0$

21. Find the equations of the lines A and B.

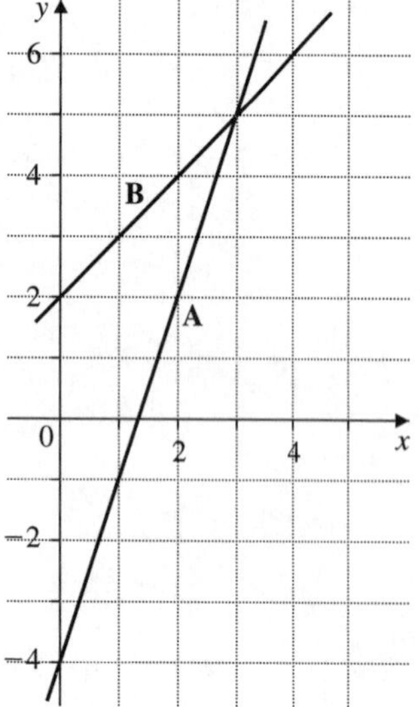

22. Find the equations of the lines C and D.

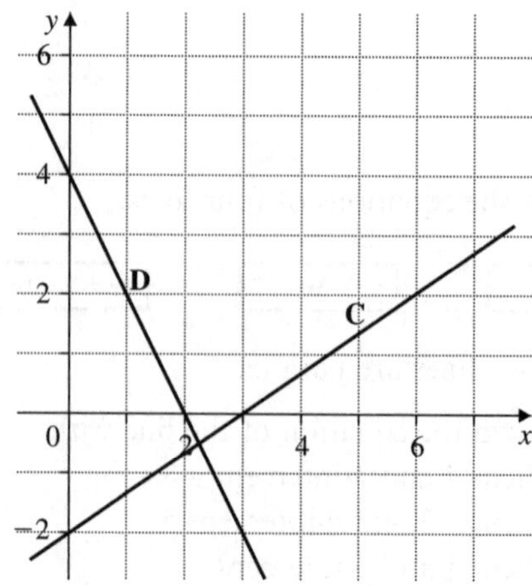

Curved graphs

Quadratic functions, $y = ax^2$

The graph of $y = ax^2$ is '∪' shaped if a is positive and '∩' shaped is a is negative.

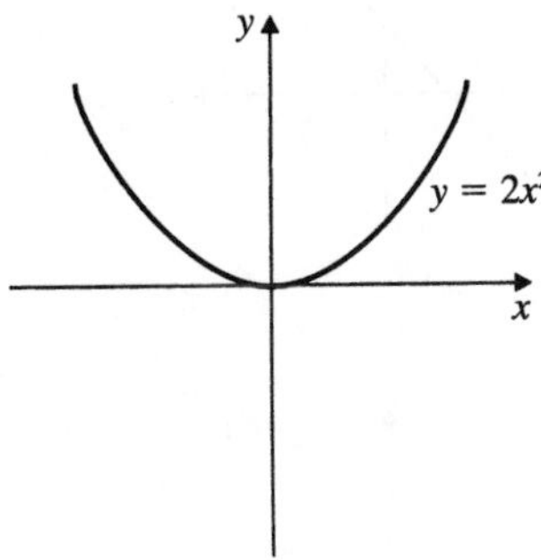

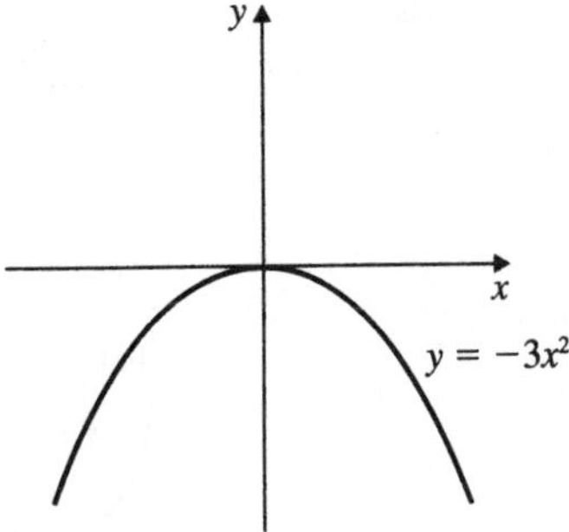

Cubic functions, $y = ax^3$

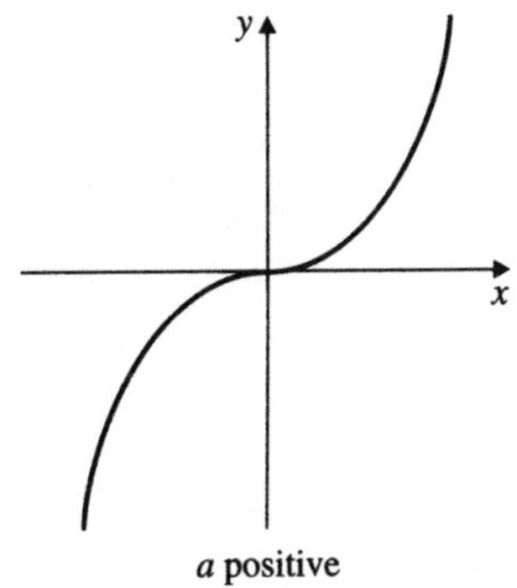

a positive

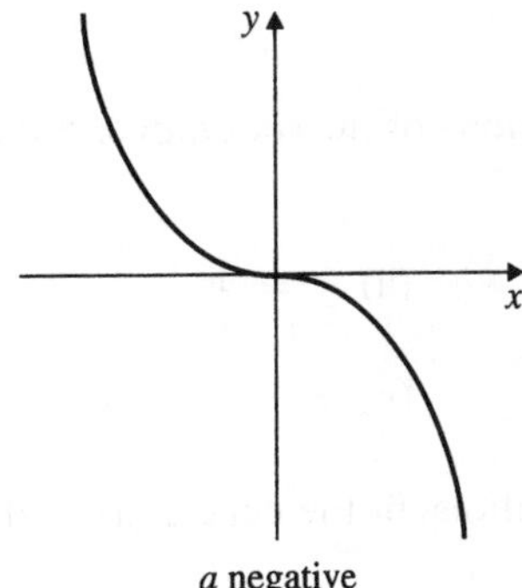

a negative

Reciprocal functions, $y = \frac{a}{x}$

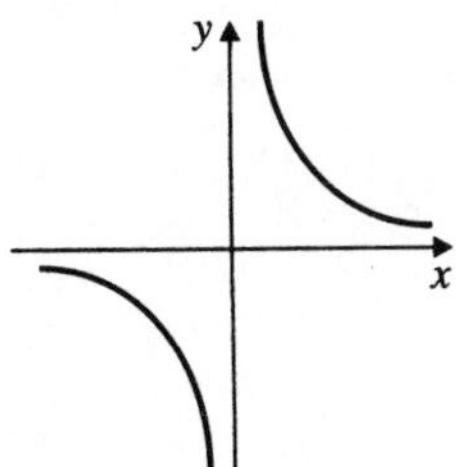

The curve has a break at $x = 0$. The x-axis and the y-axis are called *asymptotes* to the curve. The curve gets very near but never actually touches the asymptotes.

Exercise 16

1. Here are six graphs.

(a)

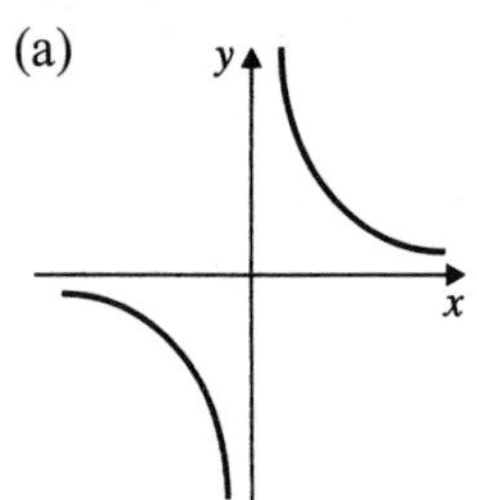

(b)

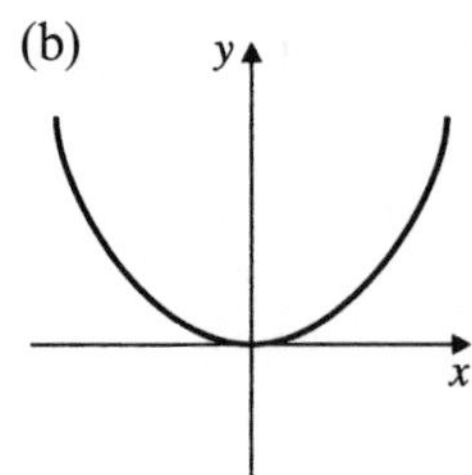

(c)

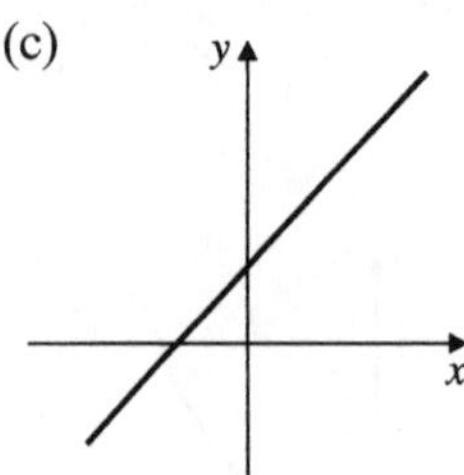

(d)

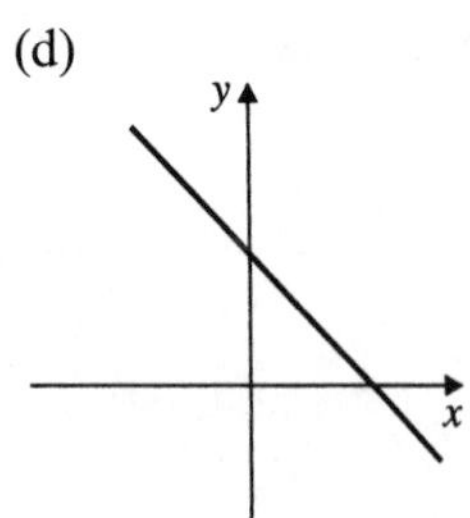

(e)

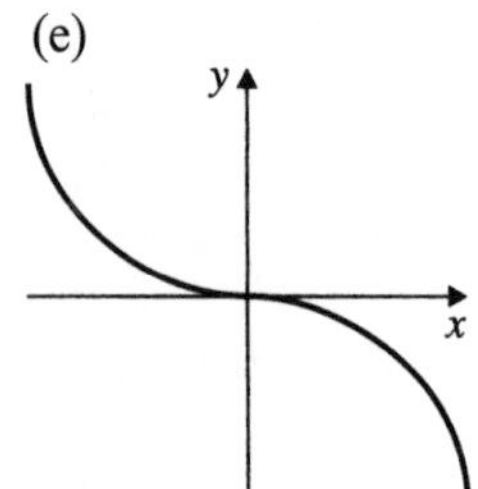

(f)

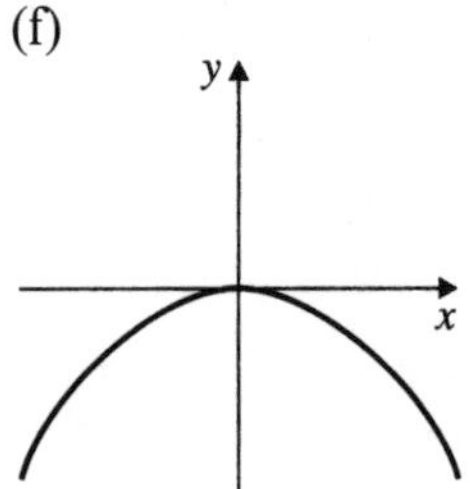

Here are the equations of the six graphs, but not in the correct order.

(i) $y = x + 1$ (ii) $y = 4x^2$ (iii) $y = -x^3$

(iv) $y = \frac{12}{x}$ (v) $y = -x + 3$ (vi) $y = -2x^2$

Decide which equations fit the curves (a) to (f).

2. For each graph in Question **1** state whether the function is:

linear | quadratic | cubic | reciprocal

3. Sketch the following graphs.

(a) $y = 2x - 5$ (b) $y = \frac{10}{x}$ (c) $y = 3x^3$

(d) $y = 5x^2$ (e) $y = \frac{1}{2}x$ (f) $y = -x^2$

(g) $y = x^2 + 5$ (h) $y = 7$ (i) $y = \frac{20}{x}$

10.4 Inequalities and regions

Symbols

- Here is the meaning of inequality symbols used.

$x < 4$ means 'x is *less than* 4'
$y > 7$ means 'y is *greater than* 7'
$z \leqslant 10$ means 'z is *less than or equal to* 10'
$t \geqslant -3$ means 't is *greater than or equal to* -3'

- With two symbols in one statement look at each part separately.
For example, if n is an *integer* and $3 < n \leqslant 7$,
n has to be greater than 3 but at the same time it has to be less than or equal to 7.
So n could be 4, 5, 6 or 7 only.

Illustrate on a number line the range of values of x stated.

(a) $x > 1$

The circle at the left hand end of the range is open. This means that 1 is not included.

(b) $x \leqslant -2$

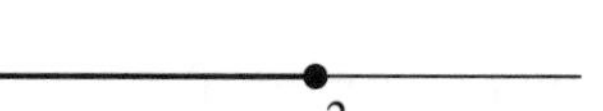

The circle at -2 is filled in to indicate that -2 is included.

(c) $1 \leqslant x < 4$

Exercise 17

1. Write down each statement with either $>$ or $<$ in the box.

(a) 3 ☐ 7 (b) 0 ☐ -2 (c) 3·1 ☐ 3·01

(d) -3 ☐ -5 (e) 100 m ☐ 1 m (f) 1 kg ☐ 1 lb

2. Write down the inequality displayed. Use x for the variable.

(a) (b) (c)

(d) (e) (f)

3. Draw a number line to display these inequalities.

(a) $x \geqslant 7$ (b) $x < 2{\cdot}5$ (c) $1 < x < 7$

(d) $0 \leqslant x \leqslant 4$ (e) $-1 < x \leqslant 5$

4. Write an inequality for each statement.

   (a) You must be at least 16 to get married. [Use A for age.]

   (b) Vitamin J1 is not recommended for people over 70 or for children 3 years or under.

   (c) To braise a rabbit the oven temperature should be between 150 °C and 175 °C. [Use T for temperature.]

   (d) Applicants for training as paratroopers must be at least 1·75 m tall. [Use h for height.]

5. Answer 'true' or 'false'.
   (a) n is an integer and $1 < n \leqslant 4$, so n can be 2, 3 or 4.
   (b) x is an integer and $2 \leqslant x < 5$, so x can be 2, 3 or 4.
   (c) p is an integer and $p \geqslant 10$, so p can be 10, 11, 12, 13 ...

Solving inequalities

We follow the same procedure used for solving equations except that when we multiply or divide by a *negative* number the inequality is *reversed.*

e.g. $4 > -2$ but multiplying by -2, $-8 < 4$

It is best to avoid dividing by a negative number as in the following example.

(a) $2x - 1 > 5$

$2x > 5 + 1$ [add 1]

$x > \frac{6}{2}$ [divide by 2]

$x > 3$

(b) $x + 1 < 3x < 2x + 2$

Solve the two inequalities separately:

$x + 1 < 3x$ $\quad$ $3x < 2x + 2$

$\frac{1}{2} < x$ $\quad$ $x < 2$

$\therefore$ The solution is $\frac{1}{2} < x < 2$.

Exercise 18

Solve the following inequalities.

1. $x - 3 > 10$	**2.** $x + 1 < 0$	**3.** $5 > x - 7$
4. $2x + 1 \leqslant 6$	**5.** $3x - 4 > 5$	**6.** $10 \leqslant 2x - 6$
7. $5x < x + 1$	**8.** $2x \geqslant x - 3$	**9.** $4 + x < -4$
10. $3x + 1 < 2x + 5$	**11.** $2(x + 1) > x - 7$	**12.** $7 < 15 - x$
13. $9 > 12 - x$	**14.** $4 - 2x \leqslant 2$	**15.** $3(x - 1) < 2(1 - x)$

16. $7 - 3x < 0$

17. $\frac{x}{3} < -1$

18. $\frac{2x}{5} > 3$

19. $2x > 0$

20. $\frac{x}{4} < 0$

21. The height of the picture has to be greater than the width.
Find the range of possible values of x.

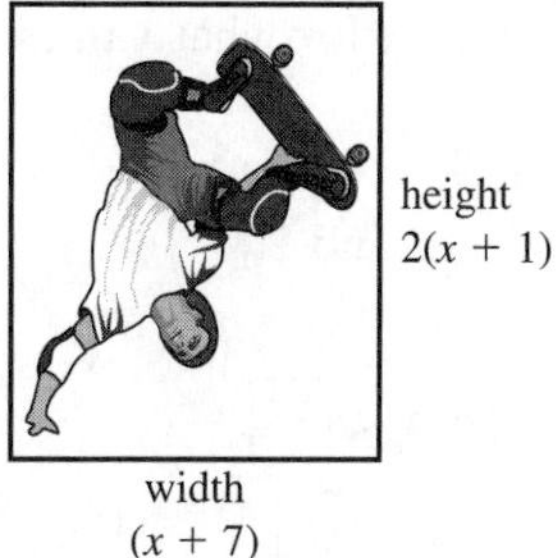

[Hint: In Questions **22** to **27**, solve the two inequalities separately.]

22. $10 \leqslant 2x \leqslant x + 9$

23. $x < 3x + 2 < 2x + 6$

24. $10 \leqslant 2x - 1 \leqslant x + 5$

25. $3 < 3x - 1 < 2x + 7$

26. $x - 10 < 2(x - 1) < x$

27. $4x + 1 < 8x < 3(x + 2)$

Exercise 19

1. The area of the rectangle must be greater than the area of the triangle.
Find the range of possible values of x.

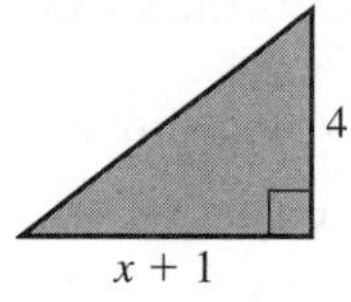

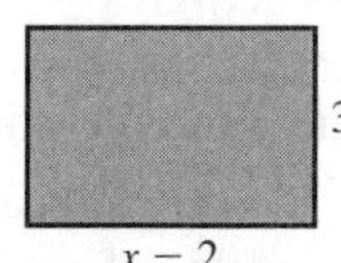

For Questions **2** to **8**, list the solutions which satisfy the given condition.

2. $3a + 1 < 20$; a is a positive integer.

3. $b - 1 \geqslant 6$; b is a prime number less than 20.

4. $1 < z < 50$; z is a square number.

5. $2x > -10$; x is a negative integer.

6. $x + 1 < 2x < x + 13$; x is an integer.

7. $0 \leqslant 2z - 3 \leqslant z + 8$; z is a prime number.

8. $\frac{a}{2} + 10 > a$; a is a positive even number.

9. Given that $4x > 1$ and $\frac{x}{3} \leqslant 1\frac{1}{3}$, list the possible integer values of x.

10. State the smallest integer n for which $4n > 19$.

11. Given that $-4 \leqslant a \leqslant 3$ and $-5 \leqslant b \leqslant 4$, find:
(a) the largest possible value of a^2
(b) the smallest possible value of ab
(c) the largest possible value of ab
(d) the value of b if $b^2 = 25$

12. For any shape of triangle ABC, complete the statement 'AB + BC □ AC', by writing $<, >$ or $=$ inside the box.

13. Find a simple fraction r such that $\frac{1}{3} < r < \frac{2}{3}$.

14. Find the largest prime number p such that $p^2 < 400$.

15. Find the integer n such that $n < \sqrt{300} < n + 1$.

16. If $f(x) = 2x - 1$ and $g(x) = 10 - x$ for what values of x is $f(x) > g(x)$?

17. (a) The solution to $x^2 < 4$ is $-2 < x < 2$
[The square roots of 4 are -2 and 2.]

(b) Copy and complete.

(i) If $x^2 < 100$, then $\square < x < \square$.

(ii) If $x^2 < 81$, then $\square < x < \square$.

(iii) If $x^2 > 36$, then $x > \square$ or $x < \square$.

Solve the inequalities.

18. $x^2 < 25$ **19.** $x^2 \leqslant 16$ **20.** $x^2 > 1$

21. $2x^2 \geqslant 72$ **22.** $3x^2 + 5 > 5$ **23.** $5x^2 - 2 < 18$

24. If $2^r > 100$, what is the smallest integer value of r?

25. Given $\left(\frac{1}{3}\right)^x < \frac{1}{200}$, what is the smallest integer value of x?

26. Find the smallest integer value of x which satisfies $x^x > 10\,000$.

27. What integer values of x satisfy
$100 < 5^x < 10\,000$?

Shading regions

It is useful to represent inequalities on a graph, particularly where two variables (x and y) are involved.

Draw a sketch graph and shade the area which represents the set of points that satisfy each of these inequalities.

(a) $x > 2$ (b) $1 \leqslant y \leqslant 5$ (c) $x + y \leqslant 8$

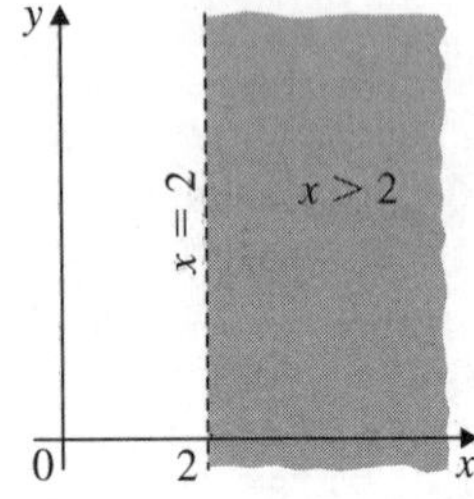

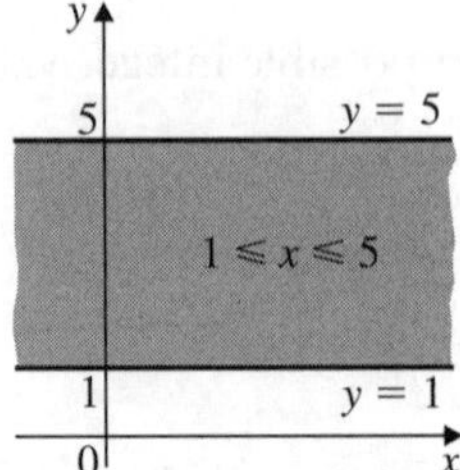

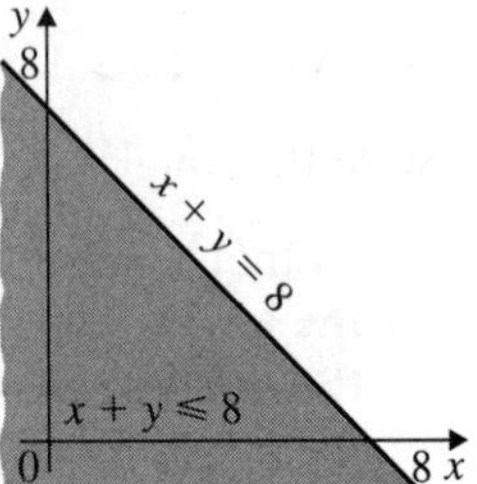

In each graph, the required region is shaded. This is done to make it clearer when several regions are shown on the same diagram.

In (a), the line $x = 2$ is shown as a broken line to indicate that the points on the line are not included.

In (b) and (c) points on the line *are* included 'in the region' and the lines are drawn unbroken.

To decide which side to shade when the line is sloping, we take a *trial point*. This can be any point which is not actually on the line.

In (c) above, the trial point could be (1, 1).

Is (1, 1) in the region $x + y \leqslant 8$?
It satisfies $x + y < 8$ because $1 + 1 = 2$, which is less than 8.
So below the line is $x + y < 8$. We have shaded the required region.

Exercise 20

In Questions **1** to **6**, describe the region shaded.

1. 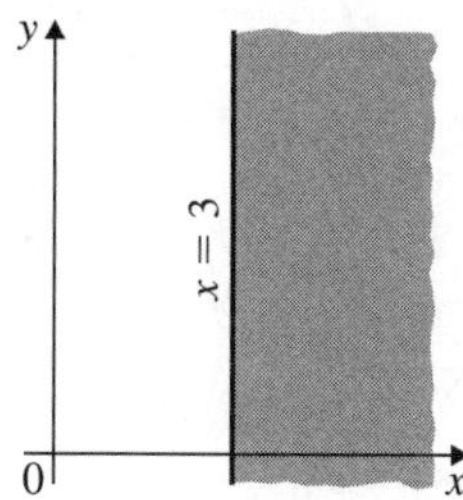

2. 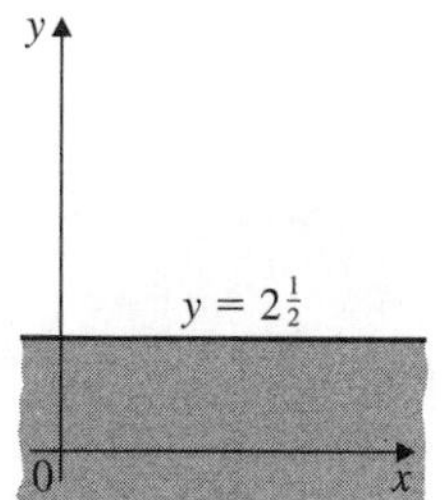

3. 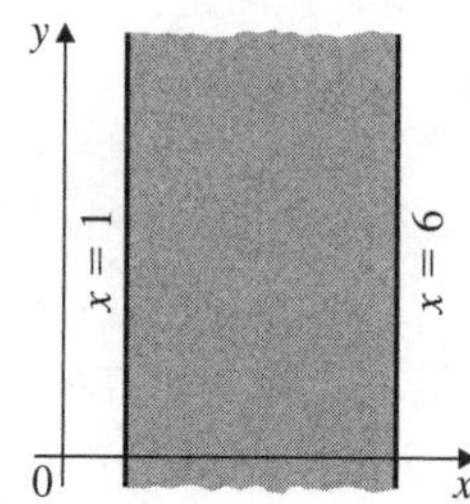

4. 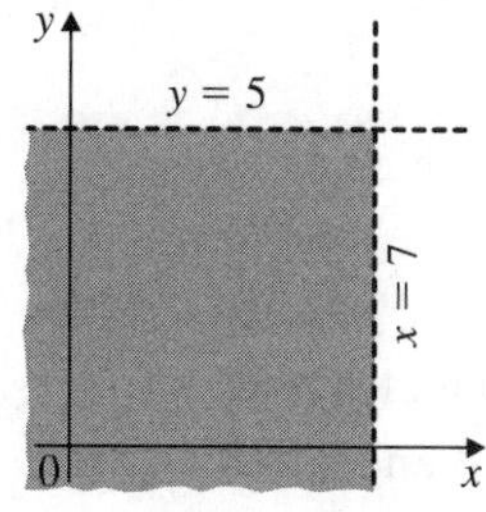

5. 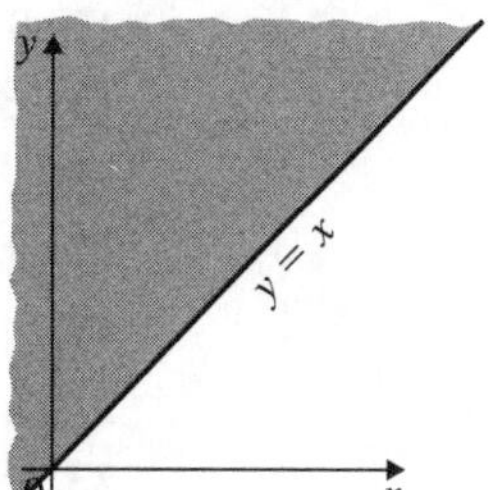

6. 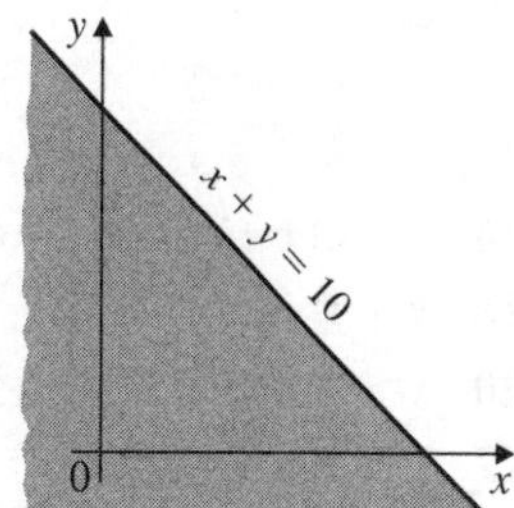

7. The point (1, 1), marked $*$, lies in the shaded region. Use this as a trial point to describe the shaded region.

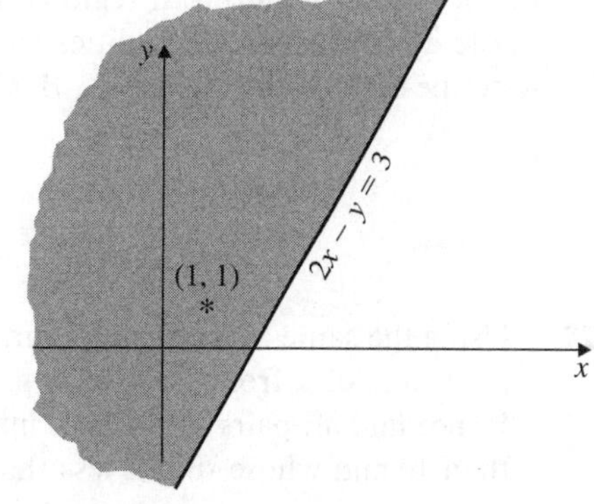

8. The point (3, 1), marked $*$, lies in the shaded triangle. Use this as a trial point to write down the three inequalities which describe the shaded region.

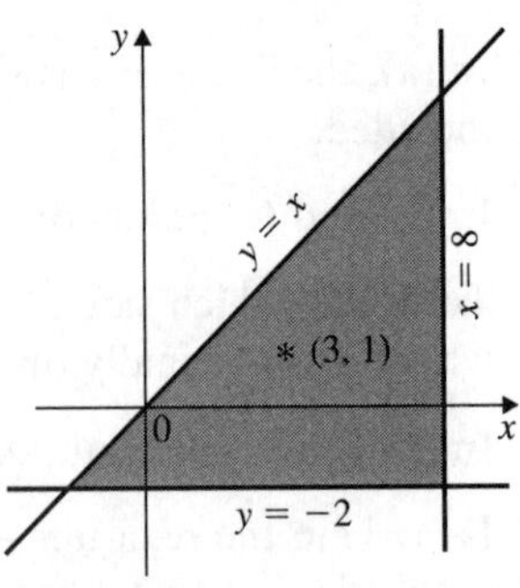

9. A trial point (1, 2) lies inside the shaded triangles. Write down the three inequalities which describe each shaded region.

(a)

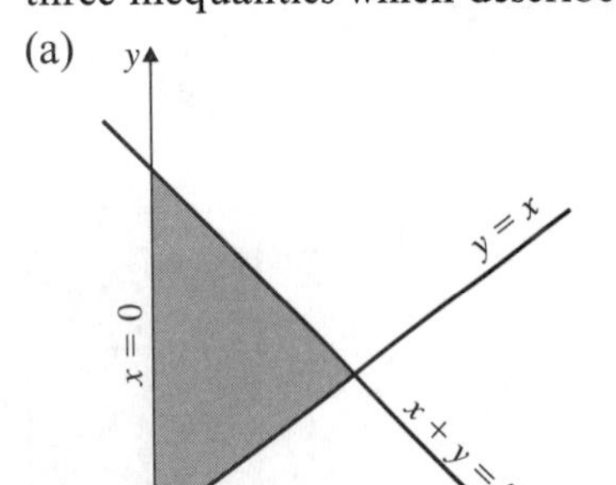

(b)

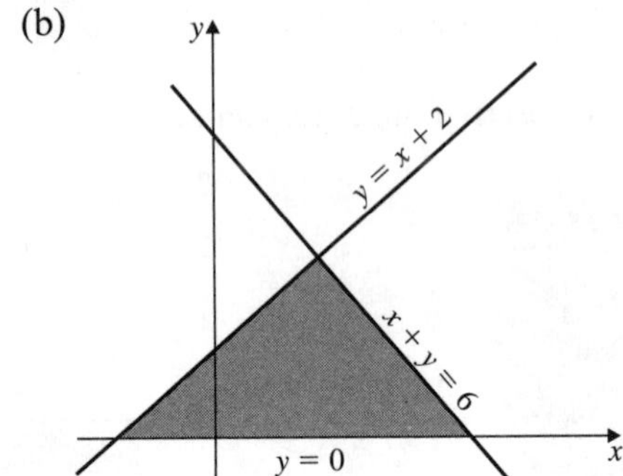

For Questions **10** to **25**, draw a sketch graph similar to those above and indicate the set of points which satisfy the inequalities by shading the region required.

10. $2 < x < 7$

11. $0 < y < 3\frac{1}{2}$

12. $-2 < x < 2$

13. $x < 6$ and $y < 4$

14. $0 < x < 5$ and $y < 3$

15. $1 < x < 6$ and $2 < y < 8$

16. $-3 < x < 0$ and $-4 < y < 2$

17. $y < x$

18. $x + y < 5$

19. $y > x + 2$ and $y < 7$

20. $x > 0$ and $y > 0$ and $x + y < 7$

21. $x > 0$ and $x + y < 10$ and $y > x$

22. $8 > y > 0$ and $x + y > 3$

23. $x + 2y < 10$ and $x > 0$ and $y > 0$

24. $3x + 2y < 18$ and $x > 0$ and $y > 0$

25. $x > 0$, $y > x - 2$, $x + y < 10$

26. The two lines $y = x + 1$ and $x + y = 5$ divide the graph into four regions A, B, C, D. Write down the two inequalities which describe each of the regions A, B, C, D.

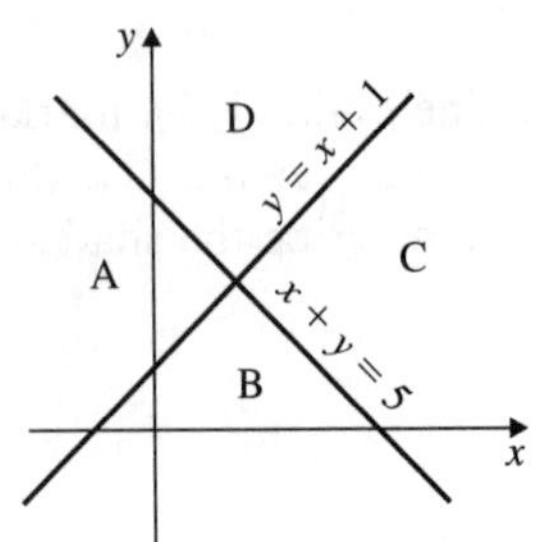

27. Using the same axes, draw the graphs of $xy = 10$ and $x + y = 9$ for values of x from 1 to 10.
Hence find all pairs of positive integers whose product is greater than 10 and whose sum is less than 9.

11 Shape and Space 3

11.1 Similar shapes

If one shape is an enlargement of another, the two shapes are mathematically *similar*.

The two triangles A and B are similar if they have the same angles.

For other shapes to be similar, not only must corresponding angles be equal, but also corresponding edges must be in the same proportion.

60°
A
80°
40°

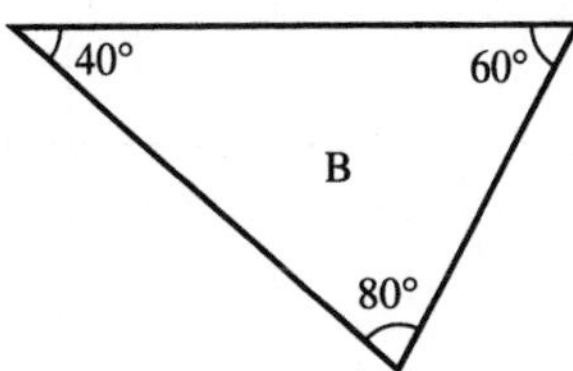

The two quadrilaterals C and D are similar. All the edges of shape D are twice as long as the edges of shape C.

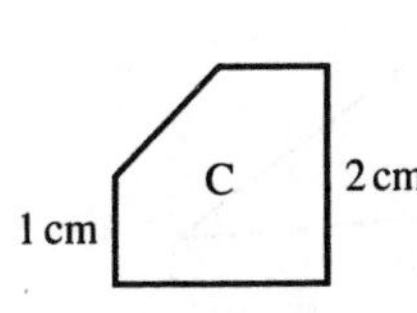

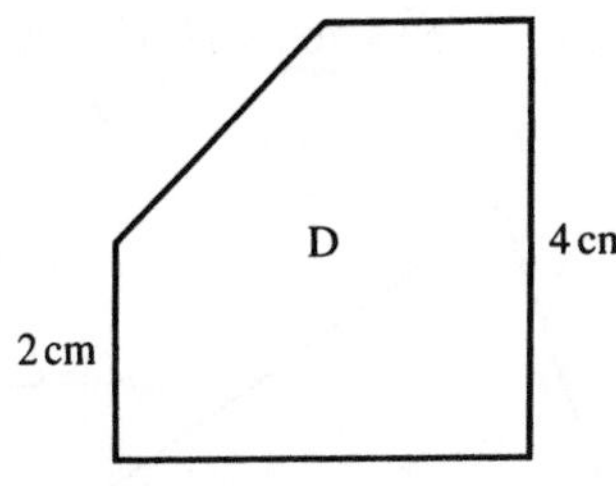

The two rectangles E and F are not similar even though they have the same angles.

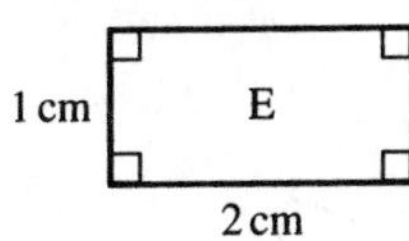

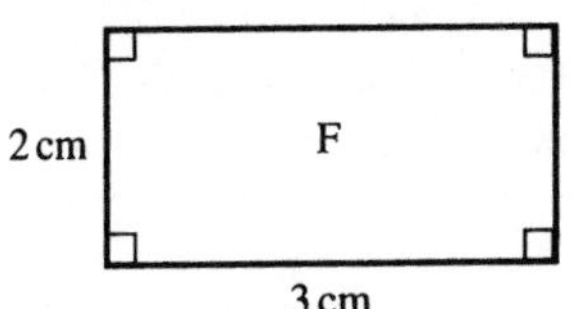

The triangles below are similar.
Find x.

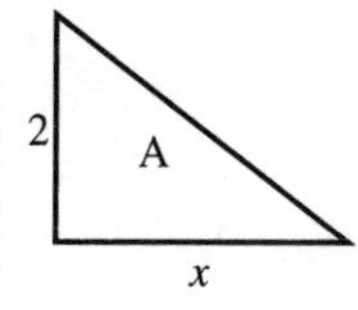

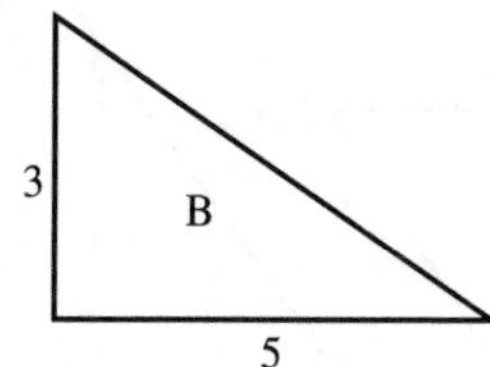

Triangle B is an enlargement of triangle A. The scale factor of the enlargement is $\frac{3}{2}$.

Corresponding sides are in the same ratio.

$$\therefore \quad \frac{x}{5} = \frac{2}{3}$$

$$x = \frac{2}{3} \times 5$$

$$x = 3\frac{1}{3}$$

Exercise 1

1. Which of the shapes B, C, D is/are similar to shape A?

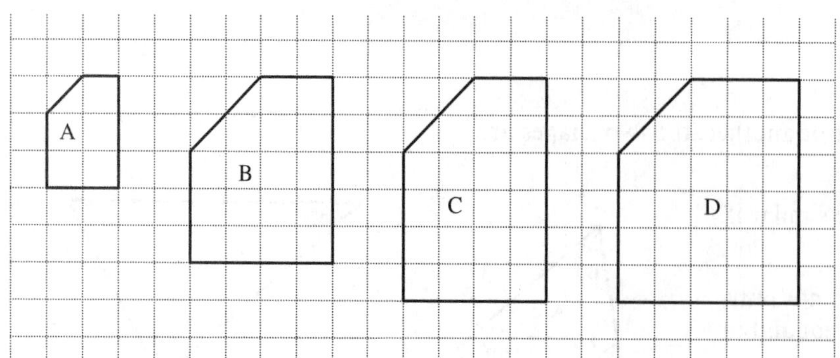

In Questions **2** to **7**, find the sides marked with letters; all lengths are given in cm. The pairs of shapes are similar.

2.

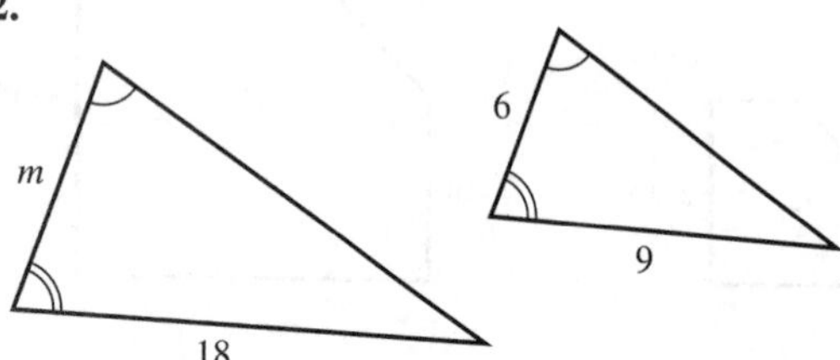

3.

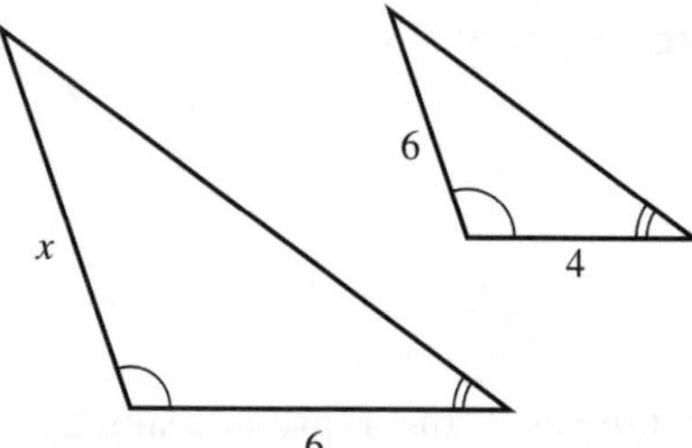

4.

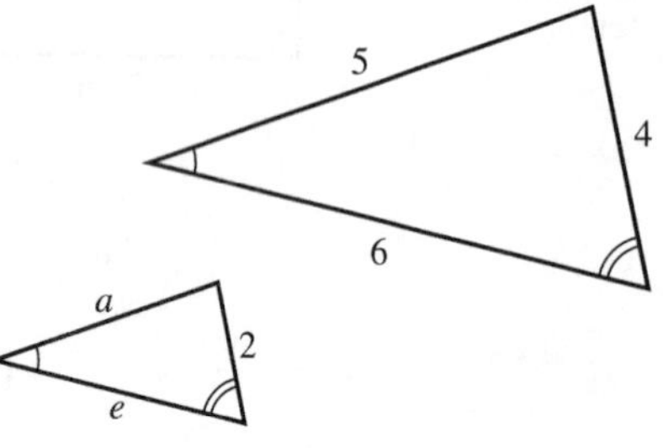

5.

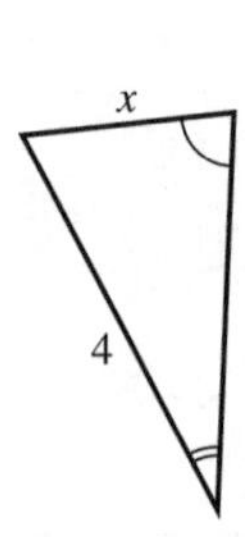

6.

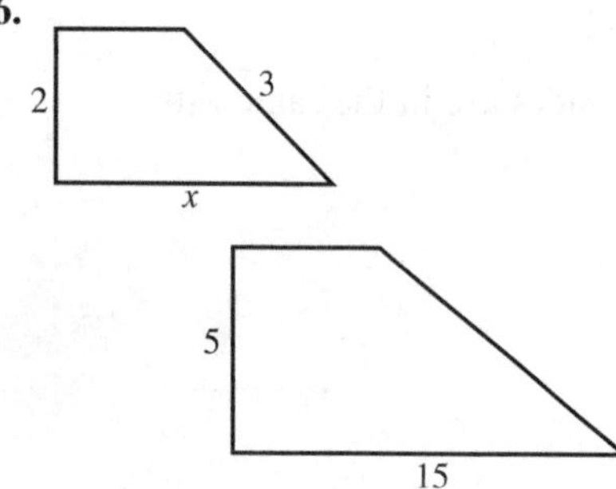

7.

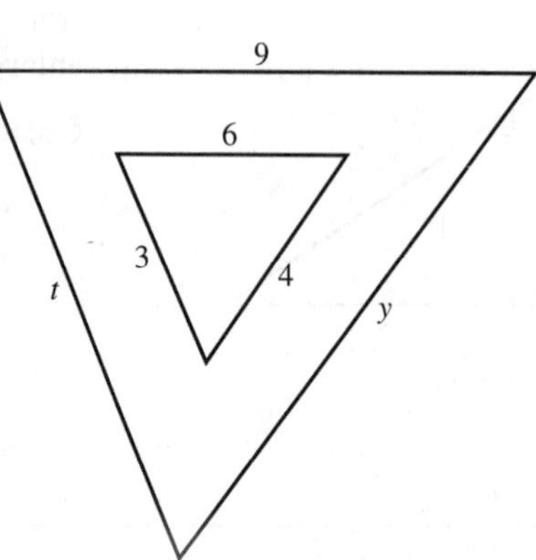

8. Picture B is an enlargement of picture A. Calculate the length x.

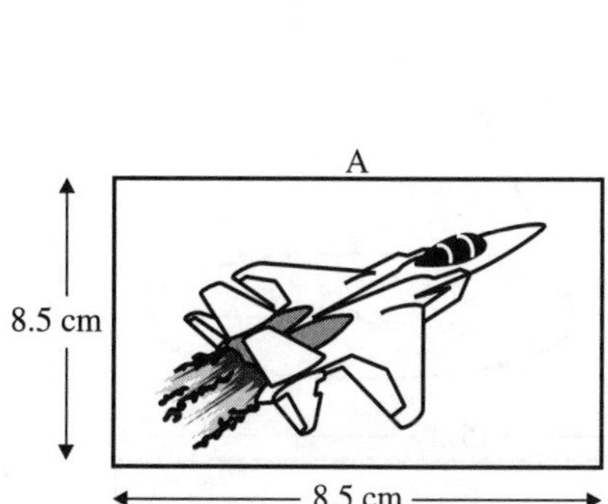

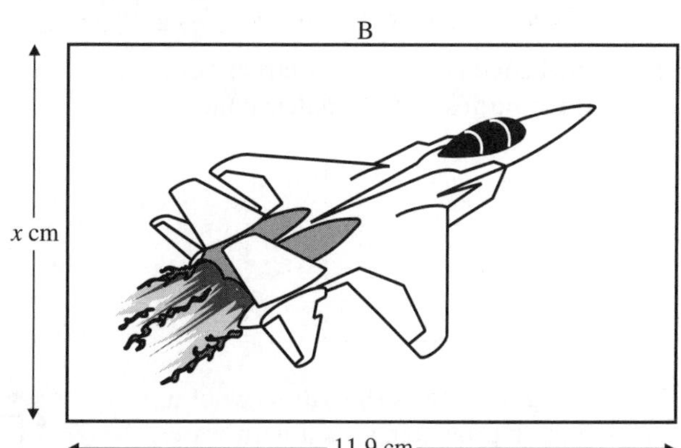

9. The drawing shows a rectangular picture 16 cm × 8 cm surrounded by a border of width 4 cm.
Are the two rectangles similar?

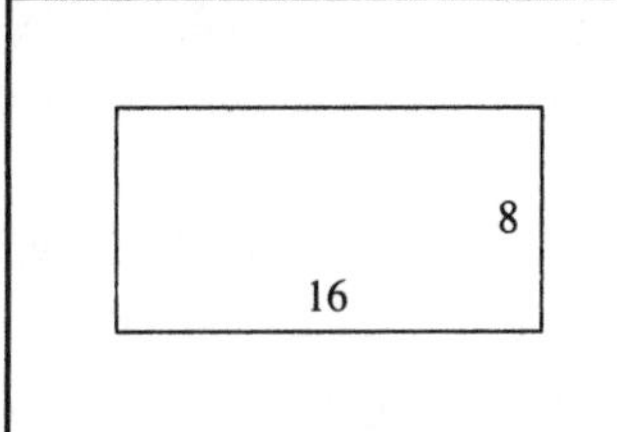

10. Which of the following *must* be similar to each other?

(a) two equilateral triangles (b) two rectangles (c) two isosceles triangles
(d) two squares (e) two regular pentagons (f) two kites
(g) two rhombuses (h) two circles.

11.

C
D
8
5
A E 7 B

(a) Explain why triangles ABC and EBD are similar.
(b) Given that EB = 7 cm, calculate the length AB.
(c) Write down the length AE.

In Questions **12, 13, 14** use similar triangles to find the sides marked with letters. All lengths are in cm.

12.

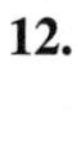

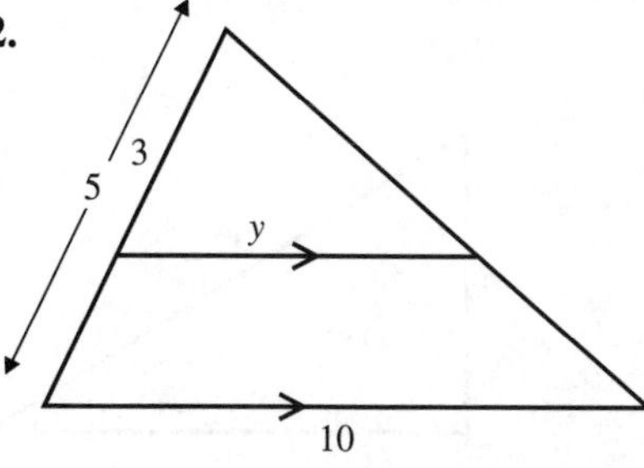

13.

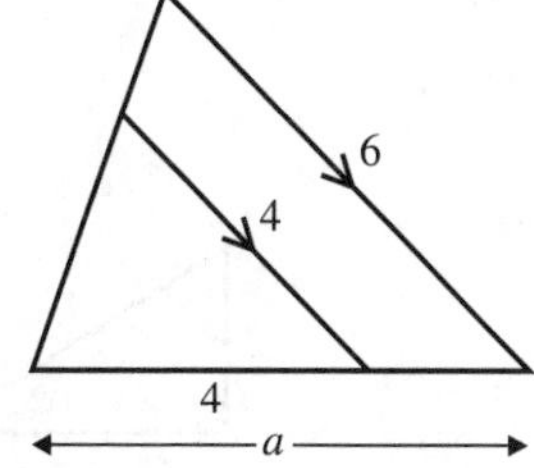

14.

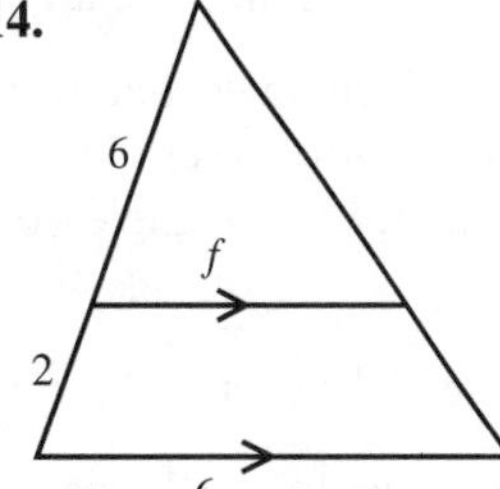

15. A tree of height 4 m casts a shadow of length 6·5 m. Find the height of a house casting a shadow 26 m long.

16. A small cone is cut from a larger cone. Find the radius of the smaller cone.

17. The diagram shows the side view of a swimming pool being filled with water. Calculate the length x.

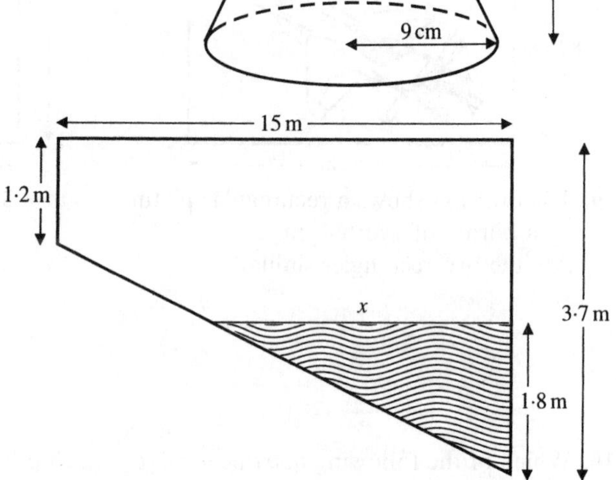

18. The diagonals of a trapezium ABCD intersect at O. AB is parallel to DC, AB = 3 cm and DC = 6 cm. Show that triangles ABO and CDO are similar. If CO = 4 cm and OB = 3 cm, find AO and DO.

11.2 Trigonometry

Trigonometry is used to calculate sides and angles in triangles. The triangle must have a right angle.

The side opposite the right angle is called the *hypotenuse* (H). It is the longest side.

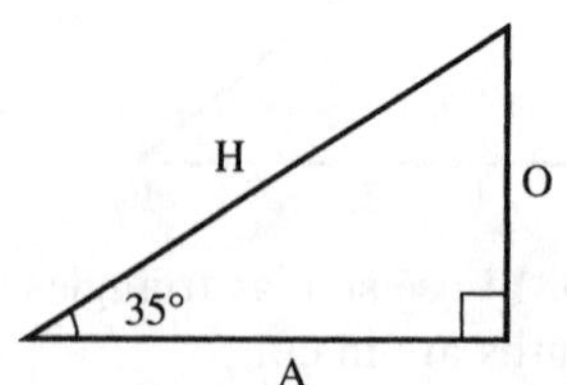

The side opposite the marked angle is called the opposite (O).

The other side is called the adjacent (A).

Consider two triangles, one of which is an enlargement of the other.
It is clear that, for the angle 30°, the ratio

$$\frac{\text{opposite}}{\text{hypotenuse}} = \frac{6}{12} = \frac{2}{4} = \frac{1}{2}$$

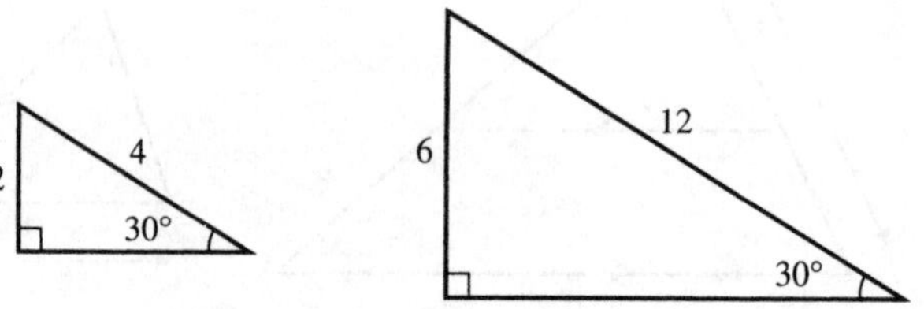

This is the same for both triangles.

Sine, cosine, tangent

Three important ratios are defined for angle x.

$\sin x = \frac{O}{H}$ $\cos x = \frac{A}{H}$ $\tan x = \frac{O}{A}$

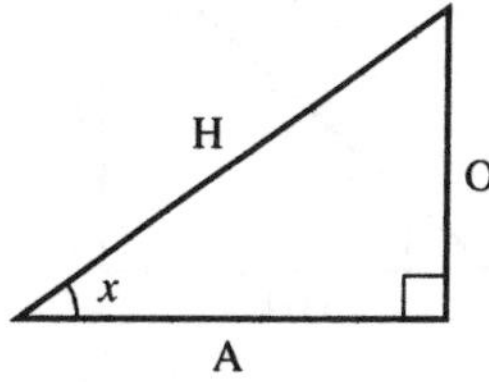

It is important to get the letters in the correct positions.

Some people find a simple sentence helpful where the first letters of each word describe sine, cosine or tangent, Hypotenuse, Opposite or Adjacent. An example is:

Silly Old Harry Caught A Herring Trawling Off Afghanistan

e.g. SOH $\sin = \frac{O}{H}$

Finding the length of a side

Find the length of l.

We have 'A' and 'H' so we use cos.

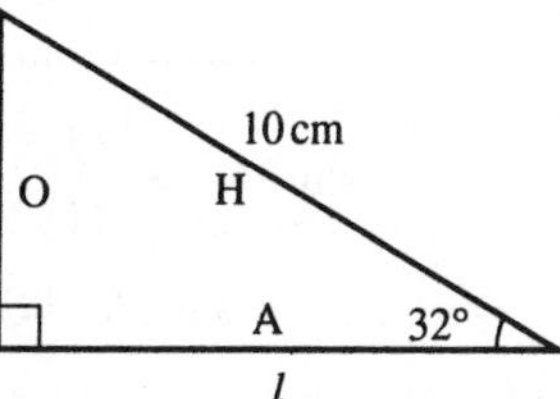

$\cos 32° = \frac{A}{H} = \frac{l}{10}$

$\therefore\ l = 10 \times \cos 32°$

$l = 8{\cdot}48$ cm (to 3 s.f.)

Exercise 2

Find the lengths marked with letters. All lengths are in cm. Give answers correct to 3 s.f.

1.
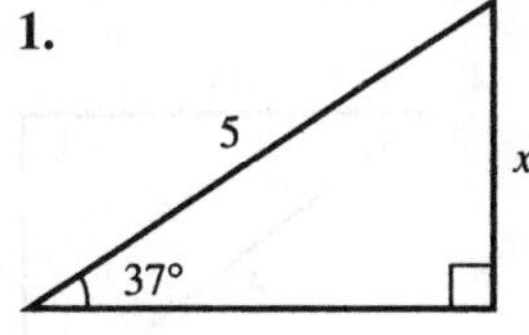

2.
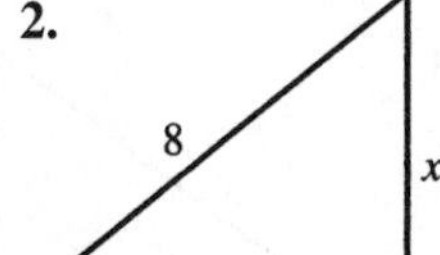

3.
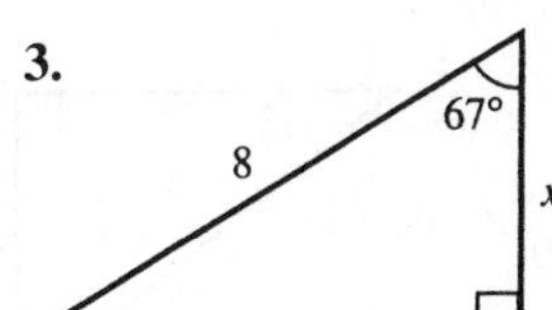

4.
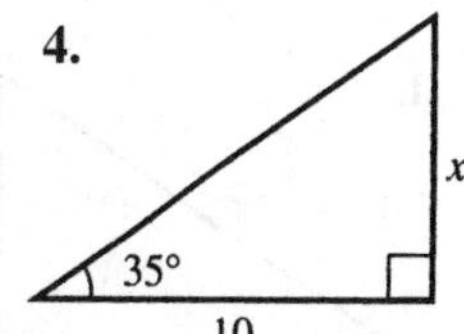

5.
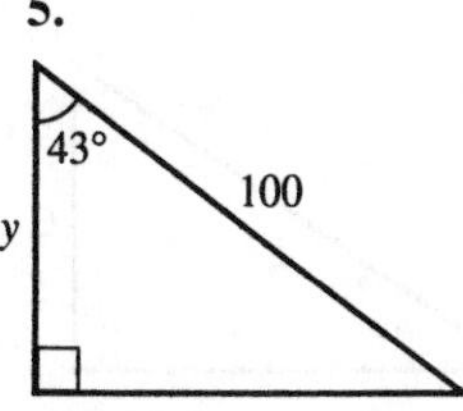

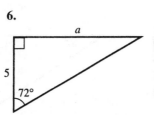

6.

7.
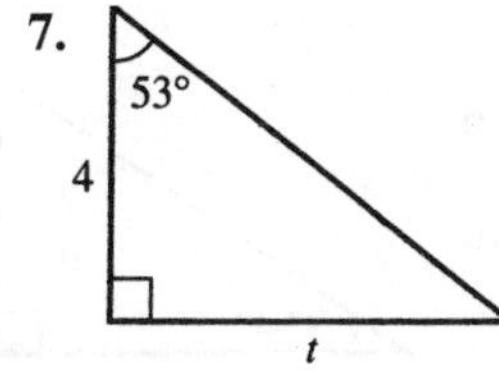

8.
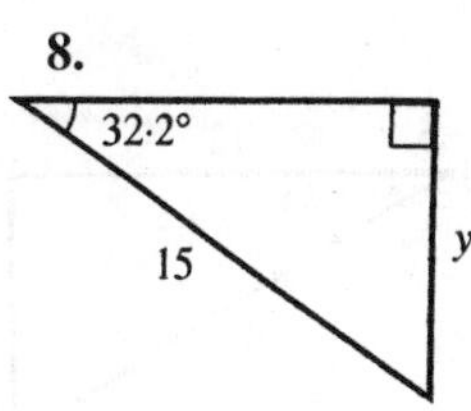

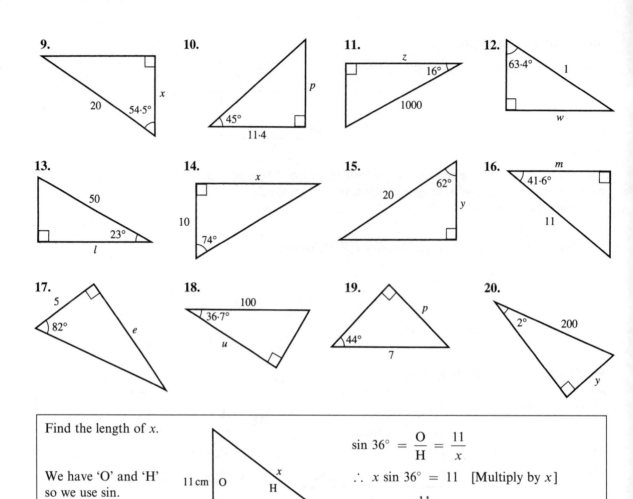

9. 20, 54·5°, x

10. 45°, 11·4, p

11. z, 16°, 1000

12. 63·4°, 1, w

13. 50, 23°, l

14. x, 10, 74°

15. 20, 62°, y

16. m, 41·6°, 11

17. 5, 82°, e

18. 100, 36·7°, u

19. p, 44°, 7

20. 2°, 200, y

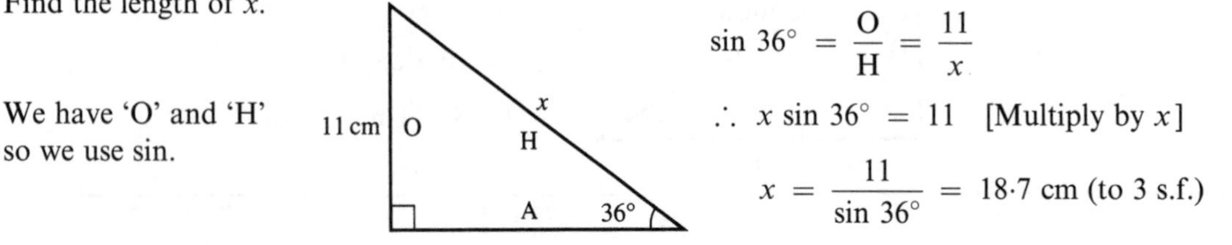

Find the length of x.

We have 'O' and 'H' so we use sin.

$$\sin 36° = \frac{O}{H} = \frac{11}{x}$$

$$\therefore\ x \sin 36° = 11 \quad \text{[Multiply by } x\text{]}$$

$$x = \frac{11}{\sin 36°} = 18{\cdot}7 \text{ cm (to 3 s.f.)}$$

Exercise 3

This exercise is more difficult. Find the lengths marked with letters.

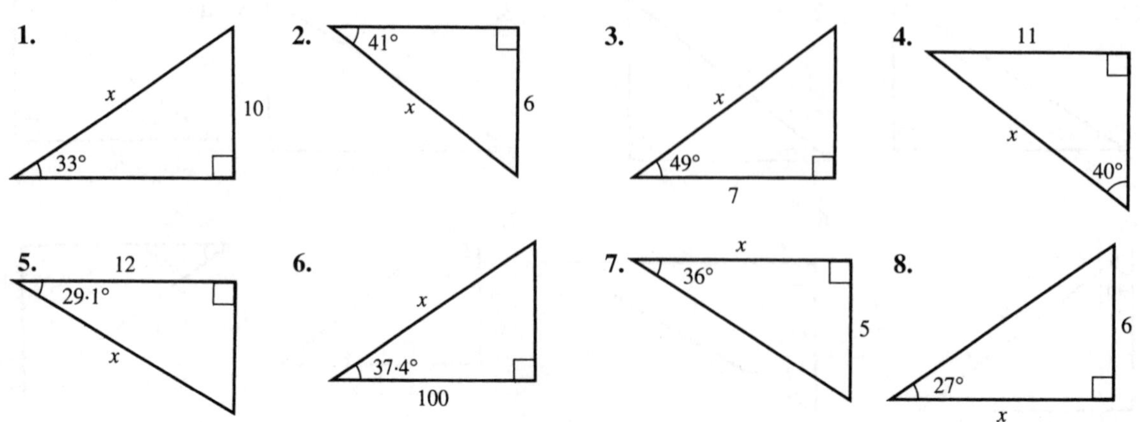

9.

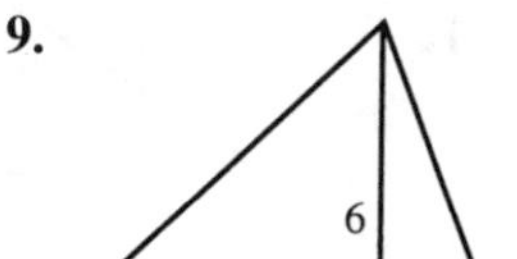

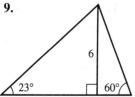

10.

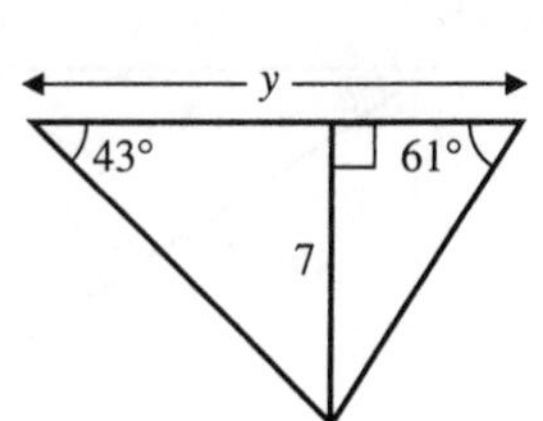

11.

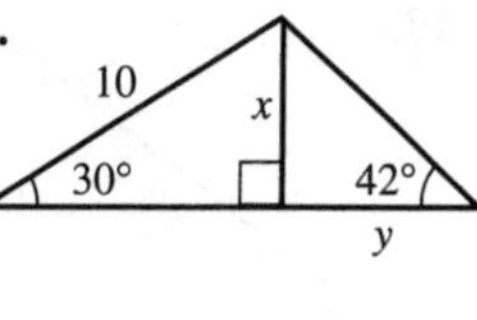

12.

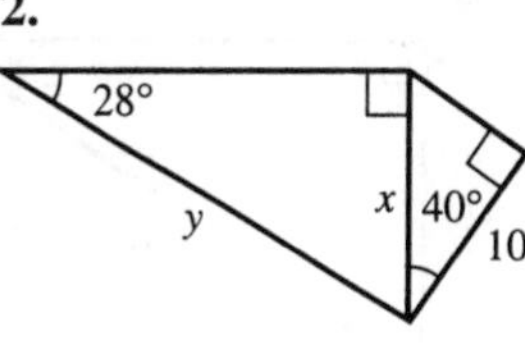

13.

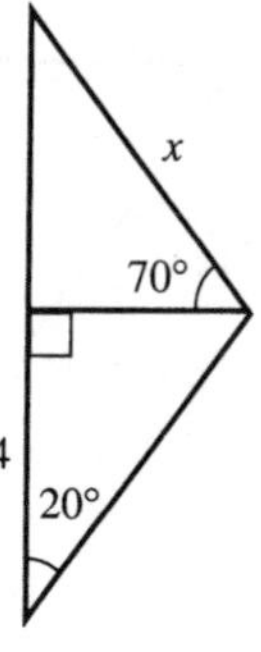

14.

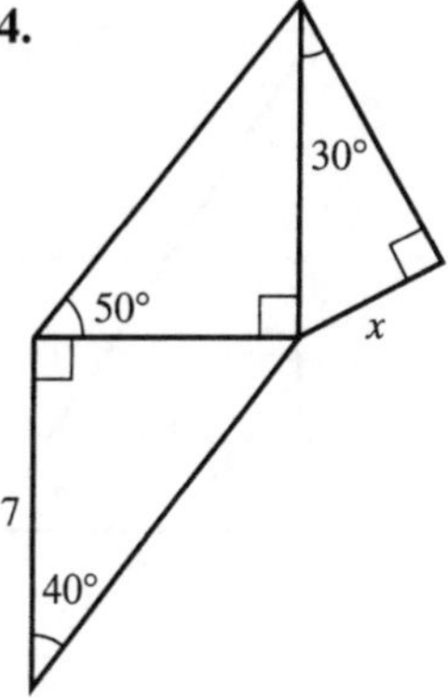

15.

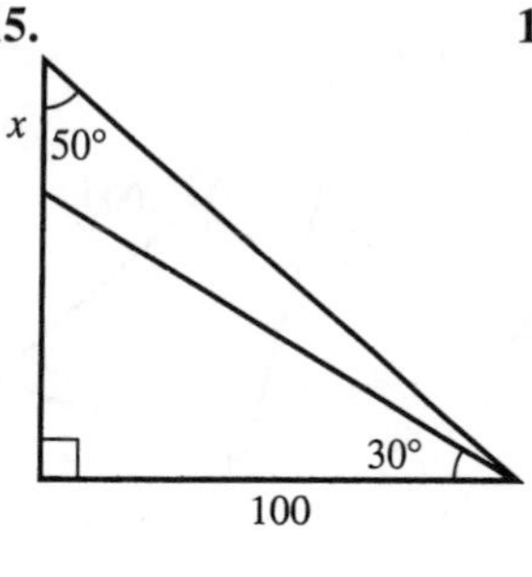

16.

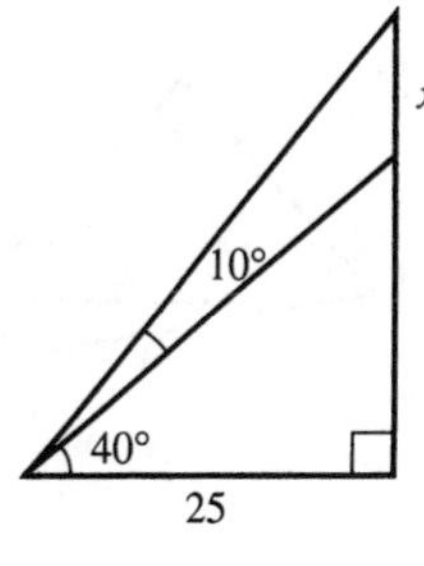

Finding angles

Find the angle x.

We have 'O' and 'A' so we use tan.

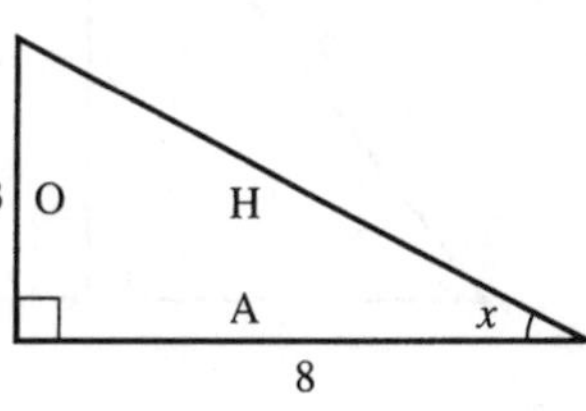

$$\tan x = \frac{O}{A} = \frac{3}{8}$$

$$\tan x = 0{\cdot}375$$
$$x = 20{\cdot}6^\circ \text{ (to 1 d.p.)}$$

On a calculator:

| 3 | ÷ | 8 | = | INV | tan |

Exercise 4

Find the angles marked with letters. Give the answers correct to 1 d.p.

1.

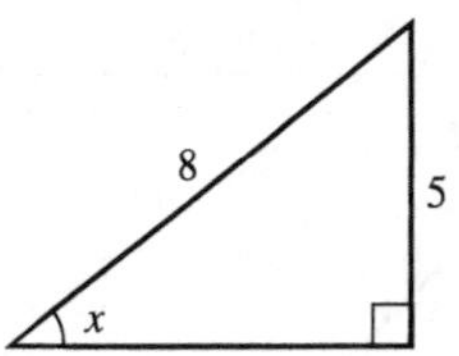

2.

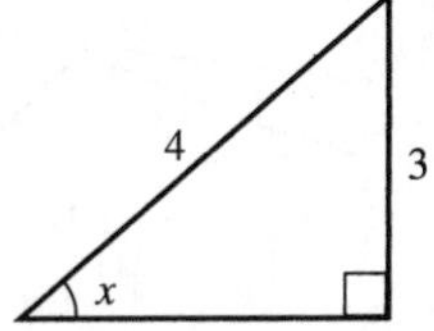

3.

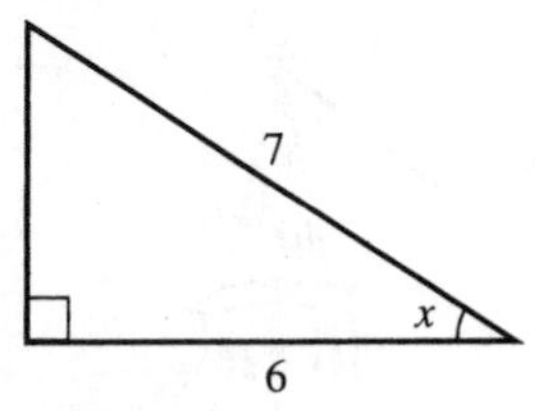

4.

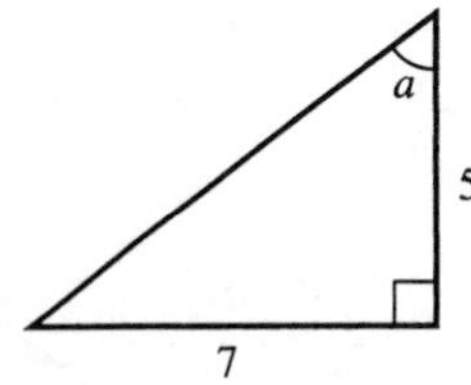

5.

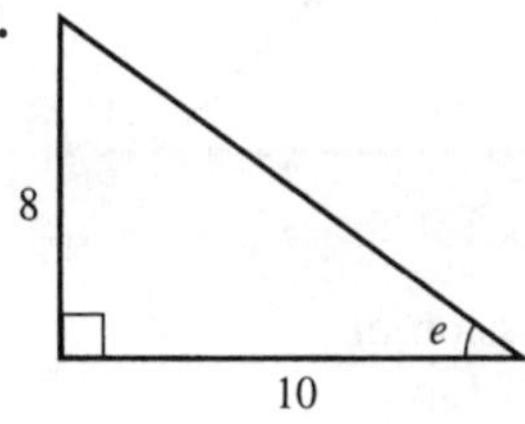

6.

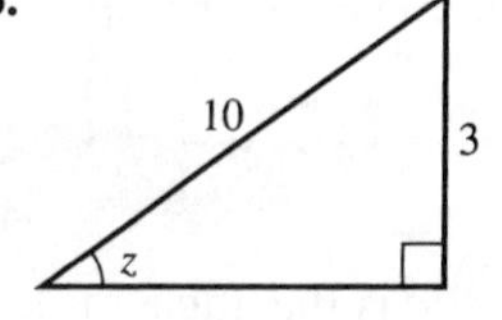

7.

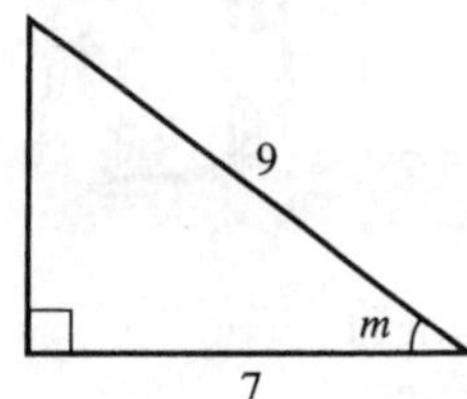

8.

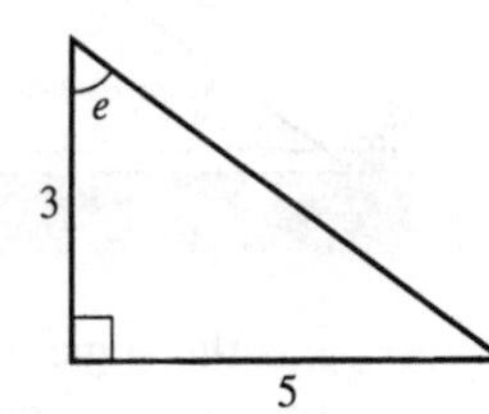

9. 33, 50, y

10. 9, 8, c

11. 7, 12, d

12. w, 4, 9

13. 2, 3, k

14. w, 1000, 215

15. 13, 4, e

16. 11, 6, z

17 5, 3, 4, x

18. y, 6, 4, 5

19. x, 7, 5, 6

20. 11, a, 7, 9

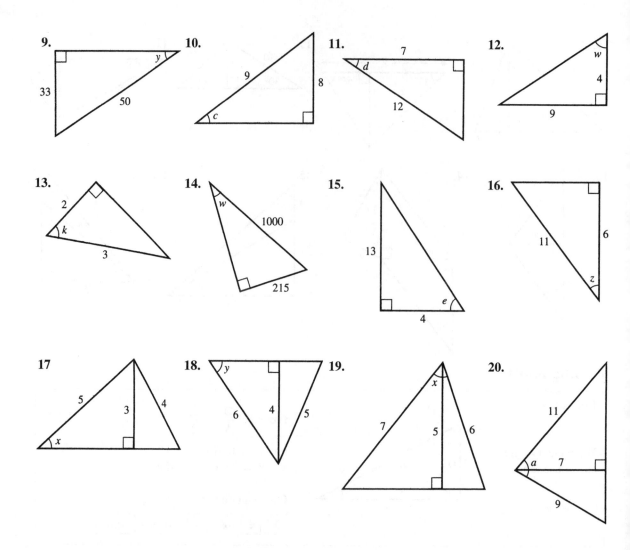

Angles of elevation and depression

(a)

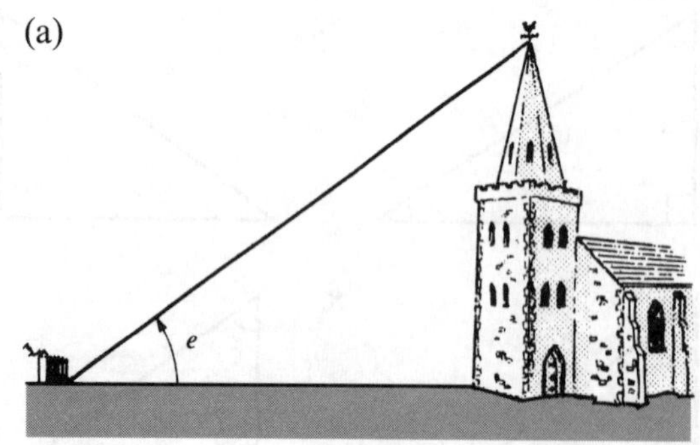

e is the angle of elevation of the Steeple from the Gate.

(b)

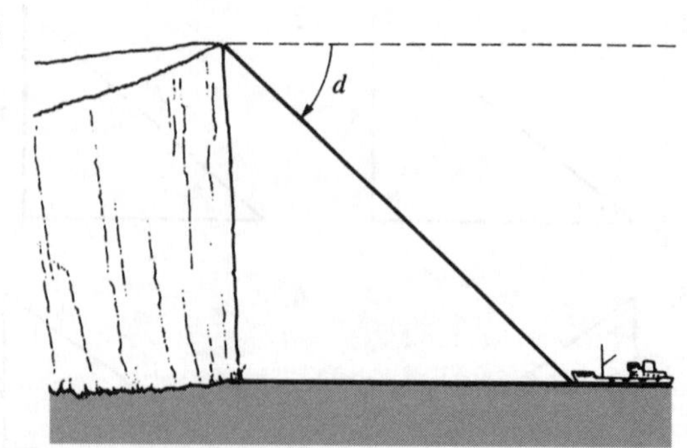

d is the angle of depression of the Boat from the Cliff top.

Exercise 5

Begin each question by drawing a large clear diagram.

1. A ladder of length 4 m rests against a vertical wall so that the base of the ladder is 1·5 m from the wall.
   Calculate the angle between the ladder and the ground.

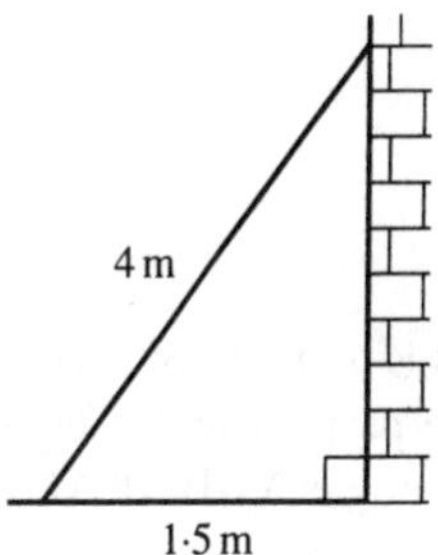

2. A ladder of length 4 m rests against a vertical wall so that the angle between the ladder and the ground is 66°. How far up the wall does the ladder reach?

3. From a distance of 20 m the angle of elevation to the top of a tower is 35°.
   How high is the tower?

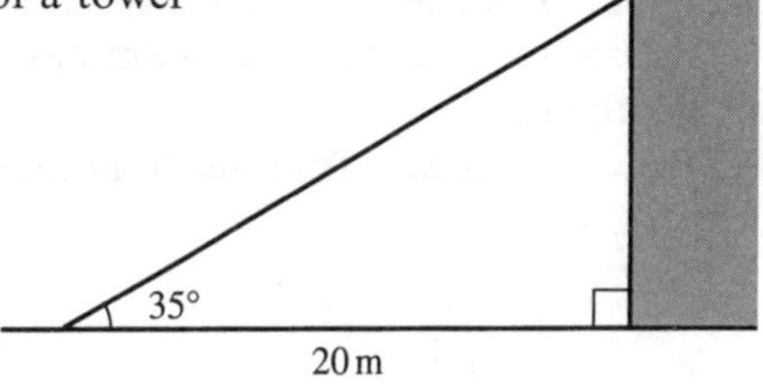

4. A point G is 40 m away from a building, which is 15 m high. What is the angle of elevation to the top of the building from G?

5. A boy is flying a kite from a string of length 60 m. If the string is taut and makes an angle of 71° with the horizontal, what is the height of the kite?
   Ignore the height of the boy.

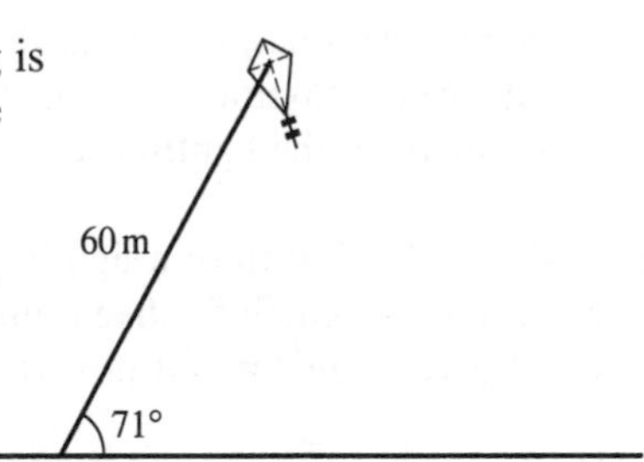

6. A straight tunnel is 80 m long and slopes downwards at an angle of 11° to the horizontal. Find the vertical drop in travelling from the top to the bottom of the tunnel.

7. The frame of a bicycle is shown in the diagram.
   Find the length of the cross bar.

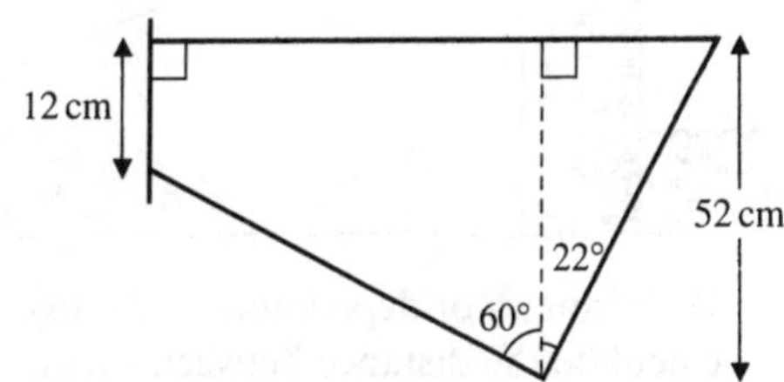

8. Calculate the length x.

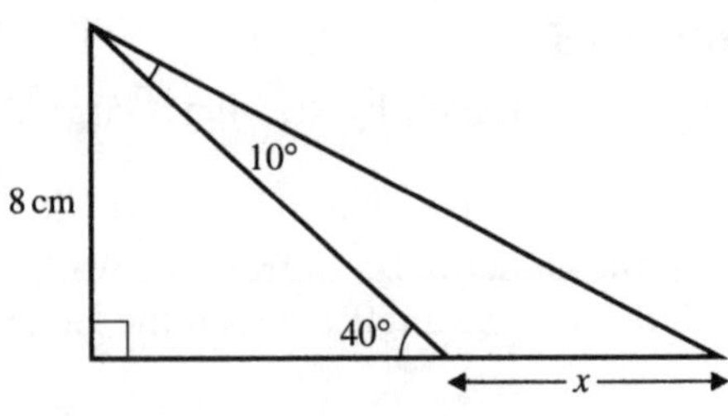

9. AB is a chord of a circle of radius 5 cm and centre O.
The perpendicular bisector of AB passes through O and also bisects the angle AOB. If $A\hat{O}B = 100°$ calculate the length of the chord AB.

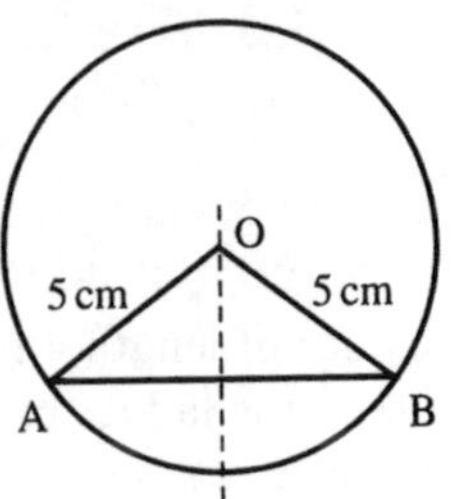

10. A ship is due South of a lighthouse L. It sails on a bearing of 055° for a distance of 80 km until it is due East of the lighthouse.
How far is it now from the lighthouse?

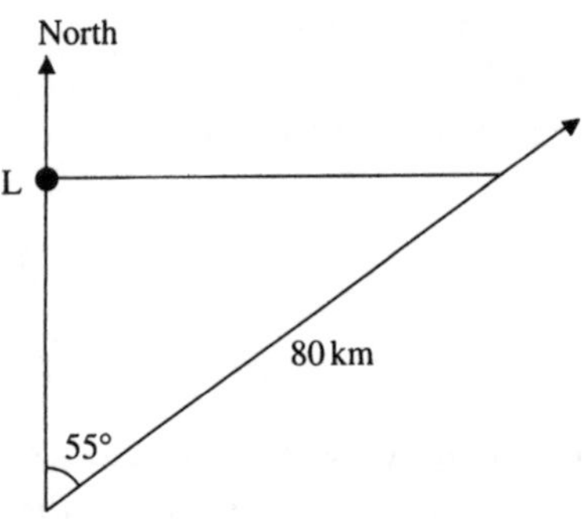

11. A ship is due South of a lighthouse. It sails on a bearing of 071° for a distance of 200 km until it is due East of the lighthouse. How far is it now from the lighthouse?

12. A ship is due North of a lighthouse. It sails on a bearing of 200° at a speed of 15 km/h for five hours until it is due West of the lighthouse. How far is it now from the lighthouse?

13. From the top of a tower of height 75 m, a guard sees two prisoners, both due East of him.

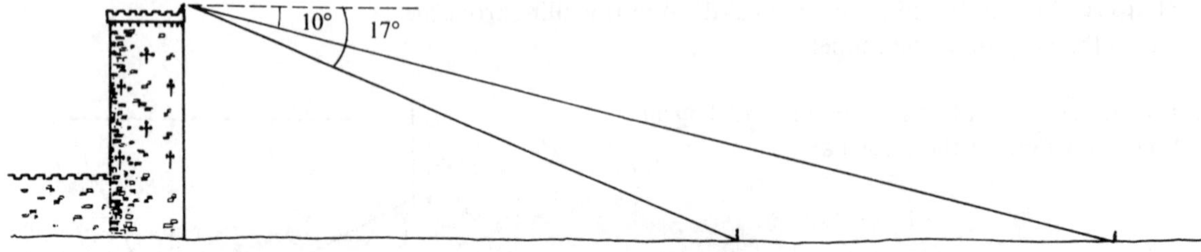

If the angles of depression of the two prisoners are 10° and 17°, calculate the distance between them.

14. From a horizontal distance of 40 m, the angle of elevation to the top of a building is 35·4°. From a point further away from the building the angle of elevation is 20·2°. What is the distance between the two points?

15. An isosceles triangle has sides of length 8 cm, 8 cm and 5 cm. Find the angle between the two equal sides.

16. The angles of an isosceles triangle are 66°, 66° and 48°. If the shortest side of the triangle is 8·4 cm, find the length of one of the two equal sides.

17. A regular pentagon is inscribed in a circle of radius 7 cm. Find the angle a and then the length of a side of the pentagon.

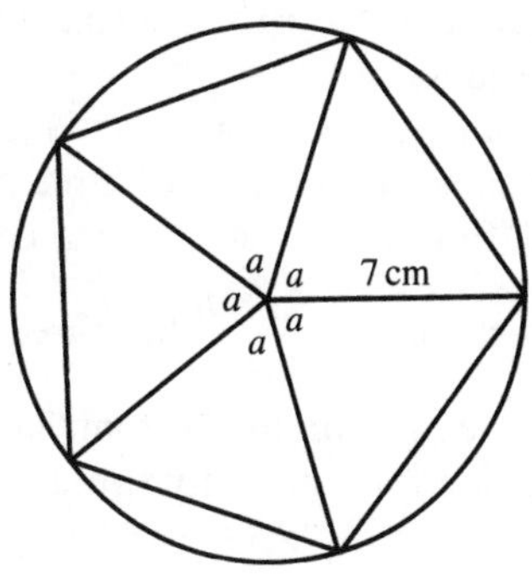

18. Find the acute angle between the diagonals of a rectangle whose sides are 5 cm and 7 cm.

11.3 Dimensions of formulas

Here are some formulas for finding volumes, areas and lengths.

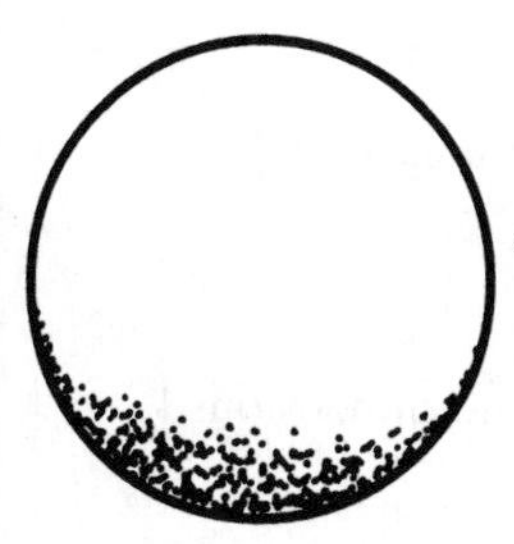

- **Sphere :** volume $= \frac{4}{3}\pi \boldsymbol{r}^3$
  surface area $= 4\pi \boldsymbol{r}^2$

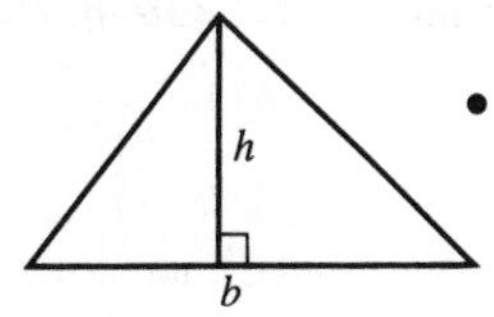

- **Triangle :** area $= \frac{1}{2}\boldsymbol{bh}$

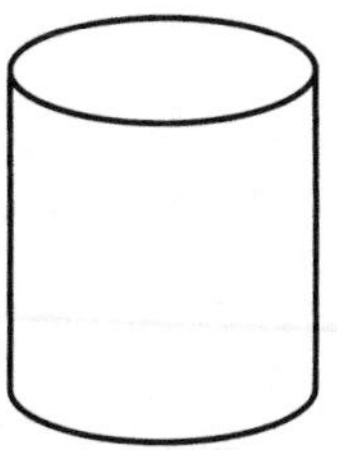

- **Cylinder :** volume $= \pi \boldsymbol{r}^2 \boldsymbol{h}$
  curved surface area $= 2\pi \boldsymbol{rh}$

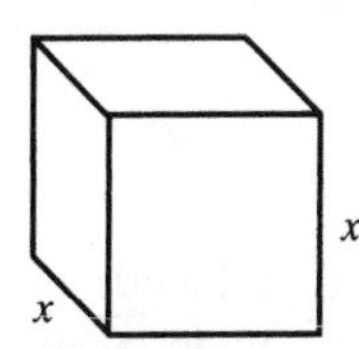

- **Cube :** volume $= \boldsymbol{x}^3$
  surface area $= 6\boldsymbol{x}^2$

All the symbols in bold type are lengths. They have the *dimension* of length and are measured in cm, metres, km, etc. The other symbols are numbers (including π) and have no dimensions.

Remember:
Numbers like 3, $\frac{1}{2}$ or π have no dimensions.

(a) It is not hard to see that all the formulas for volume have *three* lengths multiplied together. They have three dimensions.
(b) All the formulas for area have *two* lengths multiplied together. They have two dimensions.
(c) Any formula for the length of an object will involve just *one* length (or one dimension).

It is quite possible that a formula can have more than one term.
The formula $A = \pi r^2 + 3rd$ has two terms and each term has two dimensions.
It is not possible to have a mixture of terms some with, say, two dimensions and some with three dimensions.
So the formula $A = \pi r^2 + 3r^2 d$ could not possibly represent volume.

The formula $z = \dfrac{2\pi r^2 h}{L}$ has three dimensions on the top line and one dimension on the bottom. The dimensions can be 'cancelled' so the expression for z has only two dimensions and can only represent an area.
We can use these facts to check that any formula we may be using has the correct number of dimensions.

Here are four formulas where the letters c, d, r represent lengths:

(a) $t = 3c^2$ (b) $k = \frac{\pi}{3}r^3 + 4r^2 d$ (c) $m = \pi(c + d)$ (d) $f = 4c + 3cd$

State whether the formula gives:
(i) a length (ii) an area (iii) a volume
(iv) an impossible expression.

(a) $t = 3c^2 = 3c \times c$
This has *two* dimensions so t is an *area*. [Notice that the number '3' has no dimensions.]

(b) $k = \frac{\pi}{3}r^3 + 4r^2 d$

Both $\frac{\pi}{3}r^3$ and $4r^2 d$ have *three* dimensions so k is a *volume*. ['$\frac{\pi}{3}$' and '4' have no dimensions.]

(c) $m = \pi(c + d) = \pi c + \pi d$
πc is a length and πd is a length.
So m is a length plus a length.
$\therefore$ m is a length.

(d) $f = 4c + 3cd$
$4c$ is a length.
$3cd$ is a length multiplied by a length and is an area.
So f is a length plus an area which is an *impossible* expression.

Exercise 6

The symbols a, b, d, h, l, r represent lengths.

1. For each expression, decide if it represents a length, an area or a volume.

(a) $a + 3b$ (b) a^2b (c) ab
(d) $5(b - a)$ (e) $b^3 + a^3$ (f) $7ab + a^2$

2. State the number of dimensions for each of the following.

(a) πl^2 (b) $3\pi lr$ (c) $\frac{\pi}{2}b^2h$

(d) $\pi(a + b)$ (e) $\frac{ab + h^2}{6}$ (f) $abd \sin 30°$

3. Give the number of dimensions that a formula for each of the following should have.
(a) Total area of windows in a room.
(b) Volume of sand in a lorry.
(c) Area of a sports field.
(d) The diagonal of a rectangle.
(e) The capacity of an oil can.
(f) The perimeter of a trapezium.
(g) The number of tools in a van.
(h) The surface area of the roof of a house.

4. One of these equations gives the area of this shape and another gives the perimeter.

$2h + w + \frac{5}{4}w$	$w^2h + h^2$
$w + h + h + wh$	$wh + \frac{\pi}{6}wh$

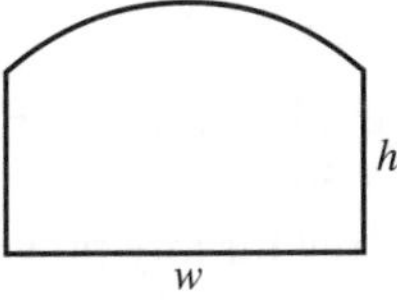

Write down the correct expression for
(a) the area (b) the perimeter.

5. From this list of expressions, choose the *two* that represent volume, the four that represent area and the *one* that represents a length. The other expression is impossible.

(a) $\pi rh + \pi r^2$ (b) $5a + 6c$
(c) $3{\cdot}5\,abd$ (d) $4hl + \pi rh$
(e) $3r^2hl$ (f) $2\pi r(r + h)$
(g) $2(rb^2 + h^3)$ (h) $\frac{\pi}{2}(l + d)^2$

6. In Sam's notes, the formula for the volume of a container was written with Tippex over the index for r. The formula was $V = \frac{\pi}{3}r^{\square}h$. What was the missing index?

7. Work out the missing index numbers in these formulas.

(a) Area $= 3(a^{\square} + bd)$ (b) Volume $= \dfrac{\pi L^{\square}}{3}$

(c) Length $= \dfrac{\pi r^{\square}}{3}$ (d) Area $= 3(a^{\square} + b^{\square}d)$

(e) Volume $= 2\pi(r^{\square} + b^{\square})$ (f) Area $= \dfrac{3\pi}{4}(a+b)^{\square}$

8. A physicist worked out a formula for the surface area of a complicated object and got

$$S = 3\pi(a+b)^2 \sin 20° + \frac{\pi}{2}a$$

Explain why the formula could not be correct.

11.4 Angles in polygons and circles

Exterior angles of a polygon

The exterior angle of a polygon is the angle between a produced side and the adjacent side of the polygon. The word 'produced' in this context means 'extended'.

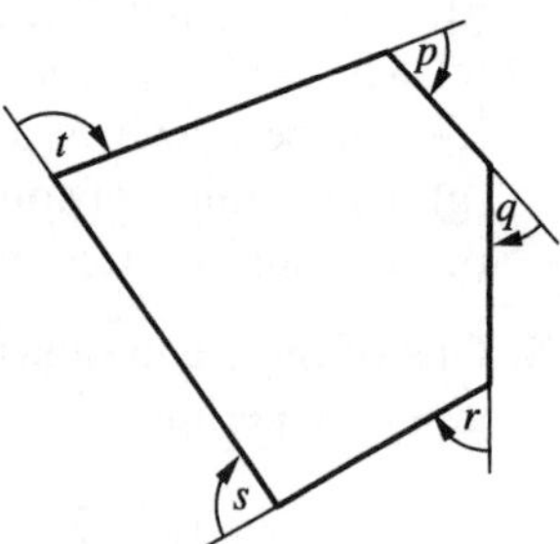

If we put all the exterior angles together we can see that the sum of the angles is 360°.
This is true for any polygon.

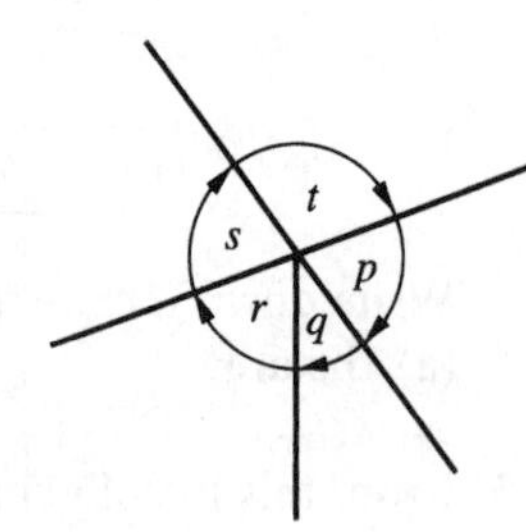

- The sum of the exterior angles of a polygon = 360°.
- In a *regular* polygon all exterior angles are equal.
- For a *regular* polygon with n sides, each exterior angle $= \dfrac{360}{n}$.

The diagram shows a regular octagon (8 sides).

(a) Calculate the size of each exterior angle (marked e).
(b) Calculate the size of each interior angle (marked i).

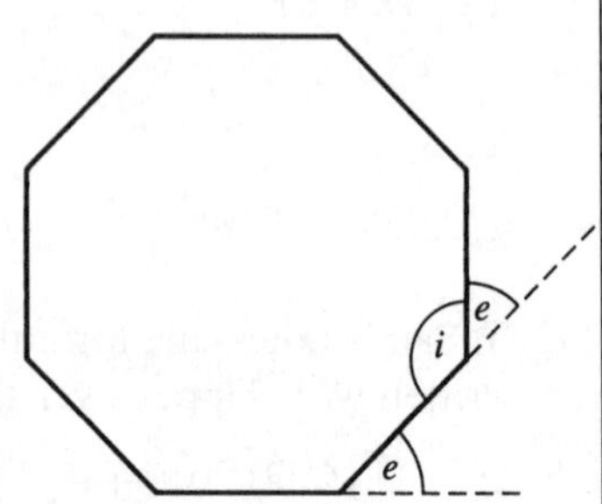

(a) There are 8 exterior angles and the sum of these angles is 360°

$\therefore$ angle $e = \frac{360}{8} = 45°$

(b) $e + i = 180°$ (angles on a straight line)

$\therefore$ $i = 135°$

Exercise 7

1. Look at the polygon shown.
   (a) Calculate each exterior angle.
   (b) Check that the total of the exterior angles is 360°.

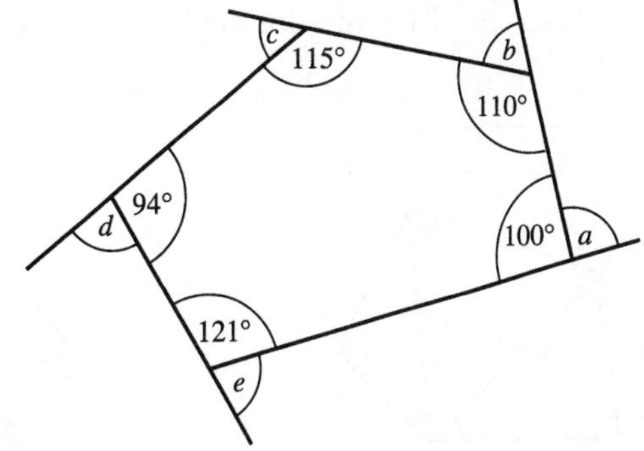

2. The diagram shows a regular decagon.
   (a) Calculate the angle *a*.
   (b) Calculate the interior angle of a regular decagon.

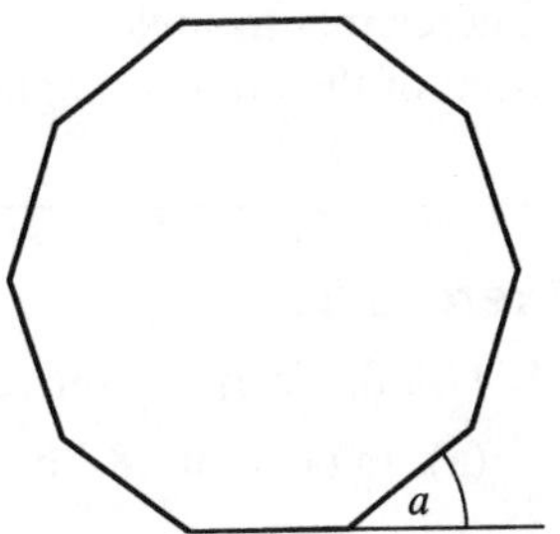

3. Find (a) the exterior angle
   (b) the interior angle

   of a regular polygon with:

   (i) 9 sides (ii) 18 sides (iii) 45 sides (iv) 60 sides

4. Find the angles marked with letters.

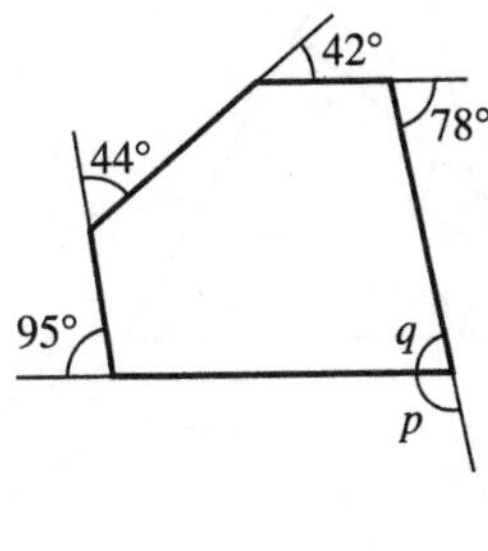

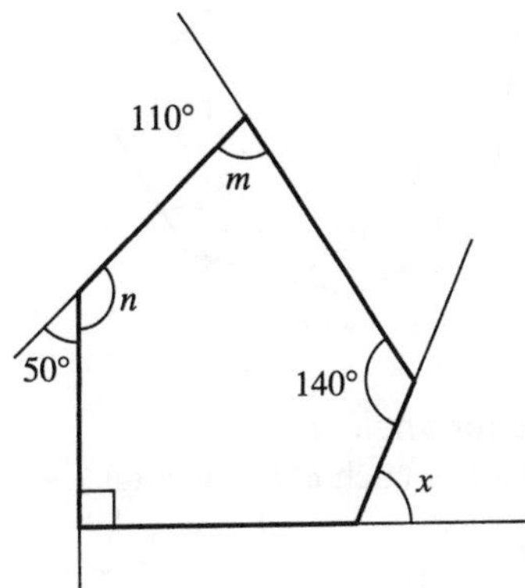

5. Each exterior angle of a regular polygon is 15°. How many sides has the polygon?

6. Each interior angle of a regular polygon is 140°. How many sides has the polygon?

7. Each exterior angle of a regular polygon is 18°. How many sides has the polygon?

Sum of the interior angles

- The sum of the interior angles of a polygon with n sides is

  $(n - 2) \times 180°$

pentagon, 5 sides ($n = 5$)

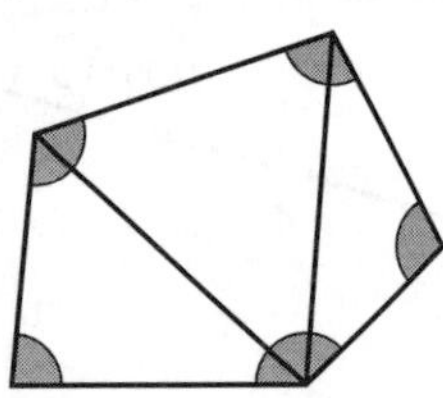

There are 3 triangles.
Sum of the interior angles $= 3 \times 180°$
$= (5 - 2) \times 180°$

hexagon, 6 sides ($n = 6$)

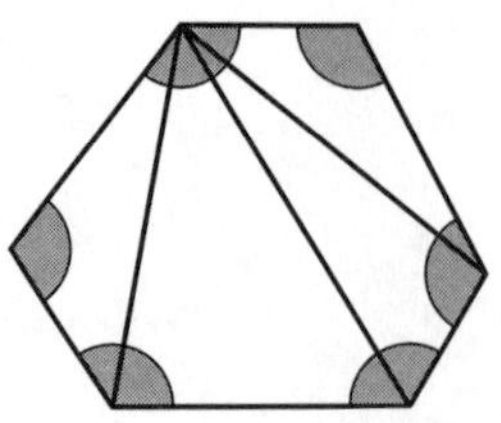

There are 4 triangles.
Sum of the interior angles $= 4 \times 180°$
$= (6 - 2) \times 180°$

Exercise 8

1. Use the formula above to find the sum of the interior angles in:
(a) an octagon (8 sides) (b) a decagon (10 sides)

2. (a) Work out the sum of the interior angles in a polygon with 20 sides.
(b) What is the size of each interior angle in a *regular* polygon with 20 sides?

3. Find the angles marked with letters.

(a)

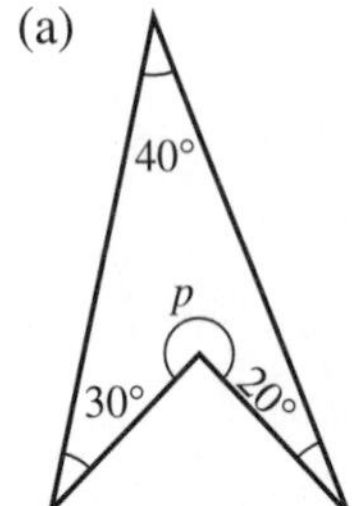

(b)

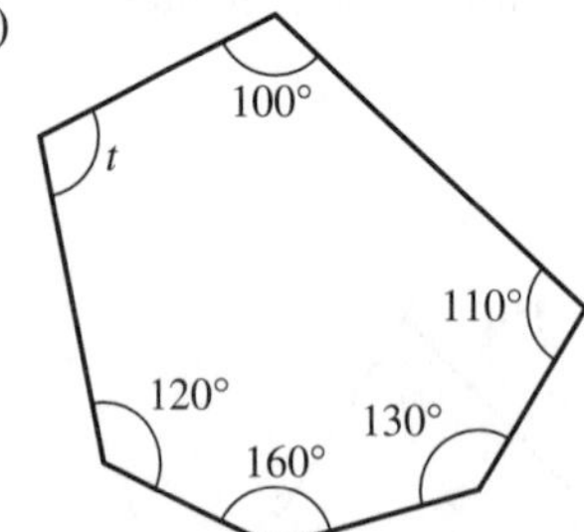

(c)

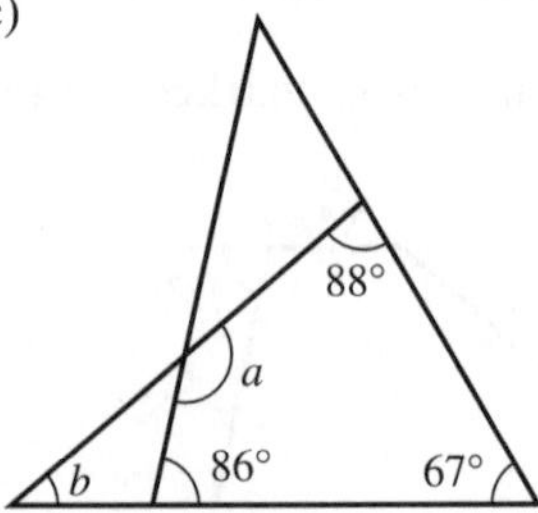

4. A regular dodecagon has 12 sides.
(a) Calculate the size of each interior angle, i.
(b) Use your answer to find the size of each exterior angle, e.

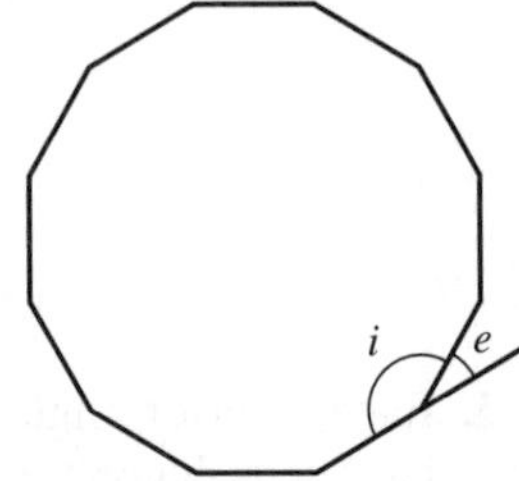

5. The sum of the interior angles of a polygon with n sides is 3600°. Find the value of n.

6. The sides of a regular polygon subtend angles of 18° at the centre of the polygon.
How many sides has the polygon?

12 REVISION

12.1 Revision exercises

Exercise 1

1. Copy the following bill and complete it by filling in the four blank spaces.

8 rolls of wallpaper at £3·20 each	=	£ ☐
3 tins of paint at £ ☐ each	=	£ 20·10
☐ brushes at £2·40 each	=	£ 9·60
Total	=	£ ☐

2. Write down each sequence and find the next two numbers.
(a) 2, 9, 16, 23
(b) 20, 18, 16, 14
(c) −5, −2, 1, 4
(d) 128, 64, 32, 16
(e) 8, 11, 15, 20

3. A man buys 500 pencils at 2·4 pence each. What change does he receive from £20?

4. Every day at school Stephen buys a roll for 14p, crisps for 11p and a drink for 21p. How much does he spend in pounds in the whole school year of 200 days?

5. An athlete runs 25 laps of a track in 30 minutes 10 seconds.
(a) How many seconds does he take to run 25 laps?
(b) How long does he take to run one lap, if he runs the 25 laps at a constant speed?

6. A pile of 250 tiles is 2 m thick. What is the thickness of one tile in cm?

7. Work out.
(a) 20% of £65
(b) 37% of £400
(c) 8·5% of £2000.

8. In a test, the marks of nine pupils were 7, 5, 2, 7, 4, 9, 7, 6, 6. Find:
(a) the mean mark
(b) the median mark
(c) the modal mark.

9. Work out.
(a) $-6-5$ (b) $-7+30$
(c) $-13+3$ (d) -4×5
(e) -3×-2 (f) $-4+-10$

10. Given $a=3$, $b=-2$ and $c=5$, work out:
(a) $b+c$ (b) $a-b$
(c) ab (d) $a+bc$

11. Solve the equations.
(a) $x-6=3$ (b) $x+9=20$
(c) $x-5=-2$ (d) $3x+1=22$

12. Which of the nets below can be used to make a cube?

(a)
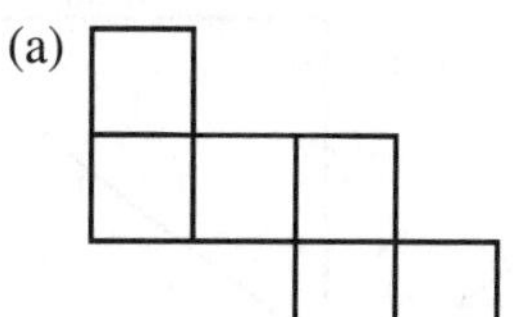

(b)
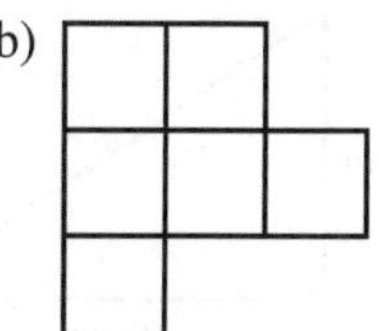

(c)
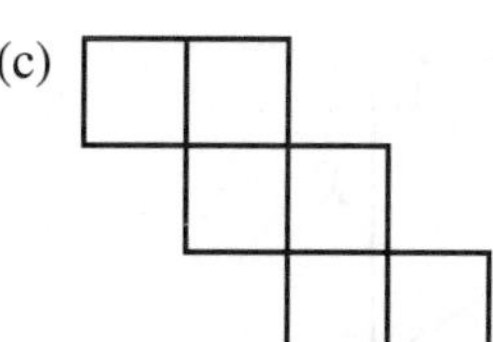

13.

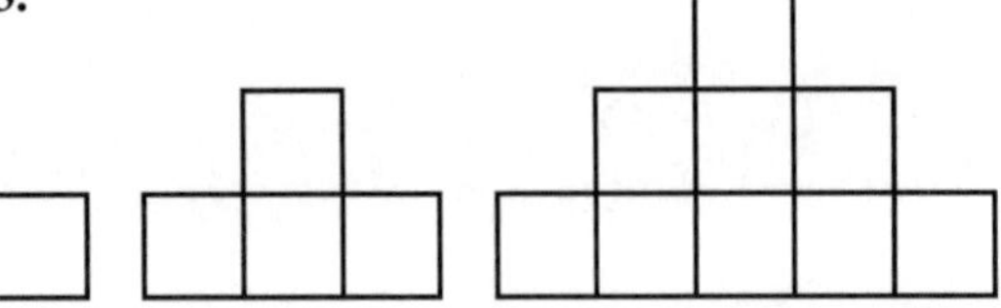

(a) Draw the next diagram in this sequence.
(b) Write down the number of squares in each diagram.
(c) Describe in words the sequence you obtain in part (b).
(d) How many squares will there be in the diagram which has 13 squares on the base?

14. *Estimate* the area of this shape correct to 1 s.f. (take $\pi = 3$).

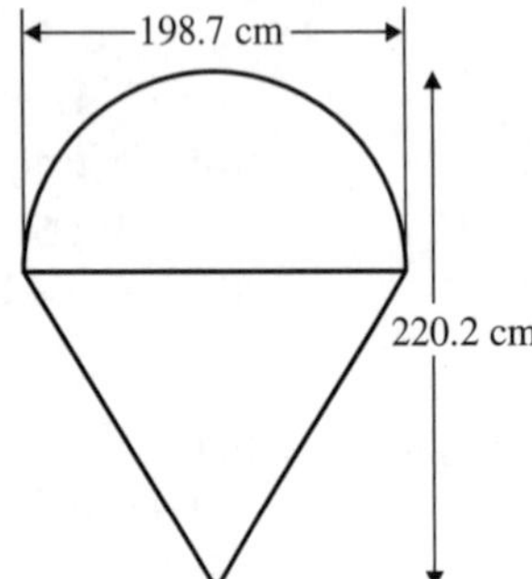

Exercise 2

1. Solve the equations.
(a) $3x - 1 = 20$ (b) $4x + 3 = 4$
(c) $5x - 7 = -3$

2. Copy the diagrams and then calculate x, correct to 3 s.f.

(a)

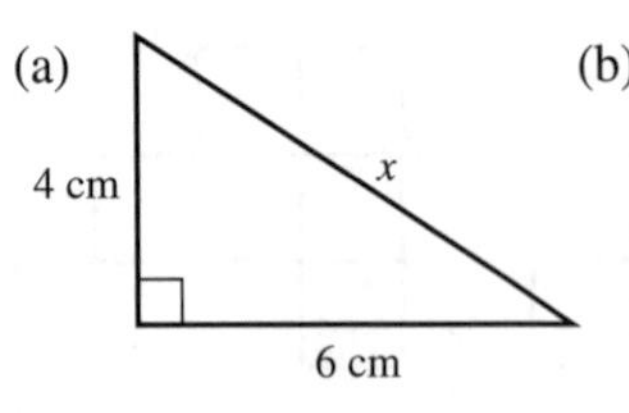

(b)

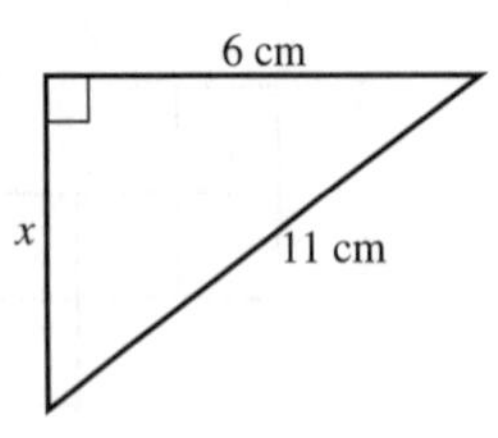

(c)

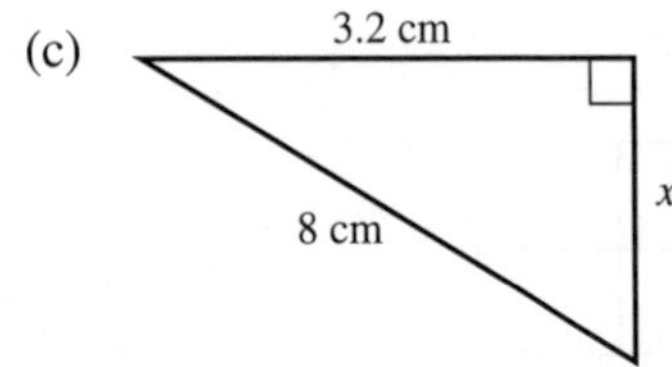

3. A bag contains 3 red balls and 5 white balls. Find the probability of selecting:
(a) a red ball
(b) a white ball.

4. A box contains 2 yellow discs, 4 blue discs and 5 green discs. Find the probability of selecting:
(a) a yellow disc
(b) a green disc
(c) a blue or a green disc.

5. A school decides to have a disco from 8 p.m. to midnight. The price of the tickets will be 20p. The costs are as follows:

Disco and D.J., £25
Hire of hall, £5 an hour
200 cans of soft drinks at 15p each
200 packets of crisps at 10p each
Printing of tickets, £5

(i) What is the total cost of putting on the disco?
(ii) How many tickets must be sold to cover the cost?
(iii) If 400 tickets are sold, all the drinks are sold at 20p each and all the packets of crisps at 12p each, calculate the profit or loss the school finally makes.

6. Work out on a calculator, correct to 4 s.f.
(a) $3{\cdot}61 - (1{\cdot}6 \times 0{\cdot}951)$
(b) $\dfrac{(4{\cdot}65 + 1{\cdot}09)}{(3{\cdot}6 - 1{\cdot}714)}$

7. Find the area, correct to 3 s.f.

(a)

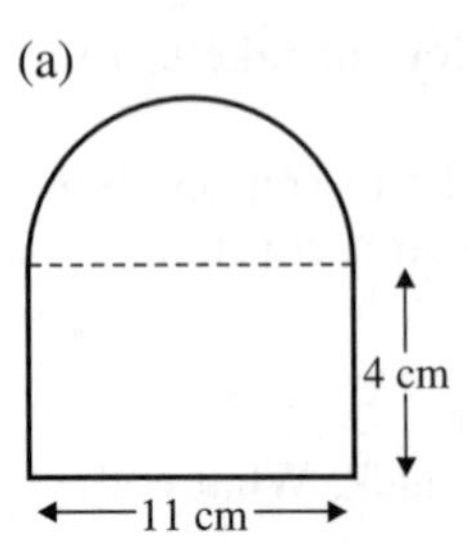

(b)

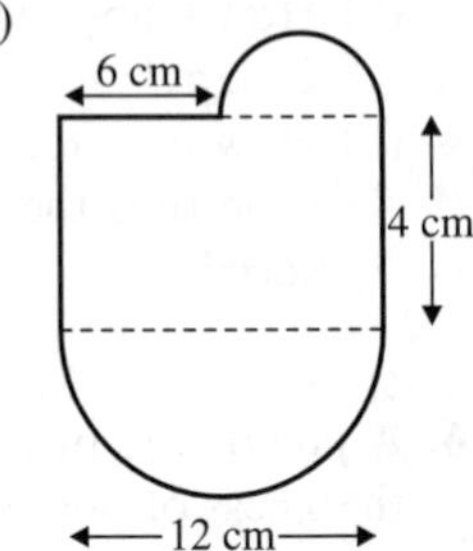

8. Look at the diagram below.

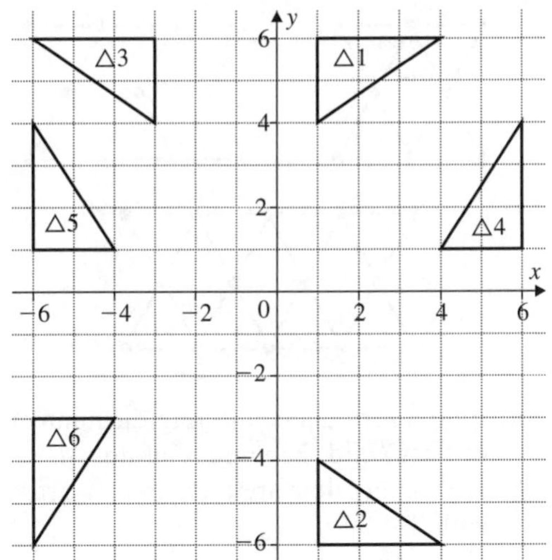

Describe fully the following transformations.
(a) △1 → △2
(b) △1 → △3
(c) △1 → △4
(d) △5 → △1
(e) △5 → △6
(f) △4 → △6

9. Plot and label the following triangles.
△1: (−3, −6), (−3, −2), (−5, −2)
△2: (−5, −1), (−5, −7), (−8, −1)
△3: (−2, −1), (2, −1), (2, 1)
△4: (6, 3), (2, 3), (2, 5)
△5: (8, 4), (8, 8), (6, 8)
△6: (−3, 1), (−3, 3), (−4, 3)

Describe fully the following transformations.
(a) △1 → △2
(b) △1 → △3
(c) △1 → △4
(d) △1 → △5
(e) △1 → △6
(f) △3 → △5
(g) △6 → △2

10. A train travels between Watford and Coventry, a distance of 108 km, in 45 minutes, at a steady speed. It passes through Rugby 40 minutes after leaving Watford. How far, in km, is it from Rugby to Coventry?

Exercise 3

1. The tables show the rail fares for adults and part of a British Rail timetable for trains between Cambridge and Bury St. Edmunds.

Fares for *one* adult

Cambridge				
£1·00	Dullingham			
£1·20	40p	Newmarket		
£1·30	£1·00	60p	Kennett	
£2·00	£1·30	£1·20	80p	Bury St. Edmunds

Train times

Cambridge	11 20
Dullingham	11 37
Newmarket	11 43
Kennett	11 52
Bury St. Edmunds	12 06

(a) How much would it cost for four adults to travel from Dullingham to Bury St. Edmunds?
(b) How long does this journey take?

2. The sketch of a clock tower is shown.

A model of the tower is made using a scale of 1 to 20.
(a) The minute hand on the tower clock is 40 cm long. What is the length of the minute hand on the model?
(b) The height of the model is 40 cm. What is the height h, in metres, of the clock tower?

3. Look at the number pattern below.

$(2 \times 1) - 1 = 2 - 1$
$(3 \times 3) - 2 = 8 - 1$
$(4 \times 5) - 3 = 18 - 1$
$(5 \times 7) - 4 = 32 - 1$
$(6 \times a) - 5 = b - 1$

(i) What number does the letter a stand for?
(ii) What number does the letter b stand for?
(iii) Write down the next line in the pattern.

4. (a) Plot and label:
$\triangle 1$: $(-3, 4)$, $(-3, 8)$, $(-1, 8)$
$\triangle 5$: $(-8, -2)$, $(-8, -6)$, $(-6, -2)$

(b) Draw the triangles $\triangle 2$, $\triangle 3$, $\triangle 4$, $\triangle 6$ and $\triangle 7$ as follows.

(i) $\triangle 1 \rightarrow \triangle 2$: translation $\begin{pmatrix} 9 \\ -4 \end{pmatrix}$.

(ii) $\triangle 2 \rightarrow \triangle 3$: translation $\begin{pmatrix} -4 \\ -8 \end{pmatrix}$.

(iii) $\triangle 3 \rightarrow \triangle 4$: reflection in the line $y = x$.

(iv) $\triangle 5 \rightarrow \triangle 6$: rotation 90° anticlockwise, centre $(-4, -1)$.

(v) $\triangle 6 \rightarrow \triangle 7$: rotation 180°, centre $(0, -1)$.

(c) Write down the coordinates of the 'pointed ends' of triangles $\triangle 2$, $\triangle 3$, $\triangle 4$, $\triangle 6$, and $\triangle 7$.

5. The faces of a round and square clock are exactly the same area. If the round clock has a radius of 10 cm, how wide is the square clock?

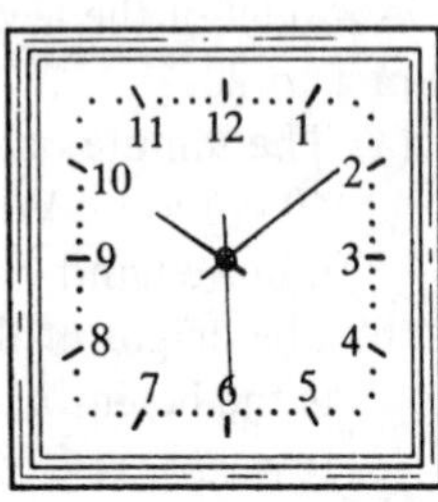

6. Here are three diagrams with lines and dots.

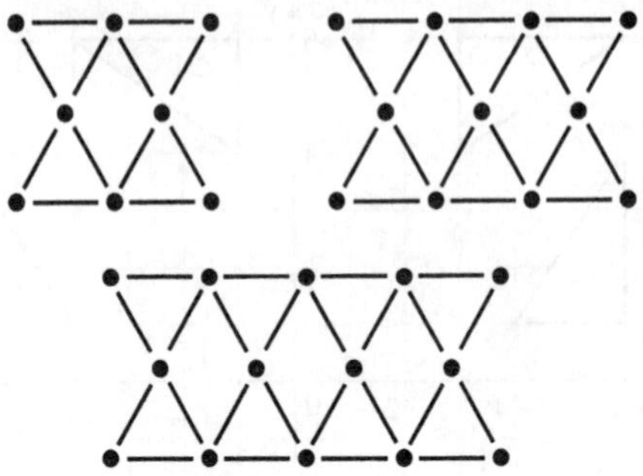

(a) Find a formula connecting the number of lines l and the number of dots d.
(b) How many dots are there in a diagram with 294 lines?

7. A factory cafeteria contains a vending machine which sells drinks. On a typical day:

the machine starts half full
no drinks are sold before 9 a.m. and after 5 p.m.
drinks are sold at a slow rate throughout the day, except during the morning and lunch breaks (10.30–11 a.m. and 1–2 p.m.) when there is a greater demand
the machine is filled up just before the lunch break. (It takes about 10 minutes to fill.)

Sketch a graph showing how the number of drinks in the machine may vary from 8 a.m. to 6 p.m.

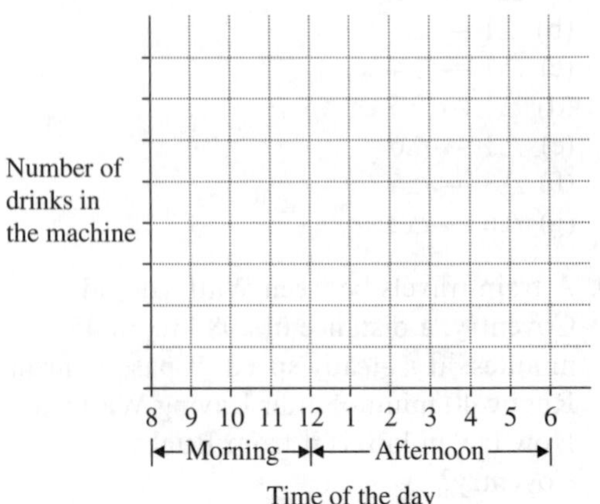

8. A metal ingot is in the form of a solid cylinder of length 7 cm and radius 3 cm.
   (a) Calculate the volume, in cm^3, of the ingot.

   The ingot is to be melted down and used to make cylindrical coins of thickness 3 mm and radius 12 mm.
   (b) Calculate the volume, in mm^3, of each coin.
   (c) Calculate the number of coins which can be made from the ingot, assuming that there is no wastage of metal.

Exercise 4

1. In December 1999, a factory employed 220 men, each man being paid £130 per week.
   (a) Calculate the total weekly wage bill for the factory.
   (b) In January 2000, the work force of 220 was reduced by 10 per cent. Find the number of men employed at the factory after the reduction.
   (c) Also in January 2000, the weekly wage of £130 was increased by 10 per cent. Find the new weekly wage.
   (d) Calculate the total weekly wage bill for the factory in January 2000.
   (e) Calculate the difference between the total weekly wage bills in December 1999 and January 2000.

2. A motorist travelled 800 miles during May, when the cost of petrol was 50 pence per litre. In June the cost of petrol increased by 10% and he reduced his mileage for the month by 5%.
   (a) What was the cost, in pence per litre, of petrol in June?
   (b) How many miles did he travel in June?

3. $1 + 3 = 2^2$. $\quad 1 + 3 + 5 = 3^2$.
   (a) $1 + 3 + 5 + 7 = x^2$. Calculate x.
   (b) $1 + 3 + 5 + \ldots + n = 100$. Calculate n.

4. The distance-time graphs for several objects are shown. Decide which line represents each of the following.
   - hovercraft from Dover
   - car ferry from Dover
   - cross-channel swimmer
   - marker buoy outside harbour
   - train from Dover
   - car ferry from Calais

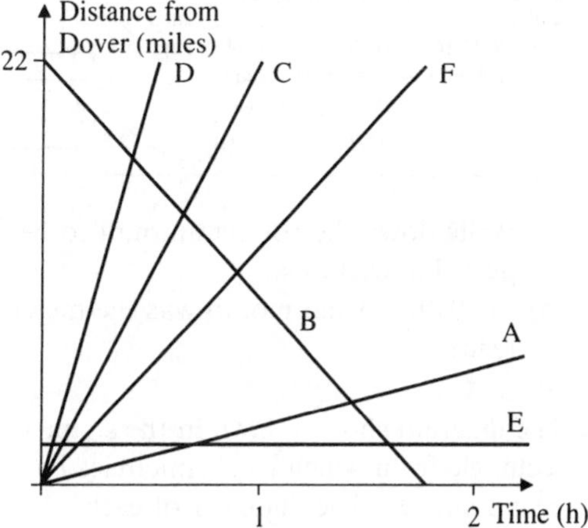

5. The mean mass of 10 boys in a class is 56 kg.
   (a) Calculate the total mass of these 10 boys.
   (b) Another boy, whose mass is 67 kg, joins the group. Calculate the mean mass of the 11 boys.

6. Two girls walk at the same speed from A to B. Aruni takes the large semicircle and Deepa takes the three small semicircles. Who arrives at B first?

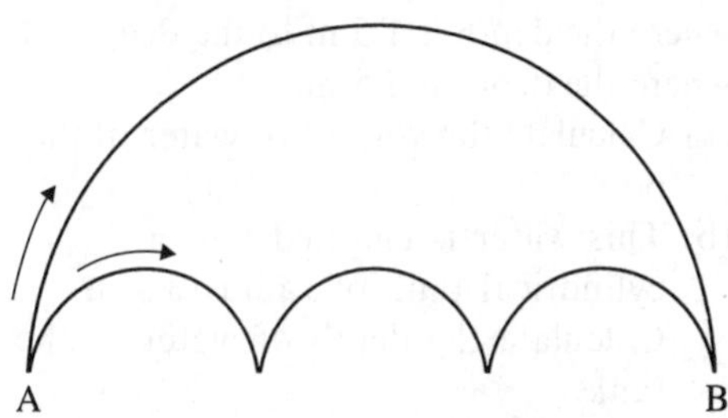

7. This electricity bill is not complete.

NEA

Northern Electricity Authority
P.O. Box 6984
Manchester M49 2QQ

Tel: 061 555 2718

Customer:
G.J. Spinner
21 Silk Street
Macclesfield SK27 3BJ

Ref: 0248-6879-5

METER READING on 07-11-99	26819 units	
METER READING on 04-02-00	[ ] units	
ELECTRICITY USED	1455 units	
1455 units at 5·44 pence per unit		£ [ ]
Quarterly charge		£ 6·27
TOTAL (now due)		£ [ ]

(a) Write down the correct amount to be placed in each box.
(b) In 1999, in what month was the meter read?

8. The diagram shows a lawn in the shape of a rectangle from which two semicircles have been removed. The diameter of each semicircle is 7 metres.

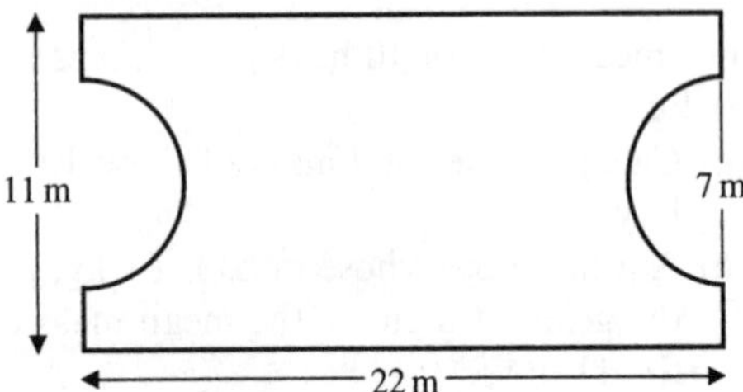

Taking π as $\frac{22}{7}$, calculate, in metres, the perimeter of the lawn.

9. A swimming pool is of width 10 m and length 25 m. The depth of water in the pool increases uniformly from the shallow end, where the depth is 1·5 m to the deep end, where the depth is 2·5 m.
(a) Calculate the volume of water in the pool.
(b) This water is emptied into a cylindrical tank of radius 3·5 m. Calculate the depth of water in the tank.

10. The following are the first six numbers, written in order of size, of a pattern.
4, 13, 28, 49, 76, 109
(a) Which of these numbers are:
 (i) odd numbers
 (ii) square numbers
 (iii) prime numbers?
(b) The difference between the first and second numbers, that is $13-4$, is 9; between the second and the third it is 15, between the third and the fourth it is 21. Work out the difference between:
 (i) the fourth and the fifth
 (ii) the fifth and the sixth.
(c) By considering your answers in (b), find the seventh and eighth numbers of the pattern.
Explain how you reached this decision.
(d) Use the method you have described to write down the next two terms in the following pattern.
1, 4, 12, 25, 43, 66, —, —

Exercise 5

1. $a=\frac{1}{2}$, $b=\frac{1}{4}$. Which one of the following has the greatest value?
(i) ab (ii) $a+b$ (iii) $\frac{a}{b}$
(iv) $\frac{b}{a}$ (v) $(ab)^2$

2. Solve the simultaneous equations.
(a) $7c+3d=29$
$5c-4d=33$
(b) $2x-3y=7$
$3x-2y=8$

3. Calculate the side or angle marked with a letter.

(a)
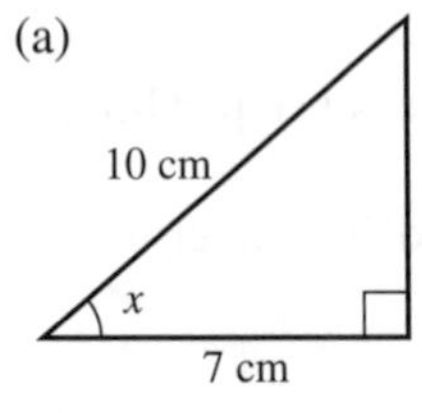

(b)
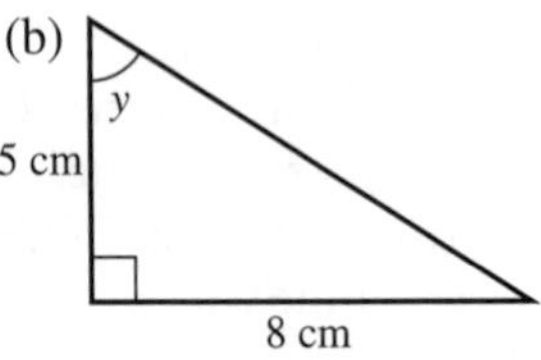

(c)
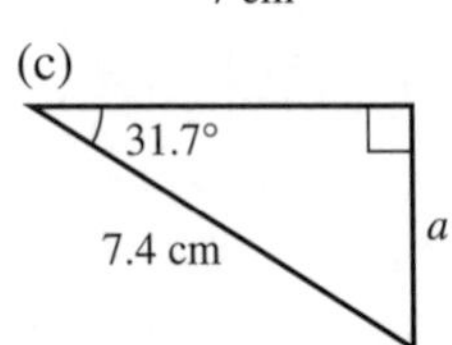

(d)
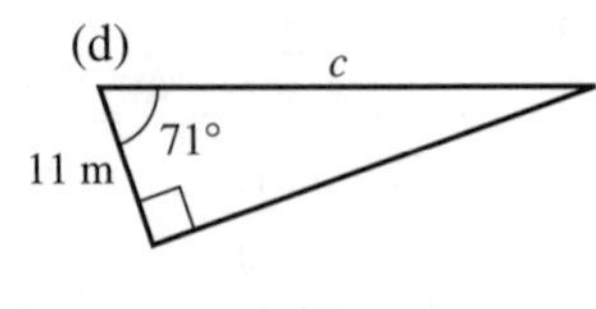

4. (a) Calculate the speed (in metres per second) of a slug which moves a distance of 300 cm in 1 minute.
   (b) Calculate the time taken for a bullet to travel 8 km at a speed of 5000 m/s.
   (c) Calculate the distance flown, in a time of four hours, by a pigeon which flies at a speed of 12 m/s.

5. Given $a = 3$, $b = 4$ and $c = -2$, evaluate:
   (a) $2a^2 - b$ (b) $a(b - c)$
   (c) $2b^2 - c^2$

6. When two dice are thrown simultaneously, what is the probability of obtaining the same number on both dice?

7. In Figure 1 a circle of radius 4 cm is inscribed in a square. In Figure 2 a square is inscribed in a circle of radius 4 cm. Calculate the shaded area in each diagram.

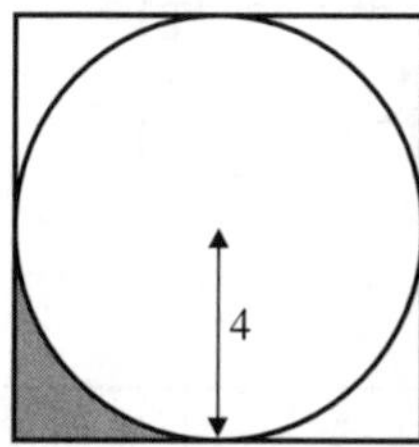

Fig. 1

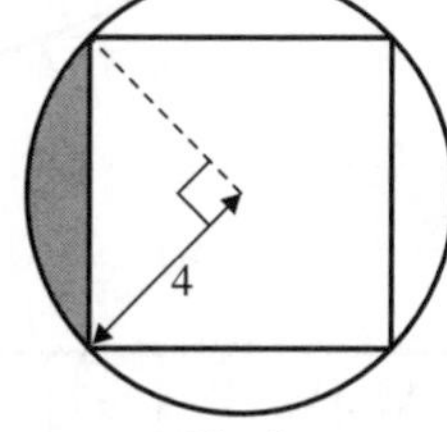

Fig. 2

8. (a) A lies on a bearing of 040° from B. Calculate the bearing of B from A.
   (b) The bearing of X from Y is 115°. Calculate the bearing of Y from X.

9. In the diagram, the equations of the lines are $y = 3x$, $y = 6$, $y = 10 - x$ and $y = \frac{1}{2}x - 3$.

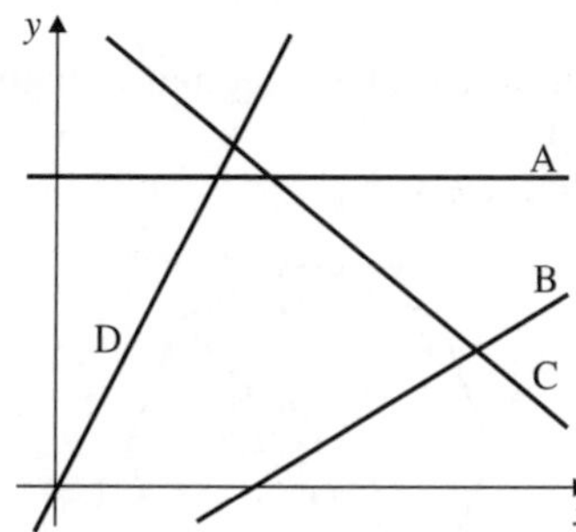

Find the equation corresponding to each line.

10. Given that $s - 3t = rt$, express:
    (a) s in terms of r and t
    (b) r in terms of s and t.

11. Find x.

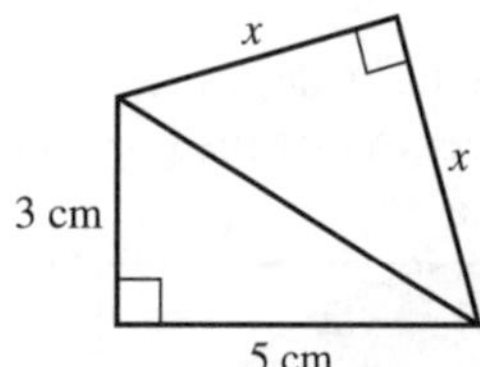

12. A cylinder of radius 8 cm has a volume of 2 litres. Calculate the height of the cylinder.

13. The shaded region A is formed by the lines $y = 2$, $y = 3x$ and $x + y = 6$. Write down the three inequalities which define A.

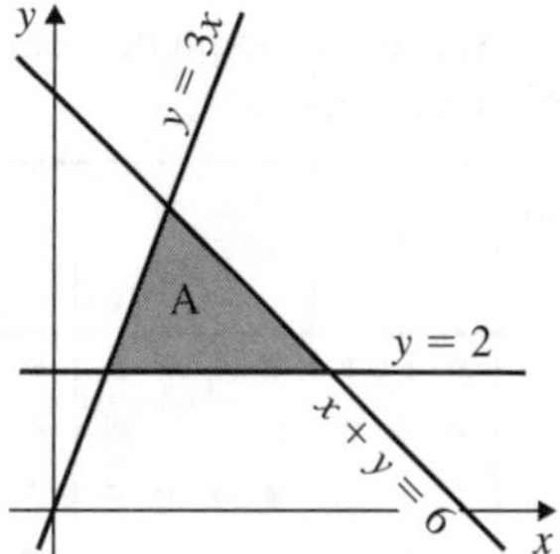

Exercise 6

1. The pump shows the price of petrol in a garage.

One day I buy £20 worth of petrol. How many litres do I buy?

2. Given that $x = 4$, $y = 3$, $z = -2$, evaluate:
   (a) $2x(y + z)$ (b) $(xy)^2 - z^2$
   (c) $x^2 + y^2 + z^2$ (d) $(x + y)(x - z)$

3. Twenty-seven small wooden cubes fit exactly inside a cubical box without a lid. How many of the cubes are touching the sides or the bottom of the box?

4. The square has sides of length 3 cm and the arcs have centres at the corners. Find the shaded area.

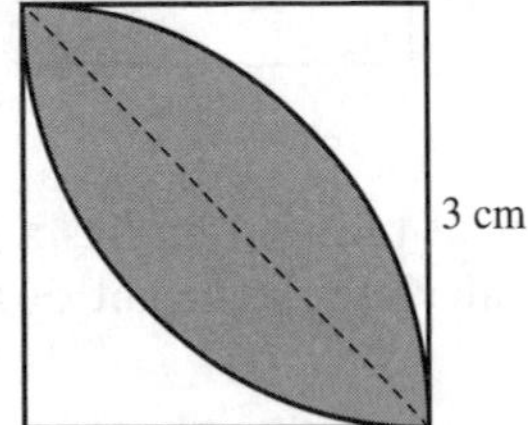

5. A coin is tossed four times. What is the probability of obtaining at least three 'heads'?

6. Each diagram in the sequence below consists of a number of dots.

Diagram number	1	2	3
	● ● ● ● ● ●	● ● ● ● ● ● ● ● ● ●	● ● ● ● ● ● ● ● ● ● ● ● ● ●

(a) Draw diagram number 4, diagram number 5 and diagram number 6.
(b) Copy and complete the table below.

Diagram number	Number of dots
1	6
2	10
3	
4	
5	
6	

(c) Without drawing the diagrams, state the number of dots in:
 (i) diagram number 10
 (ii) diagram number 15.
(d) If we write x for the diagram number and n for the number of dots, write down a formula involving x and n.

7. (a) On a map, the distance between two points is 16 cm. Calculate the scale of the map if the actual distance between the points is 8 km.
(b) On another map, two points appear 1·5 cm apart and are in fact 60 km apart. Calculate the scale of the map.

8. Write down each statement and make corrections where necessary.
(a) $t + t + t = t^3$
(b) $a^2 \times a^2 = 2a^2$
(c) $2n \times n = 2n^2$

9. Calculate the length of AB.

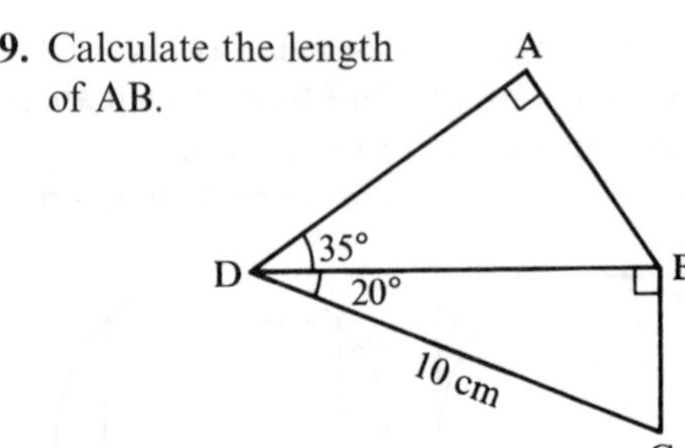

10.

Marks	3	4	5	6	7	8
Number of pupils	2	3	6	4	3	2

The table shows the number of pupils in a class who scored marks 3 to 8 in a test. Find:
(a) the mean mark
(b) the modal mark
(c) the median mark.

11. The diagram shows a regular octagon with centre O.
Find angles a and b.

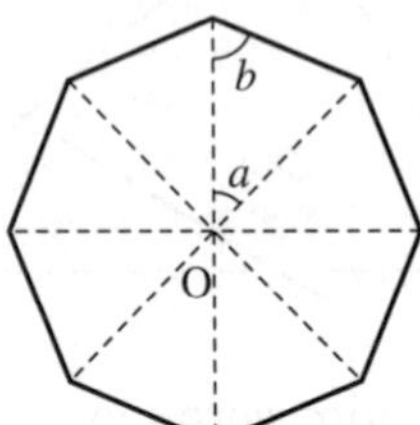

12. (a) Given that $x - z = 5y$, express z in terms of x and y.
(b) Given that $mk + 3m = 11$, express k in terms of m.
(c) For the formula $T = C\sqrt{z}$, express z in terms of T and C.

Exercise 7

1. The mass of the planet Jupiter is about 350 times the mass of the Earth. The mass of the earth is approximately $6{\cdot}03 \times 10^{21}$ tonnes. Give an estimate correct to 2 significant figures for the mass of Jupiter.

2. This graph shows a car journey from Gateshead to Middlesbrough and back again.

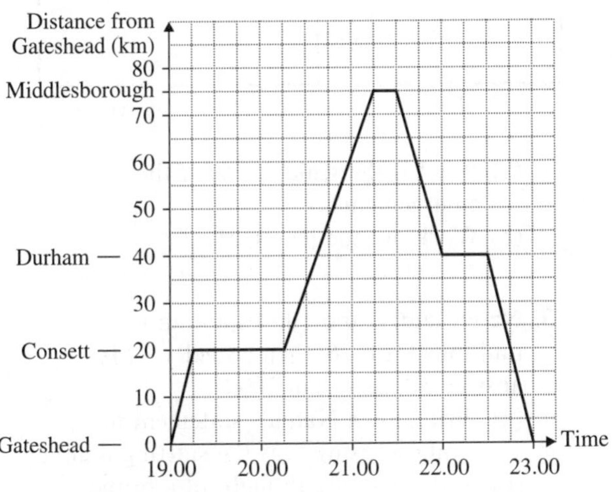

(a) Where is the car:
  (i) at 19.15 h
  (ii) at 22.15 h
  (iii) at 22.45 h?
(b) How far is it:
  (i) from Consett to Middlesbrough
  (ii) from Durham to Gateshead?
(c) At what speed does the car travel:
  (i) from Gateshead to Consett
  (ii) from Consett to Middlesbrough
  (iii) from Middlesbrough to Durham
  (iv) from Durham to Gateshead?
(d) For how long is the car stationary during the journey?

3. Work out the difference between one ton and one tonne.

1 tonne	=	1000 kg
1 ton	=	2240 lb
1 lb	=	454 g

Give your answer to the nearest kg.

4. A motorist travelled 200 miles in five hours. Her average speed for the first 100 miles was 50 m.p.h. What was her average speed for the second 100 miles?

5. Evaluate the following and give the answers to 3 significant figures.

(a) $\sqrt[3]{(9{\cdot}61 \times 0{\cdot}0041)}$

(b) $\left(\frac{1}{9{\cdot}5} - \frac{1}{11{\cdot}2}\right)^3$

(c) $\frac{15{\cdot}6 \times 0{\cdot}714}{0{\cdot}0143 \times 12}$ (d) $\sqrt[4]{\left(\frac{1}{5 \times 10^3}\right)}$

6. Throughout his life Mr Cram's heart has beat at an average rate of 72 beats per minute. Mr Cram is sixty years old. How many times has his heart beat during his life? Give the answer in standard form correct to two significant figures.

7. Two dice are thrown. What is the probability that the *product* of the numbers on top is:
(a) 12 (b) 4 (c) 11?

8. The shaded region B is formed by the lines $x = 0$, $y = x - 2$ and $x + y = 7$.

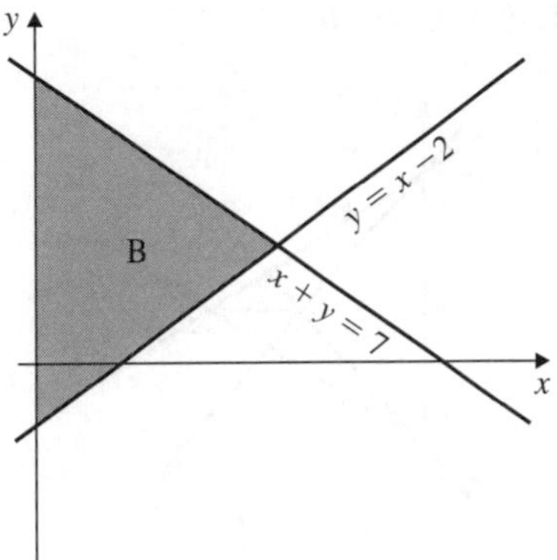

Write down the three inequalities which define B.

9. Estimate the answer correct to one significant figure. Do not use a calculator.
   (a) $(612 \times 52) \div 49{\cdot}2$
   (b) $(11{\cdot}7 + 997{\cdot}1) \times 9{\cdot}2$
   (c) $\sqrt{\left(\frac{91{\cdot}3}{10{\cdot}1}\right)}$
   (d) $\pi\sqrt{(5{\cdot}2^2 + 18{\cdot}2^2)}$

10. In the quadrilateral PQRS, PQ = QS = QR, PS is parallel to QR and $Q\hat{R}S = 70°$. Calculate:
    (a) $R\hat{Q}S$
    (b) $P\hat{Q}S$.

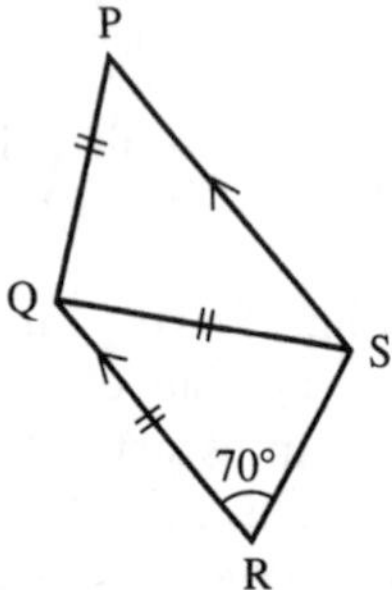

11. A bag contains x green discs and 5 blue discs. A disc is selected. Find, in terms of x, the probability of selecting a green disc.

12. In the diagram, the equations of the lines are $2y = x - 8$, $2y + x = 8$, $4y = 3x - 16$ and $4y + 3x = 16$.

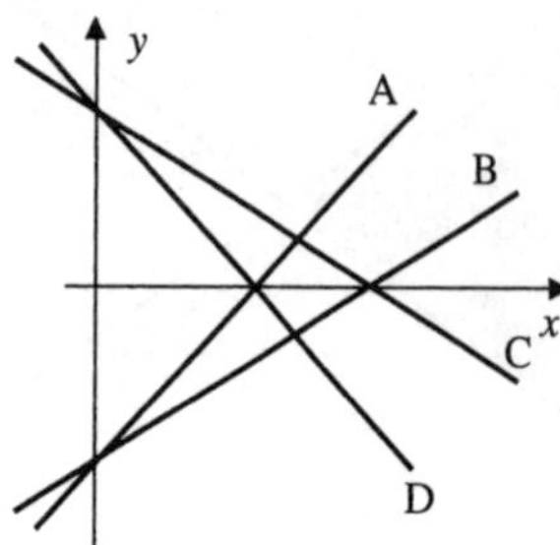

Find the equation corresponding to each line.

Exercise 8

1. Sainsburys sell their 'own-label' raspberry jam in two sizes.

Which jar represents the better value for money? You are given that 1 kg = 2·20 lb.

2. A photo 21 cm by 12 cm is enlarged as shown.

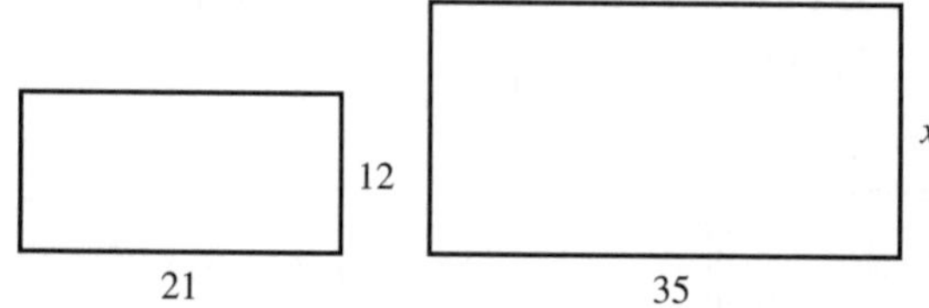

   (a) What is the scale factor of the enlargement?
   (b) Work out the length x.

3. Nadia said: 'I thought of a number, multiplied it by 6, then added 15. My answer was less than 200.'
   (a) Write down Nadia's statement in symbols, using x as the starting number.
   (b) Nadia actually thought of a prime number. What was the largest prime number she could have thought of?

4. Find the area shaded. All lengths are in cm.

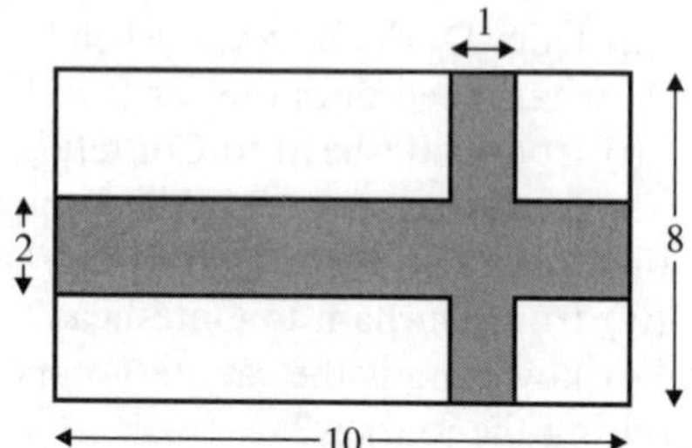

5. Solve the quadratic equations.
   (a) $x^2 + 8x + 7 = 0$
   (b) $x^2 + 8x + 15 = 0$
   (c) $x^2 + 2x - 8 = 0$

6. Point B is on a bearing 120° from point A. The distance from A to B is 110 km.

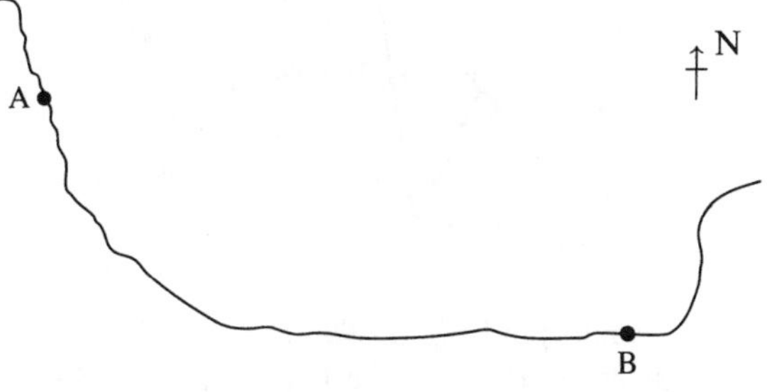

   (a) Draw a diagram showing the positions of A and B. Use a scale of 1 cm to 10 km.
   (b) Ship S is on a bearing 072° from A. Ship S is on a bearing 325° from B. Show S on your diagram and state the distance from S to B.

7. A regular octagon of side length 20 cm is to be cut out of a square card.

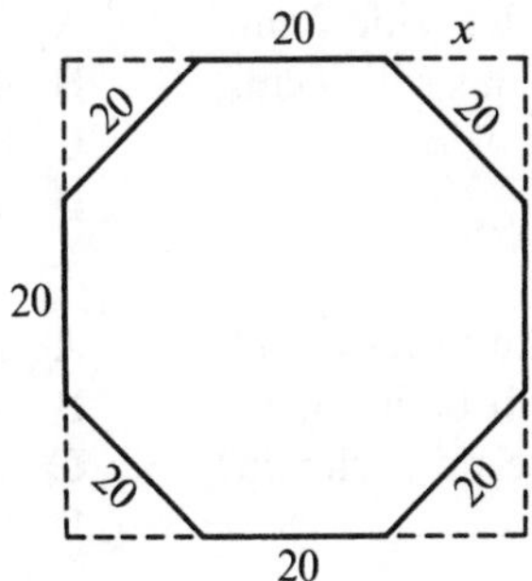

   (a) Find the length x and hence find the size of the smallest square card from which this octagon can be cut.
   (b) Calculate the area of the octagon, correct to 3 s.f.

8. Evaluate the following using a calculator (answers to 4 sig. fig.).
   (a) $\dfrac{0{\cdot}74}{0{\cdot}81 \times 1{\cdot}631}$ (b) $\sqrt{\left(\dfrac{9{\cdot}61}{8{\cdot}34 - 7{\cdot}41}\right)}$
   (c) $\left(\dfrac{0{\cdot}741}{0{\cdot}8364}\right)^4$ (d) $\dfrac{8{\cdot}4 - 7{\cdot}642}{3{\cdot}333 - 1{\cdot}735}$

9. The mean of four numbers is 21.
   (a) Calculate the sum of the four numbers.
   Six other numbers have a mean of 18.
   (b) Calculate the mean of the ten numbers.

10. Given BD = 1 m, calculate the length AC.

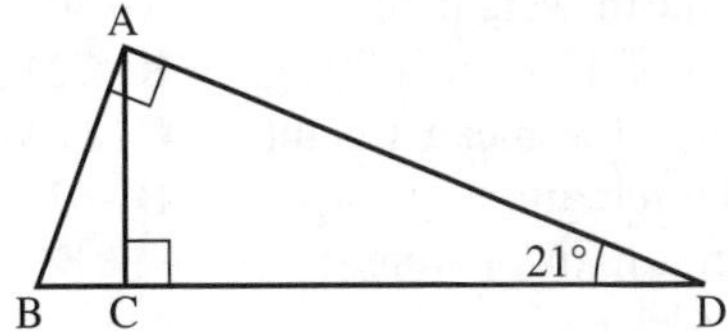

11. Use the method of trial and improvement to find a solution of the equation $x^5 = x^3 + 1$, giving your answer correct to 2 decimal places.

12. Given that $y = \dfrac{k}{k + w}$:
   (a) Find the value of y when $k = \frac{1}{2}$ and $w = \frac{1}{3}$.
   (b) Express w in terms of y and k.

12.2 Multiple choice tests

Test 1

1. How many mm are there in 1 m 1 cm?
   A 1001
   B 1110
   C 1010
   D 1100

2. If $x = 3$, then $x^2 - 2x = ?$
   A 3
   B 4
   C 0
   D 5

3. In the triangle below the value of cos x is:

A 0·8
B 1·333
C 0·75
D 0·6

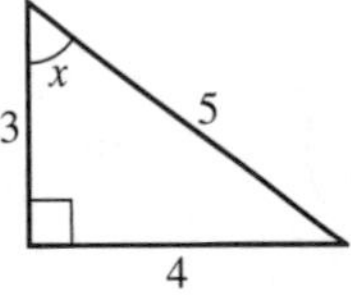

4. The gradient of the line $y = 2x - 1$ is:

A 2
B -1
C $\frac{1}{2}$
D -2

5. The mean weight of a group of 11 men is 70 kg. What is the mean weight of the remaining group when a man of weight 90 kg leaves?

A 80 kg
B 72 kg
C 68 kg
D 62 kg

6. A, B, C and D are points on the sides of a rectangle. Find the area in cm^2 of quadrilateral ABCD.

A $27\frac{1}{2}$
B 28
C $28\frac{1}{2}$
D cannot be found

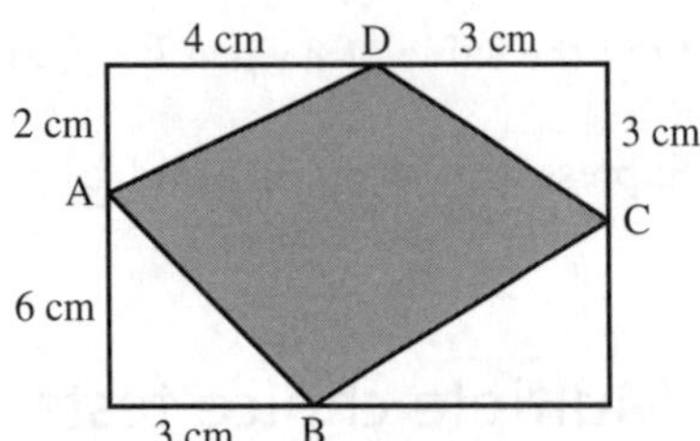

7. The formula $\frac{x}{a} + b = c$ is rearranged to make x the subject. What is x?

A $a(c - b)$
B $ac - b$
C $\frac{c - b}{a}$
D $ac + ab$

8. In standard form the value of 2000 × 80 000 is:

A 16×10^6
B $1{\cdot}6 \times 10^9$
C $1{\cdot}6 \times 10^7$
D $1{\cdot}6 \times 10^8$

9. The sum of the lengths of the edges of a cube is 36 cm. The volume, in cm^3, of the cube is:

A 36
B 27
C 64
D 48

10. In the triangle the size of angle x is:

A 35°
B 70°
C 110°
D 40°

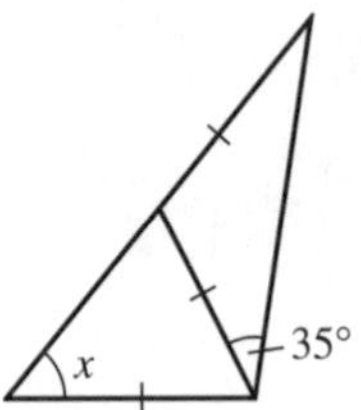

11. A man paid tax on £9000 at 30%. He paid the tax in 12 equal payments. Each payment was:

A £2·25
B £22·50
C £225
D £250

12. The approximate value of $\frac{3{\cdot}96 \times (0{\cdot}5)^2}{97{\cdot}1}$ is:

A 0·01
B 0·02
C 0·04
D 0·1

13. Given that $\frac{3}{n} = 5$, then $n = ?$

A 2
B -2
C $1\frac{2}{3}$
D 0·6

14. Cube A has side 2 cm. Cube B has side 4 cm. $\frac{\text{Volume of B}}{\text{Volume of A}} =$

A 2
B 4
C 8
D 16

15. How many tiles of side 50 cm will be needed to cover the floor shown?

A 16
B 32
C 64
D 84

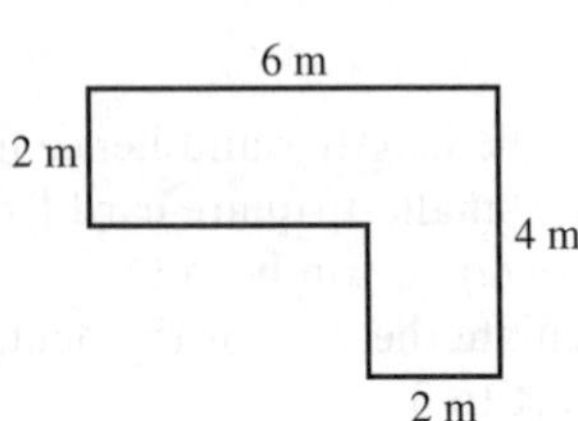

16. The equation $ax^2 + x - 6 = 0$ has a solution $x = -2$. What is a?

A 1
B -2
C $\sqrt{2}$
D 2

17. Which of the following is/are correct?
1. $\sqrt{0{\cdot}16} = 0{\cdot}4$
2. $0{\cdot}2 \div 0{\cdot}1 = 0{\cdot}2$
3. $\frac{4}{7} > \frac{3}{5}$

A **1** only
B **2** only
C **3** only
D **1** and **2**

18. How many prime numbers are there between 30 and 40?

A 0
B 1
C 2
D 3

19. A man is paid £180 per week after a pay rise of 20%. What was he paid before?

A £144
B £150
C £160
D £164

20. A car travels for 20 minutes at 45 m.p.h. How far does the car travel?

A 900 miles
B $2\frac{1}{4}$ miles
C 9 miles
D 15 miles

21. The point $(3, -1)$ is reflected in the line $y = 2$. The new coordinates are:

A $(3, 5)$
B $(1, -1)$
C $(3, 4)$
D $(0, -1)$

22. Given the equation $5^x = 120$, the best approximate solution is $x = ?$

A 2
B 3
C 4
D 22

23. The rectangle ABCD is cut out of paper and the edges AB and DC are joined to make a cylinder. The radius of the cylinder in cm is:

A 6
B 7
C $\frac{6}{\pi}$
D $\frac{12}{\pi}$

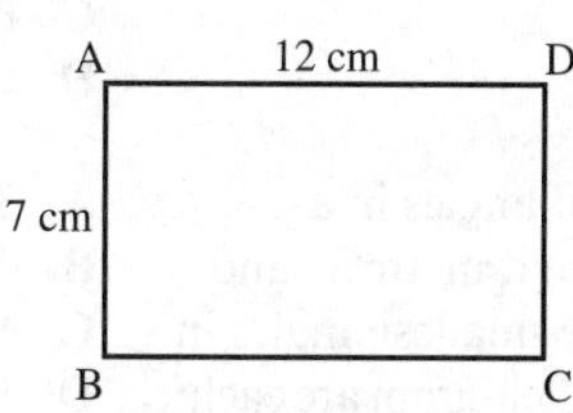

24. The shaded area in cm^2 is:

A $16 - 2\pi$
B $16 - 4\pi$
C $\frac{4}{\pi}$
D $64 - 8\pi$

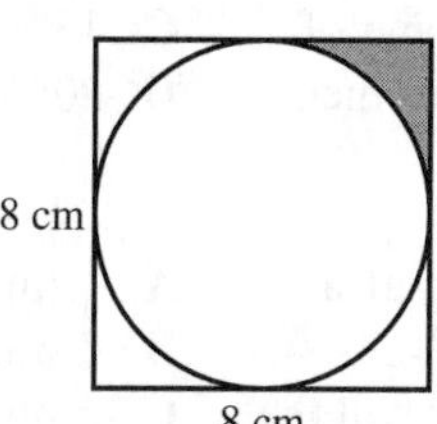

25. What is the sine of 45°?

A 1
B $\frac{1}{2}$
C $\frac{1}{\sqrt{2}}$
D $\sqrt{2}$

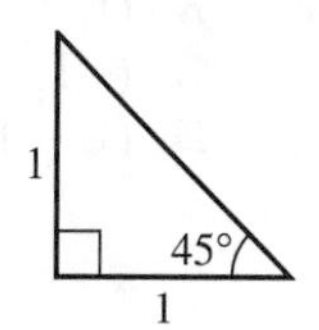

Test 2

1. What is the value of the expression $(x - 2)(x + 4)$ when $x = -1$?

A 9
B -9
C 5
D -5

2. The perimeter of a square is 36 cm. What is its area?

A 36 cm^2
B 324 cm^2
C 81 cm^2
D 9 cm^2

3. The gradient of the line $2x + y = 3$ is:

A 3
B -2
C $\frac{1}{2}$
D $-\frac{1}{2}$

4. The shape consists of four semi-circles placed round a square of side 2 m. The area of the shape, in m^2, is:

A $2\pi + 4$
B $2\pi + 2$
C $4\pi + 4$
D $\pi + 4$

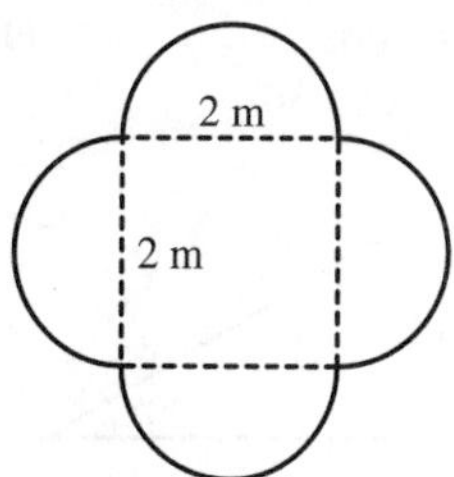

5. A firm employs 1200 people, of whom 240 are men. The percentage of employees who are men is:

A 40%
B 10%
C 15%
D 20%

6. A car is travelling at a constant speed of 30 m.p.h. How far will the car travel in 10 minutes?

A $\frac{1}{3}$ mile
B 3 miles
C 5 miles
D 6 miles

7. What are the coordinates of the point (1, −1) after reflection in the line $y = x$?

A (−1, 1)
B (1, 1)
C (−1, −1)
D (1, −1)

8. $\frac{1}{3} + \frac{2}{5} = ?$

[no calculators!]

A $\frac{2}{8}$
B $\frac{3}{8}$
C $\frac{3}{15}$
D $\frac{11}{15}$

9. In the triangle the size of the largest angle is:

A 30°
B 90°
C 120°
D 80°

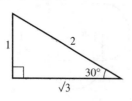

10. 800 decreased by 5% is:

A 795
B 640
C 760
D 400

11. Which of the statements is (are) true?
1. tan 60° = 2
2. sin 60° = cos 30°
3. sin 30° > cos 30°

A 1 only
B 2 only
C 3 only
D 2 and 3

12. Given $a = \frac{3}{5}$, $b = \frac{1}{3}$, $c = \frac{1}{2}$ then:

A $a < b < c$
B $a < c < b$
C $a > b > c$
D $a > c > b$

13. The *larger* angle between South-West and East is:

A 225°
B 240°
C 135°
D 315°

14. In a triangle PQR, $P\hat{Q}R = 50°$ and point X lies on PQ such that QX = XR. Calculate $Q\hat{X}R$.

A 100°
B 50°
C 80°
D 65°

15. What is the value of 1 − 0·05 as a fraction?

A $\frac{1}{20}$
B $\frac{9}{10}$
C $\frac{19}{20}$
D $\frac{5}{100}$

16. Find the length x.

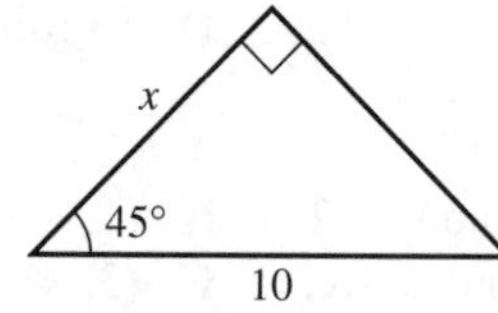

A 5
B 6
C 8
D $\sqrt{50}$

17. Given that $m = 2$ and $n = -3$, what is mn^2?

A −18
B 18
C −36
D 36

18. The graph of $y = (x - 3)(x - 2)$ cuts the y-axis at P. The coordinates of P are:

A (0, 6)
B (6, 0)
C (2, 0)
D (3, 0)

19. £240 is shared in the ratio 2 : 3 : 7. The largest share is:

A £130
B £140
C £150
D £160

20. Adjacent angles in a parallelogram are $x°$ and $3x°$. The smallest angles in the parallelogram are each:

A 30°
B 45°
C 60°
D 120°

21. A square has side 10 cm. When the sides of the square are increased by 10% the area is increased by:

A 10%
B 20%
C 21%
D 15%

22. The volume, in cm^3, of the cylinder is:

A 9π
B 12π
C 600π
D 900π

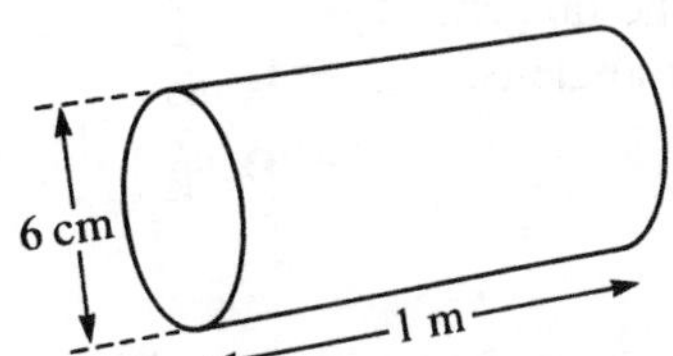

23. $3a + 2a - 7 - a = 21$
The value of a is:

A $3\frac{1}{2}$
B 7
C $4\frac{2}{3}$
D 8

24. Four people each toss a coin. What is the probability that the fourth person will toss a 'tail'?

A $\frac{1}{2}$
B $\frac{1}{4}$
C $\frac{1}{8}$
D $\frac{1}{16}$

25. What is next in the sequence
1, 3, 7, 15?

A 23
B 21
C 31
D 24

Test 3

1. The price of a T.V. changed from £240 to £300. What is the percentage increase?

A 15%
B 20%
C 60%
D 25%

2. Find the length x.

A 6
B 5
C $\sqrt{44}$
D $\sqrt{18}$

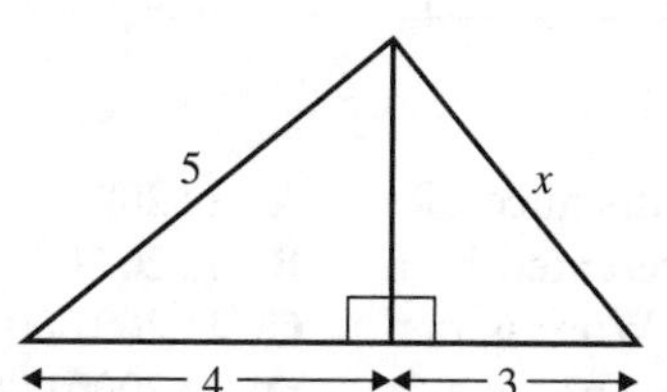

3. The bearing of A from B is 120°. What is the bearing of B from A?

A 060°
B 120°
C 240°
D 300°

4. Numbers m, x and y satisfy the equation $y = mx^2$. When $m = \frac{1}{2}$ and $x = 4$ the value of y is:

A 4
B 8
C 1
D 2

5. A school has 400 pupils, of whom 250 are boys. The ratio of boys to girls is:

A 5:3
B 3:2
C 3:5
D 8:5

6. A train is travelling at a speed of 30 km per hour. How long will it take to travel 500 m?

A 2 minutes
B $\frac{3}{50}$ hour
C 1 minute
D $\frac{1}{2}$ hour

7. The approximate value of $\dfrac{9{\cdot}65 \times 0{\cdot}203}{0{\cdot}0198}$ is:

A 99
B 9·9
C 0·99
D 180

8. Which point does *not* lie on the curve $y = \dfrac{12}{x}$?

A (6, 2)
B $(\frac{1}{2}, 24)$
C (−3, −4)
D (3, −4)

9. $t = \dfrac{c^3}{y}$, $y = ?$

A $\dfrac{t}{c^3}$
B c^3t
C $c^3 - t$
D $\dfrac{c^3}{t}$

10. The largest number of 1 cm cubes which will fit inside a cubical box of side 1 m is:

A 10^3
B 10^6
C 10^8
D 10^{12}

11. I start with x, then square it, multiply by 2 and finally subtract 3. The final result is:

A $(2x)^2 - 3$
B $(2x - 3)^2$
C $2x^2 - 3$
D $2(x - 3)^2$

12. Which of the following has the largest value?

A $\sqrt{100}$
B $\sqrt{\dfrac{1}{0.1}}$
C $\sqrt{1000}$
D $\dfrac{1}{0.01}$

13. Two dice numbered 1 to 6 are thrown together and their scores are added. The probability that the sum will be 12 is:

A $\frac{1}{6}$
B $\frac{1}{12}$
C $\frac{1}{18}$
D $\frac{1}{36}$

14. The length, in cm, of the minor arc is:

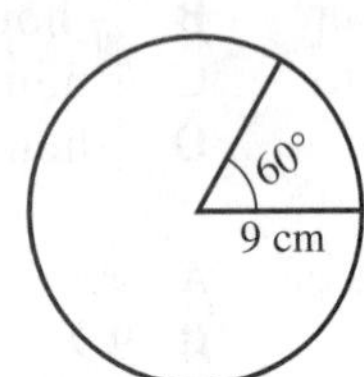

A 2π
B 3π
C 6π
D $13\frac{1}{2}\pi$

15. Metal of weight 84 kg is made into 40 000 pins. What is the weight, in kg, of one pin?

A 0·0021
B 0·0036
C 0·021
D 0·21

16. What is the value of x which satisfies both equations?
$3x + y = 1$
$x - 2y = 5$

A -1
B 1
C -2
D 2

17. What is the new fare when the old fare of £250 is increased by 8%?

A £258
B £260
C £270
D £281·25

18. Which of the following statements are true?
(a) 300 mm = 3 m
(b) $\frac{2}{5}$ is greater than $\frac{1}{3}$
(c) $2^3 > 3^2$

A (a) only
B (b) only
C (c) only
D (b) and (c)

19. What values of x satisfy the inequality $2 - 3x > 1$?

A $x < -\frac{1}{3}$
B $x > -\frac{1}{3}$
C $x > \frac{1}{3}$
D $x < \frac{1}{3}$

20. A right-angled triangle has sides in the ratio 5 : 12 : 13. The tangent of the smallest angle is:

A $\frac{12}{5}$
B $\frac{12}{13}$
C $\frac{5}{13}$
D $\frac{5}{12}$

21. To one significant figure, $\sqrt{0.1}$ is:

A 0·01
B 0·1
C 0·3
D 0·5

22. The number of letters in the word SNAIL that have line symmetry is:

A 0
B 1
C 2
D 3

23. The probability of an event occurring is 0·35. The probability of the event *not* occurring is:

A $\dfrac{1}{0.35}$
B 0·65
C 0·35
D 0

24. What fraction of the area of the rectangle is the area of the triangle?

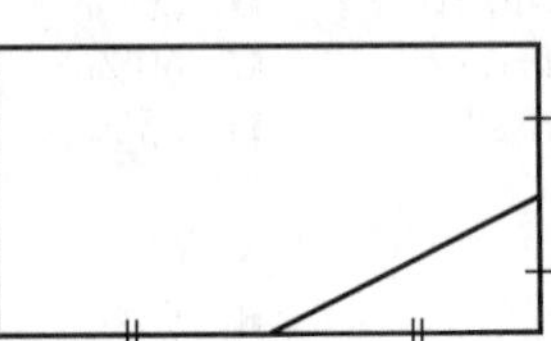

A $\frac{1}{4}$
B $\frac{1}{8}$
C $\frac{1}{16}$
D $\frac{1}{32}$

25. On a map a distance of 40 km is represented by a line of 2 cm. What is the scale of the map?

A 1 : 2000
B 1 : 20 000
C 1 : 200 000
D 1 : 2000 000

Test 4

1. What is the value of x satisfying the simultaneous equations
$3x + 2y = 13$
$x - 2y = -1$?

A 7
B 3
C $3\frac{1}{2}$
D 2

2. A straight line is 4·5 cm long. $\frac{2}{5}$ of the line is:

A 0·4 cm
B 1·8 cm
C 2 cm
D 0·18 cm

3. 7, 1, 3, 7
The median of the numbers above is:

A 5
B 4·5
C 2
D 7

4. How many cubes of edge 3 cm are needed to fill a box with internal dimensions 12 cm by 6 cm by 6 cm?

A 8
B 18
C 16
D 24

5. The value of 4865·355 correct to 2 significant figures is:

A 4865·36
B 4865·35
C 4900
D 49

6. What values of y satisfy the inequality $4y - 1 < 0$?

A $y < 4$
B $y < -\frac{1}{4}$
C $y > \frac{1}{4}$
D $y < \frac{1}{4}$

For Questions **7** to **9** use the diagram below.

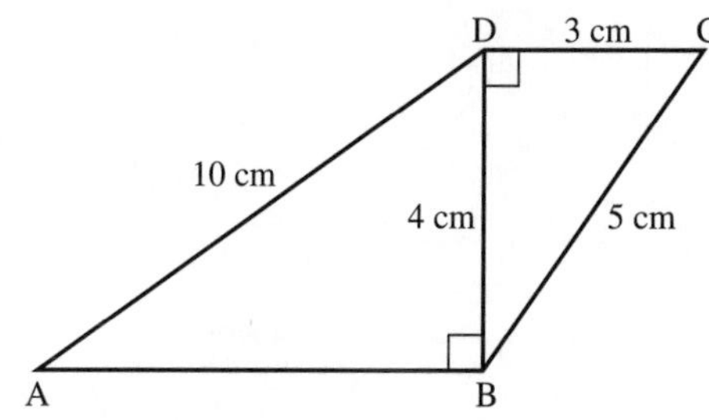

7. The length of AB, in cm, is:

A 6
B $\sqrt{116}$
C 8
D $\sqrt{84}$

8. The sine of angle DCB is:

A 0·8
B 1·25
C 0·6
D 0·75

9. The tangent of angle CBD is:

A 0·6
B 0·75
C 1·333
D 1·6

10. The area of a circle is $100\pi\,\text{cm}^2$. The radius, in cm, of the circle is:

A 50
B 10
C $\sqrt{50}$
D 5

11. $4(x + 3) - 2(x - 5) = ?$

A $2x + 2$
B $2x - 2$
C $6x + 22$
D $2x + 22$

12. An estimate of the value of $\dfrac{204 \cdot 7 \times 97 \cdot 5}{1064 \cdot 2}$, to one significant figure, is:

A 2
B 20
C 200
D 2000

13. The cube root of 64 is:

A 2
B 4
C 8
D 16

14. Here are four statements about the diagonals of a rectangle. The statement which is not *always* true is

A They are equal in length
B They divide the rectangle into four triangles of equal area
C They cross at right angles
D They bisect each other

15. Given $16^x = 4^4$, what is x?

A -2
B $-\frac{1}{2}$
C $\frac{1}{2}$
D 2

16. What is the area, in m^2, of a square with each side 0·02 m long?

A 0·0004
B 0·004
C 0·04
D 0·4

17. I start with x, then square it, multiply by 3 and finally subtract 4. The final result is:

A $(3x)^2 - 4$
B $(3x - 4)^2$
C $3x^2 - 4$
D $3(x - 4)^2$

18. How many prime numbers are there between 50 and 60?

A 1
B 2
C 3
D 4

19. What are the coordinates of the point (2, −2) after reflection in the line $y = -x$?

A (−2, 2)
B (2, −2)
C (−2, −2)
D (2, 2)

20. The area of a circle is 36π cm^2. The circumference, in cm, is:

A 6π
B 18π
C $12\sqrt{\pi}$
D 12π

21. The gradient of the line $2x - 3y = 4$ is:

A $\frac{2}{3}$
B $1\frac{1}{2}$
C $-\frac{4}{3}$
D $-\frac{3}{4}$

22. 3, 5, 7, 9
The nth term of the above sequence is:

A $2n$
B $2n - 1$
C $2n + 1$
D $2(n + 1)$

23. $a = \sqrt{\left(\frac{m}{x}\right)}$

$x = ?$

A a^2m
B $a^2 - m$
C $\frac{m}{a^2}$
D $\frac{a^2}{m}$

24. A coin is tossed three times. The probability of getting three 'heads' is:

A $\frac{1}{3}$
B $\frac{1}{6}$
C $\frac{1}{8}$
D $\frac{1}{16}$

25. A triangle has sides of length 5 cm, 5 cm and 6 cm. What is the area, in cm^2?

A 12
B 15
C 18
D 20

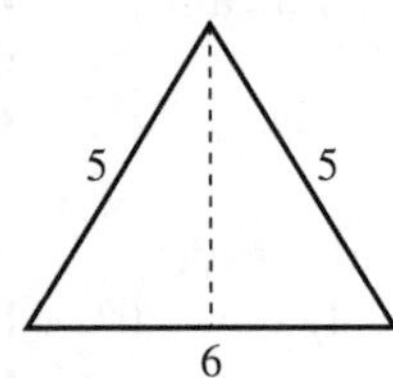

13 USING AND APPLYING MATHEMATICS

13.1 Coursework tasks

There are a large number of possible starting points for investigations here so it may be possible to allow students to choose investigations which appeal to them. On other occasions the same investigation may be set to a whole class.

Here are a few guidelines for pupils.
(a) If the set problem is too complicated try an easier case.
(b) Draw your own diagrams.
(c) Make tables of your results and be systematic.
(d) Look for patterns.
(e) Is there a rule or formula to describe the results?
(f) Can you *predict* further results?
(g) Can you *explain* any rules which you may find?
(h) Where possible extend the task further by asking questions like 'what happens if . . .'.

1 Opposite corners

Here the numbers are arranged in 9 columns.

1	2	3	4	5	6	7	8	9
10	11	12	13	14	15	16	17	18
19	20	21	22	23	24	25	26	27
28	29	30	31	32	33	34	35	36
37	38	39	40	41	42	43	44	45
46	47	48	49	50	51	52	53	54
55	56	57	58	59	60	61	62	63
64	65	66	67	68	69	70	71	72
73	74	75	76	77	78	79	80	81
82	83	84	85	86	87	88	89	90

In the 2 × 2 square . . .

6	7
15	16

$6 \times 16 = 96$
$7 \times 15 = 105$

. . . the difference between them is 9.

In the 3 × 3 square . . .

22	23	24
31	32	33
40	41	42

$22 \times 42 = 924$
$24 \times 40 = 960$

. . . the difference between them is 36.

Investigate to see if you can find any rules or patterns connecting the size of square chosen and the difference.
If you find a rule, use it to *predict* the difference for larger squares.
Test your rule by looking at squares like 8×8 or 9×9.
Can you *generalise* the rule?

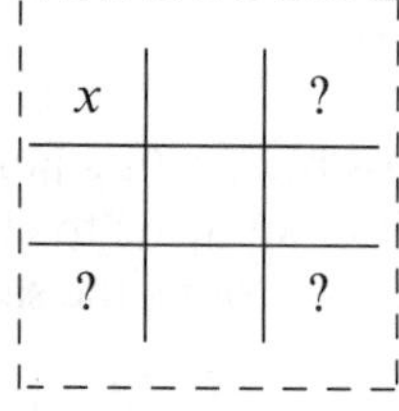

[What is the difference for a square of size $n \times n$?]

Can you *prove* the rule?

Hint:
In a 3×3 square ...

What happens if the numbers are arranged in six columns or seven columns?

1	2	3	4	5	6
7	8	9	10	11	12
13	14	15	16	17	18
19					

1	2	3	4	5	6	7
8	9	10	11	12	13	14
15	16	17	18	19	20	21
22						

2 Hiring a car

You are going to hire a car for one week (7 days).
Which of the firms below should you choose?

Gibson car hire	Snowdon rent-a-car	Hav-a-car
£170 per week unlimited mileage	£10 per day 6·5 p per mile	£60 per week 500 miles without charge 22p per mile over 500 miles

Work out as detailed an answer as possible.

3 Half-time score

The final score in a football match was 3–2. How many different scores were possible at half-time?

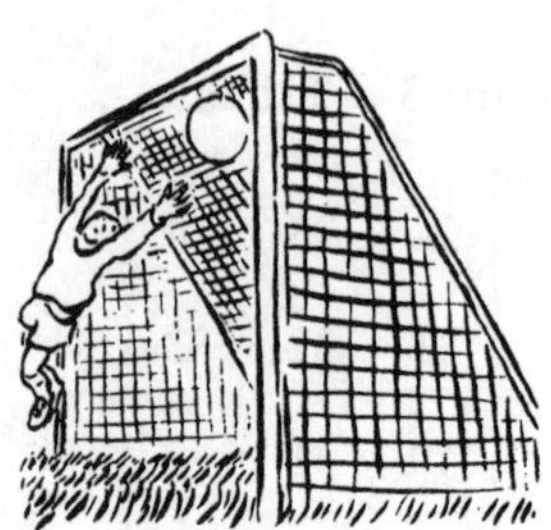

Investigate for other final scores where the difference between the teams is always one goal [1–0, 5–4, etc.]. Is there a pattern or rule which would tell you the number of possible half-time scores in a game which finished 58–57?

Suppose the game ends in a draw. Find a rule which would tell you the number of possible half-time scores if the final score was 63–63.

Investigate for other final scores [3–0, 5–1, 4–2, etc.].
Find a rule which gives the number of different half-time scores for *any* final score (say a–b).

4 An expanding diagram

Look at the series of diagrams below.

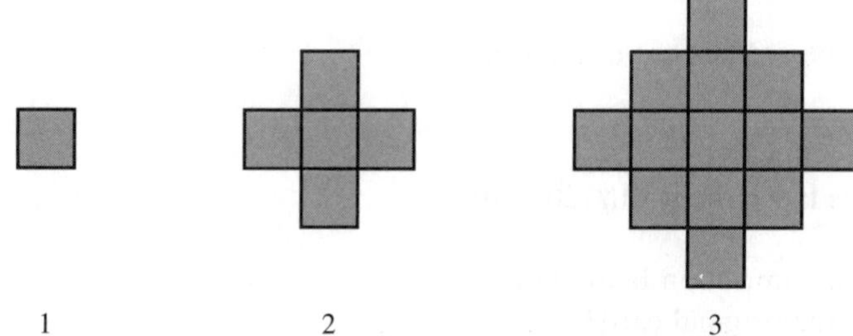

Continue the series by drawing the fourth, fifth and sixth diagrams in the sequence. Each new diagram is obtained by drawing squares all around the outside of the previous diagram. For each diagram count the number of squares it contains.

Using the results of the first six diagrams, can you predict the number of squares in the seventh diagram? See if you were right by drawing the diagram.

Can you predict the number of squares in the eighth diagram? Again draw the diagram to see if you were right.

Can you predict the number of squares in:

(a) the 12th diagram

(b) the 20th diagram?

Try to find a rule which will enable you to predict the number of squares for any member of the sequence of diagrams.

5 Maximum box

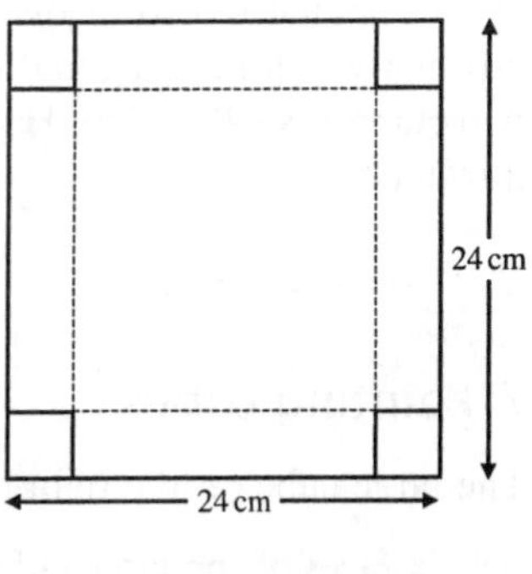

(a) You have a square sheet of card 24 cm by 24 cm.
You can make a box (without a lid) by cutting squares from the corners and folding up the sides.
What size corners should you cut out so that the volume of the box is as large as possible?
Try different sizes for the corners and record the results in a table.

Length of the side of the corner square (cm)	Dimensions of the open box (cm)	Volume of the box (cm^3)
1	$22 \times 22 \times 1$	484
2		
–		
–		

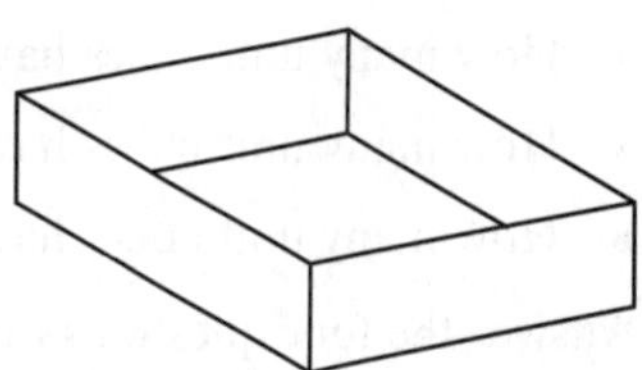

Now consider boxes made from different sized cards:
15 cm × 15 cm and 20 cm × 20 cm.
What size corners should you cut out this time so that the volume of the box is as large as possible?
Is there a connection between the size of the corners cut out and the size of the square card?

(b) Investigate the situation when the card is not square.
Take rectangular cards where the length is twice the width (20 × 10, 12 × 6, 18 × 9, etc.).
Again, for the maximum volume is there a connection between the size of the corners cut out and the size of the original card?

6 Diagonals

In a 4 × 7 rectangle, the diagonal passes through 10 squares.

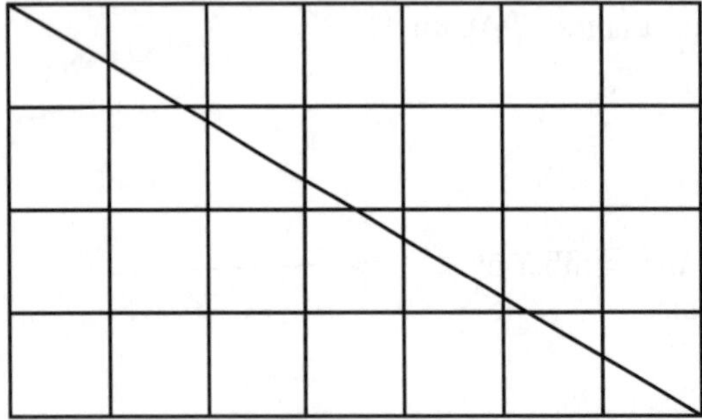

Draw rectangles of your own choice and count the number of squares through which the diagonal passes.
A rectangle is 640 × 250. How many squares will the diagonal pass through?

7 Painting cubes

The large cube on the right consists of 27 unit cubes.

All six faces of the large cube are painted green.

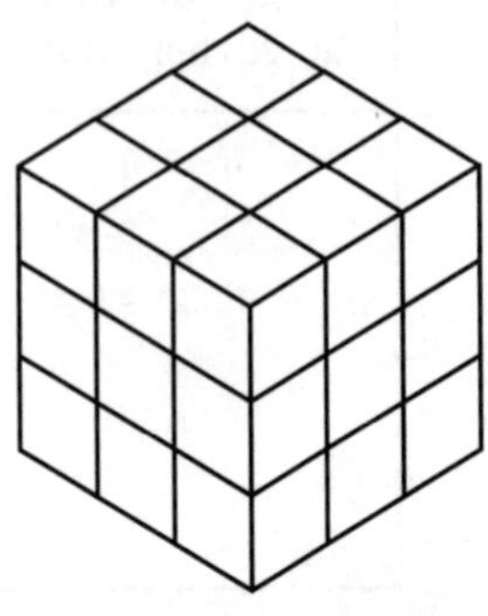

- How many unit cubes have 3 green faces?
- How many unit cubes have 2 green faces?
- How many unit cubes have 1 green face?
- How many unit cubes have 0 green faces?

Answer the four questions for the cube which is $n \times n \times n$.

13.2 Puzzles and games

1 Crossnumbers

Draw a copy of the crossnumber pattern below and work out the answers using the clues. You can check your working by doing *all* the across and *all* the down clues.

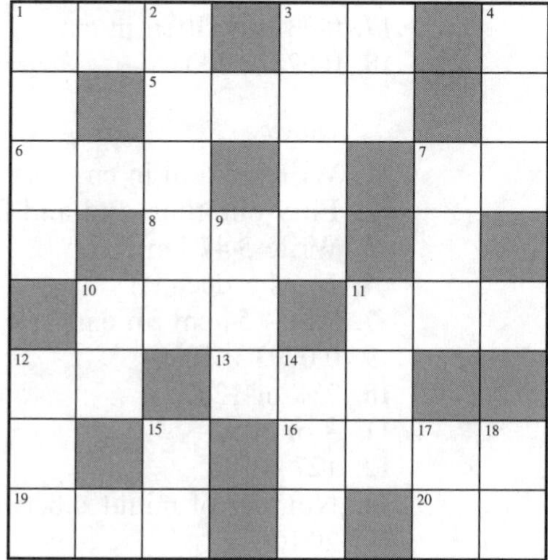

Part A

Across

1. $327 + 198$
3. $245 \div 7$
5. $3146 - 729$
6. $248 - 76$
7. 2^6
8. $850 \div 5$
10. $10^2 + 1^2$
11. $3843 \div 7$
12. $1000 - 913$
13. $37 \times 5 \times 3$
16. $152\,300 \div 50$
19. 3^6
20. $100 - \left(\frac{17 \times 10}{5}\right)$

Down

1. $3280 + 1938$
2. $65\,720 - 13\,510$
3. $3{\cdot}1 \times 1000$
4. $1284 \div 6$
7. $811 - 127$
9. 65×11
10. $(12^2 - 8) \div 8$
11. $(7^2 + 1^2) \times 11$
12. $7 + 29 + 234 + 607$
14. $800 - 265$
15. $1 + 2 + 3 + 4 + 5 + 6 + 7 + 8 + 13$
17. $(69 \times 6) \div 9$
18. $3^2 + 4^2 + 5^2 + 2^4$

Part B Draw decimal points on the lines between squares where necessary.

Across

1. $4{\cdot}2 + 1{\cdot}64$
3. $7 \times 0{\cdot}5$
5. $20{\cdot}562 \div 6$
6. $(2^3 \times 5) \times 10 - 1$
7. $0{\cdot}034 \times 1000$
8. $61 \times 0{\cdot}3$
10. $8 - 0{\cdot}36$
11. 19×50
12. $95{\cdot}7 \div 11$
13. $8{\cdot}1 \times 0{\cdot}7$
16. $(11 \times 5) \div 8$
19. $(44 - 2{\cdot}8) \div 5$
20. Number of inches in a yard

Down

1. $62{\cdot}6 - 4{\cdot}24$
2. $48{\cdot}73 - 4{\cdot}814$
3. $25 + 7{\cdot}2 + 0{\cdot}63$
4. $2548 \div 7$
7. $0{\cdot}315 \times 100$
9. $169 \times 0{\cdot}05$
10. $770 \div 100$
11. $14{\cdot}2 + 0{\cdot}7 - 5{\cdot}12$
12. $11{\cdot}4 - 2{\cdot}64 - 0{\cdot}18$
14. $0{\cdot}0667 \times 10^3$
15. $0{\cdot}6 + 0{\cdot}7 + 0{\cdot}8 + 7{\cdot}3$
17. 0·73 m written in cm
18. $0{\cdot}028 \times 200$

Part C

Across

1. Eleven squared take away six
3. Next in the sequence 21, 24, 28, 33
5. Number of minutes in a day
6. $2 \times 13 \times 5 \times 5$
7. Next in the sequence 92, 83, 74
8. 5% of 11 400
10. $98 + 11^2$
11. $(120 - 9) \times 6$
12. $1\frac{2}{5}$ as a decimal
13. $2387 \div 7$
16. $9{\cdot}05 \times 1000$
19. 8 m – 95 cm (in cm)
20. 3^4

Down

1. Write 18·6 m in cm
2. Fifty-one thousand and fifty-one
3. Write 3·47 km in m
4. $1\frac{1}{4}$ as a decimal
7. 7 m – 54 cm (in cm)
9. $0{\cdot}0793 \times 1000$
10. 2% of 1200
11. $\frac{1}{5}$ of 3050
12. $127 \div 100$
14. Number of minutes between 12 00 and 20 10
15. 4% of 1125
17. $7^2 + 3^2$
18. Last two digits of (67×3)

Part D

Across

1. $1\frac{3}{4}$ as a decimal
3. Two dozen
5. Forty less than ten thousand
6. Emergency
7. 5% of 740
8. Nine pounds and five pence
10. 1·6 m written in cm
11. $5649 \div 7$
12. One-third of 108
13. $6 - 0{\cdot}28$
16. A quarter to midnight on the 24 h clock
19. $5^3 \times 2^2 + 1^5$
20. $3300 \div 150$

Down

1. Twelve pounds 95 pence
2. Four less than sixty thousand
3. 245×11
4. James Bond
7. Number of minutes between 09 10 and 15 30
9. $\frac{1}{20}$ as a decimal
10. Ounces in a pound
11. 8·227 to two decimal places
12. 4 m – 95 cm (in cm)
14. Three to the power 6
15. 20·64 to the nearest whole number
17. $(6\frac{1}{2})^2$ to the nearest whole number
18. Number of minutes between 14 22 and 15 14

2 Crossnumbers without clues

Here we have five crossnumber puzzles with a difference. There are no clues, only answers, and it is your task to find where the answers go.

(a) Copy out the crossnumber pattern.

(b) Fit all the given numbers into the correct spaces.
Tick off the numbers from the lists as you write them in the square.

1.

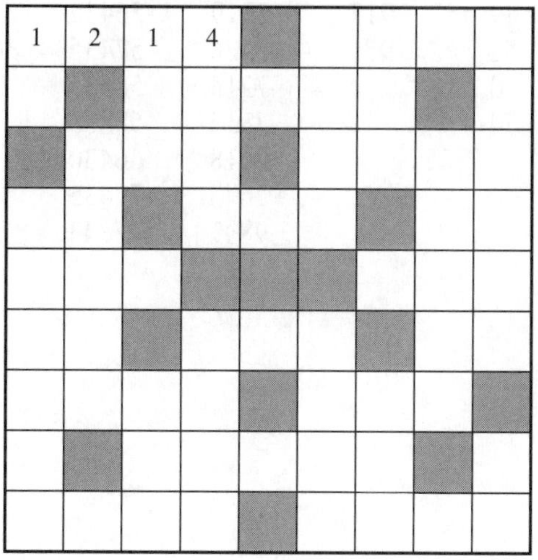

2 digits	*3 digits*	*4 digits*	*5 digits*	*6 digits*
26	215	5841	21862	134953
41	427	9217	83642	727542
19	106	9131	21362	
71	872	1624	57320	
63	725	1506		
76	385	4214		
	156	5216		
	263	4734		
	234	2007		
	180	2637		

2.

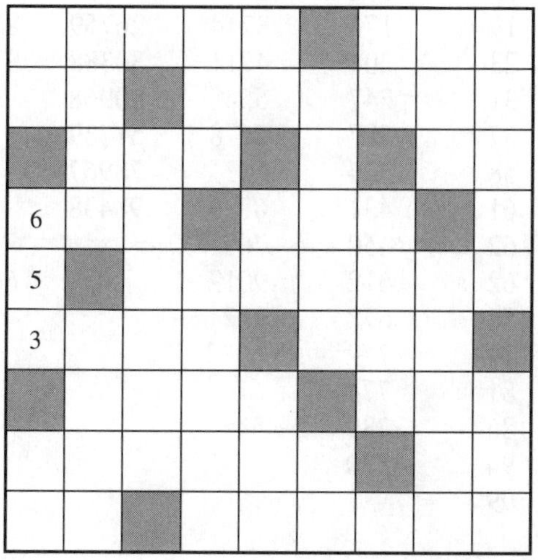

2 digits	*3 digits*	*4 digits*	*5 digits*	*6 digits*
99	571	9603	24715	387566
25	918	8072	72180	338472
52	131	4210	54073	414725
26	328	3824	71436	198264
42	906	8916	82125	
57	249			
30	653			*7 digits*
53	609			8592070
14	111			
61	127			
	276			

The next three are more difficult but they are possible! Don't give up.

3.

7

9

2 digits	*3 digits*	*4 digits*	*5 digits*	*6 digits*
26	306	3654	38975	582778
28	457	3735	49561	585778
32	504	3751	56073	728468
47	827	3755	56315	
49	917	3819	56435	*7 digits*
52	951	6426	57435	8677056
70		7214	58535	
74		7315	58835	
		7618	66430	
		7643	77435	
		9847	77543	

4.

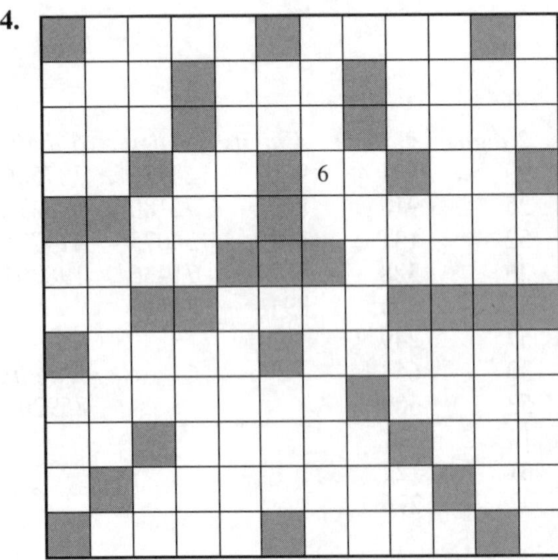

2 digits	*3 digits*	*4 digits*	*5 digits*	*6 digits*
11	121	2104	14700	216841
17	147	2356	24567	588369
18	170	2456	25921	846789
19	174	3714	26759	861277
23	204	4711	30388	876452
31	247	5548	50968	
37	287	5678	51789	
58	324	6231	78967	
61	431	6789	98438	
62	450	7630		*7 digits*
62	612	9012		6645678
70	678	9921		
74	772			
81	774			
85	789			
94	870			
99				

4 Calculator words

On a calculator the number 4915 looks like the word 'SIGH' when the calculator is held upside down.

Find the words given by the clues below.

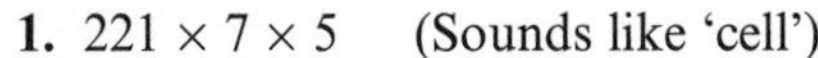

1. $221 \times 7 \times 5$ (Sounds like 'cell')
2. $5 \times 601 \times 5 \times 3$ (Wet blow)
3. $88^2 - 6$ (Ringer)
4. $0{\cdot}9 \times 5900 - 1$ (Leaves)
5. $62^2 - (4 \times 7 \times 5)$ (Nothing to it)
6. $0{\cdot}88^2 - \frac{1}{1000}$ (O Hell)
7. $(5 \times 7 \times 10^3) + (3 \times 113)$ (Gaggle)
8. $44^4 +$ Half of 67 682 (Readable)
9. $5 \times 3 \times 37 \times 1000 - 1420$ (Stick in mind)
10. $3200 - 1320 \div 11$ (Woodwind)
11. $48^4 + 8929$ (Deceitful dame)
12. $31^2 \times 32^2 - 276^2 + 30$ (Not a twig)
13. $(130 \times 135) + (23 \times 3 \times 11 \times 23)$ (Wobbly)
14. $164 \times 166^2 + 734$ (Almost big)
15. $8794^2 + 25 \times 342{\cdot}28 + 120 \times 25$ (Thin skin)
16. $0{\cdot}08 - (3^2 \div 10^4)$ (Ice house)
17. $235^2 - (4 \times 36{\cdot}5)$ (Shiny surface)
18. $(80^2 + 60^2) \times 3 + 81^2 + 12^2 + 3013$ (Ship gunge)
19. $3 \times 17 \times (329^2 + 2 \times 173)$ (Unlimbed)
20. $230 \times 230\frac{1}{2} + 30$ (Fit feet)
21. $33 \times 34 \times 35 + 15 \times 3$ (Beleaguer)
22. $0{\cdot}32^2 + \frac{1}{1000}$ (Did he or didn't he?)
23. $(23 \times 24 \times 25 \times 26) + (3 \times 11 \times 10^3) - 20$ (Help)
24. $(16^2 + 16)^2 - (13^2 - 2)$ (Slander)
25. $(3 \times 661)^2 - (3^6 + 22)$ (Pester)
26. $(22^2 + 29{\cdot}4) \times 10$; $(3{\cdot}03^2 - 0{\cdot}02^2) \times 100^2$ (Four words) (Goliath)
27. $1{\cdot}25 \times 0{\cdot}2^6 + 0{\cdot}2^2$ (Tissue time)
28. $(710 + (1823 \times 4)) \times 4$ (Liquor)
29. $(3^3)^2 + 2^2$ (Wriggler)
30. $14 + (5 \times (83^2 + 110))$ (Bigger than a duck)
31. $2 \times 3 \times 53 \times 10^4 + 9$ (Opposite to hello, almost!)
32. $(177 \times 179 \times 182) + (85 \times 86) - 82$ (Good salesman)

14 Examination Questions

Paper 1 **DO NOT** use a calculator for this paper.

1. Tom breeds hamsters for pet shops.
The number of hamsters trebles each year.
Tom has 20 hamsters at the end of Year 1.

(a) Complete the table below.

End of year	1	2	3	4	5
Number of hamsters	20				

(b) A hamster cage can hold no more than 14 hamsters.
Work out the minimum number of cages needed for 900 hamsters.
Show all your working. [Edexcel]

2. Describe fully a single transformation that would map the shaded shape on to:
(a) shape A
(b) shape B
(c) shape C. [AQA]

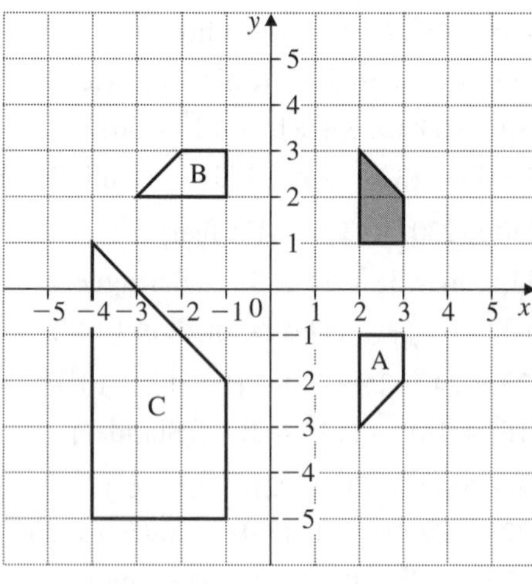

3. The expressions shown below can be used to calculate lengths, areas or volumes of various shapes.
The letters a, b, c and r represent lengths. π, 2 and $\frac{1}{2}$ are numbers which have no dimensions.

$$2a \qquad abc \qquad \pi r \qquad 2a^2b \qquad \tfrac{1}{2}ab$$
$$ab/c \qquad bc \qquad \tfrac{1}{2}\pi r^2 \qquad ab(2+c)$$

Write down the two expressions which can be used to calculate a volume. [Edexcel]

4. L-shapes are pinned on a notice board as shown below.

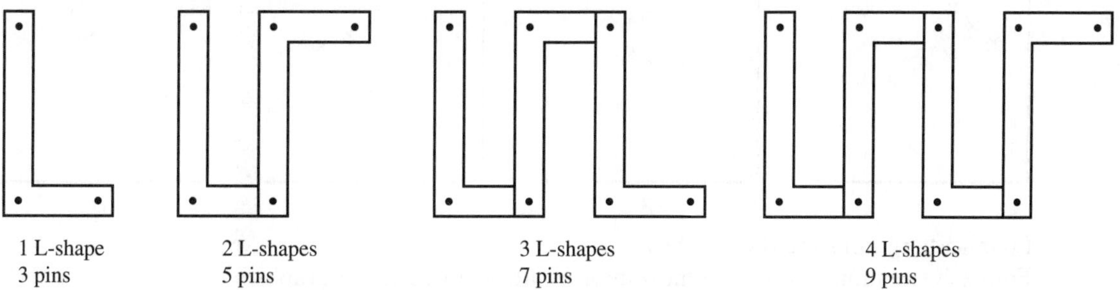

There is a rule to calculate the number of pins needed, if you know the number of L-shapes.

(a) Without drawing, calculate how many pins are used when there are 30 L-shapes pinned in this way.

(b) Write down, in words, the rule for finding the number of pins from the number of L-shapes. [WJEC]

5.

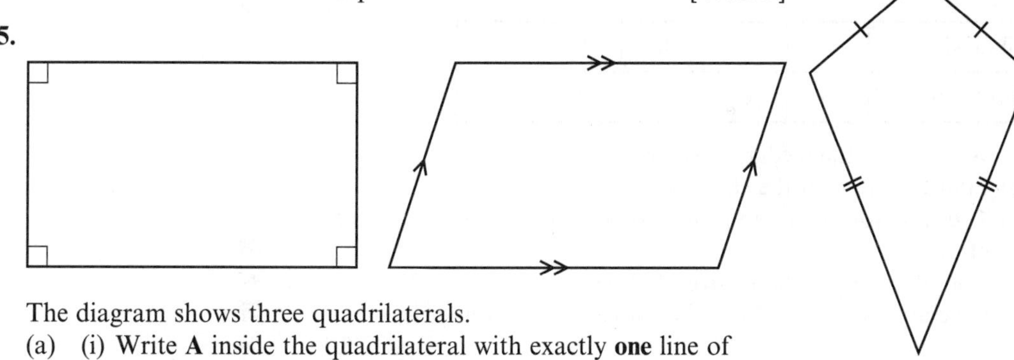

The diagram shows three quadrilaterals.

(a) (i) Write **A** inside the quadrilateral with exactly **one** line of symmetry.

(ii) Write down the mathematical name of this quadrilateral.

(b) (i) Write **B** inside the quadrilateral with rotational symmetry of order 2 **and** two lines of symmetry.

(ii) Write down the mathematical name of this quadrilateral.

(c) (i) Write **C** inside the quadrilateral with rotational symmetry of order 2 but **no** lines of symmetry.

(ii) Write down the mathematical name of this quadrilateral.

[Edexcel]

6. In a game at a fete a spinner is spun. The score obtained may be any one of 2, 4, 6, 8, 10, 12, 14, the probabilities of which are given in the following table.

Number	2	4	6	8	10	12	14
Probability	0·11	0·09	0·14	0·31	0·23	0·07	0·05

(a) Calculate the probability that the score obtained will be greater than 8.

(b) The spinner is spun 300 times. About how many times will the score be 6? [WJEC]

7. (a)

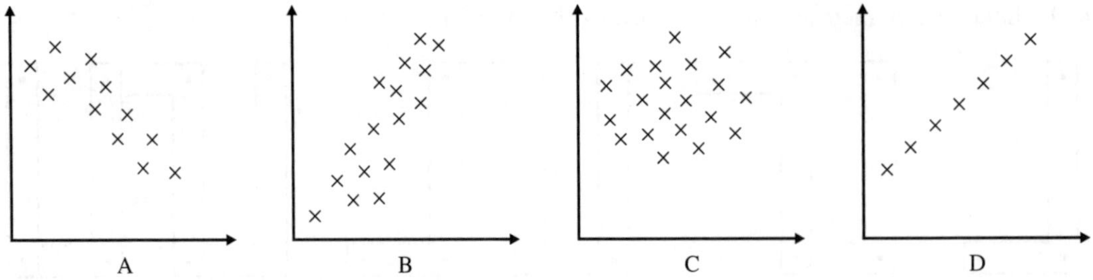

A B C D

Four scattergraphs are shown above.

For each situation, choose the most appropriate of these scattergraphs.

(i) Boys' heights and their shoe sizes.

(ii) Men's weights and the times taken for the men to complete a crossword puzzle.

(iii) Ages of cars and their selling prices.

(iv) An example of negative correlation.

(b) The shoe sizes of 28 boys are recorded in the table below.

Shoe size	6	7	8	9	10
Frequency	9	6	6	5	2

(i) Write down the median shoe size.

(ii) Find the range of the shoe sizes.

(iii) The shoe sizes of seven girls have a median of 5 and a range of 6.

One of these girls takes size 11 shoes.

Give a possible list of the shoe sizes of the seven girls.

[OCR]

8. Look at the number pattern below.

$1 \times 2 - 1 = 1$ *line 1*

$2 \times 3 - 2 = 4$ *line 2*

$3 \times 4 - 3 = 9$ *line 3*

$4 \times 5 - 4 = 16$ *line 4*

$5 \times 6 - 5 = p$ *line 5*

$\ldots \times \ldots - \ldots = q$ *line 6*

(a) (i) Calculate the value of p in *line 5*.

(ii) Complete *line 6* and so calculate the value of q.

(b) Write down *line 20* of this number pattern.

(c) Find the nth term of each of the following sequences.

(i) $1 \times 2,\quad 2 \times 3,\quad 3 \times 4,\quad 4 \times 5, \ldots$

(ii) $1, 4, 9, 16, \ldots$

[NEAB]

9. A group of 23 people share some money equally and each person gets £476. What is the total amount of money they have shared?

All working must be shown. [WEJC]

10. (a) (i) Write down the next two terms of the following sequence.

$$3, \quad 6, \quad 12, \quad 24, \quad 48, \quad \ldots\ldots$$

(ii) What is the rule for finding the next term?

(b) (i) Write down the next term of the following sequence.

$$1, \quad 4, \quad 13, \quad 40, \quad 121, \quad \ldots\ldots$$

(ii) Explain how you found this term.

(c) (i) Write down the nth term of the sequence

$$\frac{1}{3}, \quad \frac{1}{5}, \quad \frac{1}{7}, \quad \frac{1}{9}, \quad \frac{1}{11}, \quad \ldots\ldots$$

(ii) Write down the nth term of the sequence

$$\frac{1}{3}, \quad \frac{2}{7}, \quad \frac{3}{11}, \quad \frac{4}{15}, \quad \frac{5}{19}, \quad \ldots\ldots$$

[OCR]

11. A point moves around the outside of an equilateral triangle. It is always 2 cm from the nearest point on the perimeter of the triangle. Construct the locus of the point. [NEAB]

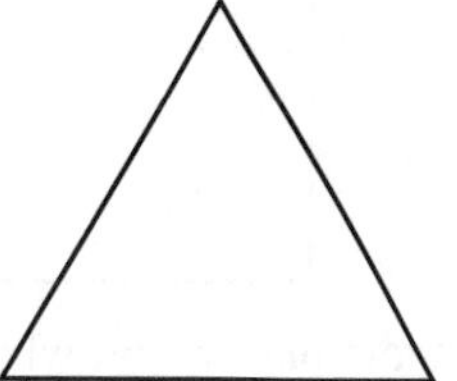

12. (a) Solve the equations.

(i) $2x = \dfrac{1}{4}$

(ii) $x^2 - 2x - 3 = 0$

(b) Solve the inequality $3(x - 2) < x + 7$. [WJEC]

13. The purpose of the set of steps given below is to work out some numbers in a number sequence.

Step 1 Write down the number 2.
Step 2 Add 2 to the number you have just written.
Step 3 Write down the answer obtained in step 2.
Step 4 If your answer in step 2 is more than 10 then stop.
Step 5 Go to step 2.

(a) Write down the numbers produced from the set of steps.
(b) Change one line of the set of steps so that it could be used to produce the first 6 odd numbers. [Edexcel]

14. This is a number pattern.

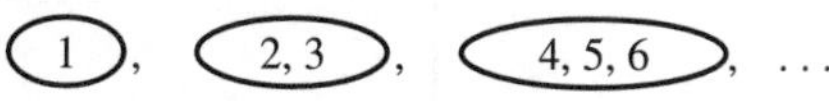

Each loop has one more number in it than the loop before.
(a) Write down the numbers that are in the next two loops.
(b) How **many** numbers are there in the 8th loop?
(c) Write down the last number in the 7th loop. [Edexcel]

15. In the diagram $CB = CD$.

(a) (i) Calculate the size of the angle marked x.

(ii) Calculate the size of the angle marked y.

(b) Does $AB = BD$?

Give a reason for your answer. [NEAB]

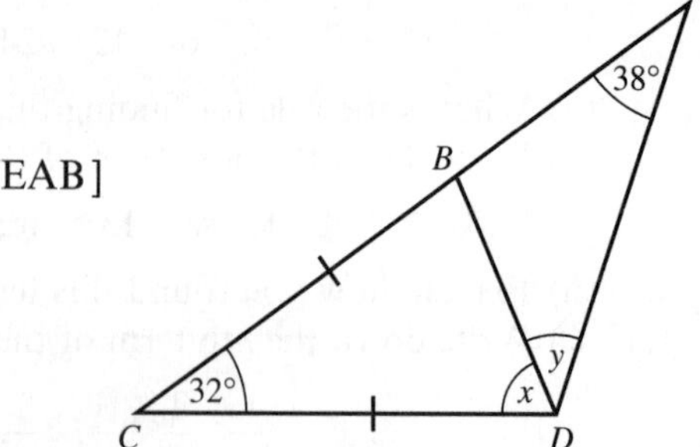

16. Kurt has to undertake a survey to find out the most popular drink in Wales. He carries out his survey by asking pupils at a school disco to answer this question:

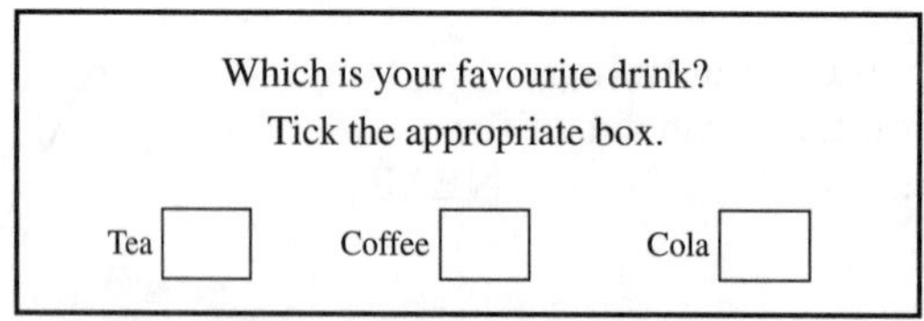

(a) State **one** reason why the design of this question is unsuitable for his survey.

(b) State **two** reasons why his survey is likely to be biased. [WJEC]

17.

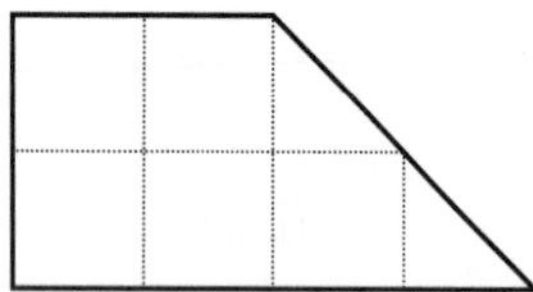

(a) Write down the geometrical name of the quadrilateral shown in the diagram.

Quadrilaterals identical to the one in (a) are to be used to tessellate the inside of the rectangle shown below.

(b) Show how the tessellation can be drawn on the grid below.

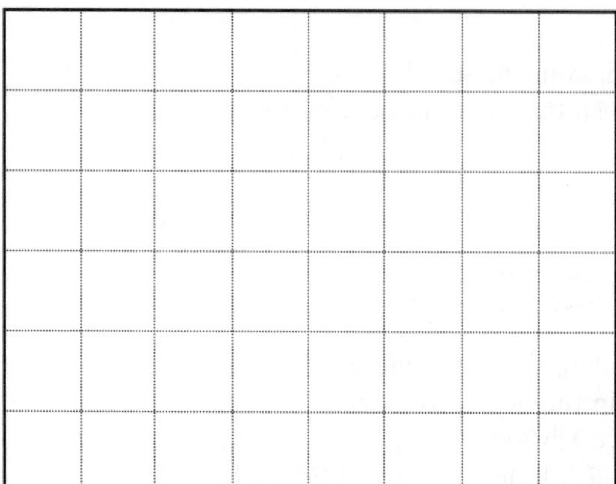

[Edexcel]

18. In a game two fair dice are thrown and the score recorded is the larger of the two numbers obtained. If the two numbers obtained are the same, the score recorded is one of them.

(a) Copy and complete this table to show the possible scores.

(b) What is the probability of obtaining:

(i) a score of 5

(ii) a score less than 3? [WJEC]

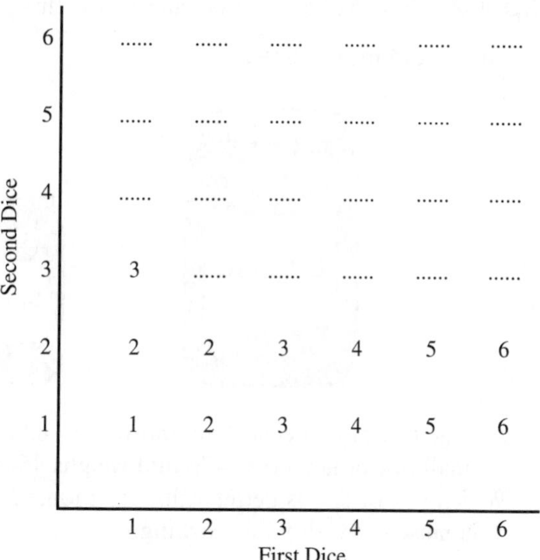

19. (a) Fill in the empty boxes in the square opposite so that each row, each column and each diagonal adds up to 0.

(b) Multiply together the three numbers in the top row and write down your answer. [CIE]

−1	4	−3
	0	

20. The video tape of *Jurassic Park* is 72 m long and can be rewound in 4 minutes.

(a) What is the speed of rewinding in cm per second?

The film *Gone with the Wind* is rewound at the same speed.
It takes 5 minutes to rewind.

(b) How long in metres is the video tape of *Gone with the Wind*?

[NISEC]

Paper 2 You **MAY** use a calculator for this paper.

1. Jam is sold in two sizes.

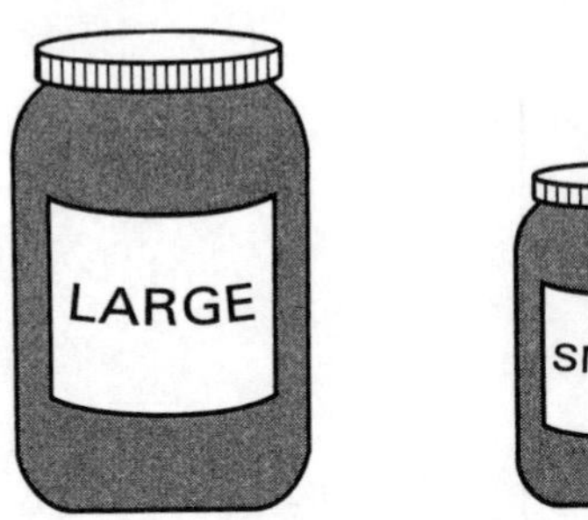

A large pot of jam costs 88p and weighs 822 g.
A small pot of jam costs 47p and weighs 454 g.
Which pot of jam is better value for money?
You **must** show all your working. [SEG]

2. In this question you **MUST** use your calculator and you **MAY** write down any stage in your calculation.

Evaluate $\dfrac{(23{\cdot}4 + 35{\cdot}6) \times 5{\cdot}7}{200{\cdot}3 \times (16{\cdot}2 - 8{\cdot}15)}$ [Edexcel]

3. James plans a game.
He hides objects at X, Y and Z and marks the positions on a plan.
The plan has been drawn using a scale of 1 cm to 100 m.

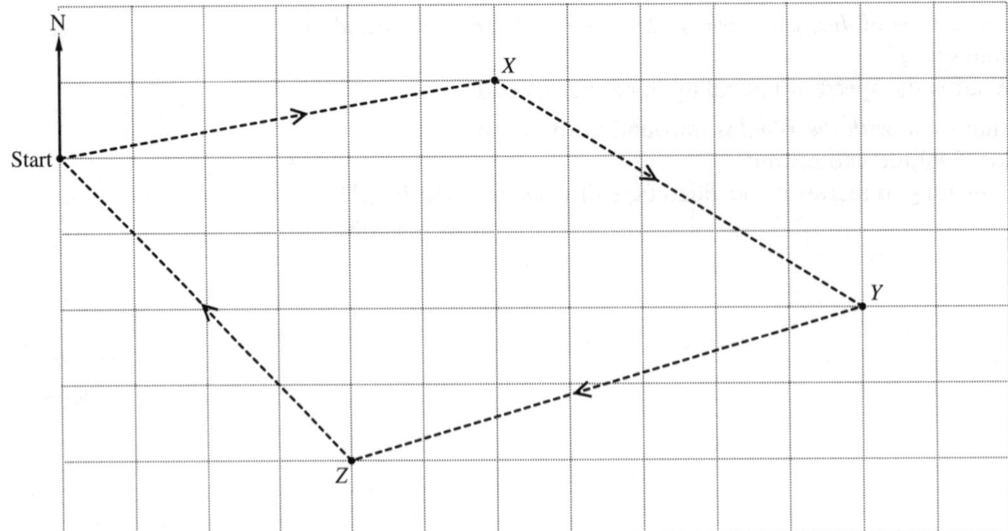

(a) Measure the bearing of Z from Y.
(b) **Calculate** the distance a competitor must walk from Y to Z.
Give your answer to the nearest metre.
You **must** show all your working. [SEG]

4.

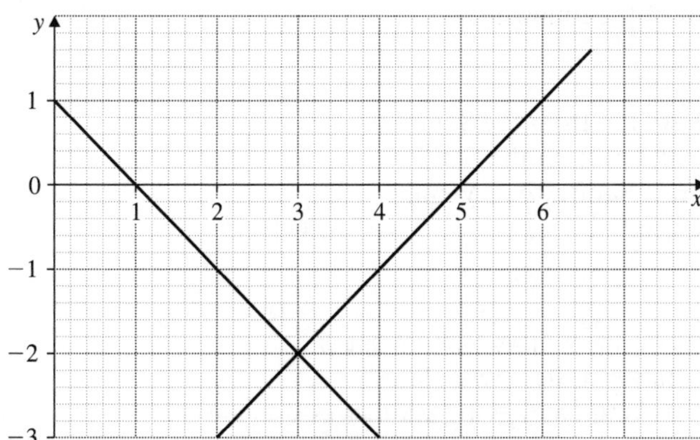

The diagram shows the graphs of the equations

$$x + y = 1 \quad \text{and} \quad y = x - 5$$

Use the diagram to solve the simultaneous equations

$$x + y = 1$$
$$y = x - 5$$

[Edexcel]

5. The graph shows the amount of petrol in a car's tank and the corresponding distances travelled for a particular journey.

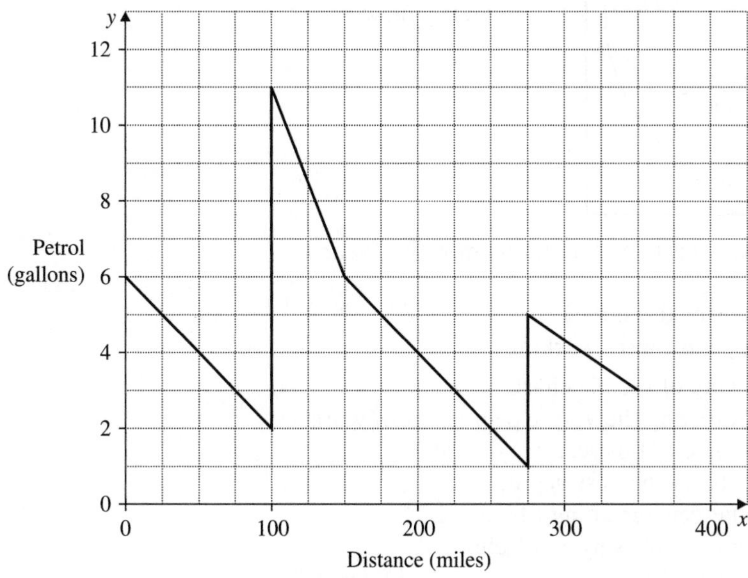

(a) At one point in the journey the tank is completely full. What is the capacity of the tank?

(b) How many gallons of petrol are used altogether?

(c) (i) Work out the number of miles travelled per gallon of petrol during the first 100 miles.

(ii) During which other part of the journey is petrol used at this rate? [NEAB]

6. (a) Work out the value of n in each of the following.
(i) $3^4 + 2^n = 97$
(ii) $y^9 \div y^3 = y^n$
(b) Saturn is approximately $1{\cdot}43 \times 10^9$ km from the Sun.
Venus is approximately $1{\cdot}08 \times 10^8$ km from the Sun.
How much further from the Sun is Saturn than Venus?
Give your answer in standard form. [SEG]

7. A map has a scale of 1 : 5000.
(a) The distance between two places on the map is 6 cm. What is the real life distance, in metres, between these two places?
(b) The real life distance between two landmarks is 1·2 kilometres. What is the distance, in cm, between these landmarks on the map? [WJEC]

8.

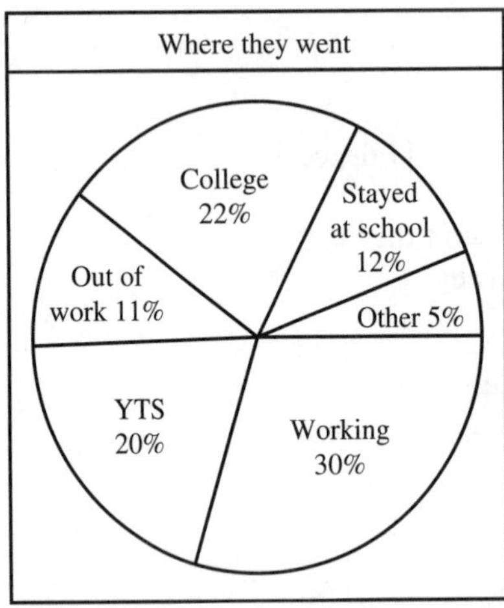

Diagram not accurately drawn

300 young people were asked what they did after completing Year 11 at school.
The pie chart shows the results of the survey.
(a) How many of the young people were working?

Gwen made an accurate drawing of the pie chart.
She first drew the sector representing the young people out of work.
(b) Calculate the size of the angle of this sector.
Give your answer correct to the nearest degree.
(c) Change to a decimal the percentage going to college.
(d) What fraction of the young people stayed at school?
Give your answer in its simplest form. [Edexcel]

9. Solve the following simultaneous equations by an algebraic (not graphical) method.
You must show all your working.

$$2x + 3y = 17$$
$$4x - y = 6$$

[WJEC]

10. Andrew has two packets of sparklers.
The rainbow packet contains

8 blue, 8 red, and 4 yellow.

The De-Lux packet contains

5 gold and 5 silver.

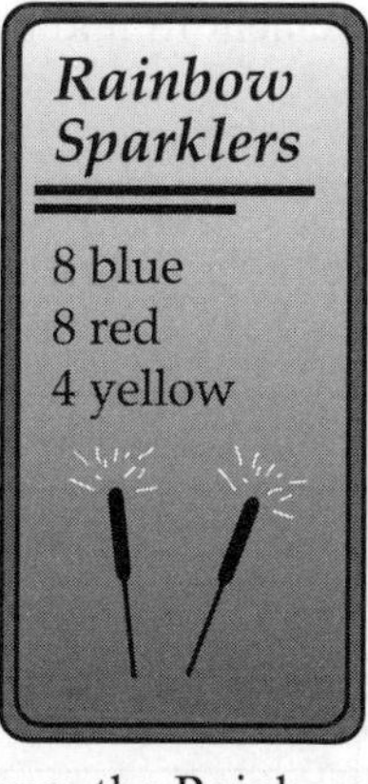

(a) Andrew takes one sparkler at random from the Rainbow packet.
What is the probability that this sparkler is blue?

(b) Andrew then takes one sparkler at random from the De-Lux packet.
List all the possible combinations of colours that Andrew could have chosen for the two sparklers.

(c) The probability of any sparkler lighting is 0·95.
Andrew tries to light a sparkler.
What is the probability that it will **not** light? [NEAB]

11. Calculate the size of the angle marked $x°$.
Give your answer correct to one decimal place. [Edexcel]

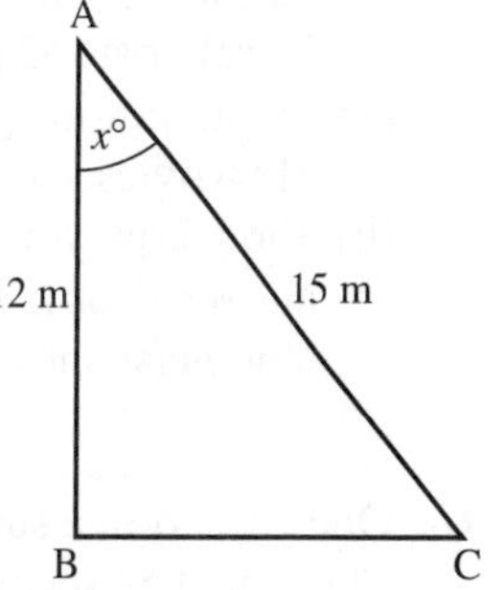

Diagram NOT accurately drawn

12. (a) Calculate the value of 2×5^9.

(b) (i) Calculate $\dfrac{28{\cdot}3 + \sqrt{0{\cdot}512}}{(18{\cdot}9 - 2{\cdot}75)^2}$.

(ii) Paul gives his answer to (i) correct to 5 significant figures.
Give one reason why this is **not** an appropriate degree of accuracy. [SEG]

13.

Continent	Population	Area (m^2)
Europe	$6{\cdot}82 \times 10^8$	$1{\cdot}05 \times 10^{10}$
Asia	$2{\cdot}96 \times 10^9$	$4{\cdot}35 \times 10^{10}$

$$\text{Population density} = \frac{\text{Population}}{\text{Area}}$$

Which of these two continents has the larger population density?
You **must** show all your working. [SEG]

14. Use the method of trial and improvement to find a solution, to 1 decimal place, of the equation

$x^3 + x = 100.$

Show all your trials in a copy of the table. A first trial has been completed for you.

Trial x	$x^3 + x$	Too high/too low
5	130	too high

[NEAB]

15. In 1995 Mr Royles drove 7764 miles in his car.
His car does 37 miles per gallon.
Petrol costs 52 pence per litre.

(a) By taking one gallon to be 4·55 litres, calculate, in £, how much Mr Royles spent on petrol in 1995.

(b) Show how you can use approximation to check that your answer is of the right order of magnitude.
You **must** show all your working. [SEG]

16. One afternoon a survey was taken of 100 customers at a supermarket. The time they spent queuing at the checkout was recorded. The results are shown below.

Time t minutes	Number of customers
$0 < t \leqslant 5$	18
$5 < t \leqslant 10$	42
$10 < t \leqslant 15$	30
$15 < t \leqslant 20$	8
$20 < t \leqslant 25$	2

(a) Calculate an estimate of the mean time these customers had to queue.

(b) On another occasion this mean time was 12·5 minutes.
Give a reason why the mean time might have changed. [NEAB]

17. *In this question take π as 3·14 or use the π button on your calculator.*

A piece of wire is bent to form a circle of radius 8 cm.
(a) What is the area of the circle?
(b) The same piece of wire is then bent to form a square. Calculate the length of each side of the square. [WJEC]

18. The table lists the weights of twelve books and the number of pages in each one.

Number of pages	80	155	100	125	145	90	140	160	135	100	115	165
Weight (g)	160	330	200	260	320	180	290	330	260	180	230	350

(a) Draw a scatter graph to show the information in the table.
(b) Describe the correlation between the number of pages in these books and their weights.
(c) Draw a line of best fit on your scatter graph.
(d) Use your line of best fit to estimate:
  (i) the number of pages in a book of weight 280 g
  (ii) the weight, in grams, of a book with 110 pages. [Edexcel]

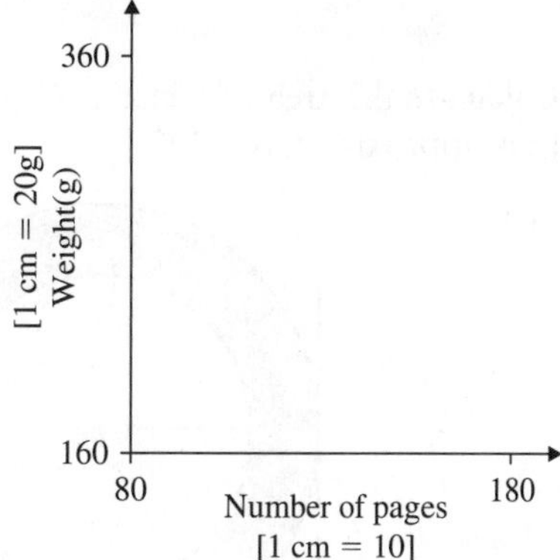

19. P and Q are two points marked on the grid.

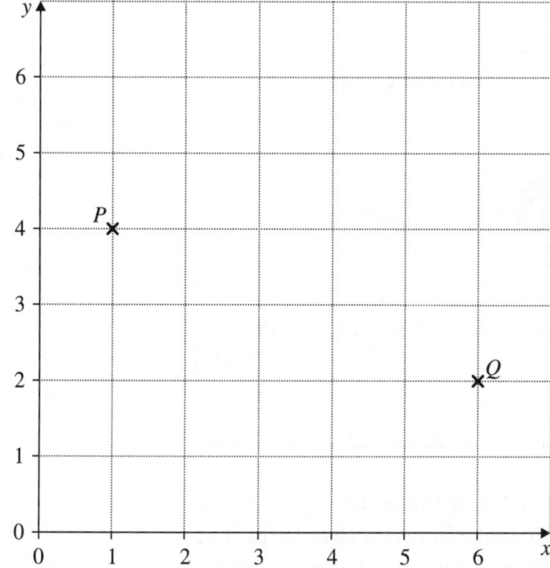

Construct accurately the locus of all points which are equidistant from P and Q. [Edexcel]

20. This diagram shows a cross-section of an artificial ski slope standing on horizontal ground $AFED$. The waiting area, BC, is horizontal and 6 m wide.
The beginners' slope, CD, is 60 m long and makes an angle of 15° with the horizontal.
The advanced slope, BA, is 37 m long.

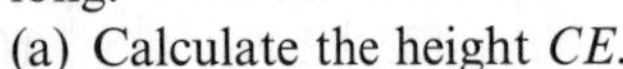

(a) Calculate the height CE.
(b) Calculate the angle the advanced slope, BA, makes with the horizontal.
(c) Calculate the horizontal distance, AD. [WJEC]

21. (a) Calculate the area of a circle of radius 3 cm.
[π is approximately 3·142.]

(b) (i)

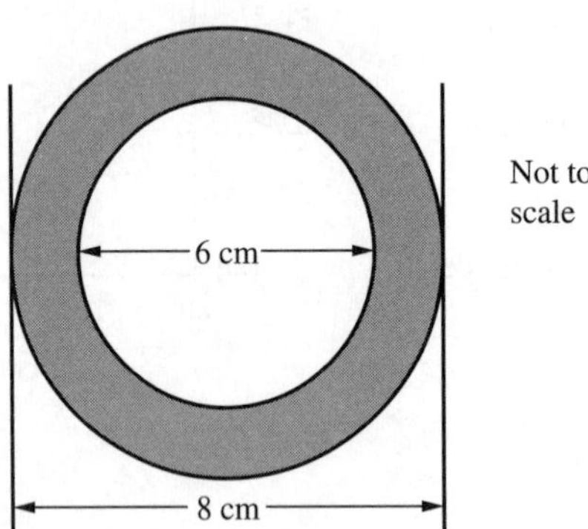

The diagram shows the cross-section of a circular ring, external **diameter** 8 cm and internal **diameter** 6 cm.
Calculate the shaded area.

(ii)

The ring is 2 millimetres thick. Calculate its volume, in cubic centimetres. [CIE]

22. The width of a wardrobe was given as 115 centimetres, measured to the nearest centimetre.
(a) Write down the lower and upper limits of the width.
The wardrobe was bought to fit into a space between two walls. The width of the space had been measured as 1·2 metres, to the nearest tenth of a metre.
(b) Explain why the wardrobe might not fit into the space. [NISEC]

Paper 3 **DO NOT** use a calculator for this paper.

1. You must write down enough working to show that you did not use a calculator.

(a) 693 fans went to a 'Take This' pop concert.
The tickets cost £14 each.
Calculate the total amount paid by the fans.

(b) (i) All of these fans travelled on 52-seater coaches.
What is the least number of coaches that could be used?
(ii) On the return journey one coach failed to turn up.
How many fans had to be left behind? [OCR]

2. Shara collected data on the colour of different vehicles passing her home. The table shows the results of her survey.

Type of Vehicle

Colour of Vehicle		Car	Van	Lorry	Bus	Total
	Red	15	2	3	5	25
	Blue	9	3	2	0	14
	White	9	4	1	0	14
	Green	2	2	2	1	7
	Total	35	11	8	6	60

(a) Which colour of vehicle is the mode?

(b) Draw a pie chart to show the proportion of each type of vehicle.
Label your pie chart clearly. [SEG]

3. A is the point (0, 3) and B is the point (3, 9).
(a) Calculate the gradient of the line AB.
(b) Write down the equation of the line AB. [NEAB]

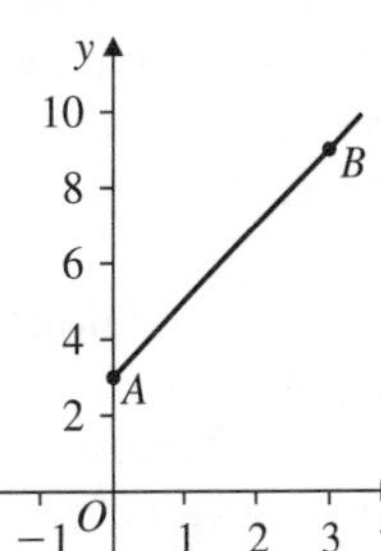

4. A cup costs n pence.
A plate costs $(n + 2)$ pence.

(a) Write an expression, in terms of n, for the cost of 6 cups.
(b) Write an expression, in terms of n, for the cost of 6 plates.
(c) George buys 6 cups and 6 plates.
He pays 96 pence.
(i) Form an equation in n.
(ii) Solve your equation to find the cost of a cup. [SEG]

5. (a) Here is a recipe for chocolate pudding for 4 people.
Nadia is making the pudding for 6 people.
(i) How many eggs will she need?
(ii) Find the amount of milk she needs.
(iii) Find the amount of vanilla essence she needs.

Rich Chocolate Pudding

100 g	Flour
75 g	Plain Chocolate
50 g	Butter
300 ml	Milk
65 g	Sugar
$\frac{1}{2}$ tsp	Vanilla essence
2	Eggs

(b) (i) Nadia weighs a bar of chocolate.
She says that the weight is 160 g correct to the nearest 10 g.
What is the minimum possible weight of the bar of chocolate?
(ii) Nadia says that a slab of butter weighs 245 g to the nearest 5 g.
What is the maximum possible weight of the butter? [OCR]

6. At a medical before entering the Army, applicants had their weights and heights recorded.
Peter made a note of his weight and height.
Peter is asked by Farah to tell her his weight and height.
In each part, write down which would be his reply using the most appropriate degree of accuracy.
(a) Peter says his weight is:
(i) 83 994 grams (ii) 83·994 kilograms
(iii) approximately 100 kilograms (iv) 84 kilograms.
(b) Peter says his height is:
(i) approximately 2 metres (ii) 170 centimetres
(iii) 1 metre 70·3 centimetres (iv) 1703 millimetres.
[OCR]

7. An examiner marked 320 examination papers.
He noted the time it took to mark each one.
The table gives a summary of these times.

Time, t minutes	Frequency	Cumulative Frequency
$0 < t \leqslant 2$	15	
$2 < t \leqslant 4$	85	
$4 < t \leqslant 6$	170	
$6 < t \leqslant 8$	40	
$8 < t \leqslant 10$	10	

(a) (i) Complete the table by filling in the cumulative frequencies.
(ii) On a graph draw a cumulative frequency diagram to show this information.

(b) Making your method clear, use your diagram to find:
(i) the median time taken to mark each paper
(ii) the interquartile range of the times taken. [NEAB]

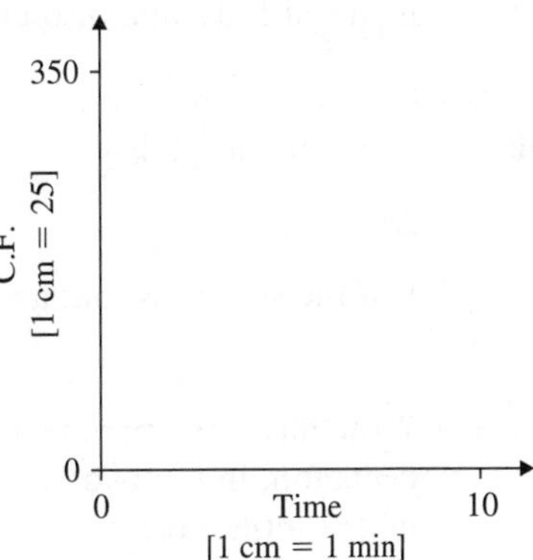

8. (a) The perimeter of a rectangle is $8x$ cm.

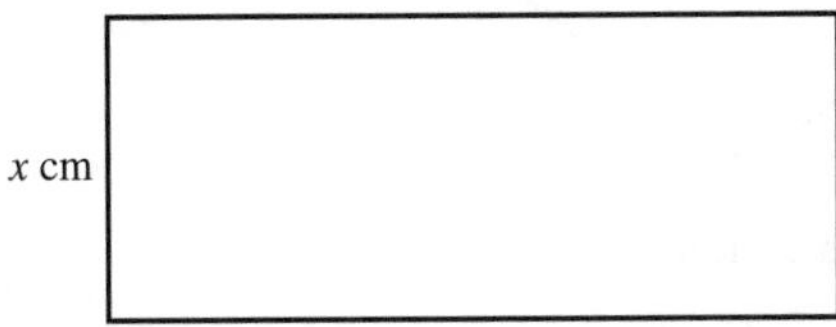

The length of the shorter side is x cm.
Write an expression, in terms of x, for the length of the longer side.

(b) The perimeters of these triangles are equal.

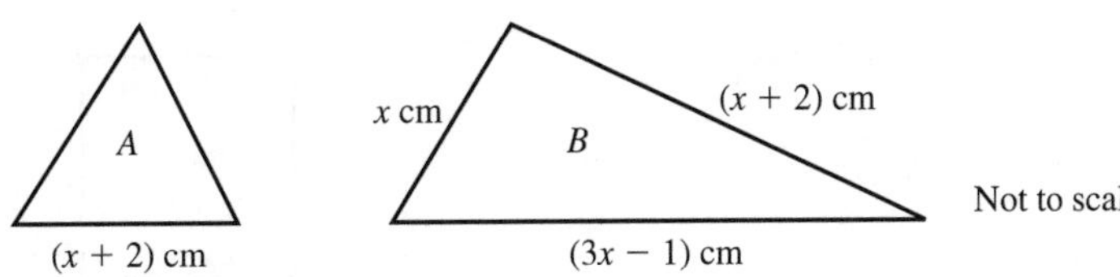

(i) Triangle A is equilateral. Its perimeter is $3(x + 2)$ cm.
Multiply out $3(x + 2)$.
(ii) Solve the equation

$$3(x + 2) = x + (x + 2) + (3x - 1)$$

(iii) Calculate the perimeter of triangle B. [SEG]

9. When a model is fired in a kiln, the probability that it shrinks is 0·95. When taken out to cool, the probability that it cracks is 0·04.

(a) What is the probability that when a model is fired in a kiln it does **not** shrink?

(b) A model is fired in a kiln, then taken out to cool. Copy and complete the tree diagram. Write all the missing probabilities on the appropriate branches.

(c) Calculate the probability that the model shrinks and also cracks. [NEAB]

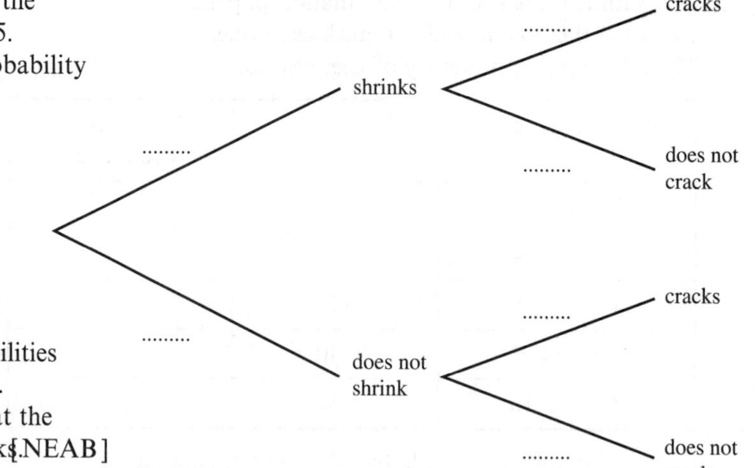

10. (i) Solve the inequality

$2n - 1 < n + 3$

(ii) List the solutions that are positive integers. [Edexcel]

11. (a) Write down the perimeter of the pentagon, in terms of a and b, in its simplest form.

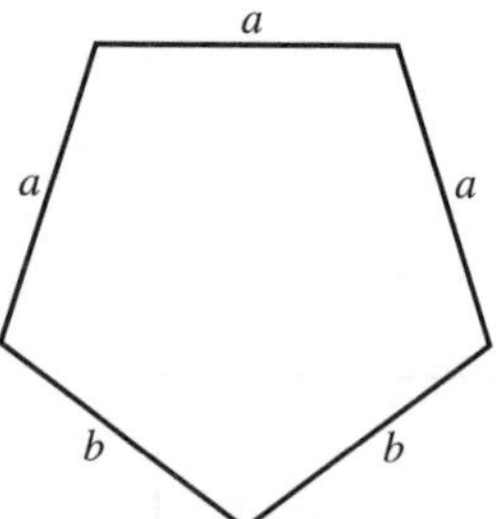

(b) (i) Write down the volume of the cuboid, in terms of x and y, in its simplest form.

(ii) Find the total area of the faces of the cuboid, in terms of x and y, in its simplest form. [NISEC]

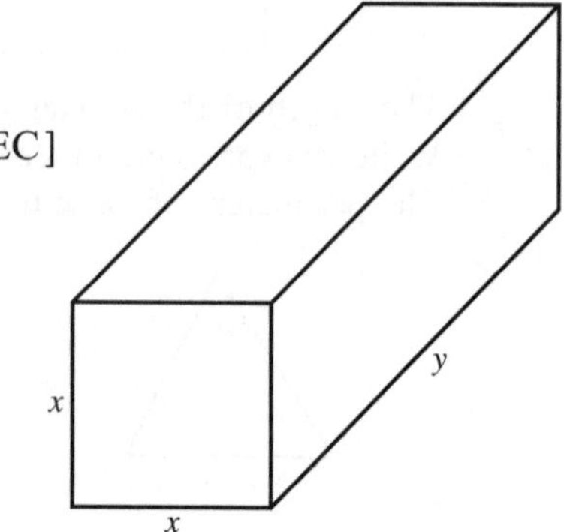

12. (a) Write, in symbols, the rule

"To find y, multiply k by 3 and then subtract 1"

(b) Work out the value of k when $y = 14$. [Edexcel]

13. *ABCD* is a rectangle.

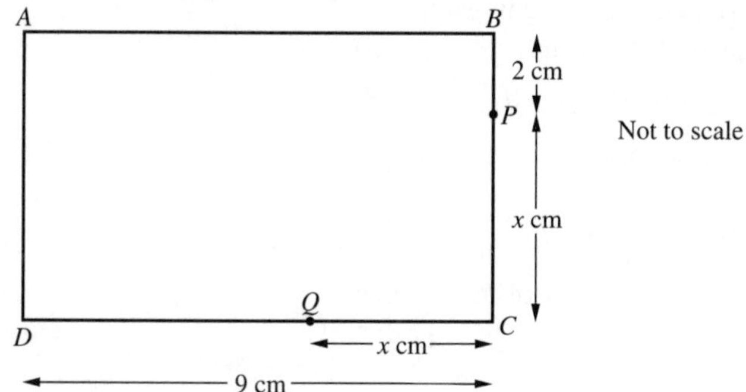

(a) Write down the expression, in terms of x, for:
   (i) the length of BC
   (ii) the length of DQ.

(b) (i) Given that $BC = DQ$, use your answers to (a) to write down an equation in terms of x.
   (ii) Solve your equation to find the value of x. [NEAB]

14. For **each** of the following sequences, find an expression, in terms of n, for the nth term.

(a) (i) 3, 6, 9, 12, 15, ...
   (ii) 4, 7, 10, 13, 16, ...

(b) 5, 6, 7, 8, 9, ... [WJEC]

15. There is to be a survey about the need for a new leisure centre in a town.

(a) State why the following question is **not** suitable for use in a questionnaire.
"Do you agree that tennis courts are more important than squash courts?"

(b) Rewrite the question in a suitable form. [SEG]

16. Look at the following list of numbers.

3, 4, 6, 8, 10, 16, 27, 35

(a) A number and its square root both appear in the list. What is the number and what is its square root?

(b) A number and its cube root both appear in the list. What is the number and what is its cube root? [NISEC]

Paper 4 You **MAY** use a calculator for this paper.

1. In 1990, a charity sold $2\frac{1}{4}$ million lottery tickets at 25p each.
80% of the money obtained was kept by the charity.

(a) Calculate the amount of money kept by the charity.

In 1991, the price of a lottery ticket fell by 20%.
Sales of lottery tickets increased by 20%.
80% of the money obtained was kept by the charity.

(b) Calculate the percentage change in the amount of money kept by the charity. [Edexcel]

2. Look at this number pattern.

$$\begin{aligned} 7^2 &= 49 \\ 67^2 &= 4489 \\ 667^2 &= 444889 \\ 6667^2 &= 44448889 \end{aligned}$$

This pattern continues.
(a) Write down the next line of the pattern.
(b) Use the pattern to work out 6666667^2.
(c) What is the square root of 4444444488888889? [NEAB]

3. (a) The cost of 15 bottles of cola is £5·25.
Find the cost of 5 bottles of cola.
(b) Pupils on a school trip were given a choice between cola and lemonade.
(i) There were 260 girls on the trip. 65% of them chose cola.
How many girls chose cola?
(ii) There were 210 boys on the trip. Two-fifths of them chose cola.
How many boys chose cola?
(iii) There were 470 pupils altogether on the trip.
What percentage of them chose cola? [OCR]

4. Use a calculator to work out the following.
In each case write down the full calculator display.

(a) $8{\cdot}6 - (3{\cdot}05 - 1{\cdot}7)$

(b) $\dfrac{6{\cdot}4 - 2{\cdot}7}{6{\cdot}4 + 2{\cdot}7}$

(c) $\dfrac{1}{4 - \sqrt{3}}$ [NEAB]

5. The diagram shows a window.
The arc AB is a semicircle. $BC = AD = 75\,\text{cm}$, $DC = 80\,\text{cm}$.

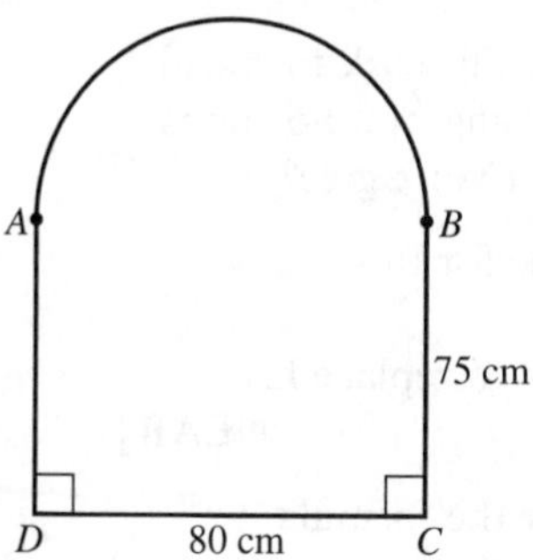

Calculate the area of the window. [SEG]

6. P, Q, R and S are four points on the circumference of a circle. PR is a diameter of the circle and PQ is parallel to SR. Angle $QPR = 42°$.

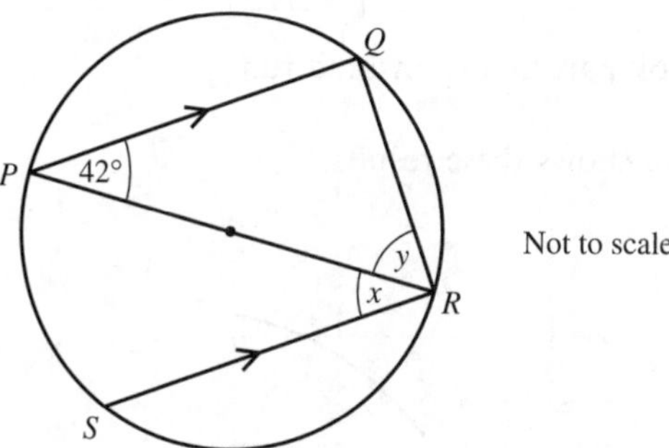

(a) (i) Write down the size of angle x giving a reason for your answer.
(ii) Work out the size of angle y.

(b) The diagram is redrawn. The points P, Q and R are marked in the same positions on the circle. The centre of the circle is O.

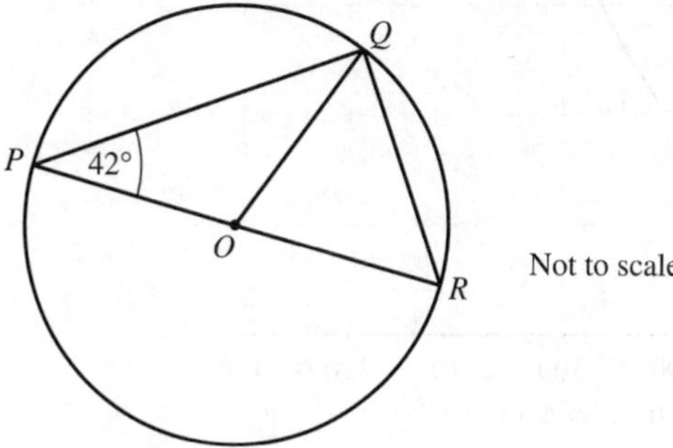

Calculate the size of angle QOR. [SEG]

7. Howard is doing a survey about shops opening on a Sunday.
Two of his questions are:

Question 1 How old are you?
Question 2 Everybody deserves to have a day off work to spend relaxing with their families, and going out. So shops shouldn't open on a Sunday, don't you agree?

(a) Explain why each question is not a good one for this questionnaire.
(b) Write a suitable question for Howard to ask to replace his question 2. [NEAB]

8. The area, A, of a cyclic quadrilateral is given by the formula

$$A = \sqrt{(S-a)(S-b)(S-c)(S-d)},$$

where a, b, c and d are the lengths of the sides of the cyclic quadrilateral and $S = \dfrac{a+b+c+d}{2}$.
When $a = 44$ cm, $b = 15$ cm, $c = 27$ cm and $d = 30$ cm, calculate:
(a) the value of S
(b) the value of A. [NEAB]

9. The finishing times of 360 people who took part in a sponsored run are recorded.
The following cumulative frequency graph shows these results.

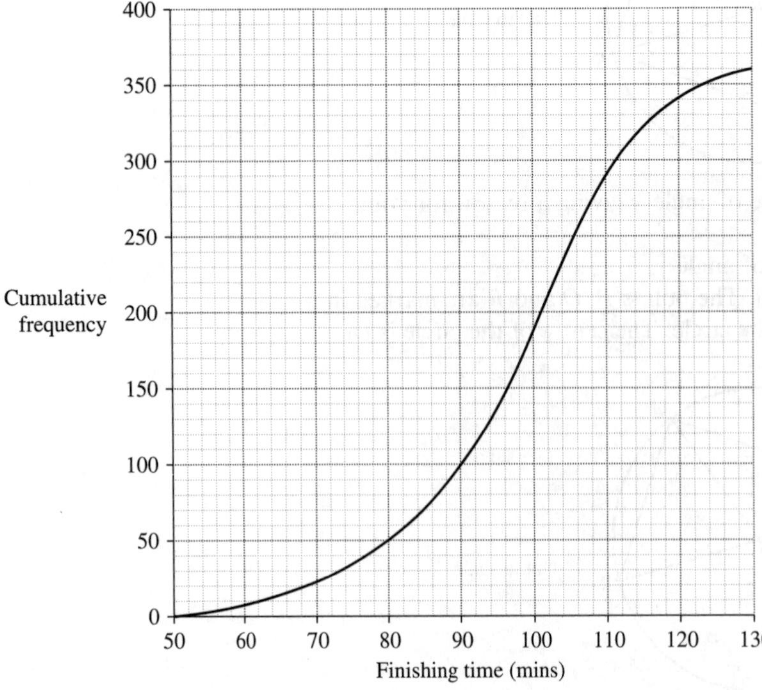

(a) What is the median finishing time?
(b) What is the interquartile range? [SEG]

10. (a) Evaluate $\dfrac{1{\cdot}67 \times 10^{-7}}{4{\cdot}38 \times 10^{3}}$ giving your answer in standard form.

(b) A book published in 1993 contained the following statement.

At a constant 80 kilometres per hour it would take 35 years to travel over the entire road network of the world.

Taking a year as 365 days, calculate the length of the road network of the world, giving your answer in standard form.

[WJEC]

11. The graph of $x = -1$ is drawn on the grid.

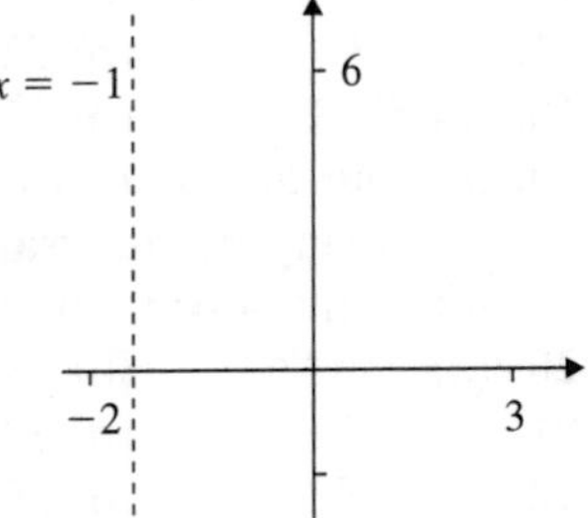

(a) Copy the diagram. On the same grid, for $-2 \leqslant x \leqslant 3$, draw the graphs of:

(i) $y = 2$
(ii) $y = 2x - 1$.

(b) Show clearly, on the grid, the region which is satisfied by the three inequalities

$x \geqslant -1, \quad y \leqslant 2 \quad$ and $\quad y \leqslant 2x - 1$. [NEAB]

12.

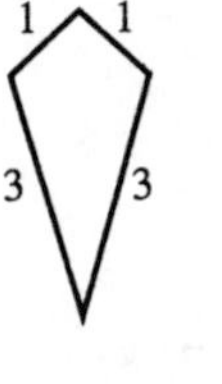

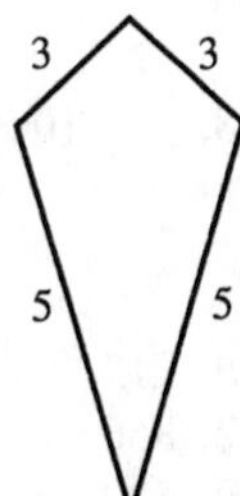

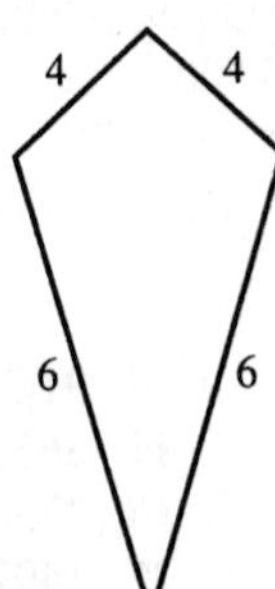

The nth shape in this series has perimeter P.

(a) Write down and simplify an expression for P in terms of n.

(b) Calculate the length of the **shortest** side of the first shape in this series for which

$P > 150$. [SEG]

13.

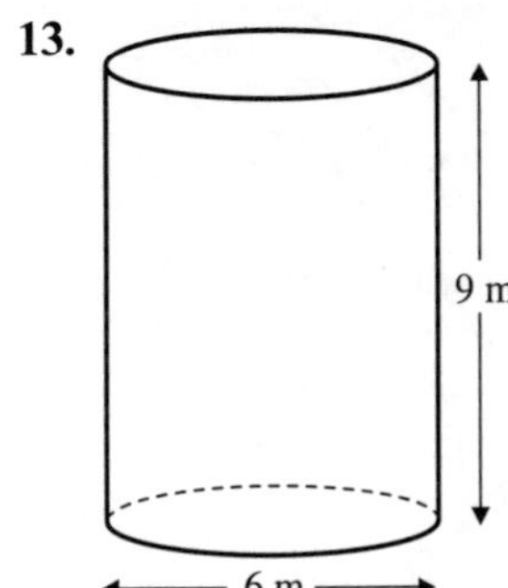

On a farm, wheat grain is stored in a cylindrical tank. The cylindrical tank has an internal diameter of 6 metres and a height of 9 metres.

(a) Calculate the volume, in m^3, of the tank.
Give your answer correct to 2 decimal places.

$1\ m^3$ of wheat grain weighs $0{\cdot}766$ tonnes.

(b) Calculate the weight, in tonnes, of wheat grain in the storage tank when it is full. [Edexcel]

Answers

Number 1

page 1 **Exercise 1**

1. 20	**2.** 400	**3.** 80	**4.** 6	**5.** 6000	**6.** 20 000
7. 5 000 000	**8.** 800 000	**9.** 200	**10.** 70	**11.** 10	**12.** 800
13. 6000	**14.** 60	**15.** 400	**16.** 70 000, 70		

17. (a) 720 (b) 5206 (c) 16 430 (d) 500 000 (e) 300 090 (f) 8500
18. (a) 8753 (b) 3578
19. (a) four thousand, six hundred and twenty (b) six hundred and seven
(c) twenty-five thousand, four hundred (d) six million, eight hundred thousand
(e) twenty-one thousand, four hundred and twenty-five
20. (a) 75 423 (b) 23 574
21. (a) 257 (b) 3221 (c) 704
22. (a) 1392 (b) 26 611 (c) 257 900
23. (a) 5□0 (b) 52 000
24. (a) 2058, 2136, 2142, 2290 (b) 5029, 5299, 5329, 5330
(c) 25 000, 25 117, 25 171, 25 200, 25 500
25. 100 **26.** 10 **27.** $a = 100$, $b = 7$ **28.** $p = 1000$, $q = 10$

page 3 **Exercise 2**

1. 3497	**2.** 2435	**3.** 785	**4.** 91 745	**5.** 212	**6.** 41	**7.** 859
8. 208	**9.** 270	**10.** 5000	**11.** 365	**12.** 856	**13.** 2528	**14.** 64 568
15. 85	**16.** 324	**17.** 639	**18.** 325	**19.** $52\frac{1}{7}$	**20.** 52	**21.** 2018
22. 4569	**23.** 7	**24.** 1080	**25.** 1492	**26.** 524	**27.** 5800	**28.** 188
29. 1641	**30.** 365	**31.** 254	**32.** 21 200			

page 3

Test 1	**Test 2**	**Test 3**	**Test 4**
1. 22	**1.** 22	**1.** 40	**1.** 35
2. 45	**2.** 27	**2.** 40	**2.** 18
3. 8	**3.** 54	**3.** 10	**3.** 83
4. 58	**4.** 45	**4.** 81	**4.** 8
5. 77	**5.** 143	**5.** 98	**5.** 32
6. 48	**6.** 9	**6.** 90	**6.** 89
7. 36	**7.** 5	**7.** 6	**7.** 29
8. 9	**8.** 1300	**8.** 35	**8.** 12
9. 110	**9.** 198	**9.** 52	**9.** 100
10. 42	**10.** 50	**10.** 190	**10.** 154
11. 48	**11.** 57	**11.** 5	**11.** 55
12. 7	**12.** 21	**12.** 8	**12.** 11
13. 116	**13.** 49	**13.** 110	**13.** 5000
14. 21	**14.** 37	**14.** 195	**14.** 225
15. 900	**15.** 12	**15.** 32	**15.** 63

page 4 **Exercise 3**

1. (a) $\begin{array}{r} 285 \\ +\ \underline{514} \\ \underline{799} \end{array}$ (b) $\begin{array}{r} 637 \\ +\ \underline{252} \\ \underline{889} \end{array}$ (c) $\begin{array}{r} 635 \\ +\ \underline{344} \\ \underline{979} \end{array}$

2. (a) $\begin{array}{r} 356 \\ +\ \underline{526} \\ \underline{882} \end{array}$ (b) $\begin{array}{r} 224 \\ +\ \underline{537} \\ \underline{761} \end{array}$ (c) $\begin{array}{r} 388 \\ +\ \underline{425} \\ \underline{813} \end{array}$

3. (a) $\begin{array}{r} 48 \\ \times\ \underline{\ \ 3} \\ \underline{144} \end{array}$ (b) $\begin{array}{r} 33 \\ \times\ \underline{\ \ 7} \\ \underline{231} \end{array}$ (c) $\begin{array}{r} 321 \\ \times\ \underline{\ \ \ 5} \\ \underline{1605} \end{array}$

4. (a) $150 \div 3 = 50$ (b) $15 \times 4 = 60$ (c) $9 \times 9 = 81$ (d) $1152 \div 6 = 192$

5. (a) $\begin{array}{r} 445 \\ +\ \underline{285} \\ \underline{730} \end{array}$ (b) $\begin{array}{r} 427 \\ +\ \underline{177} \\ \underline{604} \end{array}$ (c) $\begin{array}{r} 535 \\ +\ \underline{264} \\ \underline{799} \end{array}$

6. (a) $35 \times 7 = 245$ (b) $58 \times 10 = 580$ (c) $32 \div 4 = 8$ (d) $950 \div 5 = 190$

7. (a) $72 + 29 = 101$ (b) $108 - 17 = 91$ (c) $\begin{array}{r} 889 \\ -\ \underline{346} \\ \underline{543} \end{array}$ (d) $\begin{array}{r} 335 \\ -\ \underline{218} \\ \underline{117} \end{array}$

8. Pupils check answers

9. (a) 4 (b) 8 (c) 8

10. (a) − (b) ÷ (c) × (d) ÷ (e) +

11. (a) + (b) −, − (c) +

page 6 **Exercise 4**

1. T **2.** F **3.** T **4.** T **5.** T

6. F **7.** T **8.** T **9.** $50 + 7 + \frac{2}{10}$

10. (a) 235·1 (b) 67·23 (c) 98·32 (d) 3·167

11. 0·2, 0·31, 0·41 **12.** 0·58, 0·702, 0·75 **13.** 0·41, 0·43, 0·432

14. 0·6, 0·609, 0·61 **15.** 0·04, 0·15, 0·2, 0·35 **16.** 0·18, 0·81, 1·18, 1·8

17. 0·061, 0·07, 0·1, 0·7 **18.** 0·009, 0·025, 0·03, 0·2 **19.** CARWASH

20. (a) 32·51 (b) 0·853 (c) 1·16

21. (a) 5·69 (b) 0·552 (c) 1·30

22. (a) £3·50 (b) £0·15 (c) £0·03 (d) £0·10 (e) £12·60 (f) £0·08

23. (a) T (b) F (c) T (d) T

page 7 **Exercise 5**

1. 4·3 **2.** 0·7 **3.** 9·4 **4.** 1·2 **5.** 16 **6.** 10·7

7. 17·4 **8.** 128 **9.** 375 **10.** 0·24 **11.** 1·92 **12.** 5·2

13. 0·06 **14.** 1·76 **15.** 3·16 **16.** 105 **17.** 50 **18.** 125

page 7 **Exercise 6**

1. 6·34 **2.** 8·38 **3.** 81·5 **4.** 7·4 **5.** 7245 **6.** 32 **7.** 6·3

8. 142 **9.** 4·1 **10.** 30 **11.** 710 **12.** 39·5 **13.** 0·624 **14.** 0·897

15. 0·175 **16.** 0·236 **17.** 0·127 **18.** 0·705 **19.** 1·3 **20.** 0·08 **21.** 0·007

22. 21·8 **23.** 0·035 **24.** 0·0086 **25.** 95 **26.** 111·1 **27.** 0·32 **28.** 70

29. 5·76 **30.** 9·99 **31.** 660 **32.** 1 **33.** 0·042 **34.** 6200 **35.** 0·009

36. 0·0555 **37.** (a) 0 (b) (i) 5, 2 (ii) 5, 2, 0 (iii) 0, 5, 2 and ·

page 8 Exercise 7

1. 10·14 **2.** 20·94 **3.** 26·71 **4.** 216·95 **5.** 9·6 **6.** 23·1
7. 9·14 **8.** 17·32 **9.** 0·062 **10.** 1·11 **11.** 4·36 **12.** 2·41
13. 1·36 **14.** 6·23 **15.** 2·46 **16.** 8·4 **17.** 2·8 **18.** 10·3
19. 0·18 **20.** 4·01 **21.** 6·66 **22.** 41·11 **23.** 3·6 **24.** 6·44
25. 105·2 cm **26.** £8·96

page 9 Exercise 8

1. 0·06 **2.** 0·15 **3.** 012 **4.** 0·006 **5.** 1·8 **6.** 3·5
7. 1·8 **8.** 0·8 **9.** 0·36 **10.** 0·014 **11.** 1·26 **12.** 2·35
13. 8·52 **14.** 3·12 **15.** 0·126 **16.** 127·2 **17.** 0·17 **18.** 0·327
19. 0·126 **20.** 0·34 **21.** 0·055 **22.** 0·52 **23.** 1·3 **24.** 0·001

page 9 Exercise 9

1. 2·1 **2.** 3·1 **3.** 4·36 **4.** 4 **5.** 4 **6.** 2·5
7. 16 **8.** 200 **9.** 70 **10.** 0·92 **11.** 30·5 **12.** 6·2
13. 12·5 **14.** 122 **15.** 212 **16.** 56 **17.** 60 **18.** 1500
19. 0·3 **20.** 0·7 **21.** 0·5 **22.** 3·04 **23.** 5·62 **24.** 0·78
25. 0·14 **26.** 3·75 **27.** 0·075 **28.** 0·15 **29.** 1·22 **30.** 163·8
31. 1·75 **32.** 18·8 **33.** 8 **34.** 88 **35.** 580

page 10 Crossnumbers

A.

9	1		2	1	4	0
4		1	7		5	
	6	4		8		9
7	0		3	1	8	
4			8		3	6
4	3	7		8	1	
0		2	3		6	3

B.

9	6		1	5	7	3
3		5	6		1	
	8	3		3		8
6	6		5	9	4	
3			6		7	0
1	7	4		8	9	
8		7	0		9	3

C.

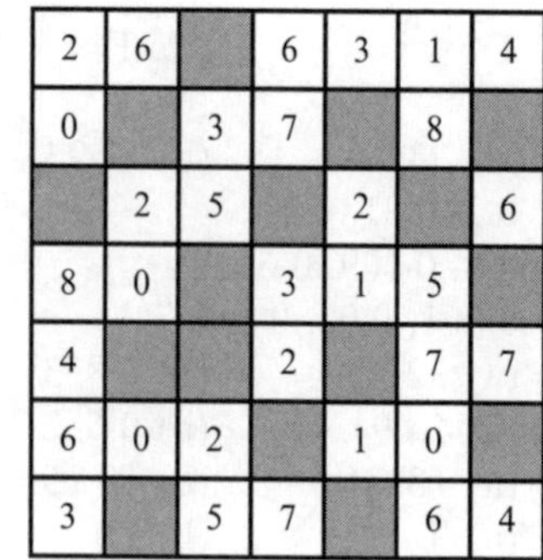

2	6		6	3	1	4
0		3	7		8	
	2	5		2		6
8	0		3	1	5	
4			2		7	7
6	0	2		1	0	
3		5	7		6	4

page 11 Exercise 10

1. (a) 11, 22, 11, 33 (b) 12, 24,13, 39 (c) 7, 14, 28, 17, 51
(d) 9, 16, 32, 21, 63 (e) 11, 18, 36, 25, 75 (f) 13, 20, 40, 29, 87

2. (a) 6, 12, 27, 20, 5 (b) 3, 6, 21, 14, $3\frac{1}{2}$ (c) 8, 16, 31, 24, 6
(d) 10, 20, 35, 28, 7 (e) 1, 2, 17, 10, $2\frac{1}{2}$ (f) 12, 24, 39, 32, 8

3. (a) 7, 22, 44, 22, $5\frac{1}{2}$ (b) 10, 25, 50, 28, 7 (c) 16, 31, 62, 40, 10
(d) $\frac{1}{2}$, $15\frac{1}{2}$, 31, 9, $2\frac{1}{4}$ (e) 100, 115, 230, 208, 52 (f) 24, 39, 78, 56, 14

4. (a) 4, 16, 48, 38, 19 (b) 5, 25, 75, 65, $32\frac{1}{2}$ (c) 6, 36, 108, 98, 49
(d) 8, 64, 192, 182, 91 (e) 1, 1, 3, −7, $-3\frac{1}{2}$ (f) 10, 100, 300, 290, 145

5. ×4, square root, −10, × − 2 **6.** reciprocal, +1, square, ÷3 **7.** +3, cube, ÷−2, +100

page 13 **Exercise 11**

1. (a) 1, 2, 3, 6 (b) 1, 3, 5, 15 (c) 1, 2, 3, 6, 9, 18
(d) 1, 3, 7, 21 (e) 1, 2, 4, 5, 8, 10, 20, 40
2. 2, 3, 5, 7, 11, 13, 17, 19
3. $2+3=5$, $2+5=7$ etc.
4. (b) 101 (d) 151 and (e) 293 are prime
5. (a) $36 = 2 \times 2 \times 3 \times 3$ (b) $60 = 2 \times 2 \times 3 \times 5$ (c) $216 = 2 \times 2 \times 2 \times 3 \times 3 \times 3$
(d) $200 = 2 \times 2 \times 2 \times 5 \times 5$ (e) $1500 = 2 \times 2 \times 3 \times 5 \times 5 \times 5$
6. $1200 = 2 \times 2 \times 2 \times 2 \times 3 \times 5 \times 5$
7. (a) 3, 6, 9, 12 (b) 4, 8, 12, 16 (c) 10, 20, 30, 40 (d) 11, 22, 33, 44 (e) 20, 40, 60, 80
8. (a) 32 (b) 56
9. 12, 24, etc.
10. (a) even (b) odd (c) even

11.

	Prime number	Multiple of 3	Factor of 16
Number greater than 5	7	9	8
Odd number	5	3	1
Even number	2	6	4

12. (a) 7 (b) 50 (c) 1 (d) 5

page 14 **Exercise 12**

1. (a) 6, 12, 18, 24 (b) 9, 18, 27, 36 (c) 18
2. (a) 9, 18, 27, 36, 45 (b) 15, 30, 45, 60 (c) 45
3. (a) 30 (b) 60 (c) 30
4. 8
5. (a) 4 (b) 3 (c) 6 (d) 5 (e) 9
6. 8 and 16 etc.
7. 11 and 22 etc.

page 15 **Exercise 13**

1. −4 **2.** −12 **3.** −11 **4.** −3 **5.** −5 **6.** 4 **7.** −5 **8.** −8
9. 19 **10.** −17 **11.** −4 **12.** −5 **13.** −11 **14.** 6 **15.** −4 **16.** 6
17. 0 **18.** −18 **19.** −3 **20.** −11 **21.** −12 **22.** 4 **23.** 4 **24.** 0
25. −8 **26.** −3 **27.** 3 **28.** −12 **29.** 18 **30.** −5 **31.** −66 **32.** 98

page 16 **Exercise 14**

1. −8 **2.** −7 **3.** 1 **4.** 1 **5.** 9 **6.** 11 **7.** −8 **8.** 42
9. 4 **10.** 15 **11.** −7 **12.** −9 **13.** −1 **14.** −7 **15.** 0 **16.** 11
17. −14 **18.** 0 **19.** 17 **20.** 3 **21.** −1 **22.** −3 **23.** 12 **24.** −9
25. 3 **26.** 0 **27.** 8 **28.** 2

29. (a)

+	−5	1	6	−2
3	−2	4	9	1
−2	−7	−1	4	−4
6	1	7	12	4
−10	−15	−9	−4	−12

(b)

+	−3	2	−4	7
5	−2	7	1	12
−2	−5	0	−6	5
10	7	12	6	17
−6	−9	−4	−10	1

page 17 **Exercise 15**

1. −6 **2.** −4 **3.** −15 **4.** 9 **5.** −8 **6.** −15 **7.** −24 **8.** 6
9. 12 **10.** −18 **11.** −21 **12.** 25 **13.** −60 **14.** 21 **15.** 48 **16.** −16
17. −42 **18.** 20 **19.** −42 **20.** −66 **21.** −4 **22.** −3 **23.** 3 **24.** −5
25. 4 **26.** −4 **27.** −4 **28.** −1 **29.** −2 **30.** 4 **31.** −16 **32.** −2
33. −4 **34.** 5 **35.** −10 **36.** 11 **37.** 16 **38.** −2 **39.** −4 **40.** −5
41. 64 **42.** −27 **43.** −600 **44.** 40 **45.** 2 **46.** 36 **47.** −2 **48.** −8

49. (a)

×	4	−3	0	−2
−5	−20	15	0	10
2	8	−6	0	−4
10	40	−30	0	−20
−1	−4	3	0	2

(b)

×	−2	5	−1	−6
3	−6	15	−3	−18
−3	6	−15	3	18
7	−14	35	−7	−42
2	−4	10	−2	−12

page 17 **Test 1**

1. −16 **2.** 64 **3.** −15 **4.** −2 **5.** 15 **6.** 18 **7.** 3
8. −6 **9.** 11 **10.** −48 **11.** −7 **12.** 9 **13.** 6 **14.** −18
15. −10 **16.** 8 **17.** −6 **18.** −30 **19.** 4 **20.** −1

page 17 **Test 2**

1. −16 **2.** 6 **3.** −13 **4.** 42 **5.** −4 **6.** −4 **7.** −12
8. −20 **9.** 6 **10.** 0 **11.** 36 **12.** −10 **13.** −7 **14.** 10
15. 6 **16.** −18 **17.** −9 **18.** 15 **19.** 1 **20.** 0

page 17 **Test 3**

1. 100 **2.** −20 **3.** −8 **4.** −7 **5.** −4 **6.** 10 **7.** 9
8. −10 **9.** 7 **10.** 35 **11.** −20 **12.** −24 **13.** −10 **14.** −7
15. −19 **16.** −1 **17.** −5 **18.** −13 **19.** 0 **20.** 8

page 18 **Test 4**

1. 5 **2.** 2 **3.** −20 **4.** 4 **5.** 1 **6.** −5
7. 1 **8.** 2 **9.** 6 **10.** 12 **11.** 0 **12.** −8

page 18 **Exercise 16**

1. 3^4 **2.** 5^2 **3.** 6^3 **4.** 10^5 **5.** 1^7 **6.** 8^4 **7.** 7^6
8. $2^3 \times 5^2$ **9.** $3^2 \times 7^4$ **10.** $3^2 \times 10^3$ **11.** $5^4 \times 11^2$ **12.** $2^2 \times 3^3$ **13.** $3^2 \times 5^3$ **14.** $2^2 \times 3^3 \times 11^2$
15. (a) 16 (b) 36 (c) 100 (d) 27 (e) 1000
16. (a) 81 (b) 441 (c) 1·44 (d) 0·04 (e) 9·61
(f) 10 000 (g) 625 (h) 75·69 (i) 0·81 (j) 6625·96
17. (a) 169 cm^2 (b) 6·25 cm^2 (c) 129·96 m^2
18. (a) a^3 (b) n^4 (c) s^5 (d) $p^2 \times q^3$ (e) b^7
19. (a) 216 (b) 256 (c) 243 (d) 100 000 (e) 64
(f) 0·001 (g) 8·3521 (h) 567 (i) 1250
20. 10^{10} **21.** 2^7 **22.** (a) $2^1, 2^2, 2^3, 2^4$ (b) 2^{25}p = £335 544·32 **23.** Yes

page 20 **Exercise 17**

1. (a) 4 (b) 6 (c) 1 (d) 10
2. (a) 9 cm (b) 7 cm (c) 12 cm
3. (a) 3·2 (b) 5·4 (c) 10·3 (d) 4·4 (e) 49·1 (f) 7·7 (g) 0·4 (h) 0·9
4. 12·2 cm **5.** 447 m **6.** 7·8 cm **7.** (a) 4 (b) 5 (c) 10 **8.** 5·8 cm

page 21 **Exercise 18**

1. $\frac{1}{3}$ **2.** $\frac{1}{4}$ **3.** $\frac{1}{10}$ **4.** 1 **5.** $\frac{1}{9}$ **6.** $\frac{1}{16}$ **7.** $\frac{1}{100}$ **8.** 1
9. $\frac{1}{49}$ **10.** 1 **11.** $\frac{1}{81}$ **12.** 1 **13.** T **14.** F **15.** T **16.** T
17. F **18.** F **19.** F **20.** T **21.** T **22.** T **23.** F **24.** F
25. F **26.** T **27.** T **28.** T **29.** T **30.** T **31.** T **32.** F

page 21 **Exercise 19**

1. 5^6 **2.** 6^5 **3.** 10^9 **4.** 7^8 **5.** 3^{10} **6.** 8^6 **7.** 2^{13} **8.** 3^4
9. 5^3 **10.** 7^4 **11.** 5^2 **12.** 3^{-4} **13.** 6^5 **14.** 5^{-10} **15.** 7^6 **16.** 7^2
17. 6^5 **18.** 8^1 **19.** 5^8 **20.** 10^2 **21.** 9^{-2} **22.** 3^{-2} **23.** 2^4 **24.** 3^{-2}
25. 7^{-6} **26.** 3^{-4} **27.** 5^{-5} **28.** 8^{-5} **29.** 5^{-5} **30.** 6^4 **31.** 3^0 **32.** 5^0
33. 3^7 **34.** 2^7 **35.** 7^2 **36.** 5^{-1}

page 22 **Exercise 20**

1. 3^6 **2.** 5^{12} **3.** 7^{10} **4.** 8^{20} **5.** x^6 **6.** a^{15} **7.** n^{14} **8.** y^9
9. 2^{-2} **10.** 3^{-4} **11.** 7^2 **12.** x^{-3} **13.** $6a^5$ **14.** $20n^4$ **15.** $14x^5$ **16.** $24y^7$
17. $5n^7$ **18.** $12y^2$ **19.** $9p^5$ **20.** $10p^6$ **21.** $8x^6$ **22.** $27a^6$ **23.** $16y^6$ **24.** $25x^8$
25. $x \pm 3$ **26.** $x = 1$ **27.** $x = 3$ **28.** $x = 0$ **29.** $x = 3$ **30.** $x = 1$ **31.** $x = 2$ **32.** $x = 3$
33. $x = -1$ **34.** $x = -1$ **35.** $x = 0$ **36.** $x = 2$ **37.** $x = 4$ **38.** $x = 0$ **39.** $x = -1$ **40.** $x = 0$

page 22 **Exercise 21**

1. (a) 0·7 (b) 2·44 (c) 3·5 **2.** 23 **3.** 130 years
4. £28·50 **5.** 1455 **6.** 15 h 5 min **7.** £10·35
8. (a)

6	13	8
11	9	7
10	5	12

(b)

11	8	5	10
2	13	16	3
14	1	4	15
7	12	9	6

9. 128 cm^2 **10.** 48

page 24 **Exercise 22**

1. (a) $\begin{array}{r} 519 \\ +\underline{346} \\ \underline{859} \end{array}$ (b) $\begin{array}{r} 334 \\ +\underline{346} \\ \underline{680} \end{array}$ (c) $160 \div 5 = 32$

2. (a) 16 384 (b) 4096 **3.** £4550
4. (a) 3·32 (b) 1·61 (c) 1·46 (d) 4·4 (e) 6·2 (f) 2·74
5. 18

6. (a)

−1	−2	3
4	0	−4
−3	2	1

(b)

4	3	−1
−3	2	7
5	1	0

(c)

0	1	−4
−5	−1	3
2	−3	−2

7. 0·05, 0·11, 0·2, 0·201, 0·21, 0·5
8. A 13°C, B −2°C, C −21°C, D 22°C
9. 9 h 15 min
10. 96 523

page 25 **Exercise 23**

1. £0·78, £1·80, £14·63
2. (a) 3^4 (b) 1^7 (c) $3^3 \times 7^2$ (d) 2^4 (e) 10^6
3. (a) 9 (b) −5 (c) −6 (d) −10 (e) 7 (f) −10
4. 140
5. (a) 50, 20, 5, 2 (b) 50, 20, 10, 5, 1 (c) £1, 50, 5, 1, 1or 50, 50, 50, 5, 2
6. m, 9, z
7. 24
8. Both same (!)
9. 1·50 m
10. (a) What time do we finish? (b) Spurs are rubbish (c) We are under attack.

page 26 **Exercise 24**

1. £3·26
2. £1·70
3. (a) 108 m^2 (b) 3
5. 100 m
6. (a) 5 (b) 27 (c) 2, 5 (d) 25, 49 (e) 8, 27
7. 10 h 30 min
8. (a) 0·54 (b) 40 (c) 0·004 (d) 2·2 (e) £9 (f) £40
9. (a) 11 (b) −4 (c) −14
10. (a) 4, 3 (b) 7, 6 (c) 8, 4 (d) 24, 2

page 27 **Exercise 25**

1. (a) 69 (b) 65
2. 120
3. 360 000 kg
4. 16
6. 64 mph
7. (a) Yes (b) No (c) Yes (d) Yes (e) Yes (f) Yes (g) Yes (h) No
8. £5·12

page 29 **Exercise 26**

1. (a) 45 (b) 30 (c) 30 (d) 20
2. 2 h 10 min
3. 2005
4. 'The London Blackout Murders'
5. 15 min
6. 225 min (= $3\frac{3}{4}$ h)
7. 11 h 5 min
8. 21.10
9. 5
10. 1 h 45 min
11. 18.00
12. 15 min
13. 15 h 10 min

Algebra 1

page 30 **Exercise 1**

1. $3x + 6$
2. $5x + 7$
3. $2x - 4$
4. $6x - y$
5. $3y + t$
6. $3(x + 4)$
7. $5(x + 3)$
8. $6(y + 11)$
9. $\frac{x + 3}{4}$
10. $\frac{x - 7}{3}$
11. $\frac{y - 8}{5}$
12. $\frac{2(4a + 3)}{5}$
13. $\frac{3(m - 6)}{4}$
14. $x^2 - 6$
15. $\frac{x^2 + 3}{4}$
16. $(n + 2)^2$
17. $(w - x)^2$
18. $\frac{x^2 - 7}{3}$
19. $(x - 9)^2 + 10$
20. $\frac{(y + 7)^2}{x}$
21. $\frac{(a - x)^3}{y}$
22. $(l - 3)$ cm
23. $(15 - x)$ cm
24. $(l + 200 - m)$ kg
25. $4(n + 2)$
26. $6w$ kg
27. xl kg
28. $\frac{n}{6}$ pence
29. £$\frac{p}{5}$
30. $\frac{12}{n}$ kg

page 32 **Exercise 2**

1. $5x+8$ **2.** $9x+5$ **3.** $7x+4$ **4.** $7x+4$
5. $7x+7$ **6.** $8x+12$ **7.** $12x-6$ **8.** $2x+5$
9. $2x-5$ **10.** $2x-5$ **11.** $13a+3b-1$ **12.** $10m+3n+8$
13. $3p-2q-8$ **14.** $2s-7t+14$ **15.** $2a+1$ **16.** $x+y+7z$
17. $5x-4y+4z$ **18.** $5k-4m$ **19.** $4a+5b-9$ **20.** $a-4x-5e$
21. x^2+7x+3 **22.** x^2+7x+8 **23.** x^2+3x+3 **24.** $3x^2+6x+5$
25. $2x^2+6x-7$ **26.** $3x^2+x+12$ **27.** $2x^2+x+3$ **28.** $2x^2-x$
29. x^2-4x-2 **30.** $3x^2-2x-2$ **31.** $4y^2+5x^2+x$ **32.** $12+x$
33. $2-6y+5y^2$ **34.** $3ab-3b$ **35.** $2cd-2d^2$ **36.** $4ab-2a^2+2$
37. $2x^3+5x^2$ **38.** $11+x^2+x^3$ **39.** $3xy$ **40.** p^2-q^2
41. $2x+8$ **42.** $2x+7$ **43.** $2x+14$ **44.** $3a+b+3$
45. $6x+2y+12$ **46.** $10x+8$

page 33 **Exercise 3**

1. $6x$ **2.** $8x$ **3.** $6x$ **4.** $15a$ **5.** $15a$ **6.** $6y$
7. $20y$ **8.** $-10t$ **9.** $21x$ **10.** $-6x$ **11.** $-20x$ **12.** $20y$
13. $-10x$ **14.** $28a$ **15.** $15a$ **16.** $1000a$ **17.** $2x^2$ **18.** $4x^2$
19. $3y^2$ **20.** $6x^2$ **21.** $8x^2$ **22.** $10y^2$ **23.** $24t^2$ **24.** $6a^2$
25. $2x^3$ **26.** $6x^3$ **27.** $8y^3$ **28.** $6a^3$ **29.** $21p^2$ **30.** $12x^2$
31. $60x^2$ **32.** $30x^2$ **33.** $6ab$ **34.** $3x^4$ **35.** $2xy$ **36.** $10pq$
37. $15xy$ **38.** $18x^3$ **39.** $24a^4$ **40.** $2a^2b$ **41.** $3xy^2$ **42.** $5c^2d$
43. a^2b^2 **44.** $2x^2y^2$ **45.** $3d^2$ **46.** $10x^2y$ **47.** $-6a^2$ **48.** $2a^2b$

page 33 **Exercise 4**

1. $2x+6$ **2.** $3x+15$ **3.** $4x+24$ **4.** $4x+2$ **5.** $10x+15$
6. $12x-4$ **7.** $12x-12$ **8.** $15x-6$ **9.** $15x-20$ **10.** $14x-21$
11. $4x+6$ **12.** $6x+3$ **13.** $5x+20$ **14.** $12x+12$ **15.** $-8x+2$
16. $-10x+10$ **17.** $-6x-3$ **18.** $-2x-1$ **19.** $-3x-2$ **20.** $-4x+5$
21. x^2+3x **22.** x^2+5x **23.** x^2-2x **24.** x^2-3x **25.** $2x^2+x$
26. $3x^2-2x$ **27.** $3x^2+5x$ **28.** $2x^2-2x$ **29.** $2x^2+4x$ **30.** $6x^2+9x$
31. $6x^2+12x$

page 34 **Exercise 5**

1. $7x+10$ **2.** $8x+2$ **3.** $5a-3$ **4.** $11a+17$
5. $8a-10$ **6.** $8t+4$ **7.** $x+4$ **8.** $x+6$
9. $2x-4$ **10.** -10 **11.** $2x^2+4x+6$ **12.** $2x^2+2x+5$
13. $7a^2+6a-4$ **14.** $5y^2+4y-3$ **15.** $5x^2+2x$ **16.** a^2+2a
17. (a) $2x-2$ (b) $x-1$ (c) $x+2$ (d) $x-3$ (e) $x+3$ (f) $x+3$

page 34 **Exercise 6**

1. (a) 17 (b) 27 (c) 48 (d) 30 (e) 12·5 (f) 121
2. (a) 11 (b) 16 (c) −1 (d) 2·4 (e) 11 (f) 0
3. (a) 7, 11, 18, 29, 47, 76, 123 (b) 12, 19, 31, 50
4. (a) $6\times 7=6+6^2$, $7\times 8=7+7^2$ (b) $10\times 11=10+10^2$, $30\times 31=30+30^2$
5. $5+9\times 1234=11\,111$
$6+9\times 12\,345=111\,111$
$7+9\times 123\,456=1\,111\,111$

6. 63, 3968
7. 3, 5, 5
8. (a) Yes (b) (i) 5 (ii) 10 (iii) 1331
9. (a) $1^3 + 2^3 + 3^3 + 4^3 = (1 + 2 + 3 + 4)^2 = 100$
$1^3 + 2^3 + 3^3 + 4^3 + 5^3 = (1 + 2 + 3 + 4 + 5)^2 = 225$
$1^3 + 2^3 + 3^3 + 4^3 + 5^3 + 6^3 = (1 + 2 + 3 + 4 + 5 + 6)^2 = 441$
(b) $(1 + 2 + 3 + 4 + \ldots + 10)^2 = 55^2 = 3025$
10. (a) 16 (b) 15 (c) 26 (d) 25
11. (a) 113 (b) (i) 90 (ii) 105 (iii) 199 (iv) 437
12. (a) (i) 24 (ii) 36 (iii) 75
(b) (i) 23 (ii) 35 (iii) 59
(c) (i) 28 (ii) 39 (iii) 50 (iv) 88
(c) (i) 40 (ii) 21 (iii) 31 (iv) 50

page 38 Exercise 7

1. 60 **2.** (a) 45 **3.** 48 **4.** (a) 14 (b) 35
5. (a) 54 (b) 21 (c) 36 **6.** (a) 42, 59 (b) 51, 67 (c) 37, 50
7. 57, 21, 6 **8.** (a) 91, 133 (b) 101, 145
9. (a) 112 (b) 217 (c) 87 **10.** 2559

page 41 Exercise 8

1. (a) $2n$ (b) $10n$ (c) $3n$ (d) $11n$ (e) $100n$ (f) $6n$ (g) $22n$ (h) $30n$
2. (a) $11 \rightarrow 55$; $n \rightarrow 5n$ (b) $20 \rightarrow 180$; $n \rightarrow 9n$ (c) $12 \rightarrow 1200$; $n \rightarrow 100n$
3. (a) $10 \rightarrow 20 \rightarrow 23$; $n \rightarrow 2n \rightarrow 2n + 3$ (b) $20 \rightarrow 60 \rightarrow 61$; $n \rightarrow 3n \rightarrow 3n + 1$
4. (a) $3 \rightarrow 18 \rightarrow 20$; $4 \rightarrow 24 \rightarrow 26$ (b) $3 \rightarrow 15 \rightarrow 13$; $4 \rightarrow 20 \rightarrow 18$
5. (a) $n \rightarrow 5n \rightarrow 5n + 1$ (b) (i) 51 (ii) $5n + 1$
6. (b) A $3n - 2$; B $4n + 2$; C $7n - 2$
7. (a) 80 (b) 76 (c) $8n$ (d) $8n - 4$
8. (a) 79 (b) 81 (c) $4n - 1$ (d) $4n + 1$
9. (a) $6n + 2$ (b) $6n - 1$ **10.** (a) $n \rightarrow n(n + 1)$ (b) $n \rightarrow n^2 + 1$
11. $n^2 + 4$ **12.** (a) 10^2 (b) n^2
13. (a) 110 (b) $n(n + 1)$ **14.** (a) $\frac{10}{11}$ (b) $\frac{n}{n+1}$
15. (a) $\frac{5}{10^2}$ (b) $\frac{5}{n^2}$ **16.** (a) 120 (b) $n(n + 2)$
17. A $3n - 4$; B $n^2 - 2$; C $n(n + 2)$

page 45 Exercise 9

1. 4 kg **2.** 3 kg **3.** 3 kg **4.** 2 kg **5.** 3 kg
6. 4 kg **7.** 4 kg **8.** 3 kg **9.** $1\frac{1}{2}$ kg **10.** 2 kg
11. 2 kg, 4 kg **12.** 6 kg, 3 kg **13.** 9 kg, 3 kg **14.** 4 kg, 8 kg

page 46 Exercise 10

1. 12 **2.** 9 **3.** 18 **4.** 4 **5.** 17 **6.** -5 **7.** 6 **8.** -7 **9.** 4 **10.** 8
11. 17 **12.** -5 **13.** 5 **14.** 6 **15.** 2 **16.** $\frac{4}{5}$ **17.** $2\frac{1}{3}$ **18.** $8\frac{1}{2}$ **19.** $1\frac{5}{6}$ **20.** 0
21. $\frac{5}{9}$ **22.** 1 **23.** $\frac{1}{5}$ **24.** $\frac{2}{7}$ **25.** $\frac{3}{4}$ **26.** $\frac{2}{3}$ **27.** $1\frac{1}{4}$ **28.** $1\frac{1}{5}$ **29.** $1\frac{5}{9}$ **30.** $\frac{1}{3}$
31. $\frac{1}{2}$ **32.** $\frac{1}{10}$ **33.** $-\frac{3}{8}$ **34.** $\frac{9}{50}$ **35.** $\frac{1}{2}$ **36.** $\frac{3}{5}$ **37.** $-\frac{4}{9}$ **38.** 0 **39.** $4\frac{5}{8}$ **40.** $-1\frac{3}{7}$
41. $2\frac{1}{3}$ **42.** $\frac{3}{4}$ **43.** 1 **44.** $3\frac{3}{5}$ **45.** $\frac{1}{3}$ **46.** $2\frac{1}{14}$ **47.** -1 **48.** $-\frac{5}{6}$ **49.** $8\frac{1}{4}$ **50.** -55

page 46 **Exercise 11**

1. $2\frac{3}{4}$ **2.** $1\frac{2}{3}$ **3.** 2 **4.** $\frac{1}{5}$ **5.** $\frac{1}{2}$ **6.** 2 **7.** $5\frac{1}{3}$ **8.** $1\frac{1}{5}$ **9.** 0 **10.** $\frac{2}{9}$
11. $1\frac{1}{2}$ **12.** $\frac{1}{6}$ **13.** $1\frac{1}{3}$ **14.** $\frac{6}{7}$ **15.** $\frac{4}{7}$ **16.** 7 **17.** $\frac{5}{8}$ **18.** 5 **19.** $\frac{2}{5}$ **20.** $\frac{1}{3}$
21. 4 **22.** -1 **23.** 1 **24.** $\frac{6}{7}$ **25.** $1\frac{1}{4}$ **26.** 1 **27.** $\frac{7}{9}$ **28.** $-1\frac{1}{2}$ **29.** $\frac{2}{9}$ **30.** $-1\frac{1}{2}$

page 47 **Exercise 12**

1. 3 **2.** 5 **3.** $10\frac{1}{2}$ **4.** -8 **5.** $\frac{1}{3}$ **6.** $-4\frac{1}{2}$ **7.** $3\frac{1}{3}$ **8.** $3\frac{1}{2}$ **9.** $3\frac{2}{3}$ **10.** -2
11. $-5\frac{1}{2}$ **12.** $4\frac{1}{5}$ **13.** $\frac{3}{7}$ **14.** $\frac{7}{11}$ **15.** $4\frac{4}{5}$ **16.** 5 **17.** 9 **18.** $-2\frac{1}{3}$ **19.** $\frac{2}{5}$ **20.** $\frac{3}{5}$
21. -1 **22.** 13 **23.** 9 **24.** $4\frac{1}{2}$ **25.** $3\frac{1}{3}$

page 47 **Exercise 13**

1. $\frac{3}{5}$ **2.** $\frac{4}{7}$ **3.** $\frac{11}{12}$ **4.** $\frac{6}{11}$ **5.** $\frac{2}{3}$ **6.** $\frac{5}{9}$ **7.** $\frac{7}{9}$ **8.** $1\frac{1}{3}$ **9.** $\frac{1}{2}$ **10.** $\frac{2}{3}$
11. 3 **12.** $1\frac{1}{2}$ **13.** 24 **14.** 15 **15.** -10 **16.** 21 **17.** 21 **18.** $2\frac{2}{3}$ **19.** $4\frac{3}{8}$ **20.** $1\frac{1}{2}$
21. $3\frac{3}{4}$ **22.** 11 **23.** 13 **24.** 10 **25.** $\frac{1}{3}$ **26.** 1 **27.** $3\frac{2}{3}$ **28.** 28 **29.** $4\frac{1}{2}$ **30.** 1
31. 220 **32.** -500 **33.** $-\frac{98}{99}$ **34.** 6 **35.** 30 **36.** $1\frac{1}{2}$ **37.** 84 **38.** 6 **39.** $\frac{5}{7}$ **40.** $\frac{3}{5}$

page 48 **Exercise 14**

1. 2 **2.** 3 **3.** 2 **4.** 2 **5.** 2 **6.** 3 **7.** 6 **8.** 1

page 49 **Exercise 15**

1. 3 **2.** $\frac{3}{4}$ **3.** $4\frac{1}{2}$ **4.** $-\frac{3}{10}$ **5.** $-\frac{1}{2}$ **6.** $17\frac{2}{3}$
7. $\frac{1}{6}$ **8.** 5 **9.** 12 **10.** $3\frac{1}{3}$ **11.** $4\frac{2}{3}$ **12.** -9

page 50 **Exercise 16**

1. $\frac{3}{4}$ **2.** $1\frac{1}{2}$ **3.** $1\frac{3}{8}$ **4.** $1\frac{1}{4}$ **5.** 7
6. (a) $3\frac{3}{5}$ (b) $\frac{3}{4}$ (c) 7 **7.** (a) 41 (b) 31 (c) 65
8. 29 **9.** 55, 56, 57 **10.** 41, 42, 43, 44
11. (a) (i) $x - 3$ (ii) $2(x - 3)$ (b) $x = 12\frac{1}{2}$
12. $x = 8$, perimeter = 60 cm **13.** (a) -6 (b) 2 (c) A and C
14. 11 **15.** £6 **16.** $x = 3$ **17.** $x = 47$ **18.** 27 cm

page 53 **Exercise 17**

Your graphs should pass through the points given.

1. (−3, −5), (−2, −3), (−1, −1), (0, 1), (1, 3), (2, 5), (3, 7)
2. (−2, −11), (−1, −8), (0, −5), (1, −2), (2, 1), (3, 4)
3. (−4, −2), (−3, −1), (−2, 0), (−1, 1), (0, 2), (1, 3), (2, 4), (3, 5), (4, 6)
4. (−2, −11), (−1, −9), (0, −7), (1, −5), (2, −3), (3, −1), (4, 1), (5, 3)
5. (−3, −11), (−2, −7), (−1, −3), (0, 1), (1, 5), (2, 9), (3, 13)
6. (−2, −5), (−1, −4), (0, −3), (1, −2), (2, −1), (3, 0), (4, 1), (5, 2)
7. (−4, −4), (−3, −2), (−2, 0), (−1, 2), (0, 4), (1, 6), (2, 8)
8. (−3, −7), (−2, −4), (−1, −1), (0, 2), (1, 5), (2, 8), (3, 11)
9. (−5, 2), (−4, 3), (−3, 4), (−2, 5), (−1, 6), (0, 7), (1, 8), (2, 9), (3, 10)
10. (−3, −15), (−2, −11), (−1, −7), (0, −3), (1, 1), (2, 5), (3, 9)
11. (−3, 10), (−2, 8), (−1, 6), (0, 4), (1, 2), (2, 0), (3, −2)
12. (−2, 12), (−1, 10), (0, 8), (1, 6), (2, 4), (3, 2), (4, 0)

page54 **Exercise 18**

14. (a) $10{\cdot}7\,\text{cm}^2$ (b) $5{\cdot}3 \times 1{\cdot}7$ (c) $12{\cdot}25\,\text{cm}^2$ (d) $3{\cdot}5 \times 3{\cdot}5$
15. (c) $x = 7$ (d) $2058\,\text{cm}^3$ **16.** (d) 3·5 s (e) 3 s (f) 20 m

page 57 **Exercise 19**

1. (a) 3·6/3·7 and −1·6/−1·7 (b) 2·4, −0·4 (c) −1, 3
2. (a) 2·4, −0·4 (b) 0, 2 **3.** (a) 0, 3 (b) 3·8, −0·8
4. (a) −1·6, 3·6 (b) 2·4, − 0·4 **5.** (a) 6·5, 0·5 (b) No intersection
6. (a) −3, 1·5 (b) 1·7, −2·7 **7.** (a) 0, 2·2, −2·2 (b) 0, 2·4, − 2·4

page 59 **Exercise 20**

1. $w = b + 4$ **2.** $w = 2b + 6$ **3.** $w = 2b - 12$ **4.** $m = 2t + 1$ **5.** $m = 3t + 2$ **6.** $s = t + 2$
7. (a) $p = 5n - 2$ (b) $k = 7n + 3$ (c) $w = 2n + 11$
8. (a) $y = 3n + 1$ (b) $h = 4n - 3$ (c) $k = 3n + 5$ **9.** $m = 8c + 4$
10. (a) $t = 2n + 4$ (b) $e = 3n + 11$ (c) $e = \dfrac{3t + 10}{2}$ **11.** $c = \dfrac{n(n - 1)}{2}$
12. (a) $m = 2n(n + 1)$ (b) 220

Shape and space 1

page 63 **Exercise 1**

1. 7·3 cm **2.** 7·9 cm **3.** 8·0 cm **4.** 10·3 cm **5.** 6·4 cm **6.** 6·8 cm
7. 9·0 cm **8.** 9·6 cm **9.** 7·6 cm **10.** 8·7 cm **11.** 8·2 cm **12.** 5·3 cm
14. $60\frac{1}{2}°$ **15.** $85\frac{1}{2}°$ **16.** 72° **17.** 121° **18.** $10\,000\,\text{m}^2$

page 65 **Exercise 2**

1. (a), (b), (d)
5. (a) triangular prism, 6 vertices, 5 faces (b) square pyramid, 5 vertices, 5 faces

page 70 **Exercise 4**

1. 70° **2.** 100° **3.** 70° **4.** 100°
5. 44° **6.** 80° **7.** 40° **8.** 48°
9. 40° **10.** 35° **11.** $a = 40°$, $b = 140°$ **12.** $x = 108°$, $y = 72°$

page 71 **Exercise 5**

1. 50° **2.** 70° **3.** 29° **4.** 30°
5. 70° **6.** 42° **7.** 40° **8.** $a = 55°$, $b = 70°$
9. 60° **10.** $x = 122°$, $y = 116°$ **11.** 135° **12.** 30°
13. 154° **14.** 75° **15.** $x = 30°$ **16.** 28°

page 72 **Exercise 6**

1. 72° **2.** 98° **3.** 80°
4. 74° **5.** 86° **6.** 88°
7. $x = 95°$, $y = 50°$ **8.** $a = 87°$, $b = 74°$ **9.** $a = 65°$, $c = 103°$
10. $a = 68°$, $b = 42°$ **11.** $y = 65°$, $z = 50°$ **12.** $a = 55°$, $b = 75°$, $c = 50°$

page 73 Exercise 7

1. 42° **2.** 68° **3.** 100°
4. 73° **5.** 120° **6.** 52°
7. 100° **8.** $a = 70°$, $b = 60°$ **9.** $x = 58°$, $y = 109°$
10. 66° **11.** 65° **12.** $e = 70°$, $f = 30°$
13. $x = 72°$, $y = 36°$ **14.** $a = 68°$, $b = 72°$, $c = 68°$ **15.** 4°
16. $28\frac{1}{2}°$ **18.** $a = 65°$, $b = 40°$ **19.** $x = 49°$, $y = 61°$
20. $a = 60°$, $b = 40°$ **21.** 136° **22.** 80°
23. $x = 65°$, $y = 35°$, $z = 55°$ **24.** 26°

page 75 Exercise 8

1. (a) 1 (b) 1 **2.** (a) 1 (b) 1 **3.** (a) 4 (b) 4
4. (a) 2 (b) 2 **5.** (a) 0 (b) 6 **6.** (a) 0 (b) 2
7. (a) 0 (b) 2 **8.** (a) 4 (b) 4 **9.** (a) 0 (b) 4
10. (a) 4 (b) 4 **11.** (a) 6 (b) 6 **12.** (a) infinite (b) infinite

page 77 Exercise 10

1. 3 **2.** (a) 1 (b) 1 (c) **3.** 9 **5.** 4

page 79 Exercise 11

1. A trapezium, B rhombus, C rectangle, D kite, E parallelogram
3. (a) 115° (b) 90° (c) 80°
5. C(5, 1), D(0, 0)

page 80 Exercise 12

1. (a) 34° (b) 56° **2.** (a) 35° (b) 35°
3. (a) 72° (b) 108° (c) 80° **4.** (a) 40° (b) 30° (c) 110°
5. (a) 116° (b) 32° (c) 58° **6.** (a) 55° (b) 55°
7. (a) 26° (b) 26° (c) 77° **8.** (a) 52° (b) 64° (c) 116°
9. (a) 110° **10.** (a) 54° (b) 72° (c) 36°
11. (a) 60° (b) 15° (c) 75°

page 81 Exercise 13

1. 34·6 cm **2.** 25·1 cm **3.** 37·7 cm **4.** 15·7 cm **5.** 28·3 cm **6.** 53·4 m
7. 44·6 m **8.** 72·3 m **9.** 13 mm **10.** 8·48 m **11.** 212 **12.** 400 m
13. 22·6 cm **14.** (a) 823 m (b) 655 **15.** 643 cm **16.** 23 or 24 **17.** 45 000

page 84 Exercise 14

1. 95·0 cm^2 **2.** 78·5 cm^2 **3.** 28·3 m^2 **4.** 38·5 m^2
5. 113 cm^2 **6.** 201 cm^2 **7.** 19·6 m^2 **8.** 380 cm^2
9. 29·5 cm^2 **10.** 125 m^2 **11.** 21·5 cm^2 **12.** 4580 g
13. 30; (a) 1508 cm^2 (b) 508 cm^2 **14.** (a) 40·8 m^2 (b) 6 **15.** 118 m^2

page 86 Exercise 15

1. 23·1 cm **2.** 38·6 cm **3.** 20·6 m **4.** 8·23 cm **5.** 28·6 cm **6.** 39·4 m
7. 17·9 cm **8.** 28·1 m **9.** 24·8 cm **10.** 46·3 m **11.** 28·8 cm

page 87 **Exercise 16**

1. 35·9 cm^2 **2.** 84·1 cm^2 **3.** 37·7 cm^2 **4.** 74·6 cm^2 **5.** 13·7 cm^2 **6.** 25·1 cm^2
7. (a) 12·5 cm^2 (b) 50 cm^2 (c) 78·5 cm^2 (d) 28·5 cm^2

page 88 **Exercise 17**

1. 2·39 cm **2.** 4·46 cm **3.** 1·11 m **4.** 4·15 cm **5.** 3·48 cm
6. 3·95 m **7.** 2·55 m **8.** 4·37 cm **9.** 4·62 cm **10.** 5·75 cm
11. 15·9 cm **12.** 5·09 cm **13.** 9·2 m **14.** 58·6 cm **15.** 5·39 cm
16. 17·8 cm **17.** 195 km **18.** 3·95 cm **19.** 215 m^2 **20.** 3·88 m
21. 575 m^2 **22.** 5·41 cm **23.** 4·5 m

page 90 **Exercise 18**

1. 24 cm^2 **2.** 14 cm^2 **3.** 36 cm^2 **4.** 77 cm^2 **5.** 54 cm^2 **6.** 25 cm^2
7. 36 cm^2 **8.** 48 cm^2 **9.** (a) C (b) A **10.** (a) 12 cm (b) 12m (c) 12 cm
11. £48 000 **12.** 80 m^2 **13.** 40 cm **14.** 32 cm **15.** 28 cm **16.** 28 cm

page 92 **Exercise 19**

1. (b) 10, 6, 3 (c) 36 (d) 17 **2.** (b) 5, 14, 6 (c) 42 (d) 17
3. $13\frac{1}{2}$ **4.** $14\frac{1}{2}$ **5.** 24 **6.** 22 **7.** 21
8. (a) 248 cm^2 (b) 120 **9.** 45 cm **10.** 96 **11.** 500 m
12. (a) 8·5 m (b) 20 cm (c) 10 m
13. 57 cm^2 **14.** 48 cm^2 **15.** 36 cm^2 **16.** 41 cm^2

page 94 **Exercise 20**

1. 42 cm^2 **2.** 22 cm^2 **3.** 103 cm^2 **4.** 60·5 cm^2 **5.** 143 cm^2
6. 9 cm^2 **7.** 47 cm^2 **8.** 81·75 cm^2 **9.** 7·2 cm **10.** £252

page 96 **Exercise 22**

1. 150 cm^3 **2.** 60 m^3 **3.** 480 cm^3 **4.** 300 cm^3 **5.** 56 m^3
6. 280 cm^3 **7.** 145 cm^3 **8.** 448 cm^3 **9.** 108 cm^3

page 97 **Exercise 23**

1. 62·8 cm^3 **2.** 113 cm^3 **3.** 198 cm^3 **4.** 763 cm^3
5. 157 cm^3 **6.** 385 cm^3 **7.** 770 cm^3 **8.** 176 m^3
9. 228 m^3 **10.** 486 cm^3 **11.** 113 litres **12.** 141 cm^3, 25·1 cm^3

page 99 **Exercise 24**

1. (a) 1·5 g/cm^3 (b) 9 g/cm^3 (c) 5·6 g/cm^3
2. 8000 g or 8 kg
3. 2400 cm^3
4. (a) 200 m^2 (b) 2400 m^3
5. 770 cm^3
6. (a) 2·25 cm^2 (b) 0·451 cm^3 (c) 4510 cm^3 **7.** 125
8. (a) 76 cm^2 (b) 30 400 cm^3 (c) 237 kg (d) 33
9. No **10.** 1570 cm^3, 12·6 kg **11.** 53 times
12. 191 cm **13.** 98 min **14.** 144

Number 2

page 102 **Exercise 1**

1. 805 **2.** 459 **3.** 650 **4.** 1333 **5.** 2745
6. 1248 **7.** 4522 **8.** 30 368 **9.** 28 224 **10.** 8568
11. 46 800 **12.** 66 281 **13.** 57 602 **14.** 89 516 **15.** 97 525

page 102 **Exercise 2**

1. 32 **2.** 25 **3.** 18 **4.** 13 **5.** 35
6. 22 r 2 **7.** 23 r 24 **8.** 18 r 10 **9.** 27 r 18 **10.** 13 r 31
11. 35 r 6 **12.** 23 r 24 **13.** 64 r 37 **14.** 151 r 17 **15.** 2961 r 15

page 103 **Exercise 3**

1. £47·04 **2.** 46 **3.** 7592 **4.** 21, 17 p change **5.** 8
6. £85 **7.** £14 million **8.** £80·64 **9.** £21 600

page 104 **Exercise 4**

1. £12 **2.** £8 **3.** £10 **4.** £3 **5.** £2·40 **6.** £24 **7.** £45
8. £72 **9.** £244 **10.** £9·60 **11.** $42 **12.** $88 **13.** 8 kg **14.** 12 kg
15. 272 g **16.** 45 m **17.** 40 km **18.** $710 **19.** 4·94 kg **20.** 60 g **21.** £204

page 104 **Exercise 5**

1. £0·28 **2.** £1·16 **3.** £1·22 **4.** £2·90 **5.** £3·57 **6.** £0·45 **7.** £0·93
8. £37·03 **9.** £16·97 **10.** £0·38 **11.** £0·79 **12.** £1·60 **13.** £13·40 **14.** £50
15. £2·94 **16.** £11·06 **17.** £1·23 **18.** £4·40 **19.** £11·25 **20.** £22·71 **21.** £9·19

page 105 **Exercise 6**

1. £63 **2.** £736 **3.** £77·55 **4.** £104 **5.** £1960 **6.** £792 **7.** £132
8. £45·75 **9.** £110·30 **10.** £42 **11.** £12·03 **12.** £9·49 **13.** £7·35 **14.** £7·01
15. £12·34 **16.** £16·92 **17.** £31·87 **18.** £9·02 **19.** £8·88 **20.** £14·14

page 105 **Exercise 7**

1. £35·20 **2.** £5724 **3.** £171·50 **4.** £88·35 **5.** 2·828 kg **6.** £58·50
7. 24 **8.** 59 400 **9.** £9·52 **10.** 3·348 kg **11.** 13·054 kg **12.** £2762·50

page 106 **Exercise 8**

1. £17·51 **2.** £40·66 **3.** £77·96 **4.** £185·34
5. (a) £28 (b) £21 **6.** (a) £480 (b) (i) £16·20 (ii) £1053

page 108 **Exercise 9**

1. £6200 **2.** £25 500
3. (a) £50 (b) £200 (c) £54 (d) £150 (e) £2400
4. 210 000 **5.** 85 kg
6. (a) £9·79 (b) £32 (c) £44·20 (d) £45
7. 8 cm × 10 cm **8.** 350 g

page 109 **Exercise 10**

1. (a) £2200 (b) £2420 (c) £2662
2. (a) £5600 (b) £7024·64
3. £13 107·96
4. (a) £36 465·19 (b) £40 202·87
5. (a) £95 400 (b) £107 191 (c) £161 176
6. (a) £14 033 (b) £734 (c) £107 946
7. £9211·88
8. No. It should be £193·48
9. 8 years
10. 11 years

page 110 **Exercise 11**

1. 8%
2. 10%
3. 25%
4. 2%
5. 4%
6. $2\frac{1}{2}$%
7. 20%
8. 50%
9. 15%
10. 80%
11. 25%
12. 20%
13. $12\frac{1}{2}$%
14. $33\frac{1}{3}$%
15. 80%
16. 5%
17. 6%
18. 20%
19. 5%
20. $2\frac{1}{2}$%

page 111 **Exercise 12**

1. 36·4%
2. 19·0%
3. 19·4%
4. 22·0%
5. 12·2%
6. 9·4%
7. 14·0%
8. 17·4%
9. 32·7%
10. 10·2%
11. 7·7%
12. 35·3%
13. 30·8%
14. 5·2%
15. 14·1%
16. 14·5%
17. 19·1%
18. 3·6%
19. 31·1%
20. 6·5%

page 111 **Exercise 13**

1. 12%
2. 29%
3. 16%
4. 0·25%
5. 15%
6. 61·1%
7. 15%
8. 14·2%
9. (a) 25 p (b) £12·80 (c) £2·80 (d) 28%
10. (a) £10 (b) (i) £4·20 (ii) 42%
11. (a) (i) 120 cm (ii) 75 cm (iii) 10 000 cm^2 (iv) 9000 cm^2 (b) 10%

page 113 **Exercise 14**

1. 200 m
2. 500 m
3. (b) 200 m (c) 1 km (d) 0·6 km
4. 63 m
5. 24 km
6. 120 m
7. (a) 2·8 km (b) 3·25 km (c) 2·7 km

page 114 **Exercise 15**

1. 150 cm
2. 125 cm
3. 28 cm
4. 5·9 cm
5. (a) 60 cm (b) 84 cm (c) 56 cm (d) 140 cm (e) 100 cm
6. 2·5 cm

page 115 **Exercise 16**

1. £10, £20
2. £45, £15
3. 330 g, 550 g
4. $480, $600
5. 36, 90
6. £10, £20, £30
7. £70
8. £50
9. 3250
10. (a) 1 : 3 (b) 2 : 7 (c) 3 : 5

page 116 **Exercise 17**

1. 8
2. 5
3. 9
4. 30 g zinc, 40 g tin
5. 24
6. 2·4 kg
7. 6
8. 18 cm
9. 22·5 cm
10. 12 cm
11. 300 g
12. 5 : 3
13. £200
14. 42c
15. £175 000
16. $\frac{1}{4}$ m^3

page 118 **Exercise 18**

1. 2·35 **2.** 0·814 **3.** 26·2 **4.** 35·6 **5.** 113 **6.** 211
7. 0·825 **8.** 0·0312 **9.** 5·9 **10.** 1·2 **11.** 0·55 **12.** 0·72
13. 0·14 **14.** 1·8 **15.** 25 **16.** 31 **17.** 486·7 **18.** 500·4
19. 2·889 **20.** 3·113 **21.** 0·07154 **22.** 3·041 **23.** 2464 **24.** 488 900
25. 0·513 **26.** 5·8 **27.** 66 **28.** 587·6 **29.** 0·6 **30.** 0·07
31. 5·84 **32.** 88 **33.** 2500 **34.** 52700 **35.** 0·006 **36.** 7000

page 118 **Exercise 19**

1. 5·38 **2.** 11·05 **3.** 0·41 **4.** 0·37 **5.** 8·02 **6.** 87·04
7. 9·01 **8.** 0·07 **9.** 8·4 **10.** 0·7 **11.** 0·4 **12.** 0·1
13. 6·1 **14.** 19·5 **15.** 8·1 **16.** 7·1 **17.** 8·16 **18.** 3·0
19. 0·545 **20.** 0·0056 **21.** 0·71 **22.** 6·83 **23.** 0·8 **24.** 19·65
25. 0·0714 **26.** 60·1 **27.** −7·3 **28.** −5·42
29. (a) 5·9 cm by 3·3 cm; 5·1 cm by 2·9 cm (b) 19·5 cm^2, 14·8 cm^2

page 119 **Exercise 20**

1. 0·57 **2.** 3·45 **3.** 431 **4.** 19·3 **5.** 0·22 **6.** 3942·7
7. 53 **8.** 18·4 **9.** 0·059 **10.** 1·1 **11.** 6140 **12.** 127·89
13. 20·3 **14.** 47·6 **15.** 599·1 **16.** 0·16

page 120 **Exercise 21**

1. 0·85 m **2.** 2400 m **3.** 63 m **4.** 0·25 m **5.** 0·7 cm
6. 20 mm **7.** 1200 m **8.** 700 cm **9.** 580 m **10.** 0·815 m
11. 0·65 km **12.** 2·5 cm **13.** 5000 g **14.** 4200 g **15.** 6400 g
16. 3000 g **17.** 800 g **18.** 0·4 kg **19.** 2000 kg **20.** 0·25 kg
21. 500 kg **22.** 620 kg **23.** 0·007 t **24.** 1·5 kg **25.** 0·8 *l*
26. 2000 ml **27.** 1 *l* **28.** 4500 ml **29.** 6000 ml **30.** 3000 cm^3
31. 2000 *l* **32.** 5500 *l* **33.** (For discussion)

page 120 **Exercise 22**

1. 24 **2.** 48 **3.** 30 **4.** 4480 **5.** 48
6. 17 600 **7.** 36 **8.** 70 **9.** 4 **10.** 880
11. 3 **12.** 2 **13.** 3520 **14.** 80 **15.** 140
16. 12 **17.** 48 **18.** 22 400 **19.** 5280 **20.** 2

page 121 **Exercise 23**

1. 25 cm **2.** 50 litres **3.** 50 kg **4.** 8 pounds **5.** 5 miles
6. 1 kg **7.** 20 miles **8.** 10 cm **9.** 2·5 kg **10.** 5 litres
11. 25 miles **12.** 20 gallons **13.** 6 pounds **14.** $\frac{5}{16}$ mile **15.** 80 gallons
16. 2 ounces **17.** 300 g **18.** 1 gallon **19.** 40 pounds **20.** 10 inches
21. 30 cm **22.** 5000 miles **23.** 50 mph **24.** Sainsbury's
25. 30 cm, 250 g, flour, 120 g sugar, 8 apples 10 cm
26. 10 g **27.** 7 m **28.** 500 ml **29.** 100 miles **30.** 3 mm
31. (a) 3 kg (b) 15 litres (c) 3 pounds **32.** $\frac{1}{8}$ inch

page 123 **Exercise 24**

1. (a) $\frac{6}{8}$ (b) $\frac{4}{10}$ (c) $\frac{3}{9}$ (d) $\frac{5}{20}$ (e) $\frac{6}{9}$ (f) $\frac{5}{10}$ (g) $\frac{3}{4}$ (h) $\frac{3}{5}$ (i) $\frac{2}{3}$
2. (a) $\frac{1}{2}$ (b) $\frac{1}{3}$ (c) $\frac{2}{5}$
3. (a) $\frac{3}{2}$ (b) $\frac{7}{4}$ (c) $\frac{9}{4}$ (d) $\frac{12}{5}$ (e) $\frac{9}{5}$ (f) $\frac{7}{2}$ (g) $\frac{27}{4}$ (h) $\frac{23}{3}$
4. (a) $1\frac{2}{5}$ (b) $2\frac{2}{3}$ (c) $2\frac{1}{2}$ (d) $2\frac{1}{3}$ (e) $4\frac{1}{2}$ (f) $1\frac{5}{7}$ (g) $6\frac{2}{3}$ (h) $2\frac{1}{4}$
5. (a) $\frac{3}{16}$ (b) $\frac{1}{2}$ (c) £400 000
6. (a) $\frac{9}{12}, \frac{8}{12}, \frac{6}{12}, \frac{3}{12}$ (b) $\frac{1}{4}, \frac{1}{2}, \frac{2}{3}, \frac{3}{4}$
7. (a) $\frac{1}{2}, \frac{7}{12}, \frac{2}{3}$ (b) $\frac{2}{3}, \frac{3}{4}, \frac{5}{6}$ (c) $\frac{1}{3}, \frac{5}{8}, \frac{17}{24}$ (d) $\frac{5}{6}, \frac{8}{9}, \frac{11}{12}$
8. (a) $\frac{1}{2}$ (b) $\frac{3}{4}$ (c) $\frac{17}{24}$ (d) $\frac{7}{18}$ (e) $\frac{3}{10}$ (f) $\frac{5}{12}$
9. (a) 9 (b) $\frac{5}{16}$ **10.** $\frac{5}{24}$ **11.** $\frac{16}{24}$

page 125 **Exercise 25**

1. (a) $\frac{6}{7}$ (b) $\frac{5}{9}$ (c) $\frac{3}{5}$ (d) 1
2. (a) $\frac{3}{8}$ (b) $\frac{9}{10}$ (c) $\frac{11}{15}$
3. (a) $\frac{5}{6}$ (b) $\frac{5}{12}$ (c) $\frac{7}{12}$ (d) $\frac{9}{20}$ (e) $1\frac{1}{15}$ (f) $\frac{13}{20}$ (g) $\frac{11}{14}$ (h) $3\frac{3}{4}$
4. (a) $\frac{1}{6}$ (b) $\frac{5}{12}$ (c) $\frac{3}{10}$ (d) $\frac{5}{12}$ (e) $\frac{1}{10}$ (f) $\frac{2}{15}$ (g) $1\frac{5}{8}$ (h) $\frac{1}{6}$
5. (a) $10\frac{3}{4}$ inches **6.** (a) $30\frac{1}{2}$ h (b) £305 **7.** $\frac{1}{4}$ **8.** 5 **9.** $\frac{7}{8}, \frac{1}{2}$

page 126 **Exercise 26**

1. (a) $\frac{2}{15}$ (b) $\frac{15}{28}$ (c) $\frac{8}{15}$ (d) $\frac{25}{42}$ (e) $\frac{10}{27}$ (f) $\frac{10}{33}$ (g) $\frac{21}{32}$ (h) $\frac{2}{3}$
2. (a) $1\frac{1}{2}$ (b) $\frac{9}{10}$ (c) $3\frac{1}{3}$ (d) $\frac{8}{9}$ (e) $1\frac{1}{9}$ (f) $\frac{20}{21}$ (g) $\frac{5}{8}$ (h) $9\frac{2}{3}$

3.

×	$\frac{2}{3}$	$\frac{3}{4}$	$\frac{1}{5}$
$\frac{1}{2}$	$\frac{1}{3}$	$\frac{3}{8}$	$\frac{1}{10}$
$\frac{1}{4}$	$\frac{1}{6}$	$\frac{3}{16}$	$\frac{1}{20}$
$\frac{2}{5}$	$\frac{4}{15}$	$\frac{3}{10}$	$\frac{2}{25}$

4. £39 **5.** 123 cm **6.** $\frac{1}{5}$

7. $\frac{1}{2} - \frac{1}{8}, \frac{1}{16} + \frac{5}{16}, \frac{3}{4} \times \frac{1}{2}, 3 \div 8$ **8.** 8

page 128 **Exercise 27**

1. 42 kg **2.** £120 **3.** (a) 7·2 (b) 11·28 (c) 0·1 (d) 0·026 (e) 28·2 (f) 0·01
4. (a) 2 (b) 11 (c) 0 (d) 5 **5.** (a) 8 hectares (b) 24 tonnes
6. £345 **7.** (a) \$6400 (b) \$83 200
8. £1·80 **9.** (a) 600 (b) £204 **10.** —

page 129 **Exercise 28**

1. (a) 15 (b) (i) 20% (ii) 16% (iii) 70% (iv) 2%
2. (a) 177 147 (b) 1 594 323 **3.** (a) 36 (b) 24 (c) 240 (d) 240
4. $7\frac{1}{2}$ cm^2 **5.** (a) 15051 (b) 110 miles
6. A = 758, B = £28·804, C = £50·304, D = £8·803, E = £59·11
7. £7400 **8.** 11·6

page 130 Exercise 29

1. (a) 410 (b) 704·5 **2.** (a) 64 (b) 1 (c) 100 (d) 3000 (e) 32 (f) 81
3. $20\,\text{cm}^2$ **4.** 000, 001, 010, 011, 100, 101, 110, 111
5. (a) £162 (b) 200 (c) F1000 **6.** 5 h 34 min
6. 5 h 34 min
7. (a) $6^2 = 5^2 + 11$, $7^2 = 6^2 + 13$ (b) $11^2 = 60 + 5^2 + 6^2$, $13^2 = 84 + 6^2 + 7^2$
8. $120\,000\,000\,\text{m}^3$ **9.** 50 m **10.** 2520

page 132 Exercise 30

1. (a) 80 g (b) 5·2 (c) 416 **2.** x, 5, t
3. (a) 12 (b) (i) 8 (ii) 48 **5.** 200 litres
6. 0·006 25 cm **7.** (a) 5·4 km (b) 0·6 cm
8. (a) $3\,\text{cm}^2$ (b) $27\,\text{cm}^2$ (c) $A = \dfrac{C^2}{12}$ **9.** 16

page 133 Exercise 31

1. 9 **2.** (a) 5 m (b) 50 m (c) 6 km **3.** 51·4°
4. (a) 40 acres (b) 15 acres (c) (i) 10% (ii) 30% (iii) 37·5% (iv) 22·5%
5. £2774 **6.** £184·50 **7.** 78 **8.** £5.85
9. (a) $99 + \frac{9}{9}$ (b) $6 + \frac{6}{6}$ (c) $55 + 5$ (d) $55 + 5 + \frac{5}{5}$ (e) $\frac{7+7}{7+7}$ (f) $\frac{88}{8}$
10. From left to right (a) 7, 3 (b) 4, 3 (c) 7, 8, 6 (d) 3, 7 0 (e) 3, 6 (f) 6, 8, 0

Algebra 2

page 135 Exercise 1

1. 36 **2.** 29 **3.** 8 **4.** 18 **5.** 84
6. 9×10^{12} **7.** 165 **8.** $\sqrt{181}$ **9.** 1·62 **10.** 650

page 136 Exercise 2

1. −5 **2.** 8 **3.** −17 **4.** 8 **5.** −2 **6.** −27 **7.** 1 **8.** −22 **9.** −22 **10.** −22
11. −10 **12.** −2 **13.** 23 **14.** −44 **15.** 26 **16.** 25 **17.** −4 **18.** 0 **19.** −16 **20.** 22
21. −5 **22.** 30 **23.** 13 **24.** 25 **25.** 40 **26.** 3 **27.** −5 **28.** −12 **29.** −34 **30.** 2
31. 12 **32.** 39 **33.** 40 **34.** 7 **35.** 3 **36.** 10 **37.** 51 **38.** −2 **39.** 1 **40.** 11

page 137 Exercise 3

1. 4 **2.** 4 **3.** 9 **4.** 16 **5.** 8 **6.** −8 **7.** −27 **8.** 64 **9.** 8 **10.** 16
11. 8 **12.** 16 **13.** 18 **14.** 36 **15.** 48 **16.** 16 **17.** 20 **18.** 54 **19.** 144 **20.** 24
21. 13 **22.** 10 **23.** 1 **24.** 18 **25.** 13 **26.** 19 **27.** 10 **28.** 32 **29.** 16 **30.** 144
31. 36 **32.** 36 **33.** 4 **34.** 1 **35.** 2 **36.** −14 **37.** −5 **38.** −5 **39.** −10 **40.** 10
41. 0 **42.** 4 **43.** 50 **44.** 4 **45.** −10 **46.** −4 **47.** −6 **48.** −16 **49.** 28 **50.** 44

page 137 Exercise 4

1. 2 **2.** $\frac{1}{2}$ **3.** 0 **4.** 18 **5.** −3 **6.** 8 **7.** 26 **8.** −24 **9.** 2
10. 0 **11.** $\frac{1}{4}$ **12.** $\frac{2}{3}$ **13.** 17 **14.** $\frac{1}{3}$ **15.** 7 **16.** $\frac{3}{4}$ **17.** $1\frac{1}{3}$ **18.** $-\frac{5}{36}$

page 138 **Exercise 5**

1. 12 cm **2.** 15×5 **3.** (a) 26×13 (b) 16×8 (c) 32×16 (d) $9 \times 4{\cdot}5$ (e) $6{\cdot}5 \times 3{\cdot}25$
4. (a) 6×5 (b) 12×11 (c) 20×19 (d) $6{\cdot}5 \times 5{\cdot}5$ (e) $8{\cdot}7 \times 7{\cdot}7$ **5.** Not given

page 139 **Exercise 6**

1. (a) 9·5 (b) 7·5
2. (a) 5·1 or −2·1 (b) 3·8 or −1·8 (c) 6·7 (d) 3·4
3. (a) 3·2 (b) 2·7 (c) 3·6
4. 2·15 **5.** 8·1 **6.** 9·56
7. (a) $x + 10$ (b) $6x(x + 10) = 9000$ (c) $34 \times 44 \times 6$
8. (a) $3\,\text{cm}^2$ (b) $x(x + 3) - 6$, $x = 3{\cdot}8$ **9.** (a) $x - 1$ (b) $x = 1{\cdot}62$

page 142 **Exercise 7**

1. (a) (3, 7) (b) (1, 3) (c) (11, −1) **2.** (2, 4) **3.** (2, 3) **4.** (3, 1) **5.** (1, 5)
6. (5, 3) **7.** (a) (4, 0) (b) (1, 6) (c) (−2, −3) (d) (8, −1) (e) (−0·6, 1·2)

page 144 **Exercise 8**

1. $x = 2, y = 1$ **2.** $x = 4, y = 2$ **3.** $x = 3, y = 1$ **4.** $x = -2, y = 1$ **5.** $x = 3, y = 2$
6. $x = 5, y = -2$ **7.** $x = 2, y = 1$ **8.** $x = 5, y = 3$ **9.** $x = 3, y = -1$ **10.** $a = 2, b = -3$
11. $a = 5, b = \frac{1}{4}$ **12.** $a = 1, b = 3$ **13.** $m = \frac{1}{2}, n = 4$ **14.** $w = 2, x = 3$ **15.** $x = 6, y = 3$
16. $x = \frac{1}{2}, z = -3$ **17.** $m = 1\frac{15}{17}, n = \frac{11}{17}$ **18.** $c = 1\frac{16}{23}, d = -2\frac{12}{23}$

page 145 **Exercise 9**

1. $x = 2, y = 4$ **2.** $x = 1, y = 4$ **3.** $x = 2, y = 5$ **4.** $x = 3, y = 7$ **5.** $x = 5, y = 2$
6. $a = 3, b = 1$ **7.** $x = 1, y = 3$ **8.** $x = 1, y = 3$ **9.** $x = -2, y = 3$ **10.** $x = 4, y = 1$
11. $x = 1, y = 5$ **12.** $x = 0, y = 2$ **13.** $x = \frac{5}{7}, y = 4\frac{3}{7}$ **14.** $x = 1, y = 2$ **15.** $x = 2, y = 3$
16. $x = 4, y = -1$ **17.** $x = 3, y = 1$ **18.** $x = 1, y = 2$ **19.** $x = 2, y = 1$ **20.** $x = -2, y = 1$

page 145 **Exercise 10**

1. $5\frac{1}{2}, 9\frac{1}{2}$ **2.** 6, 3 or $2\frac{2}{5}, 5\frac{2}{5}$ **3.** 4, 10
4. 10·5, 7·5 **5.** $a = 2, c = 7$ **6.** $m = 4, c = -3$
7. $a = 30, b = 5$ **8.** TV £200, video £450 **9.** w 2 oz, b $3\frac{1}{2}$ oz
10. 2p × 15, 5p × 25 **11.** 10p × 14, 50p × 7 **12.** 40 m, 30 m
13. (4, −3), (−2, 3) **14.** man £50, woman £70 **15.** current 4 m/s, kipper 10 m/s

page 148 **Exercise 11**

1. (a) 40 km (b) 60 km (c) York, Scarborough (d) 15 min
(e) (i) 11.00 (ii) 13.45 (f) (i) 40 km/h (ii) 60 km/h (iii) 100 km/h
2. (a) 25 km (b) 15 km (c) 09.45 (d) 1 h
(e) (i) 26·7 km/h (ii) 5 km/h (iii) 30 km/h (iv) 40 km/h
3. (a) (i) 14.00 (ii) 13.45 (b) (i) 15.45 (ii) towards Aston
(c) (i) 15 mph (ii) 40 mph (iii) 40 mph (iv) 20 mph (d) $16.07\frac{1}{2}$
4. (a) 45 min (b) 09.15 (c) 60 km/h (d) 100 km (e) 57·1 km/h
5. (a) 09.15 (b) 64 km/h (c) 37·6 km/h (d) 47 km (e) 80 km/h
6. (b) 11.05 **7.** (a) 12.42 **8.** 12.35

page 151 **Exercise 12**

1. (a) (i) £2·80 (ii) £2·30 (b) (i) €4·30 (ii) €2 (c) £35 000
3. (a) 740p (b) £280 (c) £14 000
4. (a) 5°C (b) −10°C (c) 0°C (d) second feels colder (e) (i) Bitterly cold (ii) No: too cold
5. (a) 6 gallons (b) 40 mpg; 30 mpg (c) $33\frac{1}{3}$ mpg; $5\frac{1}{2}$ gallons
6. 180 miles
7. 2·5 h

page 155 **Exercise 13**

1. B
2. D
3. (a) C (b) A (c) D (d) B
4. (a) (i) B (ii) A (b) 8 s to 18 s (c) B (d) A
6. A → Z; B → X; C → Y

Shape and space 2

page 158 **Exercise 2**

2. (d) (7, −7), (−5, 5), (5, 7)
3. (d) (7, 5), (−5, 7), (5, −7)
4. (g) (−3, 6), (−6, 6), (−6, 4)
5. (g) (3, 1), (7, 1), (7, 3)
6. (a) $y = 0$ (x-axis) (b) $x = 1$ (c) $y = 1$ (d) $y = -x$

page 160 **Exercise 3**

7. Shape 1: C, 90° CW; Shape 2: B, 180°;
   Shape 3: A, 90° ACW; Shape 4: B, 90° CW; Shape 5: F, 180°

page 161 **Exercise 4**

2. (e) (3, −4), (2, −7), (−1, −4)
3. (e) (−6, 2), (−6, 6), (−4, 4)

page 162 **Exercise 5**

4. (a) (0, 0) (b) (1, 2) (c) (0, 0) (d) (−1, 1)
5. (b) (i) (2, 3) (ii) (0, 0) (iii) (2, 0) (iv) (−1, 1)
6. (b) (i) (0, 0) (ii) (−5, 0) (iii) (−7, 4) (iv) (−1, −5)

page 164 **Exercise 6**

1. (a) Yes (b) No (c) Yes (d) Yes
2. 78 mm
3. $y = 18$ mm, $z = 66$ mm
7. OA′ = 2 × OA, OB′ = 2 × OB
9. (b) Scale factor = $1\frac{1}{2}$

page 168 **Exercise 7**

7. (e) (3, 0), (−5, −1), (3, −1)
8. (e) (3, 3), (−6, −1), (3, −3)
9. (e) (3, −1), (2, −1), (5, −7)

page 171 **Exercise 9**

1. (a) $\begin{pmatrix}4\\6\end{pmatrix}$ (b) $\begin{pmatrix}6\\4\end{pmatrix}$ (c) $\begin{pmatrix}0\\3\end{pmatrix}$ (d) $\begin{pmatrix}6\\0\end{pmatrix}$ (e) $\begin{pmatrix}5\\-2\end{pmatrix}$ (f) $\begin{pmatrix}1\\2\end{pmatrix}$ (g) $\begin{pmatrix}-2\\5\end{pmatrix}$
   (h) $\begin{pmatrix}2\\-2\end{pmatrix}$ (i) $\begin{pmatrix}-4\\-3\end{pmatrix}$ (j) $\begin{pmatrix}2\\-6\end{pmatrix}$ (k) $\begin{pmatrix}1\\-8\end{pmatrix}$ (l) $\begin{pmatrix}-6\\-1\end{pmatrix}$ (m) $\begin{pmatrix}0\\-4\end{pmatrix}$ (n) $\begin{pmatrix}6\\1\end{pmatrix}$

page 171 **Exercise 10**

1. (c) reflection in $x = 4$
2. (c) rotation 90° cw, centre (0, 0)
3. (c) reflection in $y = 0$, translation $\begin{pmatrix}-7\\0\end{pmatrix}$ (b) Yes
4. enlargement scale factor 2, reflection in $y = -x$

page 173 **Exercise 11**

2. (b) (i) true (ii) true **3.** No

4. (a) translation (b) rotation of 180° about I (there are other possible transformations) (c) DF
(d) (i) rotation 180° about I (ii) translation in direction GI
(iii) rotation 90° about F (iv) rotation 180° about I or reflection in GC

page 174 **Exercise 12**

1. A 035°, B 070°, C 155°, D 220°, E 290°, L 340°
2. A 040°, B 065°, C 130°, D 160°, E 230°, F 330°

page 175 **Exercise 13**

1. (a) $147\frac{1}{2}°$ (b) 122° (c) 090° **2.** (a) 286° (b) 225° (c) 153°
3. (a) 061° (b) $327\frac{1}{2}°$ **4.** (a) 302° (b) 344° (c) 045°

page 177 **Exercise 16**

1. 11·5 km **2.** 14·1 km **3.** 12·5 km, 032° **4.** 6·9 km
5. 8·5 km, 074° **6.** 8·4 km, 029° **7.** (b) 5·2 h **8.** No

page 179 **Exercise 17**

11. 10 cm, 40 cm **13.** a plane

page 183 **Exercise 18**

1. 10 cm **2.** 4·12 cm **3.** 10·6 cm **4.** 5·66 cm **5.** 4·24 cm **6.** 990 **7.** 4·58 cm
8. 5·20 cm **9.** 9·85 cm **10.** 9·80 cm **11.** 3·46 m **12.** 40·3 km **13.** 12·7 cm **14.** 5·7 cm

page 184 **Exercise 19**

1. (a) 5 cm (b) 40 cm² **2.** 9·49 cm **3.** 32·6 cm **4.** 5·39 units **5.** Yes
6. 6·63 cm **7.** 5·57 **8.** 8·72 **9.** 5·66 **10.** 6·63 **11.** 2·24
12. (a) (i) 13 (ii) 25 (iii) 9 **13.** (a) 5 cm (b) 7·81 cm

page 186 **Exercise 20**

1. (a) 70 cm² (b) 144 cm² (c) 12 cm²
2. (a) 4 000 000 m²; 400 hectares (b) 314 hectares; 785 acres
3. (a) 14·6 m (b) 6 (c) £19·20 (d) 11·22 m²
4. A 81 cm², B 56m² **5.** 14 × 14, 14 × 8 **6.** 460 cm² (approx), 9·7 m²
7. (a) 7 (b) (i) 35 (ii) 6 (c) (i) 1200 cm³ (ii) 14 000 cm (d) (i) 48p (ii) £5·60 (iii) £50·40
8. 45 sq units
9. (a) 6 (b) 4 (c) $a = 10$ cm, $b = 6$ cm, $c = 10$ cm, $d = 10$ cm (d) 64 cm³ **10.** 10 300 or 10 400 m²

page 189 **Exercise 21**

1. 113 litres **2.** 17·3 litres **3.** (a) $\frac{1}{3}$ (b) $\frac{4}{9}$ (c) 25 cm² **4.** 2500
5. 1100 m **6.** (a) 24 cm² (b) 35 cm² **7.** 740 cm³ **8.** 2·4 cm
9. (a) 2·5 cm (b) 3·25 cm **10.** 40 **11.** 100 **12.** 900
13. (a) 384 cm² (b) 80 cm **14.** (a) 6 (b) 12 (c) 8 (d) 1

Handling data

page 192 Exercise 1

1. (a) £425 (b) £150 (c) £250 (d) £75
2. (a) £13 333·33 (b) £15 000 (c) £6666·67 (d) £10 000 (e) £12 000
3. (a) £21 600 000 (b) £8 000 000 (c) £1 000 000
4. (a) 8 min, 34 min, 10 min (b) 18°

page 193 Exercise 2

1. (a) (i) 45° (ii) 200° (iii) 110° (iv) 5°
2. (a) $\frac{3}{10}, \frac{4}{10}, \frac{1}{5}, \frac{1}{10}$
3. $x = 60°$, $y = 210°$
4. Barley 60°, Oats 90°, Rye 165°, Wheat 45°
5. (a) 180° (b) 36° (c) 90° (d) 54°

page 195 Exercise 3

1. (a) 5 (b) 19 (c) 23 (d) 55 (e) $\frac{6}{23}$
3. (a) £3000 approx.
(b) Profits increase in months before Christmas. Very few sales after Christmas.

page 197 Exercise 4

1. (a) 5 (b) 24 (c) 35
2. (a) D (b) A (c) A (d) C (e) C (f) B
3. Field A (assuming the fertilizer increases the weight).
5. No significant change.

page 202 Exercise 5

2. (a) 25 (b) 90
5. (a) 62
(b) Sport B has more heavy people. Sport A has much smaller range of weights compared to sport B.
6. (a) Plants with fertilizer are significantly taller
(b) no significant effect

page 206 Exercise 6

1.

Stem	Leaf
1	5
2	3 7 8 9
3	2 5 6 8 9
4	0 1 2 5 6 7 8
5	1 2 3 4 9
6	5 6

2. (a)

Stem	Leaf
2	0 4 5 8
3	1 7 9
4	0 4 6
5	2 5 8 9
6	1 5 7 8
7	3 5

(b)

Stem	Leaf
2	2 8
3	0 5 8
4	1 4 6 7 7
5	3 4 9
6	7
7	2

3. (a) 50 kg (b) 15 (c) 50 kg

4.

Stem	Leaf
1	0 4 8
2	4 4 8
3	1 3 3 7 8
4	5 5 6 6 7 9
5	1 2 5 8
6	2 3 7

5. (a) 13 (b) 78

page 213 **Exercise 8**

2. (a) strong positive (b) no correlation (c) weak negative
3. (a) no correlation (b) strong negative (c) no correlation (d) weak positive
4. about 9 **5.** (b) about 44 **6.** (b) about 6·7 km
7. (b) Bogota, high in the Andes (c) about 73°

page 217 **Exercise 9**

1. (a) mean = 6, median = 5, mode = 4 (b) mean = 9, median = 7, mode = 7
(c) mean = 6·5, median = 8, mode = 9 (d) mean = 3·5, median = 3·5, mode = 4
2. 2°C, 5°C **3.** (a) 3 (b) 3 **4.** (a) 11 (b) 4
5. 2 or 45 **6.** about 4 **7.** 6
8. (a) 1·6 m (b) 1·634 m
9. (a) 7·2 (b) 5 (c) 6 **10.** £2·10
12. (a) F (b) possible (c) F (d) possible
13. (a) mean £47 920, median £22 500 (b) mean is skewed by one large salary
14. (a) mean 157·1 kg, median 91 kg (b) mean, no: over $\frac{3}{4}$ cattle below mean weight
15. (a) mean 74·5 cm, median 91 cm (b) Yes

page 220 **Exercise 10**

1. 96·25 g **2.** 51·9p **3.** 4·82 cm
4. (a) mean = 3·025, median = 3, mode = 3 (b) mean = 17·75, median = 17, mode = 17
(c) mean = 6·62, median = 8, mode = 3 (d) the mode
6. (a) 9 (b) 9 (c) 15
7. (a) 5 (b) 10 (c) 10

page 222 **Exercise 11**

1. (a) mid-points 13, 18, 23; *fx* 52, 36, 69; total 215 (b) about 10 or 11
2. about 68
3. 3·8

page 224 **Exercise 12**

1. (a) 4, 9·5 (b) 5·5
2. (a) 1·5, 5·5 (b) 4
3. (a) 10, 21 (b) 11
4. (a) 1·5, 6 (b) 4·5
5. (a) 28, 6, 12 (b) 4·8, 1·5, 2·7 (c) 33, 12, 24

page 226 **Exercise 13**

1. (a) 50 (b) 30, 60 (c) 30 (d) 30
2. (a) 43 (b) 28, 57 (c) 29 (d) 34 (all approximate)
3. (a) 100 (b) 250 (c) 2250 hours (d) 750 hours
4. (b) (i) 45 (ii) 17
5. (b) (i) about 160·5 cm (ii) about 13 cm
6. (a) about 124 (b) 52 (c) Boris is more consistent
7. (b) (i) 7·6 h (ii) about 3·3 h (c) 10%
8. (b) France 18·5; Britain 24·5 (c) 8·5
(d) Results for Britain bunched together more closely with a higher median

Number 3

page 230 **Exercise 1**

1. '$\frac{1}{3}$ off' **2.** $\frac{1}{6}$ of £5000 **3.** 25% **4.** 20%
5. (a) 0·25 (b) 0·4 (c) 0·375 (d) $0{\cdot}41\dot{6}$ (e) $0{\cdot}1\dot{6}$ (f) $0{\cdot}\dot{2}8571\dot{4}$
6. (a) $\frac{1}{5}$ (b) $\frac{9}{20}$ (c) $\frac{9}{25}$ (d) $\frac{1}{8}$ (e) $1\frac{1}{20}$ (f) $\frac{7}{1000}$
7. (a) 25% (b) 10% (c) 72% (d) 7·5% (e) 2% (f) $33\frac{1}{3}$%
8. (a) 45 000 (b) 39 600 (c) $\frac{1}{30}$
9. (a) $\frac{1}{4}$, 0·25, 25% (b) $\frac{1}{5}$, 0·2, 20% (c) $\frac{4}{5}$, 0·8, 80% (d) $\frac{1}{100}$, 0·01, 1%
(e) $\frac{3}{10}$, 0·3, 30% (f) $\frac{1}{3}$, $0{\cdot}\dot{3}$, $33\frac{1}{3}$%
10. (a) $\frac{1}{5}$ (b) $\frac{4}{10}$ (c) $\frac{11}{33}$ (d) $\frac{7}{12}$
11. A
12. (a) 0·14625 (b) £15·84
13. (a) 45%, $\frac{1}{2}$, 0·6 (b) 4%, $\frac{6}{16}$, 0·38 (c) 11%, 0·111, $\frac{1}{9}$
14. 0·58 **15.** 1·42 **16.** 0·65 **17.** 1·61 **18.** 0·07
19. 0·16 **20.** 3·64 **21.** 0·60 **22.** 62·5%

page 232 **Exercise 2**

1. 4×10^3 **2.** 5×10^2 **3.** 7×10^4 **4.** 6×10 **5.** $2{\cdot}4 \times 10^3$
6. $3{\cdot}8 \times 10^2$ **7.** $4{\cdot}6 \times 10^4$ **8.** $4{\cdot}6 \times 10$ **9.** 9×10^5 **10.** $2{\cdot}56 \times 10^3$
11. 7×10^{-3} **12.** 4×10^{-4} **13.** $3{\cdot}5 \times 10^{-3}$ **14.** $4{\cdot}21 \times 10^{-1}$ **15.** $5{\cdot}5 \times 10^{-5}$
16. 1×10^{-2} **17.** $5{\cdot}64 \times 10^5$ **18.** $1{\cdot}9 \times 10^7$ **19.** $1{\cdot}1 \times 10^9$ **20.** $1{\cdot}67 \times 10^{-24}$
21. $5{\cdot}1 \times 10^8$ **22.** $2{\cdot}5 \times 10^{-10}$ **23.** $6{\cdot}023 \times 10^{23}$ **24.** 3×10^{10} **25.** £$3{\cdot}6 \times 10^6$

page 234 **Exercise 3**

1. $1{\cdot}5 \times 10^7$ **2.** 3×10^8 **3.** $2{\cdot}8 \times 10^{-2}$ **4.** 7×10^{-9}
5. 2×10^6 **6.** 4×10^{-6} **7.** 9×10^{-2} **8.** $6{\cdot}6 \times 10^{-8}$
9. $3{\cdot}5 \times 10^{-7}$ **10.** 10^{-16} **11.** 8×10^9 **12.** $7{\cdot}4 \times 10^{-7}$
13. $4{\cdot}9 \times 10^{11}$ **14.** $4{\cdot}4 \times 10^{12}$ **15.** $1{\cdot}5 \times 10^3$ **16.** 2×10^{17}
17. $1{\cdot}68 \times 10^{13}$ **18.** $4{\cdot}25 \times 10^{11}$ **19.** $9{\cdot}9 \times 10^7$ **20.** $6{\cdot}25 \times 10^{-16}$
21. $2{\cdot}88 \times 10^{12}$ **22.** $6{\cdot}82 \times 10^{-7}$ **23.** 11 000 000 000 or $1{\cdot}1 \times 10^{10}$
24. 0·000 13 m or $1{\cdot}3 \times 10^{-4}$ **25.** *c*, *a*, *b* **26.** 13
27. 16 **28.** (a) 6×10^2 (b) $6{\cdot}67 \times 10^7$ **29.** 50 min
30. 6×10^2 **31.** (a) $9{\cdot}46 \times 10^{12}$ km (b) 144 million km

page 236 **Exercise 4**

1. B **2.** A **3.** C **4.** B **5.** C **6.** A
7. B **8.** B **9.** A **10.** C **11.** B **12.** A
13. A **14.** C **15.** C **16.** B **17.** C **18.** A
19. B **20.** B **21.** C **22.** B **23.** B **24.** A
25. B **26.** B **27.** A **28.** B **29.** A **30.** C

page 237 **Exercise 5**

1. £8000 **2.** £6 **3.** 20 min **4.** B **5.** C **6.** B
7. B **8.** C **9.** B **10.** B **11.** A
12. $1493{\cdot}2 \simeq 1500$, $23{\cdot}41° \simeq 23°$, $2108 \simeq 2000$, $5173 \simeq 5000$

page 238 **Exercise 6**

1. (a) 89·89 (b) 4·2 (c) 358·4 (d) 58·8 (e) 0·3 (f) 2·62
2. (a) 4·5 (b) 462 (c) 946·4 (d) 77·8 (e) 0·2 (f) 21
3. Yes
4. Yes
5. £5200
6. about 20
7. (a) T (b) T (c) T (d) F (e) F (f) T (g) T (h) F (i) T
8. Wrong; should be about £10 each
9. (a) (say) 200 g per paper: 3250 papers per tree
   (b) about 5×10^{11} (c) for discussion

page 241 **Exercise 7**

1. 195·5 cm
2. 36·5 kg
3. 95·55
4. 3·25 kg
5. 28·65 s
6. (a) 1·5°C, 2·5°C (b) 2·25 g, 2·35 g (c) 63·5 m, 64·5 m (d) 13·55 s, 13·65 s
7. B
8. C
9. (a) not necessarily (b) 1 cm
10. Yes, max length of card is 11·25 cm, min length of envelope is 11·5 cm.
11. 16·5, 17·5
12. 255·5, 256·5
13. 2·35, 2·45
14. 0·335, 0·345
15. 2·035, 2·045
16. 11·95, 12·05
17. 81·35, 81·45
18. 0·25, 0·35
19. 4·795, 4·805
20. 0·065, 0·075
21. 0·65, 0·75
22. 614·5, 615·5
23. 7·125, 7·135
24. 51·5 million, 52·5 million

page 242 **Test 1**

1. £3·50
2. £4·95
3. 48
4. 10p, 10p, 20p
5. $6\frac{1}{2}$
6. $\frac{1}{100}$
7. 56
8. 75%
9. 15
10. 56 p
11. 50 min
12. 6·5
13. 130 m
14. 770
15. 11
16. 25
17. $1\frac{1}{4}$
18. £10
19. 10
20. 60·5
21. 55
22. 16
23. 1 h
24. $4\frac{1}{2}$
25. 75 or 105
26. 20
27. £2·40
28. 82%
29. £4000
30. 48p

page 243 **Test 2**

1. 96
2. 19
3. 06.30
4. £2·75
5. £1·90
6. 95°
7. 5 018 001
8. 15
9. £6
10. 3·5p
11. 53
12. 800 g
13. 74
14. 280 miles
15. 40
16. 4
17. 62
18. 5
19. 5
20. 480
21. 158
22. 95
23. 0·2
24. 0·7
25. £84
26. £2455
27. 64
28. 90p
29. 55 mph
30. 28

page 244 **Test 3**

1. 70
2. 240
3. 900
4. 10 705
5. 10.45
6. 245
7. 20
8. £3·05
9. £1·76
10. 20, 20, 20, 1 or 50, 5, 5, 1
11. 0·75
12. 5
13. Tuesday
14. 1·5 kg
15. £150·50
16. 640 m
17. £722
18. £25 000
19. 4
20. £1·10
21. 28
22. 9
23. 91
24. £6
25. 98p
26. £4·46
27. £3·30
28. £42
29. 960
30. 18p

page 244 **Test 4**

1. £8·05
2. 75
3. 25
4. 0·1 cm
5. 24p
6. 104
7. 40p
8. £88
9. 5.50
10. £8·20
11. 4 km
12. 45 miles
13. £4·25
14. 998
15. 20
16. 200
17. 22·5 cm
18. 75p
19. 10
20. 16
21. 20
22. £9·82
23. 22 min
24. 1540
25. £7·94
26. 70p
27. 200
28. 35%
29. 100
30. £2500

page 245 Test 5

1. 20, 10, 5, 2 **2.** £4·40 **3.** £2·10 **4.** £26 **5.** 8 min
6. 25 **7.** 500 (± 50) **8.** $\frac{1}{1000}$ **9.** 2·65 **10.** —
11. £15 000 **12.** £3·85 **13.** £27·50 **14.** 8 **15.** 84
16. 108 **17.** 30 litres **18.** 7 cm **19.** 153 **20.** 4
21. 7 **22.** 105 sq yd **23.** 2 000 000 **24.** 51 **25.** 6
26. £6 **27.** 32 **28.** 150 **29.** 133 **30.** Wednesday

page 246 Test 6

1. 60° **2.** 0·05 **3.** 80% **4.** 8000 **5.** £16·90
6. 0·7 **7.** 5 h 20 min **8.** $12\frac{1}{2}$% **9.** 6 cm **10.** 0·001
11. 7, 8 **12.** £2 **13.** 1·8 **14.** 49·2 **15.** £12·50
16. 165 **17.** 72° **18.** 240 **19.** 34p **20.** £9
21. 60 mph **22.** 302 **23.** 50 **24.** 37 **25.** £1·11
26. £15 **27.** 12 **28.** 8, 9 **29.** £80 **30.** £13·80

page 247 Test 7

1. 82° **2.** 72p **3.** 0·25 **4.** 90 nautical miles **5.** 8
6. 11 **7.** 325 **8.** $\frac{1}{12}$ **9.** £25 000 **10.** 49 000
11. 6·3 **12.** £8·70 **13.** £2·40 **14.** 5 **15.** £37·50
16. 13·55 cm **17.** 10 cm **18.** £9 **19.** 200 **20.** £1·20
21. 250 **22.** 500 m^2 **23.** £8·70 **24.** 0·025 **25.** 2550 g
26. £40 000 **27.** 150° **28.** £150 **29.** 11 **30.** 9

page 249 Exercise 8

1. 19 **2.** 4 **3.** 3 **4.** 0 **5.** 35 **6.** 60 **7.** 16 **8.** 6 **9.** 13
10. 14 **11.** 23 **12.** 71 **13.** 20 **14.** 36 **15.** 9 **16.** 8 **17.** 32 **18.** 30
19. 4 **20.** 0 **21.** 6 **22.** 5 **23.** 1 **24.** 47 **25.** 6 **26.** 3 **27.** 16
28. 12 **29.** 52 **30.** 15 **31.** 87 **32.** 17 **33.** 23 **34.** 8 **35.** 2 **36.** 26

page 249 Exercise 9

1. $7 + 5 \times 4$ **2.** $3 \times 5 + 10$ **3.** $4 \div 2 + 3$ **4.** $11 + 3 \times 3$
5. $31 - 10 \times 2$ **6.** $10 + 6 \times 5$ **7.** $4 \times 8 - 7$ **8.** $12 + 9 \times 2$
9. $18 - 4 \times 4$ **10.** $28 - 10 \times 2$ **11.** $21 \div 3 - 5$ **12.** $7 + 3 \times 3$
13. $10 \div 2 + 3$ **14.** $10 \times 3 + 12$ **15.** $18 \div 3 + 7$ **16.** $31 + 40 \div 5$
17. $15 - 16 \div 4$ **18.** $15 + 8 \times 9$ **19.** $37 + 35 \div 5$ **20.** $11 \times 5 + 9$
21. $8 + 3 \times 2 - 4$ **22.** $12 - 3 \times 3 + 1$ **23.** $11 + 4 - 1 \times 6$ **24.** $15 \div 5 + 2 \times 4$
25. $7 \times 2 - 3 \times 3$ **26.** $12 - 2 + 3 \times 4$ **27.** $8 \times 9 - 6 \times 11$ **28.** $20 \div 20 + 9 \times 0$
29. $20 - 30 \div 10 + 8$ **30.** $30 + 6 \times 11 - 11$

page 250 Exercise 10

1. 1851 **2.** 6·889 **3.** 1·214 **4.** 0·4189 **5.** 7·889 **6.** 19·35
7. 0·049 47 **8.** 221·5 **9.** 24·37 **10.** 6·619 **11.** 3·306 **12.** 2·303
13. 41·73 **14.** 8·163 **15.** 0·1090 **16.** 0·5001 **17.** 20·63 **18.** 10·09
19. 6·191 **20.** 10·27 **21.** 8·627 **22.** 22·02 **23.** 1·093 **24.** 44·72
25. 45·66 **26.** 52·86 **27.** 22·51 **28.** 5·479 **29.** 5·272 **30.** 0·2116

page 251 Exercise 11

1. 14·52 **2.** 1·666 **3.** 1·858 **4.** 0·8264 **5.** 2·717
6. 4·840 **7.** 10·87 **8.** 7·425 **9.** 13·49 **10.** 0·7392
11. 1135 **12.** 13·33 **13.** 5·836 **14.** 86·39 **15.** 10·23
16. 5540 **17.** 14·76 **18.** 8·502 **19.** 57·19 **20.** 19·90
21. 6·578 **22.** 9·097 **23.** 0·082·80 **24.** 1855 **25.** 2·367
26. 1·416 **27.** 7·261 **28.** 3·151 **29.** 149·9 **30.** 74 020
31. 8·482 **32.** 75·21 **33.** 1·226 **34.** 6767 **35.** 5·964
36. 15·45 **37.** 25·42 **38.** 2·724 **39.** 4·366 **40.** 0·2194
41. 0·000 465 9 **42.** 0·3934 **43.** −0·7526 **44.** 2·454 **45.** 40 000
46. 3·003 **47.** 0·006 562 **48.** 0·1330

page 252 Exercise 12

1. SOIL **2.** ISLES **3.** HE LIES **4.** SOS
5. HO HO HO **6.** ESSO OIL **7.** SOLID **8.** SOLO
9. BIGGLES **10.** HE IS BOSS **11.** LODGE **12.** SIGH
13. HEDGEHOG **14.** GOSH **15.** GOBBLE **16.** BEG
17. BIG SLOB **18.** SID **19.** HILL **20.** LESLIE
21. HOBBIES **22.** GIGGLE **23.** BIBLE **24.** BOILED EGGS
25. BOBBLE **26.** HEIDI **27.** BOBBIE **28.** HIGH
29. HELLS BELLS **30.** GOD BLESS **31.** SHE DIES **32.** SOLEIL

page 253 Exercise 13

1. 4p **2.** 11p **3.** 9p **4.** 10p **5.** 4p
6. 18p **7.** 6p **8.** 13p **9.** £1·75 **10.** 36p
11. 2·5p **12.** £7·25 **13.** 15p **14.** 5p **15.** 16p
16. £0·89 **17.** 14p **18.** 2p **19.** £3·60 **20.** 15p

page 254 Exercise 14

1.

5	×	12	→	60
×		÷		
20	+	24	→	44
↓		↓		
100	×	$\frac{1}{2}$	→	50

2.

7	×	6	→	42
÷		÷		
14	−	3	→	11
↓		↓		
$\frac{1}{2}$	×	2	→	1

3.

19	×	2	→	38
−		÷		
12	×	4	→	48
↓		↓		
7	−	$\frac{1}{2}$	→	$6\frac{1}{2}$

4.

17	×	10	→	170
−		÷		
9	÷	100	→	0.09
↓		↓		
8	−	0.1	→	7.9

5.

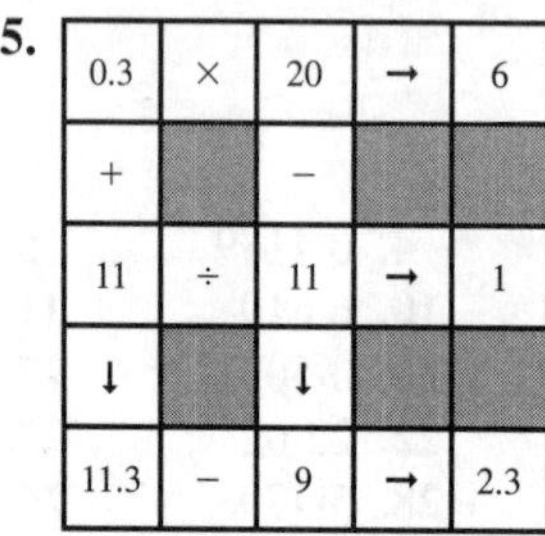

0.3	×	20	→	6
+		−		
11	÷	11	→	1
↓		↓		
11.3	−	9	→	2.3

6.

$\frac{1}{2}$	×	50	→	25
−		÷		
0.1	+	$\frac{1}{2}$	→	0.6
↓		↓		
0.4	×	100	→	40

7.

7	×	0.1	→	0.7
÷		×		
4	÷	0.2	→	20
↓		↓		
1.75	+	0.02	→	1.77

8.

1.4	+	8	→	9.4
−		×		
0.1	×	0.1	→	0.01
↓		↓		
1.3	−	0.8	→	2.1

9.

100	×	0.3	→	30
−		×		
2.5	÷	10	→	0.25
↓		↓		
97.5	+	3	→	100.5

10.

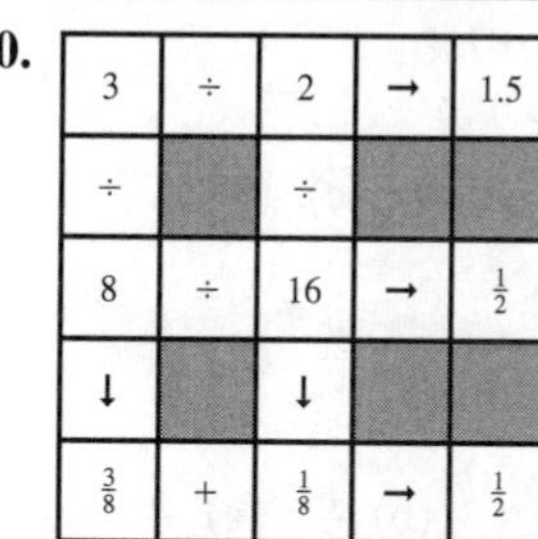

3	÷	2	→	1.5
÷		÷		
8	÷	16	→	$\frac{1}{2}$
↓		↓		
$\frac{3}{8}$	+	$\frac{1}{8}$	→	$\frac{1}{2}$

11.

$\frac{1}{4}$	−	$\frac{1}{16}$	→	$\frac{3}{16}$
×		×		
$\frac{1}{2}$	÷	4	→	$\frac{1}{8}$
↓		↓		
$\frac{1}{8}$	+	$\frac{1}{4}$	→	$\frac{3}{8}$

12.

0.5	−	0.01	→	0.49
+		×		
3.5	×	10	→	35
↓		↓		
4	÷	0.1	→	40

13.

5.2	−	1.8	→	3.4
−		÷		
4.56	×	5	→	22.8
↓		↓		
0.64	+	0.36	→	1

14.

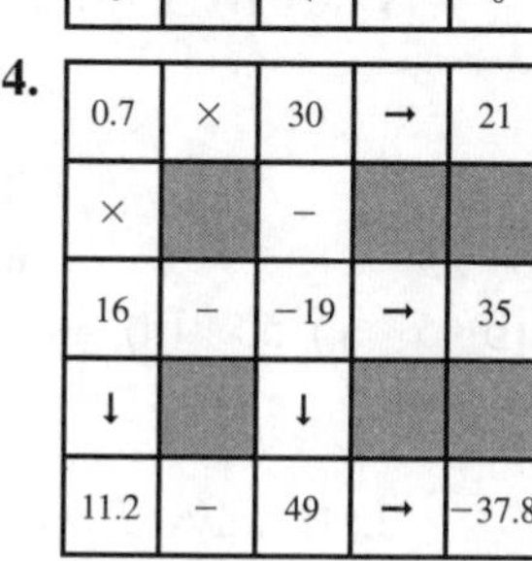

0.7	×	30	→	21
×		−		
16	−	−19	→	35
↓		↓		
11.2	−	49	→	−37.8

15.

−12	×	−6	→	72
÷		+		
4	+	7	→	11
↓		↓		
−3	+	1	→	−2

page 255 Exercise 15

1. (a) $\begin{array}{r} 5732 \\ +\ \underline{2696} \\ \underline{8428} \end{array}$ (b) $\begin{array}{r} 835 \\ -\ \underline{262} \\ \underline{573} \end{array}$ (c) $245 \div 7 = 35$ **2.** 6p

3. (a) double 18 (b) £11 111

4. 15 litres **5.** (a) £800 (b) 8% **6.** 70 mm **7.** 24 **8.** 1 (127)

9. (a) 0·3 (b) 0·003 (c) 0·115 (d) 70 000 **10.** 1·29

page 256 Exercise 16

1. 20 **2.** 200 g **3.** 6 **4.** 400 **5.** 3854 **6.** £1024

8. (a) 22 222 (b) 123 **9.** (a) 323 g (b) 23 (c) 67p (d) 29

page 257 Exercise 17

1. £10 485·76 **2.** (a) 1 (b) 15 **3.** $a = 100$, $b = 1$ **4.** 50

5. (a) 6·39 (b) 6·95 (c) 1·53 **7.** (a) $\frac{1}{36}$ (b) 16 **8.** 1105

9. 13 **10.** 10

page 259 Exercise 18

1. £1370 **2.** £2260 **3.** £4850 **4.** £1310 **5.** £1000 **6.** £6390 **7.** £5795 **8.** £3080

9. £2770 **10.** £6790 **11.** £5740 **12.** £7670 **13.** £4900 **14.** £5348 **15.** £6470

page 259 Exercise 19

1. £804 **2.** £2099·40 **3.** £1833 **4.** £1410·60 **5.** £1206 **6.** £2349 **7.** £1500

Probability

page 261 **Exercise 1**

1. B 2. C 3. A 4. B or C 5. C or D 6. A
7. B 8. B 9. C 10. D
12. Mike, with a large number of spins he should get zero with a probability of about $\frac{1}{10}$.

page 262 **Exercise 2**

1. (a) $\frac{1}{13}$ (b) $\frac{1}{52}$ (c) $\frac{1}{4}$
2. (a) $\frac{1}{9}$ (b) $\frac{1}{3}$ (c) $\frac{4}{9}$ (d) $\frac{2}{9}$
3. (a) $\frac{5}{11}$ (b) $\frac{2}{11}$ (c) $\frac{4}{11}$
4. (a) $\frac{4}{17}$ (b) $\frac{3}{17}$ (c) $\frac{11}{17}$
5. (a) $\frac{4}{17}$ (b) $\frac{8}{17}$ (c) $\frac{5}{17}$
6. (a) $\frac{2}{9}$ (b) $\frac{2}{9}$ (c) $\frac{1}{9}$ (d) 0 (e) $\frac{5}{9}$
7. (a) $\frac{1}{13}$ (b) $\frac{2}{13}$ (c) $\frac{1}{52}$ (d) $\frac{5}{52}$
8. (a) $\frac{1}{10}$ (b) $\frac{3}{10}$ (c) $\frac{3}{10}$
9. (a) $\frac{3}{13}$ (b) $\frac{5}{13}$ (c) $\frac{8}{13}$
8. (a) (i) $\frac{5}{13}$ (ii) $\frac{6}{13}$ (b) (i) $\frac{5}{12}$ (ii) $\frac{1}{12}$
11. (a) $\frac{1}{12}$ (b) $\frac{1}{40}$ (c) $\frac{1}{4}$
12. $\frac{9}{20}$
13. $\frac{1}{7}$
14. (a) (i) $\frac{1}{4}$ (ii) $\frac{1}{4}$ (iii) $\frac{1}{4}$ (b) $\frac{1}{4}$ (c) $\frac{6}{27} = \frac{2}{9}$.

page 265 **Exercise 3**

1. (a) 150 (b) 50 (c) 25
2. 25
3. 50
4. 40
5. (a) $\frac{3}{8}$ (b) 25
6. (a) $\frac{1}{2}$ (b) $\frac{1}{2}$
7. (a) 15 times (b) 105 times
8. (a) 20 (b) 5 (c) 50 (d) 40

page 267 **Exercise 4**

1. $\frac{1}{8}$
2. 16 ways
3. (b) 4 (c) $\frac{1}{9}$
4. (b) 3 (c) $\frac{1}{4}$
5. WX, WY, WZ, XY, XZ, YZ
6. (a) 30 outcomes (b) $\frac{1}{2}$
7. 12 combinations, $\frac{1}{12}$
8. 48
9. (a) 15 (b) $26 \times 26 = 676$
10. (a) 24 orders (b) 12
11. Yes
12. No, Y has the best chance.
14. lose 45p

page 272 **Exercise 6**

1. $\frac{4}{5}$
2. (a) $\frac{1}{13}$ (b) $\frac{12}{13}$ (c) $\frac{3}{13}$ (d) $\frac{10}{13}$
3. $\frac{35}{36}$
4. 0·76
5. 0·494
6. (a) $\frac{1}{4}$ (b) $\frac{3}{4}$ (c) $\frac{1}{4}$ (d) $\frac{3}{4}$ (e) 0 (f) 1
7. (a) $\frac{3}{51} = \frac{1}{17}$ (b) $\frac{16}{17}$ (c) $\frac{12}{51} = \frac{4}{17}$
8. (a) 0·3 (b) 0·9
9. (a) (i) 0·24 (ii) 0·89 (b) 575

page 275 **Exercise 7**

1. (a) $\frac{5}{11}$ (b) $\frac{7}{22}$ (c) $\frac{15}{22}$ (d) $\frac{17}{22}$
2. $\frac{1}{18}$
3. $\frac{1}{3}$
4. $\frac{1}{24}$
5. (a) 4 (b) (i) $\frac{1}{9}$ (ii) $\frac{1}{6}$ (iii) $\frac{1}{12}$
6. (a) $\frac{5}{36}$ (b) $\frac{5}{18}$ (c) $\frac{5}{18}$
7. (a) $\frac{1}{8}$ (b) $\frac{1}{4}$ (c) $\frac{3}{8}$
8. (a) 16 (b) $\frac{1}{8}$
9. (a) $\frac{2}{9}$ (b) $\frac{1}{6}$ (c) $\frac{1}{18}$ (d) 0
10. (b) (i) $\frac{1}{9}$ (ii) $\frac{1}{3}$ (iii) 0 (iv) $\frac{2}{9}$ (v) $\frac{4}{9}$
11. (a) (i) exclusive (ii) exclusive (iii) not exclusive (b) $\frac{3}{4}$
12. (a) 0·8 (b) 0·7 (c) not exclusive

page 278 **Exercise 8**

1. (a) $\frac{1}{13}$, $\frac{1}{6}$ (b) $\frac{1}{78}$
2. (a) $\frac{1}{2}$ (b) $\frac{1}{2}$ (c) $\frac{1}{4}$
3. $\frac{1}{10}$
4. (a) $\frac{1}{78}$ (b) $\frac{1}{104}$ (c) $\frac{1}{24}$
5. (a) $\frac{1}{16}$ (b) $\frac{1}{169}$ (c) $\frac{9}{169}$
6. (a) $\frac{1}{16}$ (b) $\frac{25}{144}$
7. (a) $\frac{1}{121}$ (b) $\frac{9}{121}$
8. $\frac{8}{1125}$
9. (a) $\frac{1}{288}$ (b) $\frac{1}{72}$
10. (a) $\frac{1}{9}$ (b) $\frac{4}{27}$
11. $\frac{1}{24}$
12. $\frac{1}{128}$
13. $\frac{1}{144}$

page 281 ***Exercise 9***

1. (a) $\frac{49}{100}$ (b) $\frac{9}{100}$
2. (a) $\frac{9}{64}$ (b) $\frac{15}{64}$
3. (a) $\frac{7}{15}$ (b) $\frac{1}{15}$
4. (a) $\frac{2}{9}$ (b) $\frac{2}{15}$ (c) $\frac{1}{45}$
5. (a) $\frac{1}{12}$ (b) $\frac{1}{6}$ (c) $\frac{1}{3}$ (d) $\frac{2}{9}$
6. (a) $\frac{1}{216}$ (b) $\frac{125}{216}$ (c) $\frac{25}{72}$ (d) $\frac{91}{216}$
7. (a) $\frac{1}{64}$ (b) $\frac{5}{32}$ (c) $\frac{27}{64}$
8. (a) $\frac{1}{6}$ (b) $\frac{1}{30}$ (c) $\frac{1}{30}$ (d) $\frac{29}{30}$
9. (a) $\frac{9}{16}$ (b) $\frac{1}{16}$
10. $\frac{1}{3}$
11. (a) $\frac{3}{20}$ (b) $\frac{9}{20}$
12. $\frac{3}{20} \times \frac{2}{19} \times \frac{1}{18}\ (= \frac{1}{1140})$ (b) $\frac{1}{4} \times \frac{4}{19} \times \frac{1}{6}\ (= \frac{1}{114})$ (c) $\frac{5}{20} \times \frac{4}{19} \times \frac{3}{18} \times \frac{2}{17}\ (= \frac{1}{969})$

Algebra 3

page 283 **Exercise 1**

1. $x^2 + 4x + 3$
2. $x^2 + 5x + 6$
3. $y^2 + 9y + 20$
4. $x^2 + x - 12$
5. $x^2 + 3x - 10$
6. $x^2 - 5x + 6$
7. $a^2 - 2a - 35$
8. $z^2 + 7z - 18$
9. $x^2 - 9$
10. $k^2 - 121$
11. $2x^2 - 5x - 3$
12. $3x^2 - 2x - 8$
13. $2y^2 - y - 3$
14. $49y^2 - 1$
15. $9x^2 - 4$
16. $20 + x - x^2$
17. $2x^2 + 2x - 4$
18. $6x^2 + 3x - 9$
19. $24y^2 + 4y - 8$
20. $6x^2 - 10x - 4$

page 284 **Exercise 2**

1. $x^2 + 8x + 16$
2. $x^2 + 4x + 4$
3. $x^2 - 4x + 4$
4. $4x^2 + 4x + 1$
5. $y^2 - 10y + 25$
6. $9y^2 + 6y + 1$
7. $3x^2 + 12x + 12$
8. $9 - 6x + x^2$
9. $9x^2 + 12x + 4$
10. $2x^2 + 4x + 2$
11. $2x^2 + 6x + 5$
12. $2x^2 + 2x + 13$
13. $5x^2 + 8x + 5$
14. $2y^2 - 14y + 25$
15. $10x - 5$
16. $-8x + 8$

page 284 **Exercise 3**

1. $\frac{1}{4}$
2. -3
3. 4
4. $-7\frac{2}{3}$
5. -43
6. 11
7. $-\frac{1}{2}$
8. 0
9. 1
10. $-1\frac{2}{3}$
11. 10, 8, 6
12. 13, 12, 5
13. 4 cm
14. 5 m

page 285 **Exercise 4**

1. $2(3x + 2y)$
2. $3(3x + 4y)$
3. $2(5a + 2b)$
4. $4(x + 3y)$
5. $5(2a + 3b)$
6. $6(3x - 4y)$
7. $4(2u - 7v)$
8. $5(3s + 5t)$
9. $8(3m + 5n)$
10. $9(3c - 8d)$
11. $4(5a + 2b)$
12. $6(5x - 4y)$
13. $3(9c - 11d)$
14. $7(5u + 7v)$
15. $4(3s - 8t)$
16. $8(5x - 2t)$
17. $12(2x + 7y)$
18. $4(3x + 2y + 4z)$
19. $3(4a - 2b + 3c)$
20. $5(2x - 4y + 5z)$
21. $4(5a - 3b - 7c)$
22. $8(6m + n - 3x)$
23. $7(6x + 7y - 3z)$
24. $3(2x^2 + 5y^2)$
25. $5(4x^2 - 3y^2)$
26. $7(a^2 + 4b^2)$
27. $9(3a + 7b - 4c)$
28. $6(2x^2 + 4xy + 3y^2)$
29. $8(8p - 9q - 5r)$
30. $12(3x - 5y + 8z)$
31. $3x(3 + 2y - x)$
32. $x(x - 5)$
33. $x(2x - 3)$
34. $x(7x + 1)$
35. $y(y + 4)$
36. $2x(x + 4)$
37. $4y(y - 1)$
38. $p(p - 2)$
39. $2a(3a + 1)$
40. $a(2b - 1)$
41. $x(3y + 2)$
42. $3t(1 + 3t)$
43. $4(1 - 2x^2)$
44. $5x(1 - 2x^2)$
45. $11r(4r + h)$
46. $\pi r(r + 2)$

page 286 **Exercise 5**

1. $(x+5)(x+2)$ 2. $(x+4)(x+3)$ 3. $(x+5)(x+3)$ 4. $(x+7)(x+3)$
5. $(x+6)(x+2)$ 6. $(x+7)(x+5)$ 7. $(x+8)(x+3)$ 8. $(x+5)(x+5)$
9. $(x+9)(x+4)$ 10. $(x+3)(x+2)$ 11. $(x+4)(x+2)$ 12. $(x+6)(x+3)$
13. $(x+5)(x-2)$ 14. $(x+5)(x-3)$ 15. $(x+4)(x-2)$ 16. $(x+5)(x-1)$
17. $(x+3)(x-2)$ 18. $(x+7)(x-2)$ 19. $(x-5)(x+2)$ 20. $(x-4)(x+3)$
21. $(x+3)(x-2)$ 22. $(x-7)(x+5)$ 23. $(x-8)(x+3)$ 24. $(x-4)(x-2)$
25. $(y-3)(y-2)$ 26. $(x-5)(x-3)$ 27. $(a-3)(a+2)$ 28. $(a+9)(a+5)$
29. $(b-7)(b+3)$ 30. $(x-4)(x-4)$ 31. $(y+1)(y+1)$ 32. $(y-7)(y+4)$
33. $(x-5)(x+4)$ 34. $(x-20)(x+12)$ 35. $(x+15)(x-2)$ 36. $(x-11)(x+3)$

page 287 **Exercise 6**

1. −4, −3 2. −5, −2 3. −5, 3 4. −3, 2 5. 6, 2
6. −7, −3 7. 3, 2 8. 5, −1 9. −7, 2 10. −4, −2
11. −3, −2 12. −6, −3 13. 7, −5 14. 4, −3 15. 7, 8
16. −9, 7 17. −1, −1 18. 3, 3 19. 12, −3 20. 7, 7

page 288 **Exercise 7**

1. −3, 2 2. −7, −3 3. 5, 2 4. 3, −1 5. 4, 1 6. 1, 2
7. 4, −1 8. 7, −5 9. 5 10. 8, 11 or −8, −11 11. 11

page 288 **Exercise 8**

1. $e-b$ 2. $m+t$ 3. $a+b+f$ 4. $A+B-h$ 5. y
6. $b-a$ 7. $m-k$ 8. $w+y-v$ 9. $\frac{b}{a}$ 10. $\frac{m}{h}$
11. $\frac{a+b}{m}$ 12. $\frac{c-d}{k}$ 13. $\frac{e+n}{v}$ 14. $\frac{y+z}{3}$ 15. $\frac{r}{p}$
16. $\frac{h-m}{m}$ 17. $\frac{a-t}{a}$ 18. $\frac{k+e}{m}$ 19. $\frac{m+h}{u}$ 20. $\frac{t-q}{e}$
21. $\frac{v^2+u^2}{k}$ 22. $\frac{s^2-t^2}{g}$ 23. $\frac{m^2-k}{a}$ 24. $\frac{m+v}{m}$ 25. $\frac{c-a}{b}$
26. $\frac{y-t}{s}$ 27. $\frac{z-y}{c}$ 28. $\frac{a}{h}$ 29. $\frac{2b}{m}$ 30. $\frac{cd-ab}{k}$
31. $\frac{c+ab}{a}$ 32. $\frac{e+cd}{c}$ 33. $\frac{n^2-m^2}{m}$ 34. $\frac{t+ka}{k}$ 35. $\frac{k+h^2}{h}$
36. $\frac{n-mb}{m}$ 37. $2a$ 38. $\frac{d-ac}{c}$ 39. $\frac{e-mb}{m}$

page 289 **Exercise 9**

1. mt 2. en 3. ap 4. amt 5. abc
6. ey^2 7. $a(b+c)$ 8. $t(c-d)$ 9. $m(s+t)$ 10. $k(h+i)$
11. $\frac{ab}{c}$ 12. $\frac{mz}{y}$ 13. $\frac{ch}{d}$ 14. $\frac{em}{k}$ 15. $\frac{hb}{e}$

16. $c(a+b)$ **17.** $m(h+k)$ **18.** $\frac{mu}{y}$ **19.** $t(h-k)$ **20.** $(z+t)(a+b)$

21. $\frac{e}{7}$ **22.** $\frac{e}{a}$ **23.** $\frac{h}{m}$ **24.** $\frac{bc}{a}$ **25.** $\frac{ud}{c}$

26. $\frac{m}{t^2}$ **27.** $\frac{h}{\sin 20°}$ **28.** $\frac{e}{\cos 40°}$ **29.** $\frac{m}{\tan 46°}$ **30.** $\frac{b^2c^2}{a^2}$

page 290 **Exercise 10**

1. $\pm\sqrt{\frac{h}{c}}$ **2.** $\pm\sqrt{\frac{f}{b}}$ **3.** $\pm\sqrt{\frac{m}{t}}$ **4.** $\pm\sqrt{\frac{a+b}{y}}$ **5.** $\pm\sqrt{\frac{t+a}{m}}$

6. $\pm\sqrt{(a+b)}$ **7.** $\pm\sqrt{(t-c)}$ **8.** $\pm\sqrt{(z-y)}$ **9.** $\pm\sqrt{(a^2+b^2)}$ **10.** $\pm\sqrt{(m^2-t^2)}$

11. $\pm\sqrt{(a^2-n^2)}$ **12.** $\pm\sqrt{\frac{c}{a}}$ **13.** $\pm\sqrt{\frac{n}{h}}$ **14.** $\pm\sqrt{\frac{z+k}{c}}$ **15.** $\pm\sqrt{\frac{c-b}{a}}$

16. $\pm\sqrt{\frac{h+e}{d}}$ **17.** $\pm\sqrt{\frac{m+n}{g}}$ **18.** $\pm\sqrt{\frac{z-y}{m}}$ **19.** $\pm\sqrt{\frac{f-a}{m}}$ **20.** $\pm\sqrt{(b^2-a^2)}$

21. $a-y$ **22.** $h-m$ **23.** $z-q$ **24.** $b-v$ **25.** $k-m$

26. $\frac{h-d}{c}$ **27.** $\frac{y-c}{m}$ **28.** $\frac{k-h}{e}$ **29.** $\frac{a^2-d}{b}$ **30.** $\frac{m^2-n^2}{t}$

31. $\frac{v^2-w}{a}$ **32.** $y-y^2$ **33.** $\frac{k-m}{t^2}$ **34.** $\frac{b-e}{c}$ **35.** $\frac{h-z}{g}$

36. $\frac{c-a-b}{d}$ **37.** $\frac{v^2-y^2}{k}$ **38.** $\frac{d-h}{f}$ **39.** $\frac{ab-c}{a}$ **40.** $\frac{hm-n}{h}$

page 290 **Exercise 11**

1. (a) $a=\frac{v-u}{t}$ (b) 2 **2.** $x=\frac{360\text{A}}{\pi r^2}$

3. (a) $k=\frac{Py}{m}$ (b) $y=\frac{mk}{p}$ **4.** (a) $n=pR+d$ (b) 1255

page 291 **Exercise 12**

1. $\frac{h+d}{a}$ **2.** $\frac{m-k}{z}$ **3.** $\frac{f-ed}{d}$ **4.** $\frac{d-ma}{m}$ **5.** $\frac{c-a}{b}$

6. $\pm\sqrt{\left(\frac{b}{a}\right)}$ **7.** $\pm\sqrt{\left(\frac{z}{y}\right)}$ **8.** $\pm\sqrt{(e+c)}$ **9.** $\frac{b+n}{m}$ **10.** $\frac{b-a^2}{a}$

11. $\frac{a}{d}$ **12.** mt **13.** mn **14.** $\frac{y}{d}$ **15.** $\frac{a}{t}$

16. $\frac{d}{n}$ **17.** $k(a+b)$ **18.** $\frac{v}{y}$ **19.** $\frac{m}{c}$ **20.** $\pm\sqrt{mb}$

21. $\frac{b-ag}{g}$ **22.** $\frac{x^2-h^2}{h}$ **23.** $y-z$ **24.** $\pm\sqrt{\left(\frac{c}{m}\right)}$ **25.** $\frac{t-ay}{a}$

26. $\dfrac{y^2+t^2}{u}$ **27.** $\pm\sqrt{(c-t)}$ **28.** $k-m$ **29.** $\dfrac{b-c}{a}$ **30.** $\dfrac{c-am}{m}$

31. $pq-ab$ **32.** $\dfrac{a^2-t}{b}$ **33.** $\dfrac{w}{v^2}$ **34.** $t-c$ **35.** $\dfrac{t}{x}$

36. $\dfrac{k-mn}{m}$ **37.** $\dfrac{v-t}{x}$ **38.** $\dfrac{c-ab}{a}$ **39.** $\dfrac{ma-e}{m}$ **40.** $\pm\sqrt{\dfrac{c}{b}}$

41. $\dfrac{a}{q}$ **42.** $\pm\sqrt{\left(\dfrac{a}{e}\right)}$ **43.** $\pm\sqrt{\left(\dfrac{h}{m}\right)}$ **44.** $\pm\sqrt{\left(\dfrac{v}{n}\right)}$ **45.** $\dfrac{v-t^3}{a}$

46. $\dfrac{b^3-a^3}{a}$ **47.** $\pm\sqrt{\left(\dfrac{b+d}{a}\right)}$ **48.** $\dfrac{bc-h^2}{h}$ **49.** $\pm\sqrt{(u^2-v^2)}$ **50.** $\dfrac{mb-b^3}{m}$

page 292 Exercise 13

1. $\frac{1}{5}, \frac{5}{2}, -\frac{4}{3}$ **2.** $\frac{4}{5}, -\frac{1}{6}, -5$ **3.** (a) 3 (b) $\frac{3}{2}$ (c) 4 (d) 5

4. $a = 3\frac{1}{2}$ **5.** (a) $\dfrac{n+4}{2m-3}$ (b) $n=-4$ (c) $m = 1\frac{1}{2}$

page 293 Exercise 14

1. (a) $y = 2x+1$ (b) $y = \frac{1}{2}x$ (c) $y = 4x-2$ (d) $y = -2x+5$ (e) $y = 7x$ (f) $y = -x+1$

2. $y = 3x-7$ and $y = 3x$

3. (a) $y = 4x-3$ (b) $y = -3x+5$ (c) $y = \frac{1}{3}x-2$

4. $y = 5x+c$

page 294 Exercise 15

1. (a) 1 (b) 3 **2.** (a) 1 (b) −2 **3.** (a) 2 (b) 1
4. (a) 2 (b) −5 **5.** (a) 3 (b) 4 **6.** (a) $\frac{1}{2}$ (b) 6
7. (a) 3 (b) −2 **8.** (a) 2 (b) 0 **9.** (a) $\frac{1}{4}$ (b) −4
10. (a) −1 (b) 3 **11.** (a) −2 (b) 6 **12.** (a) −1 (b) 2
13. (a) −2 (b) 3 **14.** (a) −3 (b) −4 **15.** (a) $\frac{1}{2}$ (b) 3
16. (a) $\frac{1}{3}$ (b) 3 **17.** (a) 4 (b) −5 **18.** (a) $1\frac{1}{2}$ (b) −4
19. (a) 10 (b) 0 **20.** (a) 0 (b) 4
21. A: $y = 3x-4$; B: $y = x+2$ **22.** C: $y = \frac{2}{3}x-2$; D: $y = -2x+4$

page 296 Exercise 16

1. (i) → (c) (ii) → (b) (iii) → (e) (iv) → (a) (v) → (d) (vi) → (f)
2. (a) reciprocal (b) quadratic (c) linear (d) linear (e) cubic (f) quadratic

page 297 Exercise 17

1. (a) $3 < 7$ (b) $0 > -2$ (c) $3{\cdot}1 > 3{\cdot}01$ (d) $-3 > -5$ (e) $100\,\text{m} > 1\,\text{m}$ (f) $1\,\text{kg} > 1\,\text{lb}$
2. (a) $x > 2$ (b) $x \leqslant 5$ (c) $x < 100$ (d) $-2 \leqslant x \leqslant 2$ (e) $x > -6$ (f) $3 < x \leqslant 8$

3. (a)  7 (b) 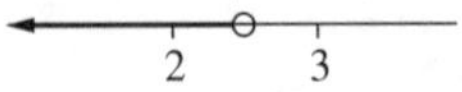 2 3 (c)  1 7
(d) 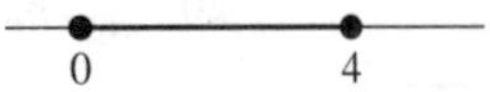 0 4 (e) 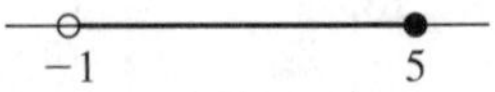 −1 5

4. (a) $A \geqslant 16$ (b) $3 \leqslant \text{age} \leqslant 70$ (c) $150 \leqslant T \leqslant 175$ (d) $h \geqslant 1{\cdot}75\,\text{m}$
5. (a) T (b) T (c) T

page 298 **Exercise 18**

1. $x > 13$ **2.** $x < -1$ **3.** $x < 12$ **4.** $x \leqslant 2\frac{1}{2}$ **5.** $x > 3$ **6.** $x \geqslant 8$
7. $x < \frac{1}{4}$ **8.** $x \geqslant -3$ **9.** $x < -8$ **10.** $x < 4$ **11.** $x > -9$ **12.** $x < 8$
13. $x > 3$ **14.** $x \geqslant 1$ **15.** $x < 1$ **16.** $x > 2\frac{1}{3}$ **17.** $x < -3$ **18.** $x > 7\frac{1}{2}$
19. $x > 0$ **20.** $x < 0$ **21.** $x > 5$ **22.** $5 \leqslant x \leqslant 9$ **23.** $-1 < x < 4$ **24.** $\frac{11}{2} \leqslant x \leqslant 6$
25. $\frac{4}{3} < x < 8$ **26.** $-8 < x < 2$ **27.** $\frac{1}{4} < x < 1\frac{1}{5}$

page 299 **Exercise 19**

1. $x > 8$ **2.** 1, 2, 3, 4, 5, 6 **3.** 7, 11, 13, 17, 19 **4.** 4, 9, 16, 25, 36, 49
5. −4, −3, −2, −1 **6.** 2, 3, 4, ... 12 **7.** 2, 3, 5, 7, 11 **8.** 2, 4, 6, ... 18
9. 1, 2, 3, 4 **10.** 5 **11.** 16, −16, 20, −5 **12.** >
13. $\frac{1}{2}$ (or others) **14.** 19 **15.** 17 **16.** $x > 3\frac{2}{3}$
17. (a) $-10 < x < 10$ (b) $-9 < x < 9$ (c) $-6 < x < 6$ **18.** $-5 < x < 5$
19. $-4 \leqslant x \leqslant 4$ **20.** $x > 1$, $x < -1$ **21.** $x \geqslant 6$, $x \leqslant -6$ **22.** all values except zero
23. $-2 < x < 2$ **24.** 7 **25.** 5 **26.** 6 **27.** 3, 4, 5

page 301 **Exercise 20**

1. $x \geqslant 3$ **2.** $y \leqslant 2\frac{1}{2}$ **3.** $1 \leqslant x \leqslant 6$ **4.** $x < 7$, $y < 5$
5. $y \geqslant x$ **6.** $x + y < 10$ **7.** $2x - y \leqslant 3$ **8.** $y \leqslant x$, $x \leqslant 8$, $y \geqslant -2$
9. (a) $x + y \leqslant 7$, $x \geqslant 0$, $y \geqslant x$ (b) $x + y \leqslant 6$, $y \geqslant 0$, $y \leqslant x + 2$
26. A: $x + y < 5$, $y > x + 1$ B: $x + y < 5$, $y < x + 1$
C: $x + y > 5$, $y < x + 1$ D: $x + y > 5$, $y > x + 1$
27. (2, 6), (3, 5), (3, 4), (4, 4), (4, 3), (5, 3), (6, 2)

Shape and space 3

page 304 **Exercise 1**

1. C only **2.** $m = 12$ **3.** $x = 9$ **4.** $a = 2\frac{1}{2}$, $e = 3$ **5.** $x = 3$
6. $x = 6$ **7.** $t = 4\frac{1}{2}$, $y = 6$ **8.** 7.7 cm **9.** No
10. (a) Yes (b) No (c) No (d) Yes (e) Yes (f) No (g) No (h) Yes
11. (b) 1·2 cm (c) 4·2 cm **12.** 6 cm **13.** 6 cm **14.** 4·5 cm
15. 16 m **16.** 3·75 cm **17.** 10·8 m **18.** AO = 2 cm, DO = 6 cm

page 307 **Exercise 2**

1. 3·01 cm **2.** 5.35 cm **3.** 3·13 cm **4.** 7·00 cm **5.** 73·1 cm
6. 15·4 cm **7.** 5·31 cm **8.** 7·99 cm **9.** 11·6 cm **10.** 11·4 cm
11. 961 cm **12.** 0·894 cm **13.** 46·0 cm **14.** 34·9 cm **15.** 9·39 cm
16. 8·23 cm **17.** 35·6 cm **18.** 80·2 cm **19.** 4·86 cm **20.** 6·98 cm

page 308 ***Exercise 3***

1. 18·4 **2.** 9.15 **3.** 10·7 **4.** 17·1
5. 13.7 **6.** 126 **7.** 6·88 **8.** 11·8
9. 17·6 **10.** 11·4 **11.** 5, 5·55 **12.** 13·1, 27·8
13. 4·26 **14.** 3·50 **15.** 26·2 **16.** 8·82

page 309 **Exercise 4**

1. 38·7° **2.** 48·6° **3.** 31·0° **4.** 54.5° **5.** 38·7° **6.** 17·5° **7.** 38·9°
8. 59·0° **9.** 41·3° **10.** 62·7° **11.** 54·3° **12.** 66·0° **13.** 48·2° **14.** 12.4°
15. 72·9° **16.** 56·9° **17.** 36·9° **18.** 41·8° **19.** 78·0° **20.** 89·4°

page 311 **Exercise 5**

1. 68·0° **2.** 3·65 m **3.** 14·0 m **4.** 20·6° **5.** 56·7 m **6.** 15.3 m **7.** 90·3 cm
8. 4·32 cm **9.** 7·66 cm **10.** 65·5 km **11.** 189 km **12.** 25·7 km **13.** 180 m **14.** 37·3 m
15. 36.4° **16.** 10·3 cm **17.** $a = 72°$, 8·23 cm **18.** 71·1°

page 315 **Exercise 6**

1. (a) length (b) volume (c) area (d) length (e) volume (f) area
2. (a) 2 (b) 2 (c) 3 (d) 1 (e) 2 (f) 3
3. (a) 2 (b) 3 (c) 2 (d) 1 (e) 3 (f) 1 (g) 0 (h) 2
4. (a) $wh + \frac{\pi}{6}wh$ (b) $2h + w + \frac{5}{4}w$
5. (a) A (b) L (c) V (d) A (e) Impossible (f) A (g) V (h) A **6.** 2
7. (a) 2 (b) 3 (c) 1 (d) 2, 1 (e) 3, 3 (f) 2

page 317 **Exercise 7**

1. (a) $a = 80°, b = 70°, c = 65°, d = 86°, e = 59°$ **2.** (a) $a = 36°$ (b) 144°
3. (a) (i) 40° (ii) 20° (iii) 8° (iv) 6° (b) (i) 140° (ii) 160° (iii) 172° (iv) 174°
4. $p = 101°, q = 79°, x = 70°, m = 70°, n = 130°$ **5.** 24 **6.** 9 **7.** 20

page 319 **Exercise 8**

1. (a) 1080° (b) 1440° **2.** (a) 3240° (b) 162°
3. (a) 270° (b) 100° (c) $a = 119°, b = 25°$
4. (a) 150° (b) 30° **5.** 22 **6.** 20

Revision

page 319 **Exercise 1**

1. £25·60, £6·70, 4, £55·30 **2.** (a) 30, 37 (b) 12, 10 (c) 7, 10 (d) 8, 4 (e) 26, 33
3. £8 **4.** £92 **5.** (a) 1810 s (b) 72·4 s **6.** 0·8 cm
7. (a) £13 (b) £148 (c) £170 **8.** (a) 5·89 (b) 6 (c) 7
9. (a) −11 (b) 23 (c) −10 (d) −20 (e) 6 (f) −14
10. (a) 3 (b) 5 (c) −6 (d) −7 **11.** (a) 9 (b) 11 (c) 3 (d) 7
12. (a) Yes (b) No (c) Yes **13.** (c) Sequence of square numbers (d) 49
14. 30 000 cm^2

page 320 **Exercise 2**

1. (a) 7 (b) $\frac{1}{4}$ (c) $\frac{4}{5}$ **2.** (a) 7·21 cm (b) 9·22 cm (c) 7·33 cm
3. (a) $\frac{3}{8}$ (b) $\frac{5}{8}$ **4.** (a) $\frac{2}{11}$ (b) $\frac{5}{11}$ (c) $\frac{9}{11}$
5. (i) £100 (ii) 500 (iii) £44 profit **6.** (a) 2·088 (b) 3·043
7. (a) 91·5 cm^2 (b) 119 cm^2

8. (a) reflection in the x-axis (b) reflection in $x = -1$ (c) reflection in $y = x$
(d) rotation, centre (0, 0), 90° clockwise (e) reflection in $y = -1$
(f) rotation, centre (0, −1), 180°

9. (a) enlargement; scale factor $1\frac{1}{2}$, (1, −4) (b) rotation 90° clockwise, (0, −4)
(c) reflection in $y = -x$ (d) translation $\begin{pmatrix} 11 \\ 10 \end{pmatrix}$
(e) enlargement; scale factor $\frac{1}{2}$, (−3, 8) (f) rotation 90° anticlockwise, $(\frac{1}{2}, 6\frac{1}{2})$
(g) enlargement; scale factor 3, (−2, 5)

10. 12 km

page 321 Exercise 3

1. (a) £5·20 (b) 29 min **2.** (a) 2 cm (b) 8 m
3. (i) 9 (ii) 50 (iii) $(7 \times 11) - 6 = 72 - 1$
4. (c) △2 (6, 0); △3 (2, −8); △4 (−8, 2); △6 (1, −5); △7 (−1, 3)
5. 17·7 cm **6.** (a) $l = 2d - 4$ (b) 149
8. (a) 198 cm^3 (b) 1357 mm^3 (c) 145

page 323 Exercise 4

1. (a) £28 600 (b) 198 (c) £143 (d) £28 314 (e) £286 **2.** (a) 55p (b) 760
3. (a) 4 (b) 19 **4.** A swimmer, B car ferry from Calais, C hovercraft, D train from Dover, E marker buoy, F car ferry from Dover
5. (a) 560 kg, 57 kg (b) 50 kg **6.** Both arrive at the same time
7. 28 274, £79·15, £85·42, November **8.** 74 m **9.** (a) 500 m^3 (b) 13 m
10. (a) (i) 13, 49, 109 (ii) 4, 49 (iii) 13, 109 (b) (i) 27 (ii) 33 (c) 148, 193 (d) 94, 127

page 324 Exercise 5

1. $\frac{a}{b}$ **2.** (a) $c = 5, d = -2$ (b) $x = 2, y = -1$
3. (a) 45·6° (b) 58·0° (c) 3·89 cm (d) 33·8 m **4.** (a) 0·05 m/s (b) 1·6 s (c) 173 km
5. (a) 14 (b) 18 (c) 28 **6.** $\frac{1}{6}$ **7.** 3·43 cm^2, 4·57 cm^2 **8.** (a) 220° (b) 295°
9. A: $y = 6$; B: $y = \frac{1}{2}x - 3$; C: $y = 10 - x$; D: $y = 3x$
10. (a) $s = t(r + 3)$ (b) $r = \frac{s - 3t}{t}$ **11.** 4·12 cm **12.** 9·95 cm **13.** $y \geqslant 2, x + y \leqslant 6; y \leqslant 3x$

page 325 Exercise 6

1. 26·2 litres **2.** (a) 8 (b) 140 (c) 29 (d) 42 (e) 6 (f) −6
3. 25 **4.** 5·14 cm^2 **5.** $\frac{5}{16}$
6. (b) 3 → 14, 4 → 18, 5 → 22, 6 → 26 (c) (i) 42 (ii) 62 (d) $n = 4x + 2$
7. (a) 1 : 50 000 (b) 1 : 4 000 000 **8.** (a) $t + t + t = 3t$ (b) $a^2 \times a^2 = a^4$ (c) correct
9. 5·39 cm **10.** (a) 5·45 (b) 5 (c) 5
11. $a = 45°, b = 67\frac{1}{2}°$ **12.** (a) $z = x - 5y$ (b) $k = \frac{11 - 3m}{m}$ (c) $z = \frac{T^2}{C^2}$

page 324 Exercise 7

1. $2{\cdot}1 \times 10^{24}$ tonnes
2. (a) (i) Consett (ii) Durham (iii) Consett (b) (i) 55 km (ii) 40 km
(c) (i) 80 km/h (ii) 55 km/h (iii) 70 km/h (iv) 80 km/h (d) $1\frac{3}{4}$ hours

3. 17 kg
4. $33\frac{1}{3}$ mph
5. (a) 0·340 (b) $4{\cdot}08 \times 10^{-6}$ (c) 64·9 (d) 0·119
6. $2{\cdot}3 \times 10^9$
7. (a) $\frac{1}{9}$ (b) $\frac{1}{12}$ (c) 0
8. $x \geqslant 0, y \geqslant x - 2, x + y \leqslant 7$
9. (a) 600 (b) 9000 or 10 000 (c) 3 (d) 60
10. 40° (b) 100°
11. $\dfrac{x}{x+5}$
12. A: $4y = 3x - 16$; B: $2y = x - 8$; C: $2y + x = 8$; D: $4y + 3x = 16$

page 328 Exercise 8

1. 95p for 1 lb
2. (a) $1\frac{2}{3}$ (b) 20 cm
3. (a) $6x + 15 < 200$ (b) 29
4. 24 cm^2
5. (a) −7, −1 (b) −5, −3 (c) −4, 2
6. (b) 85·5 km (± 1·5 km)
7. (a) $x = 14{\cdot}1$ cm, size of card = 48·3 cm (b) 1930 cm^2
8. (a) 0·5601 (b) 3·215 (c) 0·6161 (d) 0·4743
9. (a) 84 (b) 19·2
10. 0·335 m
11. 1·24
12. (a) $\frac{3}{5}$ (b) $w = \dfrac{k(1-y)}{y}$

page 329 Test 1

1. C	2. A	3. D	4. A	5. C
6. C	7. A	8. D	9. B	10. B
11. C	12. A	13. D	14. C	15. C
16. D	17. A	18. C	19. B	20. D
21. A	22. B	23. C	24. B	25. C

page 331 Test 2

1. B	2. C	3. B	4. A	5. D
6. C	7. A	8. D	9. B	10. C
11. B	12. D	13. A	14. C	15. C
16. D	17. B	18. A	19. B	20. B
21. C	22. D	23. B	24. A	25. C

page 333 Test 3

1. D	2. D	3. D	4. B	5. A
6. C	7. A	8. D	9. D	10. B
11. C	12. D	13. D	14. B	15. A
16. B	17. C	18. B	19. D	20. D
21. C	22. C	23. B	24. B	25. D

page 335 Test 4

1. B	2. B	3. A	4. C	5. C
6. D	7. D	8. A	9. B	10. B
11. D	12. B	13. B	14. C	15. D
16. A	17. C	18. B	19. B	20. D
21. A	22. C	23. C	24. C	25. A

Examination Questions

Exam groups accept no responsibility whatsoever for the accuracy or method of working in the answers given.

page 346 **Paper 1**

1. (a) 60, 180, 540, 1620 (b) 65 cages
2. (a) Reflection in x-axis (b) rotation 90° anticlockwise, centre (0, 0)
(c) enlargement, scale factor 3, centre (5, 4)
3. abc, $2a^2b$ **4.** number of pins = twice the number of L-shapes and then add one
5. (a) kite (b) rectangle (c) parallelogram **6.** (a) 0·35 (b) 42
7. (a) (i) B (ii) C (iii) A (iv) A (b) (i) 7 (ii) 4 (iii) several answers
8. (a) (i) $p = 25$ (ii) $q = 36$ (b) $20 \times 21 - 20 = 400$ (c) (i) $n(n+1)$ (ii) n^2
9. £10 948
10. (a) (i) 96,192 (ii) double the last term
(b) (i) 364 (ii) treble the last term and then add one (c) (i) $\dfrac{1}{2n+1}$ (ii) $\dfrac{n}{4n-1}$
12. (a) (i) $\frac{1}{8}$ (ii) 3, −1 (b) $x < 6\frac{1}{2}$
13. (a) 2, 4, 6, 8, 10, 12 (b) Step 1. Write down the number 1.
14. (a) 7, 8, 9, 10; 11, 12, 13, 14, 15 (b) 8 (c) 28
15. (a) (i) 74° (ii) 36° (b) No. Triangle is not isosceles
16. (a) Not enough answers boxes (b) Age group small, answers are suggested.
17. Trapezium **18.** (b) (i) $\frac{1}{4}$ (ii) $\frac{1}{9}$
19. (a)

−1	4	−3
−2	0	2
3	−4	1

(b) 12 **20.** (a) 30 cm/s (b) 90 m

page 352 **Paper 2**

1. small pot is better value **2.** 0·209
3. (a) 254° (b) 728 m **4.** $x = 3$, $y = -2$
5. (a) 11 gallons (b) 16 gallons (c) (i) 25 m.p.g. (ii) 150 → 275 miles
6. (a) (i) 4 (ii) 6 (b) $1{\cdot}322 \times 10^9$
8. (a) 90 (b) 40° (c) 0·22 (d) $\frac{3}{25}$ **9.** $x = 2\frac{1}{2}$, $y = 4$
10. (a) $\frac{8}{20} = \frac{2}{5}$ (b) bg, bs, rg, rs, yg, ys (c) 0·05 **11.** 36·9°
12. (a) 3 906 250 (b) (i) 0·111 (3 s.f.) (ii) numbers are given to only 3 s.f.
13. Asia (0·068 people/m^2) **14.** 4·6 **15.** (a) £496·48
16. (a) 9·2 (b) shop more busy, fewer tills in operation ...
17. (a) 201 cm^2 (b) 12·6 cm
18. (b) strong positive correlation (d) (i) about 135 pages (ii) about 220 g
19. perpendicular bisector of PQ
20. (a) 15·5 m (b) 25° (nearest degree) (c) 97·5 m
21. (a) 28·3 cm^2 (b) (i) 22·0 cm^2 (ii) 4·40 cm^3
22. (a) lower limit 114·5, upper limit 115·5
(b) lower limit of space between walls = 1·15 m which is less than the upper limit of the wardrobe.

page 359 **Paper 3**

1. (a) £9702 (b) (i) 14 (ii) 17
2. (a) Red (b) Angles: 150°, 84°, 84°, 42°
3. (a) 2 (b) $y = 2x + 3$
4. (a) $6n$ (b) $6n + 12$ (c) (ii) 7 pence
5. (a) (i) 3 (ii) 450 ml (iii) $\frac{3}{4}$ tsp (b) (i) 155 (ii) 247·5
6. (a) 84 kg (b) 170 cm
7. (a) (i) C.F. 15, 100, 270, 310, 320 (b) (i) about 4·7 minutes (ii) about 2 minutes
8. (a) $3x$ cm (b) (i) $3x + 6$ (ii) $x = 2\frac{1}{2}$ (iii) $13\frac{1}{2}$ cm
9. (a) 0·05 (c) 0·038
10. (i) $n < 4$ (ii) 1, 2, 3
11. (a) $3a + 2b$ (b) (i) x^2y (ii) $2x^2 + 4xy$
12. (a) $y = 3k - 1$ (b) $k = 5$
13. (a) (i) $x + 2$ (ii) $9 - x$ (b) (ii) $3\frac{1}{2}$
14. (a) (i) $3n$ (ii) $3n + 1$ (b) $n + 4$
15. (a) question is biased
16. (a) 16, 4 (b) 27, 3

page 364 **Paper 4**

1. (a) £450 000 (b) 4%
2. (a) $66667^2 = 4444488889$ (b) 44444448888889 (c) 66666667
3. (a) £1·75 (b) 0·4065934 (c) 0·4409269
5. 8510 cm^2
6. (a) (i) 42° (ii) 48° (b) 84°
7. (a) Question 1: People often don't like to state their age; Data is not easy to analyse if not in groups. Question 2: Leading question

   (b) 'Do you think shops should open on Sundays?' Yes ☐ No ☐ Don't know ☐
8. (a) 58 (b) 723 cm^2
9. (a) 99 min (b) 21 min
10. (a) $3{\cdot}81 \times 10^{-11}$ (b) $2{\cdot}45 \times 10^7$ km
12. (a) $P = 4n + 4$ (b) 37
13. (a) 254·47 m^3 (b) 195 tonnes

Index